HAESE MATHEMATICS

Specialists in mathemat

C000244953

Mathematics

Analysis and Approaches SL

2

Michael Haese

Mark Humphries

Chris Sangwin

Ngoc Vo

**for use with
IB Diploma
Programme**

MATHEMATICS: ANALYSIS AND APPROACHES SL

Michael Haese	B.Sc.(Hons.), Ph.D.
Mark Humphries	B.Sc.(Hons.)
Chris Sangwin	M.A., M.Sc., Ph.D.
Ngoc Vo	B.Ma.Sc.

Published by Haese Mathematics
152 Richmond Road, Marleston, SA 5033, AUSTRALIA
Telephone: +61 8 8210 4666, Fax: +61 8 8354 1238
Email: info@haesemathematics.com
Web: www.haesemathematics.com

National Library of Australia Card Number & ISBN 978-1-925489-56-9

© Haese & Harris Publications 2019

First Edition	2019
Reprinted	2020

Editorial review by Denes Tilistyak (Western International School of Shanghai).

Cartoon artwork by John Martin.

Artwork by Brian Houston, Charlotte Frost, Yi-Tung Huang, and Nicholas Kellett-Southby.

Typeset by Deanne Gallasch and Charlotte Frost. Typeset in Times Roman 10.

Computer software by Yi-Tung Huang, Huda Kharrufa, Brett Laishley, Bronson Mathews, Linden May, Joshua Douglass-Molloy, Jonathan Petrinolis, and Nicole Szymanczyk.

Production work by Sandra Haese, Bradley Steventon, Nicholas Kellett-Southby, Cashmere Collins-McBride, and Joseph Small.

We acknowledge the contribution of Marjut Mäenpää, Mal Coad, and Glen Whiffen, for material from previous courses which now appears in this book. The publishers wish to make it clear that acknowledging these individuals does not imply any endorsement of this book by any of them, and all responsibility for the content rests with the authors and publishers.

Printed in China by Prolong Press Limited.

FOREWORD

This book has been written for the International Baccalaureate Diploma Programme course *Mathematics: Analysis and Approaches SL*, for first teaching in August 2019, and first assessment in May 2021.

This book is designed to complete the course in conjunction with the **Mathematics: Core Topics SL** textbook. It is expected that students will start using this book approximately 6-7 months into the two-year course, upon the completion of the Mathematics: Core Topics SL textbook.

SL Mathematics

The *Mathematics: Analysis and Approaches* courses have a focus on algebraic rigour, and the book has been written with this focus in mind. The material is presented in a clear, easy-to-follow style, free from unnecessary distractions, while effort has been made to contextualise questions so that students can relate concepts to everyday use.

Each chapter begins with an Opening Problem, offering an insight into the application of the mathematics that will be studied in the chapter. Important information and key notes are highlighted, while worked examples provide step-by-step instructions with concise and relevant explanations. Discussions, Activities, and Investigations are used throughout the chapters to develop understanding, problem solving, and reasoning.

In this changing world of mathematics education, we believe that the contextual approach shown in this book, with the associated use of technology, will enhance the students' understanding, knowledge and appreciation of mathematics, and its universal application.

We welcome your feedback.

Email: info@haesemathematics.com   Web: www.haesemathematics.com

PMH, MAH, CS, NV

ACKNOWLEDGEMENTS

The photo of Dr Jonathon Hare and Dr Ellen McCallie on page 56 was reproduced from www.creative-science.org.uk/parabola.html with permission.

ONLINE FEATURES

With the purchase of a new textbook you will gain 24 months subscription to our online product. This subscription can be renewed for a small fee.

Access is granted through **SNOWFLAKE**, our book viewing software that can be used in your web browser or may be installed to your tablet or computer.

Students can revisit concepts taught in class and undertake their own revision and practice online.

COMPATIBILITY

For iPads, tablets, and other mobile devices, some of the interactive features may not work. However, the digital version of the textbook can be viewed online using any of these devices.

REGISTERING

You will need to register to access the online features of this textbook.

Visit www.haesemathematics.com/register and follow the instructions. Once registered, you can:
- activate your digital textbook
- use your account to make additional purchases.

To activate your digital textbook, contact Haese Mathematics. On providing proof of purchase, your digital textbook will be activated. **It is important that you keep your receipt as proof of purchase.**

For general queries about registering and subscriptions:
- Visit our **SNOWFLAKE** help page: https://snowflake.haesemathematics.com.au/help
- Contact Haese Mathematics: info@haesemathematics.com

SELF TUTOR

Simply 'click' on the ◀) **Self Tutor** (or anywhere in the example box) to access the worked example, with a teacher's voice explaining each step necessary to reach the answer.

Play any line as often as you like. See how the basic processes come alive using movement and colour on the screen.

Example 3	◀) **Self Tutor**

Solve for x on the domain $0 \leqslant x \leqslant 2\pi$:

a $\cos x = -\frac{\sqrt{3}}{2}$ b $2\sin x - 1 = 0$ c $\tan x + \sqrt{3} = 0$

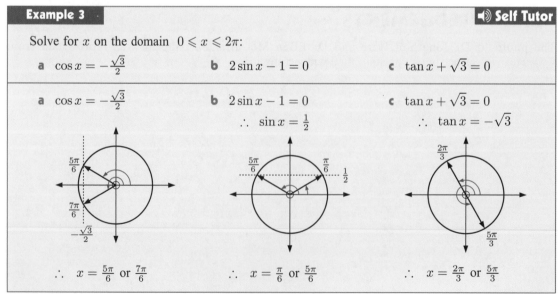

a $\cos x = -\frac{\sqrt{3}}{2}$

$\therefore \quad x = \frac{5\pi}{6}$ or $\frac{7\pi}{6}$

b $2\sin x - 1 = 0$

$\therefore \quad \sin x = \frac{1}{2}$

$\therefore \quad x = \frac{\pi}{6}$ or $\frac{5\pi}{6}$

c $\tan x + \sqrt{3} = 0$

$\therefore \quad \tan x = -\sqrt{3}$

$\therefore \quad x = \frac{2\pi}{3}$ or $\frac{5\pi}{3}$

See **Chapter 9**, **Trigonometric equations and identities**, p. 228

INTERACTIVE LINKS

Interactive links to in-browser tools which complement the text are included to assist teaching and learning.

Icons like this will direct you to:

- interactive demonstrations to illustrate and animate concepts
- games and other tools for practising your skills
- graphing and statistics packages which are fast, powerful alternatives to using a graphics calculator
- printable pages to save class time.

Save time, and make learning easier!

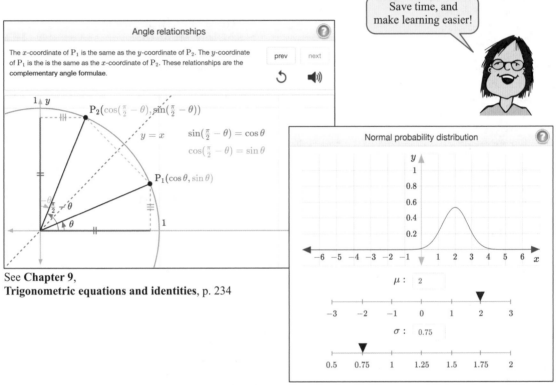

See **Chapter 9**,
Trigonometric equations and identities, p. 234

See **Chapter 21, The normal distribution**, p. 509

GRAPHICS CALCULATOR INSTRUCTIONS

Graphics calculator instruction booklets are available for the **Casio fx-CG50**, **TI-84 Plus CE**, **TI-$n$spire**, and the **HP Prime**. Click on the relevant icon below.

CASIO
fx-CG50

TI-84 Plus CE

TI-$n$spire

HP Prime

When additional calculator help may be needed, specific instructions are available from icons within the text.

GRAPHICS
CALCULATOR
INSTRUCTIONS

TABLE OF CONTENTS

SYMBOLS AND NOTATION USED IN THIS COURSE

$\mathbb{N}$	the set of positive integers and zero, $\{0, 1, 2, 3, ...\}$		d	the common difference of an arithmetic sequence
$\mathbb{Z}$	the set of integers, $\{0, \pm1, \pm2, \pm3, ...\}$		r	the common ratio of a geometric sequence
$\mathbb{Z}^+$	the set of positive integers, $\{1, 2, 3, ...\}$		S_n	the sum of the first n terms of a sequence, $u_1 + u_2 + ... + u_n$
$\mathbb{Q}$	the set of rational numbers		S_∞ or S	the sum to infinity of a sequence, $u_1 + u_2 + ...$
$\mathbb{Q}'$	the set of irrational numbers			
$\mathbb{R}$	the set of real numbers			
$\{x_1, x_2, ...\}$	the set with elements x_1, x_2, ...		$\sum_{i=1}^{n} u_i$	$u_1 + u_2 + ... + u_n$
$n(A)$	the number of elements in set A			
$\{x \mid ....$	the set of all x such that		$n!$	$n \times (n-1) \times (n-2) \times .... \times 3 \times 2 \times 1$
$\in$	is an element of		$\binom{n}{r}$ or ^nC_r	the rth binomial coefficient, $r = 0, 1, 2, ...$ in the expansion of $(a+b)^n$
$\notin$	is not an element of			
$\varnothing$ or $\{\ \}$	the empty (null) set			
U	the universal set		$f : x \mapsto y$	f is a function which maps x onto y
$\cup$	union		$f(x)$	the image of x under the function f
$\cap$	intersection		f^{-1}	the inverse function of the function f
$\subset$	is a proper subset of		$f \circ g$	the composite function of f and g
$\subseteq$	is a subset of		$\lim_{x \to a} f(x)$	the limit of $f(x)$ as x tends to a
A'	the complement of the set A			
$a^{\frac{1}{n}}, \sqrt[n]{a}$	a to the power of $\frac{1}{n}$, nth root of a (if $a \geqslant 0$ then $\sqrt[n]{a} \geqslant 0$)		$\dfrac{dy}{dx}$	the derivative of y with respect to x
			$f'(x)$	the derivative of $f(x)$ with respect to x
$a^{\frac{1}{2}}, \sqrt{a}$	a to the power $\frac{1}{2}$, square root of a (if $a \geqslant 0$ then $\sqrt{a} \geqslant 0$)		$\dfrac{d^2y}{dx^2}$	the second derivative of y with respect to x
$|x|$	the modulus or absolute value of x $|x| = \begin{cases} x \text{ for } x \geqslant 0 & x \in \mathbb{R} \\ -x \text{ for } x < 0 & x \in \mathbb{R} \end{cases}$		$f''(x)$	the second derivative of $f(x)$ with respect to x
			$\int y\, dx$	the indefinite integral of y with respect to x
$\equiv$	identity or is equivalent to			
$\approx$	is approximately equal to		$\int_a^b y\, dx$	the definite integral of y with respect to x between the limits $x = a$ and $x = b$
$>$	is greater than			
$\geq$ or $\geqslant$	is greater than or equal to			
$<$	is less than		e^x	exponential function of x
$\leq$ or $\leqslant$	is less than or equal to		$\log_a x$	the logarithm in base a of x
$\ngtr$	is not greater than		$\ln x$	the natural logarithm of x, $\log_e x$
$\nless$	is not less than		$\sin, \cos, \tan$	the circular functions
u_n	the nth term of a sequence or series		$\sin^{-1}, \cos^{-1}, \tan^{-1}$	the inverse circular functions

A(x, y)	the point A in the plane with Cartesian coordinates x and y
[AB]	the line segment with end points A and B
AB	the length of [AB]
(AB)	the line containing points A and B
$\widehat{A}$	the angle at A
$\widehat{CAB}$	the angle between [CA] and [AB]
$\triangle$ABC	the triangle whose vertices are A, B, and C
$\parallel$	is parallel to
$\perp$	is perpendicular to
P(A)	probability of event A
P(A')	probability of the event 'not A'
P$(A \mid B)$	probability of the event A given B
$x_1, x_2,$	observations of a variable
$f_1, f_2,$	frequencies with which the observations $x_1, x_2, x_3,$ ..... occur
$p_1, p_2,$	probabilities with which the observations $x_1, x_2, x_3,$ ..... occur
P$(X = x)$	the probability distribution function of the discrete random variable X
$P(x)$	the probability mass function of a discrete random variable X
E(X)	the expected value of the random variable X
μ	population mean
σ	population standard deviation
σ^2	population variance
$\overline{x}$	sample mean
s^2	sample variance
s	standard deviation of the sample
B(n, p)	binomial distribution with parameters n and p
N(μ, σ^2)	normal distribution with mean μ and variance σ^2
$\sim$	is distributed as
z	standardised normal z-score, $z = \dfrac{x - \mu}{\sigma}$
r	Pearson's product-moment correlation coefficient

THEORY OF KNOWLEDGE

Theory of Knowledge is a Core requirement in the International Baccalaureate Diploma Programme.

Students are encouraged to think critically and challenge the assumptions of knowledge. Students should be able to analyse different ways of knowing and areas of knowledge, while considering different cultural and emotional perceptions, fostering an international understanding.

The activities and discussion topics in the below table aim to help students discover and express their views on knowledge issues.

Chapter 3: Functions p. 93	**THE SYNTAX OF MATHEMATICS**
Chapter 6: Logarithms p. 156	**IS MATHEMATICS AN INVENTION OR A DISCOVERY?**
Chapter 7: The unit circle and radian measure p. 180	**MEASURES OF ANGLE**
Chapter 10: Reasoning and proof p. 256	**DEFINITIONS IN MATHEMATICS**
Chapter 10: Reasoning and proof p. 258	**AXIOMS**
Chapter 11: Introduction to differential calculus p. 271	**ZENO'S PARADOXES**
Chapter 14: Applications of differentiation p. 359	**SNELL'S LAW**
Chapter 19: Bivariate statistics p. 469	**MATHEMATICAL EXTRAPOLATION**
Chapter 19: Bivariate statistics p. 474	**LINEAR REGRESSION**

THEORY OF KNOWLEDGE

Snell's law states the relationship between the angles of incidence and refraction when a ray of light passes from one medium to another with different optical density. It was first discovered in 984 AD by the Persian scientist **Ibn Sahl**, who was studying the shape of lenses. However, it is named after **Willebrord Snellius**, who rediscovered it during the Renaissance. The law was published by **René Descartes** in his *Discourse on the Method* published in 1637.

Willebrord Snellius

In the figure alongside, a ray passes from A to B via point R. We suppose the refractive indices of the two media are n and m, the angle of incidence is α, and the angle of refraction is β.

Snell's law states that: $n \sin \alpha = m \sin \beta$.

The law follows from Fermat's *principle of least time*, which says that a ray of light travelling between two points will take the path of least time.

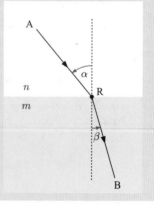

1 Is optimisation a mathematical principle?

2 Is mathematics an intrinsic or natural part of other subjects?

See **Chapter 14, Applications of differentiation**, p. 359

GEOMETRIC FACTS

TRIANGLE FACTS

- The sum of the interior angles of a triangle is 180°.

- In any isosceles triangle:
    - the base angles are equal
    - the line joining the apex to the midpoint of the base bisects the vertical angle and meets the base at right angles.

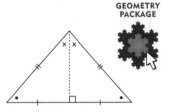

GEOMETRY PACKAGE

QUADRILATERAL FACTS

- The sum of the interior angles of a quadrilateral is 360°.
- A **parallelogram** is a quadrilateral which has opposite sides parallel.

Properties:
- opposite sides are equal in length
- opposite angles are equal in size
- diagonals bisect each other.

GEOMETRY PACKAGE

- A **rectangle** is a parallelogram with four equal angles of 90°.

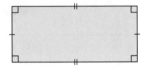

Properties:
- opposite sides are parallel and equal
- diagonals bisect each other
- diagonals are equal in length.

GEOMETRY PACKAGE

- A **rhombus** is a parallelogram in which all sides are equal in length.

Properties:
- opposite sides are parallel
- opposite angles are equal in size
- diagonals bisect each other at right angles
- diagonals bisect the angles at each vertex.

GEOMETRY PACKAGE

- A **square** is a rhombus with four equal angles of 90°.

Properties:
- opposite sides are parallel
- diagonals bisect each other at right angles
- diagonals bisect the angles at each vertex
- diagonals are equal in length.

GEOMETRY PACKAGE

- A **trapezium** is a quadrilateral which has a pair of parallel opposite sides.

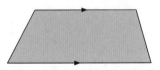

- A **kite** is a quadrilateral which has two pairs of adjacent sides equal in length.

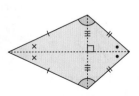

Properties:
- one diagonal is a line of symmetry
- one pair of opposite angles are equal
- diagonals cut each other at right angles
- **one** diagonal bisects **one** pair of angles at the vertices
- one of the diagonals bisects the other.

CIRCLE FACTS

Name of theorem	Statement	Diagram
Angle in a semi-circle	The angle in a semi-circle is a right angle.	$A\hat{B}C = 90°$ GEOMETRY PACKAGE
Chords of a circle	The perpendicular from the centre of a circle to a chord bisects the chord.	$AM = BM$ GEOMETRY PACKAGE
Radius-tangent	The tangent to a circle is perpendicular to the radius at the point of contact.	$O\hat{A}T = 90°$ GEOMETRY PACKAGE
Tangents from an external point	Tangents from an external point are equal in length.	$AP = BP$ GEOMETRY PACKAGE
Angle at the centre	The angle at the centre of a circle is twice the angle on the circle subtended by the same arc.	$A\hat{O}B = 2 \times A\hat{C}B$ GEOMETRY PACKAGE
Angles subtended by the same arc	Angles subtended by an arc on the circle are equal in size.	$A\hat{D}B = A\hat{C}B$ GEOMETRY PACKAGE
Angle between a tangent and a chord	The angle between a tangent and a chord at the point of contact is equal to the angle subtended by the chord in the alternate segment.	$B\hat{A}S = A\hat{C}B$ GEOMETRY PACKAGE

USEFUL FORMULAE

PERIMETER FORMULAE

square	rectangle	triangle	circle	arc
$P = 4l$	$P = 2(l + w)$	$P = a + b + c$	$C = 2\pi r$ or $C = \pi d$	$l = \left(\frac{\theta}{360}\right) 2\pi r$

AREA FORMULAE

Shape	Diagram	Formula
Rectangle		$A = \text{length} \times \text{width}$
Triangle		$A = \frac{1}{2} \times \text{base} \times \text{height}$
Parallelogram		$A = \text{base} \times \text{height}$
Trapezium or Trapezoid		$A = \left(\frac{a + b}{2}\right) \times h$
Circle		$A = \pi r^2$
Sector		$A = \left(\frac{\theta}{360}\right) \times \pi r^2$

SURFACE AREA FORMULAE

RECTANGULAR PRISM

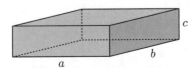

$$A = 2(ab + bc + ac)$$

CYLINDER

Object	Outer surface area
Hollow cylinder 	$A = 2\pi rh$ (no ends)
Open cylinder	$A = 2\pi rh + \pi r^2$ (one end)
Solid cylinder	$A = 2\pi rh + 2\pi r^2$ (two ends)

CONE

Object	Outer surface area
Open cone	$A = \pi rs$ (no base)
Solid cone	$A = \pi rs + \pi r^2$ (solid)

SPHERE

$A = 4\pi r^2$

VOLUME FORMULAE

Object	Diagram	Volume
Solids of uniform cross-section	height ... end ... height ... end	$V = $ **area of end $\times$ length**
Pyramids and cones	height ... base ... height h ... base	$V = \frac{1}{3}($**area of base $\times$ height**$)$
Spheres	r	$V = \frac{4}{3}\pi r^3$

Chapter 1

The binomial theorem

Contents:

OPENING PROBLEM

The cube alongside has sides of length $(a + b)$ cm. Its volume is $(a + b)^3$ cm^3.

The cube has been subdivided into smaller blocks by making 3 cuts parallel to the cube's surfaces as shown.

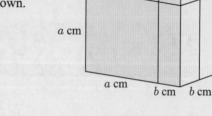

Things to think about:

a How many blocks have been created?

b How many blocks are:

    i a by a by a

    ii a by a by b

    iii a by b by b

    iv b by b by b?

c By adding the volumes of the blocks, can you write an expression which is equivalent to $(a + b)^3$?

The sum $a + b$ is called a **binomial** as it contains two terms.

Any expression of the form $(a + b)^n$ is called a **power of a binomial**.

In this Chapter we derive a concise formula for the **binomial expansion** of $(a + b)^n$. However, before we can achieve this, we need some notation associated with **combinations**.

A   FACTORIAL NOTATION

For $n \geqslant 1$, $n!$ is the product of the first n positive integers.

$$n! = n(n - 1)(n - 2) \dots 3 \times 2 \times 1$$

$n!$ is read "n factorial".

For example, $5 \times 4 \times 3 \times 2 \times 1 = 5!$

An alternative definition of factorial numbers is that $n! = n \times (n - 1)!$ for $n \geqslant 1$.

For example, $6! = 6 \times 5!$

Under this rule we notice that $1! = 1 \times 0!$

We therefore define $0! = 1$

DISCUSSION

- Is the definition $0! = 1$ "arbitrary"?

- Is it logical to extend the definition of factorials to include $0!$, even though it is not meaningful in the context of the original definition "product of the first n positive integers"? Can you think of other areas of mathematics in which a definition is similarly expanded?

Example 1   ◀)) **Self Tutor**

Express in factorial form:

a $9 \times 8 \times 7$

b $\dfrac{11 \times 10 \times 9 \times 8}{4 \times 3 \times 2 \times 1}$

a $9 \times 8 \times 7 = \dfrac{9 \times 8 \times 7 \times 6 \times 5 \times 4 \times 3 \times 2 \times 1}{6 \times 5 \times 4 \times 3 \times 2 \times 1} = \dfrac{9!}{6!}$

b $\dfrac{11 \times 10 \times 9 \times 8}{4 \times 3 \times 2 \times 1} = \dfrac{11 \times 10 \times 9 \times 8 \times 7 \times 6 \times 5 \times 4 \times 3 \times 2 \times 1}{4 \times 3 \times 2 \times 1 \times 7 \times 6 \times 5 \times 4 \times 3 \times 2 \times 1} = \dfrac{11!}{4!7!}$

EXERCISE 1A

1 Evaluate:

   a $2!$ **b** $3!$ **c** $4!$ **d** $5!$ **e** $6!$ **f** $10!$

2 Express in factorial form:

   a $4 \times 3 \times 2 \times 1$ **b** $7 \times 6 \times 5 \times 4 \times 3 \times 2 \times 1$ **c** 6×5

   d $8 \times 7 \times 6$ **e** $10 \times 9 \times 8 \times 7$ **f** $15 \times 14 \times 13 \times 12$

   g $\dfrac{9 \times 8 \times 7}{3 \times 2 \times 1}$ **h** $\dfrac{13 \times 12 \times 11 \times 10}{4 \times 3 \times 2 \times 1}$ **i** $\dfrac{15 \times 14 \times 13 \times 12 \times 11}{5 \times 4 \times 3 \times 2 \times 1}$

3 Simplify without using a calculator:

   a $\dfrac{7!}{6!}$ **b** $\dfrac{8!}{6!}$ **c** $\dfrac{12!}{10!}$ **d** $\dfrac{120!}{119!}$ **e** $\dfrac{10!}{8! \times 2!}$ **f** $\dfrac{100!}{98! \times 2!}$

4 Simplify:

   a $\dfrac{n!}{(n-1)!}$ **b** $\dfrac{(n+2)!}{n!}$ **c** $\dfrac{(n+1)!}{(n-1)!}$

B   BINOMIAL EXPANSIONS

We have often used the perfect square expansion: $(a+b)^2 = a^2 + 2ab + b^2$.

We can use this rule to expand $(a+b)^3$ as follows:

$$\begin{aligned}(a+b)^3 &= (a+b)(a+b)^2 \\ &= (a+b)(a^2 + 2ab + b^2) \quad \text{\{perfect square expansion\}} \\ &= a^3 + 2a^2b + ab^2 \\ &\quad + a^2b + 2ab^2 + b^3 \\ &= a^3 + 3a^2b + 3ab^2 + b^3 \quad \text{\{collecting like terms\}}\end{aligned}$$

> The **binomial expansion** of $(a+b)^2$ is $a^2 + 2ab + b^2$.
>
> The **binomial expansion** of $(a+b)^3$ is $a^3 + 3a^2b + 3ab^2 + b^3$.

In the following **Investigation** we will discover a method to expand $(a+b)^n$ for higher integer values of n.

INVESTIGATION 1   THE BINOMIAL EXPANSION

What to do:

1   Expand $(a+b)^4$ using $(a+b)^4 = (a+b)(a+b)^3$.

2   Hence expand $(a+b)^5$ using $(a+b)(a+b)^4$.

3   The cubic expansion $(a+b)^3 = a^3 + 3a^2b + 3ab^2 + b^3$ contains 4 terms. They are written in order so that the powers of a decrease. We observe that their coefficients are: 1   3   3   1

    a With the terms written in this order, what happens to the powers of b?

    b Does the pattern in **a** continue for the expansions of $(a+b)^4$ and $(a+b)^5$?

    c Use your results to continue this pattern of coefficients up to the case $n = 5$.

$$
\begin{array}{ccccccc}
n = 1 & & & 1 & & 1 & \\
n = 2 & & 1 & & 2 & & 1 \\
n = 3 & 1 & & 3 & & 3 & & 1 \longleftarrow \text{row 3} \\
& & & & \vdots & &
\end{array}
$$

4   The triangle of numbers we are considering is called **Pascal's triangle**.

    a How can each row of Pascal's triangle be predicted from the previous one?

    b Predict the elements of the 6th row of Pascal's triangle.

    c Hence write down the binomial expansion of $(a+b)^6$.

    d Check your result algebraically by using $(a+b)^6 = (a+b)(a+b)^5$ and your results from **2**.

You should have observed that in Pascal's triangle, the values on the end of each row are always 1. Each of the remaining values is found by adding the two values diagonally above it.

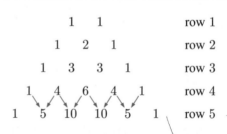

$$
\begin{array}{cccccccc}
& & & 1 & & 1 & & & \text{row 1} \\
& & 1 & & 2 & & 1 & & \text{row 2} \\
& 1 & & 3 & & 3 & & 1 & \text{row 3} \\
1 & & 4 & & 6 & & 4 & & 1 \quad \text{row 4} \\
1 & & 5 & & 10 & & 10 & & 5 \quad 1 \quad \text{row 5}
\end{array}
$$

You should have also found that
$$
\begin{aligned}
(a+b)^4 &= a^4 + 4a^3b + 6a^2b^2 + 4ab^3 + b^4 \\
&= a^4b^0 + 4a^3b^1 + 6a^2b^2 + 4a^1b^3 + a^0b^4
\end{aligned}
$$

Notice in this expansion that:

• As we look from left to right across the expansion, the powers of a decrease by 1, while the powers of b increase by 1.

• The sum of the powers of a and b in each term of the expansion is 4.

• The number of terms in the expansion is $4 + 1 = 5$.

• The coefficients of the terms are row 4 of Pascal's triangle.

For the expansion of $(a+b)^n$ where $n \in \mathbb{N}$:

• As we look from left to right across the expansion, the powers of a *decrease* by 1, while the powers of b *increase* by 1.

• The sum of the powers of a and b in each term of the expansion is n.

• The number of terms in the expansion is $n + 1$.

• The coefficients of the terms are row n of Pascal's triangle.

In the following Examples we see how the general binomial expansion $(a + b)^n$ may be put to use.

Example 2 ◀)) **Self Tutor**

Use $(a + b)^3 = a^3 + 3a^2b + 3ab^2 + b^3$ to find the binomial expansion of:

a $(2x + 3)^3$ **b** $(x - 5)^3$

---

a In the expansion of $(a + b)^3$ we substitute $a = (2x)$ and $b = (3)$.

$$\therefore \ (2x + 3)^3 = (2x)^3 + 3(2x)^2(3) + 3(2x)^1(3)^2 + (3)^3$$
$$= 8x^3 + 36x^2 + 54x + 27$$

b We substitute $a = (x)$ and $b = (-5)$

$$\therefore \ (x - 5)^3 = (x)^3 + 3(x)^2(-5) + 3(x)(-5)^2 + (-5)^3$$
$$= x^3 - 15x^2 + 75x - 125$$

Brackets are essential!

Example 3 ◀)) **Self Tutor**

Find the:

a 5th row of Pascal's triangle   **b** binomial expansion of $\left(x - \dfrac{2}{x}\right)^5$.

---

a
$$1 \quad 1 \longleftarrow \text{the 1st row, for } (a + b)^1$$
$$1 \quad 2 \quad 1$$
$$1 \quad 3 \quad 3 \quad 1$$
$$1 \quad 4 \quad 6 \quad 4 \quad 1$$
$$1 \quad 5 \quad 10 \quad 10 \quad 5 \quad 1 \longleftarrow \text{the 5th row, for } (a + b)^5$$

b Using the coefficients obtained in **a**, $(a + b)^5 = a^5 + 5a^4b + 10a^3b^2 + 10a^2b^3 + 5ab^4 + b^5$

Letting $a = (x)$ and $b = \left(\dfrac{-2}{x}\right)$,

$$\left(x - \frac{2}{x}\right)^5$$
$$= (x)^5 + 5(x)^4\left(\frac{-2}{x}\right) + 10(x)^3\left(\frac{-2}{x}\right)^2 + 10(x)^2\left(\frac{-2}{x}\right)^3 + 5(x)\left(\frac{-2}{x}\right)^4 + \left(\frac{-2}{x}\right)^5$$
$$= x^5 - 10x^3 + 40x - \frac{80}{x} + \frac{80}{x^3} - \frac{32}{x^5}$$

EXERCISE 1B

1 Use the binomial expansion of $(a + b)^3$ to expand and simplify:

a $(p + q)^3$ **b** $(x + 1)^3$ **c** $(x - 3)^3$

d $(2 + x)^3$ **e** $(3x - 1)^3$ **f** $(2x + 5)^3$

g $(2a - b)^3$ **h** $\left(3x - \dfrac{1}{3}\right)^3$ **i** $\left(2x + \dfrac{1}{x}\right)^3$

j $(\sqrt{x} - 1)^3$ **k** $(x^2 + 2)^3$ **l** $\left(x^2 - \dfrac{1}{x^2}\right)^3$

2 Use $(a + b)^4 = a^4 + 4a^3b + 6a^2b^2 + 4ab^3 + b^4$ to expand and simplify:

    a $(1 + x)^4$
    b $(p - q)^4$
    c $(x - 2)^4$

    d $(3 - x)^4$
    e $(1 + 2x)^4$
    f $(2x - 3)^4$

    g $(2x + b)^4$
    h $\left(x + \dfrac{1}{x}\right)^4$
    i $\left(2x - \dfrac{1}{x}\right)^4$

3 **a** Expand and simplify:

      i $(a - b)^3$
      ii $(a - b)^4$

    b Compare the expansions in **a** with those of $(a + b)^3$ and $(a + b)^4$. Discuss the signs of the corresponding terms.

4 **a** Write down the 5th row of Pascal's triangle.

    b Hence copy and complete: $(a + b)^5 = \ldots\ldots$

    c Find the binomial expansion of:

      i $(x + 2)^5$
      ii $(1 - x)^5$
      iii $(1 + 2x)^5$

      iv $(x - 2y)^5$
      v $(x^2 + 1)^5$
      vi $\left(x - \dfrac{1}{x}\right)^5$

5 **a** Write down the 6th row of Pascal's triangle.

    b Hence copy and complete: $(a + b)^6 = \ldots\ldots$

    c Find the binomial expansion of:

      i $(x + 2)^6$
      ii $(2x - 1)^6$
      iii $\left(x + \dfrac{1}{x}\right)^6$

6 Expand and simplify:

    a $\left(1 + \sqrt{2}\right)^3$
    b $\left(\sqrt{5} + 2\right)^4$
    c $\left(2 - \sqrt{2}\right)^5$

7 **a** Expand $(2 + x)^6$.
    b Hence find the value of $(2.01)^6$.

8 Expand and simplify:

    a $(2x + 3)(x + 1)^4$
    b $(x - 1)(2x + 1)^3$

9 Find the coefficient of:

    a a^3b^2 in the expansion of $(3a + b)^5$
    b a^3b^3 in the expansion of $(2a + 3b)^6$.

ACTIVITY

Suppose "shallow diagonals" are drawn on Pascal's triangle as shown below:

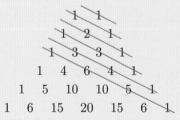

What to do:

  1 Find the sum of the numbers in each diagonal.

  2 Do you recognise the sequence of numbers formed by your answers to **1**? Can you explain why this occurs?

THE BINOMIAL THEOREM

For higher powers of a binomial, generating rows of Pascal's triangle by hand is very tedious. To efficiently expand $(a+b)^n$, we need a general formula for each term of the expansion.

INVESTIGATION 2   THE BINOMIAL COEFFICIENT

PART 1: COUNTING

The mathematical principle of **counting** is not formally a part of this course. However, it is necessary to understand how the binomial expansion $(a+b)^n$ is developed.

Suppose there are 10 members in a debating club. 4 members are to be randomly chosen to represent the club in a competition.

What to do:

1 Suppose the members of the club are listed. There are 10 options for who can be listed first, and 9 options for who can be listed second.

> Enrique
> Amélie
> Francesca
> Kristian
> Betina
> ....

   a How many options are there for who can be listed:

      i third   **ii** fourth   **iii** fifth?

   b Explain why the total number of orders in which the members can be listed is $10 \times 9 \times 8 \times .... \times 3 \times 2 \times 1 = 10!$

2 Now suppose the top four members on the list are the ones chosen to represent the club.

   a Explain why the total number of ways in which the first four members can be listed is $10 \times 9 \times 8 \times 7$.

   b Write $10 \times 9 \times 8 \times 7$ in the form $\dfrac{10!}{k!}$.

   c In how many ways could the 6 people *not* in the team be ordered?

   d Complete the sentence: Since the order of the 6 people left out of the team is not important, we divided the total number of orders in which the members can be listed by ......

3 State the number of ways in which the 4 members who *are* in the team can be ordered.

4 Hence explain why the total number of ways in which the team of 4 can be chosen from 10 members is $\dfrac{10!}{4! \times 6!}$.

5 Now suppose there are n members in the club and r members are chosen for the team. In how many ways could the team be chosen?

PART 2: THE BINOMIAL COEFFICIENT

Consider the expansion of $(a+b)^n = (a+b)(a+b)(a+b)....(a+b)$.

What to do:

1 Suppose you expanded the brackets completely *without* simplifying "like" terms. How many terms would there be?

2 Each of these terms is generated by selecting one term, either a or b, from each of the n sets of brackets.

   a If you choose b r times, how many times do you choose a?

   b In how many ways can you choose r lots of b from the n sets of brackets?

   c When you collect the "like" terms, how many terms of the form $a^{n-r}b^r$ will there be? This value is called the *binomial coefficient*.

From the **Investigation**, you should have found that:

- If there are n distinct objects and we choose r of them at a time, the total number of possible **combinations** is $\dfrac{n!}{(n-r)! \times r!}$.

  We abbreviate this formula as ^nC_r or $\binom{n}{r}$.

  ^nC_r is read as "n choose r".

- The value $\binom{n}{r} = \dfrac{n!}{(n-r)! \times r!}$ is called the **binomial coefficient** because $\binom{n}{r}$ is the coefficient of $a^{n-r}b^r$ in the expansion of $(a+b)^n$.

  For a given value of n, we can calculate $\binom{n}{r}$ for $r = 0, 1, 2, ..., n$.

We can evaluate $\binom{n}{r}$ using the formula $\binom{n}{r} = \dfrac{n!}{r!(n-r)!}$, or our graphics calculator.

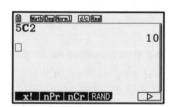

GRAPHICS CALCULATOR INSTRUCTIONS

For example,

$$\binom{5}{2} = \frac{5!}{2!3!} = \frac{5 \times 4 \times 3 \times 2 \times 1}{2 \times 1 \times 3 \times 2 \times 1} = 10.$$

To find *all* the values of $\binom{n}{r}$ for a particular value of n, you can use a list on your calculator.

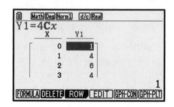

GRAPHICS CALCULATOR INSTRUCTIONS

For example, for $n = 4$ we see $\binom{n}{0} = 1$, $\binom{n}{1} = 4$, $\binom{n}{2} = 6$, $\binom{n}{3} = 4$, and $\binom{n}{4} = 1$.

INVESTIGATION 3   THE BINOMIAL THEOREM

What to do:

1 Evaluate this triangle of numbers:

Use your calculator to list the binomial coefficients for each whole row.

$$\binom{1}{0} \quad \binom{1}{1}$$
$$\binom{2}{0} \quad \binom{2}{1} \quad \binom{2}{2}$$
$$\binom{3}{0} \quad \binom{3}{1} \quad \binom{3}{2} \quad \binom{3}{3}$$
$$\binom{4}{0} \quad \binom{4}{1} \quad \binom{4}{2} \quad \binom{4}{3} \quad \binom{4}{4}$$
$$\binom{5}{0} \quad \binom{5}{1} \quad \binom{5}{2} \quad \binom{5}{3} \quad \binom{5}{4} \quad \binom{5}{5}$$
$$\binom{6}{0} \quad \binom{6}{1} \quad \binom{6}{2} \quad \binom{6}{3} \quad \binom{6}{4} \quad \binom{6}{5} \quad \binom{6}{6}$$

2 Copy and complete: *The rth number in the nth row of Pascal's triangle is* ......

From the **Investigation**, you should have observed that the rth number of the nth row of Pascal's triangle is $\binom{n}{r}$ where $n, r \in \mathbb{N}$, $r \leqslant n$. This confirms that the coefficients in the expansion of $(a+b)^n$ are the values $\binom{n}{r}$ for $r = 0, 1, 2, ..., n$.

The **binomial theorem** states that

$$(a+b)^n = a^n + \binom{n}{1}a^{n-1}b + ... + \binom{n}{r}a^{n-r}b^r + ... + b^n$$

$$= \sum_{r=0}^{n} \binom{n}{r}a^{n-r}b^r$$

where $\binom{n}{r}$ is the **binomial coefficient** of $a^{n-r}b^r$ and $r = 0, 1, 2, 3, ..., n$.

The binomial theorem allows us to perform a binomial expansion or find a particular term in a binomial expansion, without having to draw Pascal's triangle each time.

The **general term** or $(r+1)$th term in the binomial expansion $(a+b)^n$ is
$$T_{r+1} = \binom{n}{r}a^{n-r}b^r.$$

Example 4 ◀)) **Self Tutor**

Write down the first three and last two terms of the expansion of $\left(2x + \dfrac{1}{x}\right)^{12}$.
Do not simplify your answer.

$\left(2x + \dfrac{1}{x}\right)^{12} = \sum\limits_{r=0}^{12} \binom{12}{r}(2x)^{n-r}\left(\dfrac{1}{x}\right)^r$

$\qquad = (2x)^{12} + \binom{12}{1}(2x)^{11}\left(\dfrac{1}{x}\right)^1 + \binom{12}{2}(2x)^{10}\left(\dfrac{1}{x}\right)^2 + ...$

$\qquad .... + \binom{12}{11}(2x)^1\left(\dfrac{1}{x}\right)^{11} + \left(\dfrac{1}{x}\right)^{12}$

Example 5 ◀)) **Self Tutor**

Find the 7th term of $\left(3x - \dfrac{4}{x^2}\right)^{14}$. Do not simplify your answer.

$a = (3x)$, $b = \left(\dfrac{-4}{x^2}\right)$, and $n = 14$

Given the general term $T_{r+1} = \binom{n}{r}a^{n-r}b^r$, we let $r = 6$

$\qquad \therefore \ T_7 = \binom{14}{6}(3x)^8 \left(\dfrac{-4}{x^2}\right)^6$

EXERCISE 1C

1   Write down the first three and last two terms of the following binomial expansions. Do not simplify your answers.

   a $(1 + 2x)^{11}$

   b $\left(3x + \dfrac{2}{x}\right)^{15}$

   c $\left(2x - \dfrac{3}{x}\right)^{20}$

2 Without simplifying, write down:

    a the 6th term of $(2x + 5)^{15}$ **b** the 4th term of $(x^2 + y)^9$

    c the 10th term of $\left(x - \dfrac{2}{x}\right)^{17}$ **d** the 9th term of $\left(2x^2 - \dfrac{1}{x}\right)^{21}$.

3 Show that $(a - b)^n = \displaystyle\sum_{r=0}^{n} \binom{n}{r}(-1)^r a^{n-r} b^r$.

Example 6   ◀)) **Self Tutor**

In the expansion of $\left(x^2 + \dfrac{4}{x}\right)^{12}$, find:

    a the coefficient of x^6 **b** the constant term.

$a = (x^2)$, $b = \left(\dfrac{4}{x}\right)$, and $n = 12$

$\therefore$ the general term $T_{r+1} = \binom{12}{r}(x^2)^{12-r}\left(\dfrac{4}{x}\right)^r$

$\qquad\qquad\qquad\qquad = \binom{12}{r} x^{24-2r} \times \dfrac{4^r}{x^r}$

$\qquad\qquad\qquad\qquad = \binom{12}{r} 4^r x^{24-3r}$

  a If $24 - 3r = 6$ **b** If $24 - 3r = 0$

    then $3r = 18$ then $3r = 24$

      $\therefore r = 6$ $\therefore r = 8$

  $\therefore T_7 = \binom{12}{6} 4^6 x^6$ $\therefore T_9 = \binom{12}{8} 4^8 x^0$

  $\therefore$ the coefficient of x^6 is $\therefore$ the constant term is

    $\binom{12}{6} 4^6$ or $3\,784\,704$. $\binom{12}{8} 4^8$ or $32\,440\,320$.

---

4 Consider the expansion of $(x + 2)^8$.

    a Write down the general term of the expansion.

    b Find the coefficient of x^5.

5 Consider the expansion of $(x + b)^7$.

    a Write down the general term of the expansion.

    b Find b given that the coefficient of x^4 is -280.

6 Find the constant term in the expansion of:

    a $\left(x + \dfrac{2}{x^2}\right)^{15}$ **b** $\left(x - \dfrac{3}{x^2}\right)^9$

7 Find the coefficient of:

    a x^{10} in the expansion of $(3 + 2x^2)^{10}$ **b** x^3 in the expansion of $\left(2x^2 - \dfrac{3}{x}\right)^6$

    c $x^6 y^3$ in the expansion of $(2x^2 - 3y)^6$ **d** x^{12} in the expansion of $\left(2x^2 - \dfrac{1}{x}\right)^{12}$.

8 Consider the expression $\left(x^2y - 2y^2\right)^6$. Find the term in which x and y are raised to the same power.

9 The third term of $(1+x)^n$ is $36x^2$. Find n, and hence find the fourth term.

10 Find a if the coefficient of x^{11} in the expansion of $\left(x^2 + \dfrac{1}{ax}\right)^{10}$ is 15.

Example 7 ◄⑴ **Self Tutor**

Find the coefficient of x^5 in the expansion of $(x+3)(2x-1)^6$.

$(x+3)(2x-1)^6$
$= (x+3)[(2x)^6 + \binom{6}{1}(2x)^5(-1) + \binom{6}{2}(2x)^4(-1)^2 + ...]$
$= (x+3)(2^6x^6 - \binom{6}{1}2^5x^5 + \binom{6}{2}2^4x^4 - ....)$

with arrows labelled (1) and (2)

So, the terms containing x^5 are $\binom{6}{2}2^4x^5$ from (1)

and $-3\binom{6}{1}2^5x^5$ from (2)

$\therefore$ the coefficient of x^5 is $\binom{6}{2}2^4 - 3\binom{6}{1}2^5 = -336$

---

11 Find:
  a the coefficient of x^4 in the expansion of $(x+4)(x-3)^6$
  b the coefficient of x^5 in the expansion of $(x+2)(x^2+1)^8$
  c the term containing x^6 in the expansion of $(2-x)(3x+1)^9$.

12 If $(1+kx)^n = 1 - 12x + 60x^2 - ....$, $n \in \mathbb{Z}^+$, find the values of k and n.

13 **a** Write down the first 5 rows of Pascal's triangle.
  b Find the sum of the numbers in:
    i row 1   **ii** row 2   **iii** row 3   **iv** row 4   **v** row 5.
  c Copy and complete: "The sum of the numbers in row n of Pascal's triangle is ......"
  d Show that $(1+x)^n = \binom{n}{0} + \binom{n}{1}x + \binom{n}{2}x^2 + ... + \binom{n}{n-1}x^{n-1} + \binom{n}{n}x^n$.
  e Hence deduce that:
    i $\binom{n}{0} + \binom{n}{1} + \binom{n}{2} + ... + \binom{n}{n-1} + \binom{n}{n} = 2^n$
    ii $\binom{n}{0} - \binom{n}{1} + \binom{n}{2} - \binom{n}{3} + ... + (-1)^n\binom{n}{n} = 0$
  f By considering the binomial expansion of $(1+x)^n$, find $\displaystyle\sum_{r=0}^{n} 2^r\binom{n}{r}$.

14 **a** Write down the first four and last two terms of the binomial expansion $(3+x)^n$.
  b Hence simplify $3^n + \binom{n}{1}3^{n-1} + \binom{n}{2}3^{n-2} + \binom{n}{3}3^{n-3} + ... + 3n + 1$.

DISCUSSION

$$\begin{array}{ccccccc} & & & 1 & & 1 & \\ & & 1 & & 2 & & 1 \\ & 1 & & 3 & & 3 & & 1 \\ 1 & & 4 & & 6 & & 4 & & 1 \\ 1 & & 5 & & 10 & & 10 & & 5 & & 1 \end{array}$$

$$\begin{array}{ccccc} & & \binom{1}{0} & \binom{1}{1} & \\ & \binom{2}{0} & \binom{2}{1} & \binom{2}{2} & \\ \binom{3}{0} & \binom{3}{1} & \binom{3}{2} & \binom{3}{3} & \\ \binom{4}{0} & \binom{4}{1} & \binom{4}{2} & \binom{4}{3} & \binom{4}{4} \\ \binom{5}{0} & \binom{5}{1} & \binom{5}{2} & \binom{5}{3} & \binom{5}{4} & \binom{5}{5} \end{array}$$

These alternative representations of Pascal's triangle allow us to deduce some properties of the binomial coefficient $\binom{n}{r}$.

For example:

* The values of the coefficients at the end of each row are 1, suggesting that $\binom{n}{0} = 1$ and $\binom{n}{n} = 1$ for all $n \in \mathbb{N}$.

* The remaining values in each row are found by adding the two values diagonally above it, giving us **Pascal's Rule** $\binom{n}{r} + \binom{n}{r+1} = \binom{n+1}{r+1}$.

* The symmetry of Pascal's triangle suggests that $\binom{n}{r} = \binom{n}{n-r}$ for all $r, n \in \mathbb{N}$, $r \leqslant n$.

Can you explain, in the context of combinations, why these properties are true?

HISTORICAL NOTE   THE BINOMIAL THEOREM

The binomial theorem is one of the most important results in mathematics.

The process of multiplying out binomial terms dates back to the beginning of algebra. Mathematicians had noticed relationships between the coefficients for many centuries, and Pascal's triangle was certainly widely used long before Pascal.

Sir Isaac Newton discovered the binomial theorem in 1665, but he did not publish his results until much later. Newton was the first person to give a formula for the binomial coefficients. He did this because he wanted to go further. Newton's ground-breaking result included a generalisation of the binomial theorem to the case of $(a+b)^n$ where n is a rational number, such as $\frac{1}{2}$. In doing this, Newton was the first person to confidently use the exponential notation that we recognise today for both negative and fractional powers.

Sir Isaac Newton

REVIEW SET 1A

1 Express in factorial form:

    a $8 \times 7 \times 6 \times 5 \times 4 \times 3 \times 2 \times 1$ **b** $10 \times 9 \times 8$

2 Simplify:

    a $\dfrac{n!}{(n-2)!}$ **b** $\dfrac{n! + (n+1)!}{n!}$

3 Use the binomial expansion to expand and simplify:

    a $(x+3)^3$ **b** $(x-2)^5$

4 Without simplifying, write down:

    a the 5th term of $(2x+3)^9$ **b** the 8th term of $\left(3x-\dfrac{1}{x}\right)^{12}$.

5 Expand and simplify:

    a $\left(5+\sqrt{3}\right)^3$ **b** $(x+3)(x-1)^4$

6 Use the expansion of $(4+x)^3$ to find the exact value of $(4.02)^3$.

7 Use Pascal's triangle to expand $(a+b)^6$.

    Hence find the binomial expansion of: **a** $(x-3)^6$ **b** $\left(2+\dfrac{1}{x}\right)^6$

8 Find the coefficient of x^{-6} in the expansion of $\left(2x-\dfrac{3}{x^2}\right)^{12}$.

9 Find the coefficient of x^5 in the expansion of $(2x+3)(x-2)^6$.

10 Find c given that the expansion $(1+cx)(1+x)^4$ includes the term $22x^3$.

11   **a** Write down the first four and last two terms of the binomial expansion $(2+x)^n$.

      b Hence simplify $2^n+\binom{n}{1}2^{n-1}+\binom{n}{2}2^{n-2}+\binom{n}{3}2^{n-3}+....+2n+1$.

12 Find the possible values of a if the coefficient of x^3 in $\left(2x+\dfrac{1}{ax^2}\right)^9$ is 288.

REVIEW SET 1B

1 Simplify: **a** $\dfrac{9!}{7!}$ **b** $\dfrac{8!}{3!5!}$

2 Express in factorial form:

    a $7\times6\times5\times4$ **b** $\dfrac{11\times10\times9}{3\times2\times1}$

3 Use the binomial expansion to find:

    a $(x-2y)^3$ **b** $(3x+2)^4$

4 Find the coefficient of x^3 in the expansion of $(2x+5)^6$.

5 Find the constant term in the expansion of $\left(2x^2-\dfrac{1}{x}\right)^6$.

6 Expand and simplify:

    a $\left(2-\sqrt{2}\right)^6$ **b** $(x+3)(2x+1)^3$

7 Write down the first three and last two terms of the following binomial expansions. Do not simplify your answers.

    a $(2x-7)^{10}$ **b** $\left(3x+\dfrac{4}{x}\right)^{13}$

8 Find the coefficient of x^{10} in the expansion of $\left(\dfrac{3}{x^2} - 4x\right)^{10}$.

9 In the expansion of $\left(3x^2 + \dfrac{1}{x}\right)^9$, find:

    a the coefficient of x^{12} **b** the constant term.

10 The first three terms in the expansion of $(1 + kx)^n$, $n \in \mathbb{Z}^+$, are $1 - 4x + \frac{15}{2}x^2$. Find k and n.

11 Find k in the expansion $(m - 2n)^{10} = m^{10} - 20m^9n + km^8n^2 - \dots + 1024n^{10}$.

12 Find the possible values of q if the constant terms in the expansions of $\left(x^3 + \dfrac{q}{x^3}\right)^8$ and $\left(x^3 + \dfrac{q}{x^3}\right)^4$ are equal.

Chapter 2

Quadratic functions

Contents:

OPENING PROBLEM

Energy-conscious Misha wants to use solar energy to heat his cup of coffee. He has decided to build a reflecting surface to focus the sun's light on the cup.

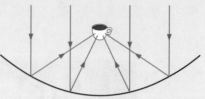

He understands that the sun's rays will arrive parallel, and that each ray will bounce off the surface according to the law of reflection:

    angle of incidence = angle of reflection

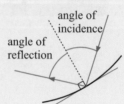

Things to think about:

a What *shape* should the surface have?

b Can we write a *formula* which defines the shape of the surface?

In this Chapter we will study **quadratic functions** and investigate their graphs which are called **parabolas**. There are many examples of parabolas in everyday life, including water fountains, bridges, and radio telescopes.

We will see how the curve Misha needs in the **Opening Problem** is actually a parabola, and how the **Opening Problem** relates to the geometric definition of a parabola.

ACTIVITY 1   CONIC SECTIONS

A cone is *right-circular* if its apex is directly above the centre of the base.

Suppose we have two right-circular cones, and we place one upside-down on the first. Now suppose the cones are infinitely tall.

We call the resulting shape a **double inverted right-circular cone**.

When a double inverted right-circular cone is cut by a plane, 7 possible intersections may result, called **conic sections**:

- a point
- a line
- a line-pair
- a circle
- an ellipse
- a parabola
- a hyperbola

Click on the icon to explore the conic sections.

You should observe how the parabola results when cutting the cone parallel to its slant edge.

DEMO

A   # QUADRATIC FUNCTIONS

A **quadratic function** is a relationship between two variables x and y which can be written in the form $y = ax^2 + bx + c$ where a, b, c are constants, $a \neq 0$.

FINDING y GIVEN x

For any value of x, the corresponding value of y can be found by substitution.

Example 1	🔊 Self Tutor

If $y = -2x^2 + 3x + 1$ find the value of y when:

a $x = 0$ **b** $x = 2$ **c** $x = -3$.

a When $x = 0$,
$$y = -2(0)^2 + 3(0) + 1$$
$$= 0 + 0 + 1$$
$$= 1$$

b When $x = 2$,
$$y = -2(2)^2 + 3(2) + 1$$
$$= -8 + 6 + 1$$
$$= -1$$

c When $x = -3$,
$$y = -2(-3)^2 + 3(-3) + 1$$
$$= -18 - 9 + 1$$
$$= -26$$

SUBSTITUTING POINTS

We can test whether an ordered pair (x, y) satisfies a quadratic function by substituting the x-coordinate into the function, and seeing whether the result matches the y-coordinate.

Example 2	🔊 Self Tutor

Determine whether the given point satisfies the quadratic function:

a $y = 3x^2 + 2x$ $(2, 16)$ **b** $y = -x^2 - 2x + 1$ $(-3, 1)$

a When $x = 2$,
$$y = 3(2)^2 + 2(2)$$
$$= 12 + 4$$
$$= 16$$
$\therefore$ $(2, 16)$ satisfies the function $y = 3x^2 + 2x$.

b When $x = -3$,
$$y = -(-3)^2 - 2(-3) + 1$$
$$= -9 + 6 + 1$$
$$= -2$$
$\therefore$ $(-3, 1)$ does not satisfy the function $y = -x^2 - 2x + 1$.

FINDING x GIVEN y

When we substitute a value for y into a quadratic function, we are left with a quadratic equation. Solving the quadratic equation gives us the values of x corresponding to that y-value. There may be 0, 1, or 2 solutions.

Example 3   ◀) **Self Tutor**

If $y = x^2 - 2x + 3$, find the value(s) of x when:

   a $y = 2$ **b** $y = 18$.

a If $y = 2$ then	**b** If $y = 18$ then
$x^2 - 2x + 3 = 2$	$x^2 - 2x + 3 = 18$
$\therefore\ x^2 - 2x + 1 = 0$	$\therefore\ x^2 - 2x - 15 = 0$
$\therefore\ (x-1)^2 = 0$	$\therefore\ (x-5)(x+3) = 0$
$\therefore\ x = 1$	$\therefore\ x = -3$ or 5

EXERCISE 2A

1 Which of the following are quadratic functions?

   a $y = 2x^2 - 4x + 10$ **b** $y = 8x + 3$

   c $y = -2x^2$ **d** $y = \frac{1}{3}x + 6 - x^2$

   e $2y + x - 3 = 0$ **f** $y - 2x^2 = 3x - 1$

2 For each of the following functions, find the value of y for the given value of x:

   a $y = x^2 + 3x - 7$ when $x = 1$

   b $y = -2x^2 + 5x + 2$ when $x = -2$

   c $y = 3x^2 - 2x - 5$ when $x = 3$

   d $y = -3x^2 + 7x - 2$ when $x = -1$

3 Copy and complete each table of values:

   a $y = x^2 - 3x + 1$

x	-2	-1	0	1	2
y					

   b $y = x^2 + 2x - 5$

x	-2	-1	0	1	2
y					

   c $y = 2x^2 - x + 3$

x	-4	-2	0	2	4
y					

   d $y = -3x^2 + 2x + 4$

x	-4	-2	0	2	4
y					

4 Determine whether the given point satisfies the quadratic function:

   a $y = 2x^2 + 5$ $(0, 4)$ **b** $y = x^2 - 3x + 2$ $(2, 0)$

   c $y = -x^2 + 2x - 5$ $(-1, -8)$ **d** $y = -2x^2 - x + 6$ $(3, -15)$

   e $y = 3x^2 - 4x + 10$ $(2, 10)$ **f** $y = -\frac{1}{2}x^2 + 4x - 1$ $(2, 5)$

5 For each of the following quadratic functions, find the value(s) of x for the given value of y:

   a $y = x^2 + 3x + 6$ when $y = 4$ **b** $y = x^2 - 4x + 7$ when $y = 3$

   c $y = x^2 - 6x + 1$ when $y = -4$ **d** $y = 2x^2 + 5x + 1$ when $y = 4$

   e $y = \frac{1}{2}x^2 + \frac{5}{2}x - 2$ when $y = 1$ **f** $y = -\frac{1}{2}x^2 + 2x - 1$ when $y = 2$

B — GRAPHS OF QUADRATIC FUNCTIONS

The simplest quadratic function is $y = x^2$. Its graph can be drawn from a table of values.

x	-3	-2	-1	0	1	2	3
y	9	4	1	0	1	4	9

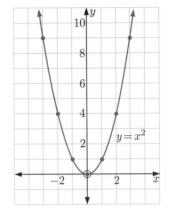

The graph of a quadratic function is called a **parabola**.

The point where the graph "turns" is called the **vertex**.

If the graph opens upwards, the vertex is the **minimum** or **minimum turning point**, and the graph is **concave upwards**.

If the graph opens downwards, the vertex is the **maximum** or **maximum turning point**, and the graph is **concave downwards**.

The vertical line that passes through the vertex is called the **axis of symmetry**. Every parabola is symmetrical about its axis of symmetry.

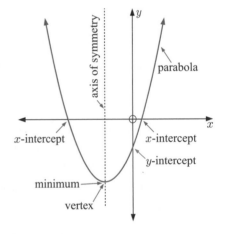

The value of y where the graph crosses the y-axis is the **y-intercept**.

The values of x (if they exist) where the graph crosses the x-axis are called the **x-intercepts**. They correspond to the **roots** of the quadratic equation $ax^2 + bx + c = 0$.

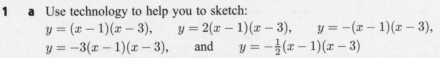

INVESTIGATION 1 — GRAPHING $y = a(x-p)(x-q)$

In this Investigation we consider the properties of the graph of a quadratic stated in factored form. It is best done using a **graphing package** or **graphics calculator**.

What to do:

GRAPHING PACKAGE

1 a Use technology to help you to sketch:

$y = (x-1)(x-3)$, $y = 2(x-1)(x-3)$, $y = -(x-1)(x-3)$,

$y = -3(x-1)(x-3)$,   and $y = -\frac{1}{2}(x-1)(x-3)$

b Find the x-intercepts for each function in **a**.

c What is the geometrical significance of a in $y = a(x-1)(x-3)$?

2 a Use technology to help you to sketch:

$$y = 2(x-1)(x-4), \quad y = 2(x-3)(x-5), \quad y = 2(x+1)(x-2),$$
$$y = 2x(x+5), \quad \text{and} \quad y = 2(x+2)(x+4)$$

b Find the x-intercepts for each function in **a**.

c What is the geometrical significance of p and q in $y = 2(x-p)(x-q)$?

3 a Use technology to help you to sketch:

$$y = 2(x-1)^2, \quad y = 2(x-3)^2, \quad y = 2(x+2)^2, \quad \text{and} \quad y = 2x^2$$

b Find the x-intercept for each function in **a**.

c What is the geometrical significance of p in $y = 2(x-p)^2$?

4 Copy and complete:

• If a quadratic has the form $y = a(x-p)(x-q)$ then it ...... the x-axis at ......

• If a quadratic has the form $y = a(x-p)^2$ then it ...... the x-axis at ......

INVESTIGATION 2   **GRAPHING** $y = a(x-h)^2 + k$

In this Investigation we consider the properties of the graph of a quadratic stated in completed square form. It is best done using a **graphing package** or **graphics calculator**.

What to do:

GRAPHING
PACKAGE

1 a Use technology to help you to sketch:

$$y = (x-3)^2 + 2, \quad y = 2(x-3)^2 + 2, \quad y = -2(x-3)^2 + 2,$$
$$y = -(x-3)^2 + 2, \quad \text{and} \quad y = -\tfrac{1}{3}(x-3)^2 + 2$$

b Find the coordinates of the vertex for each function in **a**.

c What is the geometrical significance of a in $y = a(x-3)^2 + 2$?

2 a Use technology to help you to sketch:

$$y = 2(x-1)^2 + 3, \quad y = 2(x-2)^2 + 4, \quad y = 2(x-3)^2 + 1,$$
$$y = 2(x+1)^2 + 4, \quad y = 2(x+2)^2 - 5, \quad \text{and} \quad y = 2(x+3)^2 - 2$$

b Find the coordinates of the vertex for each function in **a**.

c What is the geometrical significance of h and k in $y = 2(x-h)^2 + k$?

3 Copy and complete:

If a quadratic has the form $y = a(x-h)^2 + k$ then its vertex has coordinates ......

Quadratic form, $a \neq 0$	Graph	Facts
$y = a(x-p)(x-q)$ where $p, q \in \mathbb{R}$		• x-intercepts are p and q • axis of symmetry is $x = \dfrac{p+q}{2}$ • vertex has x-coordinate $\dfrac{p+q}{2}$

Quadratic form, $a \neq 0$	Graph	Facts
$y = a(x - h)^2$ where $h \in \mathbb{R}$	$x = h$ $V(h, 0)$ x	• touches x-axis at h • axis of symmetry is $x = h$ • vertex is $(h, 0)$
$y = a(x - h)^2 + k$ where $h, k \in \mathbb{R}$	$x = h$ $V(h, k)$	• axis of symmetry is $x = h$ • vertex is (h, k)

You should have found that a, the coefficient of x^2, controls the width of the graph and whether it opens upwards or downwards.

> For a quadratic function $y = ax^2 + bx + c$, $a \neq 0$:
>
> • $a > 0$ produces the shape $\smile$ called concave up.
>
> $a < 0$ produces the shape $\frown$ called concave down.
>
> • If $-1 < a < 1$, $a \neq 0$ the graph is wider than $y = x^2$.
> If $a < -1$ or $a > 1$ the graph is narrower than $y = x^2$.

Example 4 ◀ׁ) **Self Tutor**

Sketch the graph using axes intercepts, and state the equation of the axis of symmetry:

a $y = 2(x + 3)(x - 1)$ **b** $y = -2(x - 1)(x - 2)$ **c** $y = \frac{1}{2}(x + 2)^2$

a $y = 2(x + 3)(x - 1)$
has x-intercepts -3, 1
When $x = 0$,
$\quad y = 2(3)(-1)$
$\quad = -6$
$\therefore$ y-intercept is -6

b $y = -2(x - 1)(x - 2)$
has x-intercepts 1, 2
When $x = 0$,
$\quad y = -2(-1)(-2)$
$\quad = -4$
$\therefore$ y-intercept is -4

c $y = \frac{1}{2}(x + 2)^2$
touches x-axis at -2
When $x = 0$,
$\quad y = \frac{1}{2}(2)^2$
$\quad = 2$
$\therefore$ y-intercept is 2

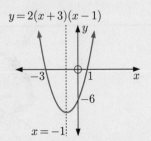

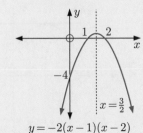

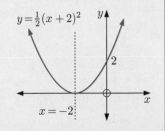

EXERCISE 2B.1

1 Sketch the graph using axes intercepts, and state the equation of the axis of symmetry:

The axis of symmetry is midway between the x-intercepts.

   a $y = (x - 4)(x + 2)$ **b** $y = -(x - 4)(x + 2)$

   c $y = 2(x + 3)(x + 5)$ **d** $y = -3(x + 1)(x + 5)$

   e $y = 2(x + 3)^2$ **f** $y = -\frac{1}{4}(x + 2)^2$

2 Match each quadratic function with its corresponding graph.

   a $y = 2(x - 1)(x - 4)$ **b** $y = -(x + 1)(x - 4)$ **c** $y = (x - 1)(x - 4)$

   d $y = (x + 1)(x - 4)$ **e** $y = 2(x + 4)(x - 1)$ **f** $y = -3(x + 4)(x - 1)$

   g $y = 2(x + 1)(x + 4)$ **h** $y = -(x - 1)(x - 4)$ **i** $y = -3(x - 1)(x - 4)$

A
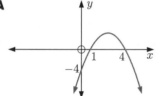

B
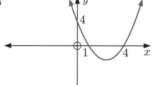

C
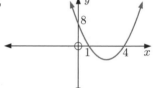

D
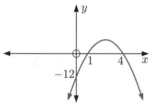

E
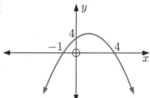

F
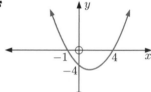

G
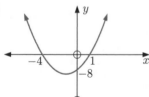

H
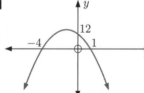

I
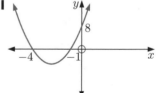

Example 5   ◀)) **Self Tutor**

Use the vertex, axis of symmetry, and y-intercept to graph $y = -2(x + 1)^2 + 4$.

$y = a(x - h)^2 + k$ is called **completed square form**.

The axis of symmetry is $x = -1$.

The vertex is $(-1, 4)$.

When $x = 0$, $y = -2(1)^2 + 4$
                $= 2$

$a < 0$ so the shape is $\frown$

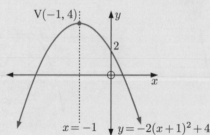

3 Use the vertex, axis of symmetry, and y-intercept to graph:

a $y = (x-1)^2 + 3$ **b** $y = 2(x+2)^2 + 1$ **c** $y = -2(x-1)^2 - 3$

d $y = \frac{1}{2}(x-3)^2 + 2$ **e** $y = -\frac{1}{3}(x-1)^2 + 4$ **f** $y = -\frac{1}{10}(x+2)^2 - 3$

4 Match each quadratic function with its corresponding graph:

a $y = -(x+1)^2 + 3$ **b** $y = -2(x-3)^2 + 2$ **c** $y = x^2 + 2$

d $y = -(x-1)^2 + 1$ **e** $y = (x-2)^2 - 2$ **f** $y = \frac{1}{3}(x+3)^2 - 3$

g $y = -x^2$ **h** $y = -\frac{1}{2}(x-1)^2 + 1$ **i** $y = 2(x+2)^2 - 1$

A
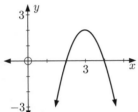

B
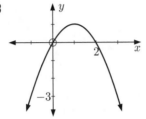

C
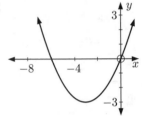

D
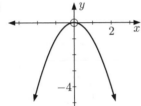

E
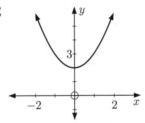

F
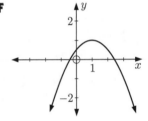

G
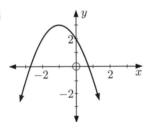

H
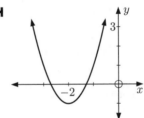

I
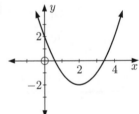

SKETCHING GRAPHS BY "COMPLETING THE SQUARE"

If we wish to graph a quadratic given in general form $y = ax^2 + bx + c$, one approach is to use "**completing the square**" to convert it to the completed square form $y = a(x-h)^2 + k$. We can then read off the coordinates of the vertex (h, k).

Consider the simple case $y = x^2 - 6x + 7$, for which $a = 1$.

$$y = x^2 - 6x + 7$$
$$\therefore \ y = \underbrace{x^2 - 6x + 3^2} \ \underbrace{+7 - 3^2}$$
$$\therefore \ y = \quad (x-3)^2 \quad - 2$$

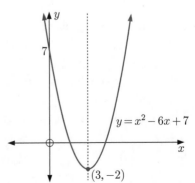

So, the axis of symmetry is $x = 3$ and the vertex is $(3, -2)$.

When $x = 0$, $y = 7$, so the y-intercept is 7.

Example 6   ◄⑨ **Self Tutor**

Write $y = x^2 + 4x + 3$ in the form $y = (x - h)^2 + k$ by "completing the square".
Hence sketch $y = x^2 + 4x + 3$, stating the coordinates of the vertex.

$y = x^2 + 4x + 3$
$\therefore\ y = x^2 + 4x + 2^2 + 3 - 2^2$
$\therefore\ y = (x + 2)^2 - 1$

So, the axis of symmetry is $x = -2$
and the vertex is $(-2, -1)$.

When $x = 0$, $y = 3$
$\therefore$ the y-intercept is 3.

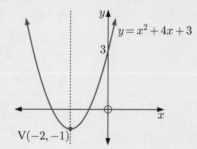

Example 7   ◄⑨ **Self Tutor**

a Convert $y = 3x^2 - 4x + 1$ to the completed square form $y = a(x - h)^2 + k$.
b Hence write down the coordinates of the vertex, and sketch the quadratic.

a $y = 3x^2 - 4x + 1$
$= 3[x^2 - \frac{4}{3}x + \frac{1}{3}]$
$= 3[x^2 - 2(\frac{2}{3})x + (\frac{2}{3})^2 + \frac{1}{3} - (\frac{2}{3})^2]$
$= 3[(x - \frac{2}{3})^2 + \frac{3}{9} - \frac{4}{9}]$
$= 3[(x - \frac{2}{3})^2 - \frac{1}{9}]$
$= 3(x - \frac{2}{3})^2 - \frac{1}{3}$

b The vertex is $(\frac{2}{3}, -\frac{1}{3})$
and the y-intercept is 1.

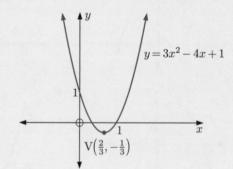

EXERCISE 2B.2

1 Write the following quadratics in the form $y = (x - h)^2 + k$ by "completing the square". Hence sketch each function, stating the coordinates of the vertex.

a $y = x^2 - 2x + 3$ **b** $y = x^2 + 4x - 2$ **c** $y = x^2 - 4x$

d $y = x^2 + 3x$ **e** $y = x^2 + 5x - 2$ **f** $y = x^2 - 3x + 2$

g $y = x^2 - 6x + 5$ **h** $y = x^2 + 8x - 2$ **i** $y = x^2 - 5x + 1$

2 For each of the following quadratics:

i Write the quadratic in the completed square form $y = a(x - h)^2 + k$.

ii State the coordinates of the vertex.

iii Find the y-intercept.

iv Sketch the graph of the quadratic.

> Take out the factor a, then complete the square.

a $y = 2x^2 + 4x + 5$ **b** $y = 2x^2 - 8x + 3$

c $y = 2x^2 - 6x + 1$ **d** $y = 3x^2 - 6x + 5$

e $y = -x^2 + 4x + 2$ **f** $y = -2x^2 - 5x + 3$

SKETCHING QUADRATICS IN THE GENERAL FORM $y = ax^2 + bx + c$

We now consider a method of graphing quadratics of the form $y = ax^2 + bx + c$ directly, without having to first convert them to a different form.

We know that the quadratic equation $ax^2 + bx + c = 0$

has solutions $\dfrac{-b \pm \sqrt{\Delta}}{2a}$ where $\Delta = b^2 - 4ac$.

If $\Delta \geqslant 0$, these are the x-intercepts of the graph of the quadratic function $y = ax^2 + bx + c$.

The average of the values is $\dfrac{-b}{2a}$, so we conclude that:

- the axis of symmetry is $x = \dfrac{-b}{2a}$
- the vertex of the quadratic has x-coordinate $\dfrac{-b}{2a}$.

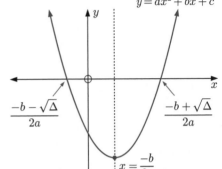

To graph a quadratic of the form $y = ax^2 + bx + c$:

- Find the axis of symmetry $x = \dfrac{-b}{2a}$.
- Substitute this value to find the y-coordinate of the vertex.
- State the y-intercept c.
- Find the x-intercepts by solving $ax^2 + bx + c = 0$, either by factorisation or using the quadratic formula.
- Graph the quadratic using the information you have found.

Example 8   ◀ Self Tutor

Consider the quadratic $y = 2x^2 + 8x - 10$.

   a Find the axis of symmetry.
   b Find the coordinates of the vertex.
   c Find the axes intercepts.
   d Hence sketch the quadratic.

$y = 2x^2 + 8x - 10$ has $a = 2$, $b = 8$, and $c = -10$. Since $a > 0$, the shape is $\smile$

a $\dfrac{-b}{2a} = \dfrac{-8}{2(2)} = -2$

   The axis of symmetry is $x = -2$.

b When $x = -2$,
$$y = 2(-2)^2 + 8(-2) - 10$$
$$= -18$$
The vertex is $(-2, -18)$.

c The y-intercept is -10.
   When $y = 0$, $2x^2 + 8x - 10 = 0$
      $\therefore \;\; 2(x^2 + 4x - 5) = 0$
      $\therefore \;\; 2(x + 5)(x - 1) = 0$
             $\therefore \;\; x = -5$ or 1
   $\therefore$ the x-intercepts are -5 and 1.

d
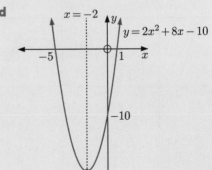

EXERCISE 2B.3

1 For each of the following quadratics:

    i Locate the vertex.

    ii State whether the vertex is a minimum turning point or a maximum turning point.

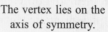

> The vertex lies on the axis of symmetry.

a $y = x^2 - 4x + 2$ **b** $y = x^2 + 2x - 3$

c $y = 2x^2 + 4$ **d** $y = -3x^2 + 1$

e $y = 2x^2 + 8x - 7$ **f** $y = -x^2 - 4x - 9$

g $y = 2x^2 + 6x - 1$ **h** $y = 2x^2 - 10x + 3$

i $y = -\frac{1}{2}x^2 + x - 5$ **j** $y = \frac{1}{4}x^2 - 7x + 6$

2 For each of the following quadratics:

    i State the axis of symmetry.   **ii** Find the coordinates of the vertex.

    iii Find the axes intercepts.   **iv** Hence sketch the quadratic.

a $y = x^2 - 8x + 7$ **b** $y = -x^2 - 6x - 8$ **c** $y = 6x - x^2$

d $y = -x^2 + 3x - 2$ **e** $y = 2x^2 + 4x - 24$ **f** $y = -3x^2 + 4x - 1$

g $y = 2x^2 - 5x + 2$ **h** $y = 4x^2 - 8x - 5$ **i** $y = -\frac{1}{4}x^2 + 2x - 3$

ACTIVITY 2

Click on the icon to run a card game for quadratics.

CARD GAME

C   USING THE DISCRIMINANT

The discriminant of the quadratic equation $ax^2 + bx + c = 0$ is $\Delta = b^2 - 4ac$.

We have used Δ to determine the number of real roots of the equation. If they exist, these roots correspond to zeros of the quadratic $y = ax^2 + bx + c$. Δ therefore tells us about the relationship between the graph of a quadratic function and the x-axis.

The graphs of $y = x^2 - 2x - 3$, $y = x^2 - 2x + 1$, and $y = x^2 - 2x + 3$ all have the same axis of symmetry, $x = 1$.

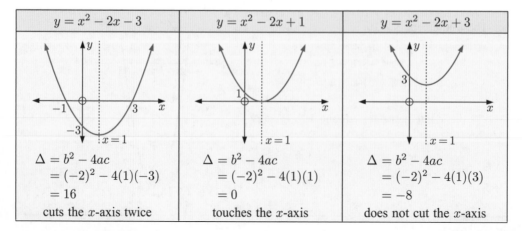

$y = x^2 - 2x - 3$	$y = x^2 - 2x + 1$	$y = x^2 - 2x + 3$
$\Delta = b^2 - 4ac$ $= (-2)^2 - 4(1)(-3)$ $= 16$	$\Delta = b^2 - 4ac$ $= (-2)^2 - 4(1)(1)$ $= 0$	$\Delta = b^2 - 4ac$ $= (-2)^2 - 4(1)(3)$ $= -8$
cuts the x-axis twice	touches the x-axis	does not cut the x-axis

For a quadratic function $y = ax^2 + bx + c$, we consider the discriminant $\Delta = b^2 - 4ac$.

- If $\Delta > 0$, the graph cuts the x-axis twice.
- If $\Delta = 0$, the graph *touches* the x-axis.
- If $\Delta < 0$, the graph does not cut the x-axis.

POSITIVE DEFINITE AND NEGATIVE DEFINITE QUADRATICS

Positive definite quadratics are quadratics which are positive for all values of x. So, $ax^2 + bx + c > 0$ for all $x \in \mathbb{R}$.

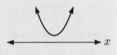

A quadratic is **positive definite** if and only if $a > 0$ and $\Delta < 0$.

Negative definite quadratics are quadratics which are negative for all values of x. So, $ax^2 + bx + c < 0$ for all $x \in \mathbb{R}$.

A quadratic is **negative definite** if and only if $a < 0$ and $\Delta < 0$.

Example 9   ◀ **Self Tutor**

Use the discriminant to determine the relationship between the graph of each function and the x-axis:

a $y = x^2 + 3x + 4$ **b** $y = -2x^2 + 5x + 1$

a $a = 1$, $b = 3$, $c = 4$
$\therefore \ \Delta = b^2 - 4ac$
$\quad = 9 - 4(1)(4)$
$\quad = -7$

Since $\Delta < 0$, the graph does not cut the x-axis.
Since $a > 0$, the graph is concave up.
The graph is positive definite. It lies entirely above the x-axis.

b $a = -2$, $b = 5$, $c = 1$
$\therefore \ \Delta = b^2 - 4ac$
$\quad = 25 - 4(-2)(1)$
$\quad = 33$

Since $\Delta > 0$, the graph cuts the x-axis twice.
Since $a < 0$, the graph is concave down.
The quadratic is neither positive definite nor negative definite.

EXERCISE 2C

1 Use the discriminant to determine the relationship between the graph of each function and the x-axis:

a $y = x^2 + x - 2$ **b** $y = x^2 - 4x + 1$ **c** $y = -x^2 - 3$

d $y = x^2 + 7x - 2$ **e** $y = x^2 + 8x + 16$ **f** $y = -2x^2 + 3x + 1$

g $y = 6x^2 + 5x - 4$ **h** $y = -x^2 + x + 6$ **i** $y = 9x^2 + 6x + 1$

2 Consider the graph of $y = 2x^2 - 5x + 1$.

   a Describe the shape of the graph.

   b Use the discriminant to show that the graph cuts the x-axis twice.

   c Find the x-intercepts, rounding your answers to 2 decimal places.

   d State the y-intercept.

   e Hence sketch the function.

3 Consider the graph of $y = -x^2 + 4x - 7$.

   a Use the discriminant to show that the graph does not cut the x-axis.

   b Is the graph positive definite or negative definite? Explain your answer.

   c Find the vertex and y-intercept.

   d Hence sketch the function.

4 Show that:

   a $2x^2 - 4x + 7$ is positive definite
        b $-2x^2 + 3x - 4$ is negative definite

   c $x^2 - 3x + 6 > 0$ for all x
           d $4x - x^2 - 6 < 0$ for all x.

5 Consider the graphs illustrated.

Let $y = ax^2 + bx + c$ have discriminant Δ_1, and $y = dx^2 + ex + f$ have discriminant Δ_2.

Copy and complete the following table by indicating whether each constant is positive, negative, or zero:

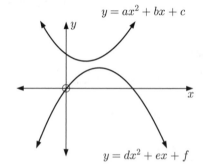

Constant	a	b	c	d	e	f	Δ_1	Δ_2
Sign								

Example 10　　　　　　　　　　　　　　　　　　　　　　🔊 **Self Tutor**

Find the value(s) of k for which the function $y = x^2 - 6x + k$:

   a cuts the x-axis twice
     b touches the x-axis
     c misses the x-axis.

$a = 1, \ b = -6, \ c = k$

$\therefore \ \Delta = b^2 - 4ac$

$ = (-6)^2 - 4(1)(k)$

$ = 36 - 4k$

  a The graph cuts the
    x-axis twice if $\Delta > 0$.

    $\therefore \ 36 - 4k > 0$

    $\therefore \ \ 4k < 36$

    $\therefore \ \ k < 9$

  b The graph touches the
    x-axis if $\Delta = 0$.

    $\therefore \ 36 - 4k = 0$

    $\therefore \ \ k = 9$

  c The graph does not cut
    the x-axis if $\Delta < 0$.

    $\therefore \ 36 - 4k < 0$

    $\therefore \ \ 4k > 36$

    $\therefore \ \ k > 9$

---

6 For each quadratic function, find the value(s) of k for which the function:

     i cuts the x-axis twice
     ii touches the x-axis
     iii misses the x-axis.

   a $y = x^2 + 3x + k$
     b $y = kx^2 - 4x + 1$
     c $y = (k+1)x^2 - 2kx + (k-4)$

7 Explain why $3x^2 + kx - 1$ is never positive definite for any value of k.

8 Find the value of k such that $y = \frac{1}{2}x^2 + (k-2)x + k^2 + 4$ is *not* positive definite. What relationship does the graph have with the x-axis in this case?

D   FINDING A QUADRATIC FROM ITS GRAPH

If we are given sufficient information on or about a graph, we can determine the quadratic in whatever form is required.

Example 11   ◀)) **Self Tutor**

Find the equation of the quadratic with graph:

a

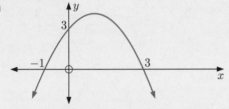

b

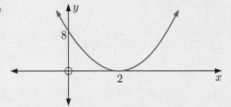

a Since the x-intercepts are -1 and 3,
$y = a(x+1)(x-3)$.
The graph is concave down, so $a < 0$.
When $x = 0$, $y = 3$
$\therefore \quad 3 = a(1)(-3)$
$\therefore \quad a = -1$
The quadratic is $y = -(x+1)(x-3)$.

b The graph touches the x-axis at $x = 2$,
so $y = a(x-2)^2$.
The graph is concave up, so $a > 0$.
When $x = 0$, $y = 8$
$\therefore \quad 8 = a(-2)^2$
$\therefore \quad a = 2$
The quadratic is $y = 2(x-2)^2$.

Example 12   ◀)) **Self Tutor**

Find the equation of the quadratic with graph:

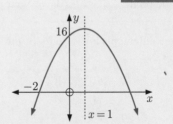

The axis of symmetry $x = 1$ lies midway between the x-intercepts.
$\therefore$ the other x-intercept is 4.
$\therefore$ the quadratic has the form
$\qquad y = a(x+2)(x-4)$ where $a < 0$
But when $x = 0$, $y = 16$
$\therefore \quad 16 = a(2)(-4)$
$\therefore \quad a = -2$
The quadratic is $y = -2(x+2)(x-4)$.

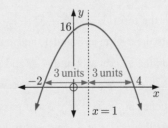

EXERCISE 2D

1 Find the equation of the quadratic with graph:

a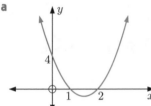

b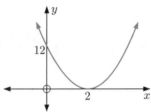

c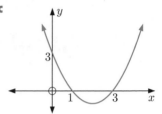

d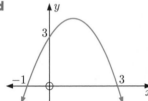

e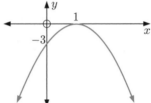

f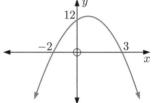

2 Find the equation of the quadratic with graph:

a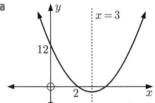

b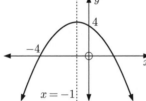

c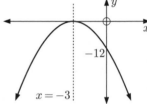

Example 13   ◀) **Self Tutor**

Find the equation of the quadratic whose graph cuts the x-axis at 4 and -3, and which passes through the point $(2,\ -20)$. Give your answer in the form $y = ax^2 + bx + c$.

Since the x-intercepts are 4 and -3, the quadratic has the form $y = a(x - 4)(x + 3),\ a \neq 0$.

When $x = 2,\quad y = -20$

$\quad\quad \therefore\ -20 = a(2 - 4)(2 + 3)$ The quadratic is $y = 2(x - 4)(x + 3)$

$\quad\quad \therefore\ -20 = a(-2)(5)$ $= 2(x^2 - x - 12)$

$\quad\quad\quad \therefore\ a = 2$ $= 2x^2 - 2x - 24$

---

3 Find, in the form $y = ax^2 + bx + c$, the equation of the quadratic whose graph:

  a cuts the x-axis at 5 and 1, and passes through $(2,\ -9)$

  b cuts the x-axis at 2 and $-\frac{1}{2}$, and passes through $(3,\ -14)$

  c touches the x-axis at 3 and passes through $(-2,\ -25)$

  d touches the x-axis at -2 and passes through $(-1,\ 4)$

  e cuts the x-axis at 3, passes through $(5,\ 12)$, and has axis of symmetry $x = 2$

  f cuts the x-axis at 5, passes through $(2,\ 5)$, and has axis of symmetry $x = 1$.

Example 14   ◀ﾘ **Self Tutor**

Find the equation of the quadratic with graph:

a

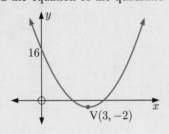

b

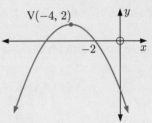

a Since the vertex is $(3, -2)$, the quadratic has the form $y = a(x - 3)^2 - 2$ where $a > 0$.
When $x = 0$, $y = 16$
$\therefore$ $16 = a(-3)^2 - 2$
$\therefore$ $16 = 9a - 2$
$\therefore$ $18 = 9a$
$\therefore$ $a = 2$
The quadratic is $y = 2(x - 3)^2 - 2$.

b Since the vertex is $(-4, 2)$, the quadratic has the form $y = a(x + 4)^2 + 2$ where $a < 0$.
When $x = -2$, $y = 0$
$\therefore$ $0 = a(2)^2 + 2$
$\therefore$ $4a = -2$
$\therefore$ $a = -\frac{1}{2}$
The quadratic is $y = -\frac{1}{2}(x + 4)^2 + 2$.

4 If V is the vertex, find the equation of the quadratic with graph:

a

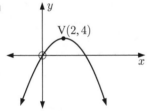

b

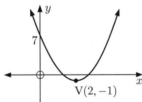

c

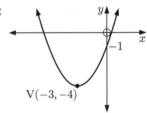

d

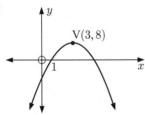

e

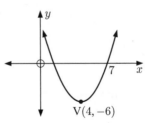

f

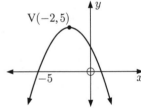

g

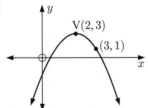

h

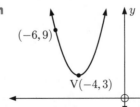

i

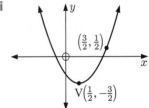

5 A quadratic has vertex $(2, -5)$, and passes through the point $(-1, 13)$. Find the value of the quadratic when $x = 4$.

INVESTIGATION 3   FINDING QUADRATICS

For the quadratic $y = 2x^2 + 3x + 7$ we can construct a table of values for $x = 0, 1, 2, 3, 4, 5$.

x	0	1	2	3	4	5
y	7	12	21	34	51	72

We turn this table into a **difference table** by adding two further rows:

- the row Δ_1 gives the differences between successive y-values
- the row Δ_2 gives the differences between successive Δ_1-values.

x	0	1	2	3	4	5
y	7	12	21	34	51	72
Δ_1		5	9	13	17	21
Δ_2			4	4	4	4

$$9 - 5 \qquad 34 - 21 \qquad 72 - 51$$

What to do:

1 Construct difference tables for $x = 0, 1, 2, 3, 4, 5$ for each of the following quadratics:

    a $y = x^2 + 4x + 3$ **b** $y = 3x^2 - 4x$ **c** $y = 5x - x^2$ **d** $y = 4x^2 - 5x + 2$

2 What do you notice about the Δ_2 row for each quadratic in **1**?

3 Consider the general quadratic $y = ax^2 + bx + c$, $a \neq 0$.

    a Copy and complete the following difference table:

x	0	1	2	3	4	5
y	ⓒ	$a+b+c$	$4a+2b+c$	......	......	......
Δ_1	○		......	......	......	......
Δ_2		○	......	......	......	

    b Comment on the Δ_2 row.

    c What can the circled numbers be used for?

4 Use your observations in **3** to determine, if possible, the quadratics with the following tables of values:

    a

x	0	1	2	3	4
y	6	5	8	15	26

    b

x	0	1	2	3	4
y	8	10	18	32	52

    c

x	0	1	2	3	4
y	1	2	-1	-8	-19

    d

x	0	1	2	3	4
y	5	3	-1	-7	-15

5 We wish to determine the **maximum** number of pieces into which a pizza can be cut using n cuts across it.

For example, for $n = 1$ we have

which has 2 pieces

for $n = 3$ we have

which has 7 pieces.

a Copy and complete:

Number of cuts, n	0	1	2	3	4	5
Maximum number of pieces, P_n						

b Complete the Δ_1 and Δ_2 rows. Hence determine a quadratic formula for P_n.

c For a huge pizza with 12 cuts across it, find the maximum number of pieces which can result.

E   THE INTERSECTION OF GRAPHS

Consider the graphs of a quadratic function and a linear function on the same set of axes.

There are three possible scenarios for intersection:

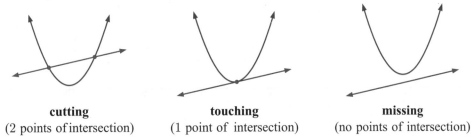

cutting
(2 points of intersection)

touching
(1 point of intersection)

missing
(no points of intersection)

If the line *touches* the curve, we say that the line is a **tangent** to the curve.

The x-coordinates of any intersection points of the graphs can be found by solving the two equations **simultaneously**.

Example 15   ◄)) Self Tutor

Find the coordinates of the point(s) of intersection of the graphs with equations $y = x^2 - x - 18$ and $y = x - 3$.

$y = x^2 - x - 18$ meets $y = x - 3$ where

$\qquad x^2 - x - 18 = x - 3$

$\therefore \ x^2 - 2x - 15 = 0 \qquad \{\text{RHS} = 0\}$

$\therefore \ (x - 5)(x + 3) = 0 \qquad \{\text{factorising}\}$

$\qquad \qquad \therefore \ x = 5 \text{ or } -3$

Substituting into $y = x - 3$, when $x = 5$, $y = 2$ and when $x = -3$, $y = -6$.

$\therefore$ the graphs meet at $(5, 2)$ and $(-3, -6)$.

Graphing each side of an inequality helps us to illustrate its solutions. Any points where the graphs intersect will lie at the endpoints of the interval(s) in the solution.

Example 16   ◄» **Self Tutor**

Consider the curves $y = x^2 + 5x + 6$ and $y = 2x^2 + 2x - 4$.

a Solve for x: $x^2 + 5x + 6 = 2x^2 + 2x - 4$.

b Graph the two curves on the same set of axes.

c Hence solve for x: $x^2 + 5x + 6 > 2x^2 + 2x - 4$.

a $x^2 + 5x + 6 = 2x^2 + 2x - 4$

∴ $x^2 - 3x - 10 = 0$

∴ $(x + 2)(x - 5) = 0$

∴ $x = -2$ or 5

b $y = x^2 + 5x + 6$

$= (x + 2)(x + 3)$ has zeros -2 and -3.

$y = 2x^2 + 2x - 4$

$= 2(x^2 + x - 2)$

$= 2(x + 2)(x - 1)$ has zeros -2 and 1.

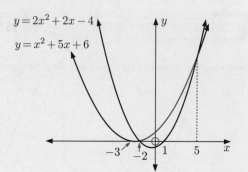

c If $x^2 + 5x + 6 > 2x^2 + 2x - 4$, the graph of $y = x^2 + 5x + 6$ is above the graph of
$y = 2x^2 + 2x - 4$.

This occurs when $-2 < x < 5$.

EXERCISE 2E

1 Find the coordinates of the point(s) of intersection of:

a $y = x^2 - 2x + 8$ and $y = x + 6$ b $y = -x^2 + 3x + 9$ and $y = 2x - 3$

c $y = x^2 - 4x + 3$ and $y = 2x - 6$ d $y = -x^2 + 4x - 7$ and $y = 5x - 4$

2 Use technology to find the coordinates of the points of intersection of the graphs with equations:

a $y = x^2 - 3x + 7$ and $y = x + 5$

b $y = x^2 - 5x + 2$ and $y = x - 7$

c $y = -x^2 - 2x + 4$ and $y = x + 8$

d $y = -x^2 + 4x - 2$ and $y = 5x - 6$.

GRAPHING PACKAGE

3 Consider the graphs with equations $y = x^2$ and $y = x + 2$.

a Find the points where the graphs intersect.

b Plot the graphs on the same set of axes.

c Hence solve for x: $x^2 > x + 2$.

> The solutions to $x^2 > x + 2$
> are the values of x for which
> $y = x^2$ is above $y = x + 2$.

4 Consider the graphs with equations $y = x^2 + 2x - 3$ and $y = x - 1$.

a Find the points where the graphs intersect.

b Plot the graphs on the same set of axes.

c Hence solve for x: $x^2 + 2x - 3 > x - 1$.

5   Consider the curves $y = 2x^2 - x + 3$ and $y = 2 + x + x^2$.

   a Find the points where the curves intersect.

   b Plot the curves on the same set of axes.

   c Hence solve for x: $2x^2 - x + 3 > 2 + x + x^2$.

6 Consider the graphs with equations $y = \dfrac{4}{x}$ and $y = x + 3$.

   a Solve $\dfrac{4}{x} = x + 3$ using algebra.

   b Use technology to plot the graphs on the same set of axes.

   c Hence solve for x: $\dfrac{4}{x} > x + 3$.

Example 17	◀)) **Self Tutor**

$y = 2x + k$ is a tangent to $y = 2x^2 - 3x + 4$.   Find k.

$y = 2x + k$ meets $y = 2x^2 - 3x + 4$ where
$$2x^2 - 3x + 4 = 2x + k$$
$$\therefore\ 2x^2 - 5x + (4 - k) = 0$$

Since the graphs touch, this quadratic has $\Delta = 0$
$$\therefore\ (-5)^2 - 4(2)(4 - k) = 0$$
$$\therefore\ 25 - 8(4 - k) = 0$$
$$\therefore\ 25 - 32 + 8k = 0$$
$$\therefore\ 8k = 7$$
$$\therefore\ k = \tfrac{7}{8}$$

A *tangent* is a line which *touches* the curve.

---

7   For what value of c is the line $y = 3x + c$ a tangent to the parabola with equation $y = x^2 - 5x + 7$?

8   Find the values of m for which the lines $y = mx - 2$ are tangents to the curve with equation $y = x^2 - 4x + 2$.

9   Find the gradients of the lines with y-intercept 1 that are tangents to the curve alongside.

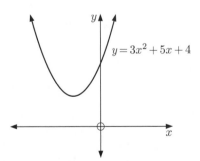

$y = 3x^2 + 5x + 4$

10   **a** For what values of c do the lines $y = x + c$ never meet the parabola with equation $y = 2x^2 - 3x - 7$?

   b Choose one of the values of c found in part **a**. Illustrate with a sketch that these graphs never meet.

11 Prove that two quadratic functions can intersect at most twice.

12 Consider the curve $y = x^2 + 4x - 1$ and the line $y = 2x + c$. Find the values of c for which the line:

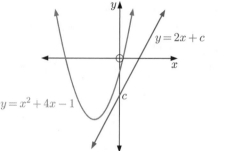

    a meets the curve twice

    b is a tangent to the curve

    c does not meet the curve.

13

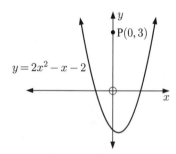

Show that any linear function passing through $P(0, 3)$ will meet the curve $y = 2x^2 - x - 2$ twice.

14 The graphs of $y = (x - 2)^2$ and $y = -x^2 + bx + c$ touch when $x = 3$.
Find the values of b and c.

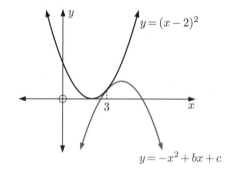

F   PROBLEM SOLVING WITH QUADRATICS

Some real-world problems can be solved using a quadratic equation.

Any answer we obtain must be checked to see if it is reasonable. For example:

- if we are finding a length then it must be positive and we reject any negative solutions
- if we are finding "how many people are present" then the answer must be a positive integer.

We employ the following general problem solving method:

Step 1:	If the information is given in words, translate it into algebra using a variable such as x. Be sure to define what x represents, and include units if appropriate. Write down the resulting equation.
Step 2:	Solve the equation by a suitable method.
Step 3:	Examine the solutions carefully to see if they are acceptable.
Step 4:	Give your answer in a sentence, making sure you answer the question.

Example 18   ◀》 **Self Tutor**

A rectangle has length 3 cm longer than its width, and its area is 42 cm². Find the width
of the rectangle.

If the width is x cm then the length is $(x+3)$ cm.

$$\therefore \ x(x+3) = 42 \quad \{\text{equating areas}\}$$
$$\therefore \ x^2 + 3x - 42 = 0$$
$$\therefore \ x = \frac{-3 \pm \sqrt{3^2 - 4(1)(-42)}}{2}$$
$$\therefore \ x = \frac{-3 \pm \sqrt{177}}{2}$$
$$\therefore \ x \approx -8.15 \ \text{ or } \ 5.15$$

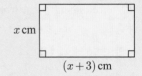

We reject the negative solution as lengths are positive.

The width is about 5.15 cm.

EXERCISE 2F

1 Two integers differ by 12, and the sum of their squares is 74. Find the integers.

2 The sum of a number and its reciprocal is $\frac{26}{5}$. Find the number.

3 The sum of a natural number and its square is 210. Find the number.

4 The product of two consecutive even numbers is 360. Find the numbers.

5 The product of two consecutive odd numbers is 255. Find the numbers.

6 The number of diagonals of an n-sided polygon is given by the formula $D = \frac{n}{2}(n-3)$.
   A polygon has 90 diagonals. How many sides does it have?

7 The length of a rectangle is 4 cm longer than its width. The rectangle has area 26 cm². Find its
   width.

8 A rectangular box has a square base. Its height is 1 cm longer than its
   base side length. The total surface area of the box is 240 cm².
   Suppose the sides of the base are x cm long.

   a Show that the total surface area is given by $A = 6x^2 + 4x$ cm².

   b Find the dimensions of the box.

9

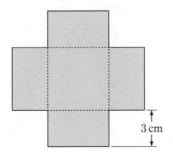

An open box can hold 80 cm³. It is made from a square piece
of tinplate with 3 cm squares cut from each of its 4 corners.
Find the dimensions of the original piece of tinplate.

Example 19 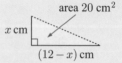 **Self Tutor**

Is it possible to bend a 12 cm length of wire to form the perpendicular sides of a right angled triangle with area 20 cm²?

Suppose the wire is bent x cm from one end.

The area $A = \frac{1}{2}x(12 - x)$

$\therefore \ \frac{1}{2}x(12 - x) = 20$

$\therefore \ x(12 - x) = 40$

$\therefore \ 12x - x^2 - 40 = 0$

$\therefore \ x^2 - 12x + 40 = 0$

Now $\Delta = (-12)^2 - 4(1)(40)$
$= -16$ which is < 0

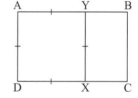

There are no real solutions, indicating this situation is **impossible**.

---

10 Is it possible to bend a 20 cm length of wire into a rectangle with area 30 cm²?

11 The rectangle ABCD is divided into a square and a smaller rectangle by [XY] which is parallel to its shorter sides.
The smaller rectangle BCXY is *similar* to the original rectangle, so rectangle ABCD is a **golden rectangle**.

The ratio $\dfrac{AB}{AD}$ is called the **golden ratio**.

Show that the golden ratio is $\dfrac{1 + \sqrt{5}}{2}$.

Hint: Let $AB = x$ units and $AD = 1$ unit.

12 Two trains travel along a 160 km track each day. The express travels 10 km h⁻¹ faster and takes 30 minutes less time than the normal train. Find the speed of the express.

13
A group of elderly citizens chartered a bus for $160. Unfortunately, 8 of them fell ill and had to miss the trip. As a consequence, the other citizens had to pay an extra $1 each. How many elderly citizens went on the trip?

14 A truck carrying a wide load needs to pass through the parabolic tunnel shown. The units are metres.
The truck is 5 m high and 4 m wide.

  a Find the quadratic function which describes the shape of the tunnel.

  b Determine whether the truck will fit.

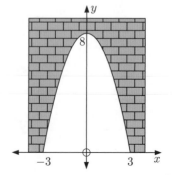

15 A stone is thrown into the air from the top of a cliff 60 m above sea level. The stone reaches a maximum height of 80 m above sea level after 2 seconds.

   a Find the quadratic function which describes the stone's height above sea level.

   b Find the stone's height above sea level after 3 seconds.

   c How long will it take for the stone to hit the water?

G   OPTIMISATION WITH QUADRATICS

The process of finding a maximum or minimum value is called **optimisation**.

For the quadratic $y = ax^2 + bx + c$, we have seen that the vertex has x-coordinate $-\dfrac{b}{2a}$.

- If $a > 0$, the **minimum** value of y occurs at $x = -\dfrac{b}{2a}$.

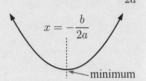

- If $a < 0$, the **maximum** value of y occurs at $x = -\dfrac{b}{2a}$.

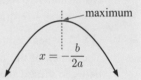

Example 20   ◆) Self Tutor

Find the maximum or minimum value of the following quadratics, and the corresponding value of x:

   a $y = x^2 + x - 3$ **b** $y = 3 + 3x - 2x^2$

a $y = x^2 + x - 3$ has $a = 1$, $b = 1$, and $c = -3$.

Since $a > 0$, the shape is $\smile$

The minimum value occurs when $x = \dfrac{-b}{2a} = -\dfrac{1}{2}$

and $y = (-\frac{1}{2})^2 + (-\frac{1}{2}) - 3 = -3\frac{1}{4}$

So, the minimum value of y is $-3\frac{1}{4}$, occurring when $x = -\frac{1}{2}$.

b $y = -2x^2 + 3x + 3$ has $a = -2$, $b = 3$, and $c = 3$.

Since $a < 0$, the shape is $\frown$

The maximum value occurs when $x = \dfrac{-b}{2a} = \dfrac{-3}{-4} = \dfrac{3}{4}$

and $y = -2(\frac{3}{4})^2 + 3(\frac{3}{4}) + 3 = 4\frac{1}{8}$

So, the maximum value of y is $4\frac{1}{8}$, occurring when $x = \frac{3}{4}$.

EXERCISE 2G

1 Find the maximum or minimum value for each quadratic, and the corresponding value of x:

   a $y = x^2 - 2x$ **b** $y = 7 - 2x - x^2$ **c** $y = 8 + 2x - 3x^2$

   d $y = 2x^2 + x - 1$ **e** $y = 4x^2 - x + 5$ **f** $y = 7x - 2x^2$

2 The profit in manufacturing x refrigerators per day, is given by $P = -3x^2 + 240x - 800$ euros.

   a How many refrigerators should be made each day to maximise the total profit?

   b What is the maximum profit?

Example 21   ◀) **Self Tutor**

A gardener has 40 m of fencing to enclose a rectangular garden plot, where one side is an existing brick wall. Suppose the two new equal sides are x m long.

  a Show that the area enclosed is given by $A = x(40 - 2x)$ m^2.

  b Find the dimensions of the garden of maximum area.

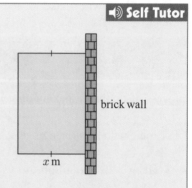

  a Side [XY] has length $(40 - 2x)$ m.

     Now, area = length × width

       $\therefore$ $A = x(40 - 2x)$ m^2

  b $A = 0$ when $x = 0$ or 20.

     The vertex of the function lies midway between these values, so $x = 10$.

     Since $a < 0$, the shape is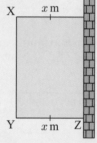

    $\therefore$ the area is maximised when $YZ = 10$ m and $XY = 20$ m.

---

3 A rectangular plot is enclosed by 200 m of fencing and has an area of A square metres. Show that:

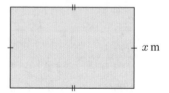

  a $A = 100x - x^2$ where x m is the length of one of its sides

  b the area is maximised if the rectangle is a square.

4 Three sides of a rectangular paddock are to be fenced, the fourth side being an existing straight water drain. If 1000 m of fencing is available, what dimensions should be used for the paddock to maximise its area?

5 1800 m of fencing is available to fence six identical pens as shown in the diagram.

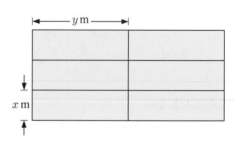

  a Explain why $9x + 8y = 1800$.

  b Show that the area of each pen is given by $A = -\frac{9}{8}x^2 + 225x$ m^2.

  c If the area enclosed is to be maximised, what are the dimensions of each pen?

6 500 m of fencing is available to make 4 rectangular pens of identical shape. Find the dimensions that maximise the area of each pen if the plan is:

a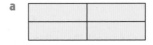

b

7 A tightrope connects two elevated platforms. The curve of the tightrope is given by the equation $y = 0.008x^2 - 0.8x + 50$. The units are metres.

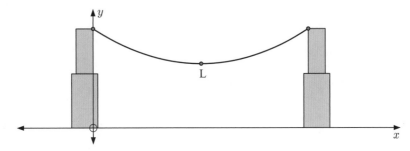

a Find the height of the platforms.

b L is the lowest point along the tightrope. Determine the height of L above ground level.

8

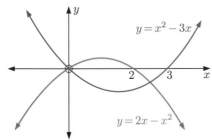

The graphs of $y = x^2 - 3x$ and $y = 2x - x^2$ are illustrated.

a Show that the graphs meet where $x = 0$ and $x = 2\frac{1}{2}$.

b Find the maximum vertical separation between the curves for $0 \leqslant x \leqslant 2\frac{1}{2}$.

9 Infinitely many rectangles may be inscribed within the right angled triangle shown alongside. One of them is illustrated.

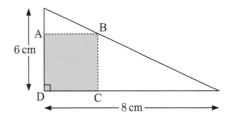

a Let $AB = x$ cm and $BC = y$ cm. Use similar triangles to find y in terms of x.

b Find the dimensions of rectangle ABCD of maximum area.

INVESTIGATION 4   THE GEOMETRIC DEFINITION OF A PARABOLA

A **parabola** is defined as the locus of all points which are equidistant from a fixed point called the **focus** and a fixed line called the **directrix**.

Suppose the focus is $F(0, a)$ and the directrix is the horizontal line $y = -a$. The parabola is the set of all points P such that $FP = NP$ where N is the closest point on the directrix to P.

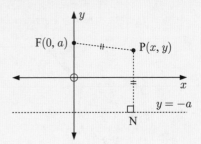

What to do:

1 Suggest why it is convenient to let the focus be at $(0, a)$ and the directrix be the line $y = -a$.

2 Use the circular-linear graph paper provided to graph the parabola which has focus $F(0, 2)$ and directrix $y = -2$.

3 Using the definition on the previous page:

   a Write down the coordinates of N.

   b Write expressions for FP and NP.

   c Show that the parabola has the equation $y = \dfrac{x^2}{4a}$.

4 Consider a point $P\left(X, \dfrac{X^2}{4a}\right)$ on the parabola

$y = \dfrac{x^2}{4a}$ with focus $F(0, a)$ and directrix

$y = -a$.

Let N be the closest point on the directrix to P.

   a Find the coordinates of the midpoint M of [FN].

   b Show that [MP] has equation

$$y = \dfrac{X}{2a}\left(x - \dfrac{X}{2}\right).$$

   c Hence prove that (MP) is a tangent to the parabola.

   d Let B lie on the normal to the parabola as shown. Suppose a ray of light shines vertically down onto the parabola with angle of incidence θ as shown. Notice that [BP] is parallel to [FN].

      i Explain why $M\widehat{N}P$ must equal θ.

     ii Hence explain why $M\widehat{F}P$ must equal θ.

    iii Hence explain why $F\widehat{P}B$ must equal θ.

    iv Hence explain why any vertical ray of light shining down onto a parabolic mirror will be reflected to the focus of the parabola F.

     v Explain what shape Misha needs in the **Opening Problem** and where he needs to place his cup.

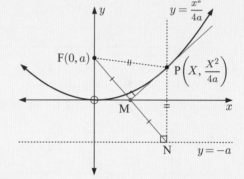

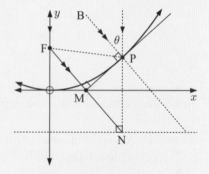

This experiment was performed by Dr Jonathon Hare and Dr Ellen McCallie for the television series "Rough Science".

QUADRATIC INEQUALITIES

> A **quadratic inequality** can be written in either the form $ax^2 + bx + c \geqslant 0$
> or $ax^2 + bx + c > 0$ where $a \neq 0$.

We have seen that the solutions to a quadratic equation are the x-intercepts of the corresponding quadratic function.

In a similar way, the solutions to a quadratic *inequality* are the values of x for which the corresponding function has a particular *sign*.

SIGN DIAGRAMS

A **sign diagram** is a number line which indicates the values of x for which a function is negative, zero, positive, or undefined.

A sign diagram consists of:

- a **horizontal line** which represents the x-axis
- **positive** $(+)$ and **negative** $(-)$ signs indicating where the graph is **above** and **below** the x-axis respectively
- the **zeros** of the function, which are the x-intercepts of its graph.

Consider the three functions below:

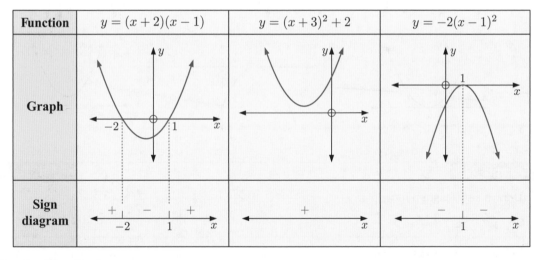

Function	$y = (x+2)(x-1)$	$y = (x+3)^2 + 2$	$y = -2(x-1)^2$

You should notice that:

- A sign change occurs about a zero of the function for single linear factors such as $(x+2)$ and $(x-1)$. This indicates **cutting** of the x-axis.
- No sign change occurs about a zero of the function for squared linear factors such as $(x-1)^2$. This indicates **touching** of the x-axis.

DEMO

> In general:
> - when a linear factor has an **odd power** there is a change of sign about that zero
> - when a linear factor has an **even power** there is no sign change about that zero.

Example 22   ◀)) **Self Tutor**

Draw a sign diagram for:

a
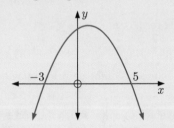

b
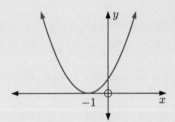

a
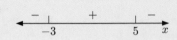

b
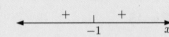

EXERCISE 2H.1

1 Draw a sign diagram for each graph:

a
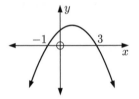

b
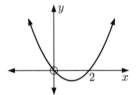

c
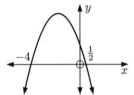

d
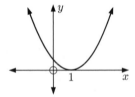

e
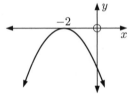

f
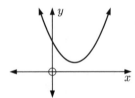

Example 23   ◀)) **Self Tutor**

Draw a sign diagram for:

a $x^2 + 2x - 3$

b $-4(x - 3)^2$

a $x^2 + 2x - 3 = (x + 3)(x - 1)$
which has zeros -3 and 1.

When $x = 2$ we have $(5)(1) > 0$,
so we put a $+$ sign here.

As the factors are single, the signs
alternate.

b $-4(x - 3)^2$ has zero 3.

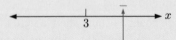

When $x = 4$ we have $-4(1)^2 < 0$,
so we put a $-$ sign here.

As the factor is squared, the signs do not
change.

2 Draw a sign diagram for:

   a $(x+4)(x-2)$ **b** $(x+1)(x-5)$ **c** $x(x-3)$

   d $x(x+2)$ **e** $(2x+1)(x-4)$ **f** $-(x+1)(x-3)$

   g $-(3x-2)(x+1)$ **h** $(2x-1)(3-x)$ **i** $(5-x)(1-2x)$

3 Draw a sign diagram for:

   a $(x+2)^2$ **b** $(x-3)^2$ **c** $-(x-4)^2$

   d $2(x+1)^2$ **e** $-3(x+4)^2$ **f** $-\frac{1}{2}(2x+5)^2$

4 Draw a sign diagram for:

   a x^2-9 **b** $4-x^2$ **c** $5x-x^2$

   d x^2-3x+2 **e** $2-8x^2$ **f** $6x^2+x-2$

   g $6-16x-6x^2$ **h** $-2x^2+9x+5$ **i** $-15x^2-x+2$

5 Draw a sign diagram for:

   a $x^2+10x+25$ **b** x^2-2x+1 **c** $-x^2+4x-4$

   d $4x^2-4x+1$ **e** $-x^2-6x-9$ **f** $-4x^2+12x-9$

QUADRATIC INEQUALITIES

To solve quadratic inequalities we use the following procedure:

- Make the RHS zero by shifting all terms to the LHS.
- Fully factorise the LHS.
- Draw a sign diagram for the LHS.
- Determine the values required from the sign diagram.

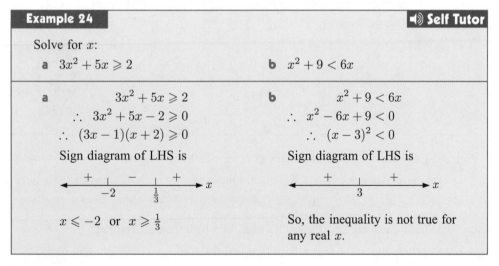

Example 24	◀ Self Tutor

Solve for x:

  a $3x^2+5x \geqslant 2$ **b** $x^2+9<6x$

a
$$3x^2+5x \geqslant 2$$
$$\therefore \ 3x^2+5x-2 \geqslant 0$$
$$\therefore \ (3x-1)(x+2) \geqslant 0$$

Sign diagram of LHS is

$$x \leqslant -2 \ \text{ or } \ x \geqslant \tfrac{1}{3}$$

b
$$x^2+9<6x$$
$$\therefore \ x^2-6x+9<0$$
$$\therefore \ (x-3)^2<0$$

Sign diagram of LHS is

So, the inequality is not true for any real x.

EXERCISE 2H.2

1 Solve for x:

   a $(x-2)(x+5) \leqslant 0$ **b** $(2-x)(x+3) \geqslant 0$ **c** $(x-1)^2<0$

   d $(x+5)^2 \geqslant 0$ **e** $(2x+1)(3-x)>0$ **f** $(x-4)(2x+3)<0$

2 Solve for x:

    a $x^2 - x \geqslant 0$
        b $3x^2 + 2x < 0$
        c $x^2 + 4x + 4 > 0$

    d $x^2 + 2x - 15 \leqslant 0$
        e $x^2 - 4x - 12 > 0$
        f $3x^2 + 9x - 12 < 0$

3 Solve for x:

    a $x^2 \geqslant 3x$
        b $x^2 < 4$
        c $2x^2 \geqslant 4$

    d $x^2 - 21 \leqslant 4x$
        e $x^2 + 30 > 11x$
        f $x + 42 < x^2$

    g $2x^2 \geqslant x + 3$
        h $4x^2 - 4x + 1 < 0$
        i $6x^2 + 7x < 3$

    j $3x^2 > 8(x + 2)$
        k $2x^2 - 4x + 2 > 0$
        l $6x^2 + 1 \leqslant 5x$

    m $1 + 5x < 6x^2$
        n $12x^2 \geqslant 5x + 2$
        o $2x^2 + 9 > 9x$

Example 25   ◀) Self Tutor

Find the value(s) of k for which the function $y = kx^2 + (k + 3)x - 1$:

    a cuts the x-axis twice
    b touches the x-axis
    c misses the x-axis.

$a = k, \ b = k + 3, \ c = -1$

$\therefore \ \Delta = b^2 - 4ac$

$\qquad = (k + 3)^2 - 4(k)(-1)$

$\qquad = k^2 + 6k + 9 + 4k$ So, Δ has sign diagram:

$\qquad = k^2 + 10k + 9$

$\qquad = (k + 9)(k + 1)$

a The graph cuts the x-axis twice if $\Delta > 0$

    $\therefore \ k < -9$ or $k > -1, \ k \neq 0$.

b The graph touches the x-axis if $\Delta = 0$

    $\therefore \ k = -9$ or $k = -1$.

c The graph misses the x-axis if $\Delta < 0$

    $\therefore \ -9 < k < -1$.

> The discriminant Δ is a quadratic in k, so we must solve a quadratic inequality.

---

4 For each quadratic function, find the values of k for which the function:

    i cuts the x-axis twice
    ii touches the x-axis
    iii misses the x-axis.

    a $y = 2x^2 + kx - k$
      b $y = kx^2 - 2x + k$
      c $y = x^2 + (k + 2)x + 4$

5 For each quadratic equation, find the values of k for which the equation has:

    i two real roots
    ii a repeated real root
    iii no real roots.

    a $2x^2 + (k - 2)x + 2 = 0$
      b $x^2 + (3k - 1)x + (2k + 10) = 0$

    c $(k + 1)x^2 + kx + k = 0$

6 For what values of m is $y = (m - 2)x^2 + 6x + 3m$:

    a positive definite
    b negative definite?

7 Consider the curve $y = -x^2 + 3x - 6$ and the line $y = mx - 2$. Find the values of m for which the line:

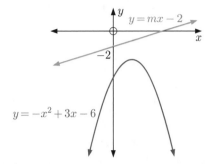

    a meets the curve twice

    b is a tangent to the curve

    c does not meet the curve.

REVIEW SET 2A

1 Use the vertex, axis of symmetry, and y-intercept to graph:

    a $y = (x - 2)^2 - 4$ **b** $y = -\frac{1}{2}(x + 4)^2 + 6$

2 Find, in the form $y = ax^2 + bx + c$, the equation of the quadratic whose graph:

    a touches the x-axis at 4 and passes through $(2, 12)$

    b has vertex $(-4, 1)$ and passes through $(1, 11)$.

3 Find the maximum or minimum value of $y = -2x^2 + 4x + 3$, and the value of x at which this occurs.

4 Find the points of intersection of $y = x^2 - 3x$ and $y = 3x^2 - 5x - 24$.

5 For what values of k does the graph of $y = -2x^2 + 5x + k$ *not* cut the x-axis?

6 Find the values of m for which $2x^2 - 3x + m = 0$ has:

    a a repeated root   **b** two distinct real roots   **c** no real roots.

7 The sum of a number and its reciprocal is $2\frac{1}{30}$. Find the number.

8 Show that no line with a y-intercept of 10 will ever be tangential to the curve with equation $y = 3x^2 + 7x - 2$.

9   **a** Write the quadratic $y = 2x^2 + 6x - 3$ in the form $y = a(x - h)^2 + k$.

    b Hence sketch the graph of the quadratic.

10 Find the equation of the quadratic with graph:

    a   **b**   **c**

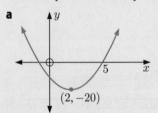
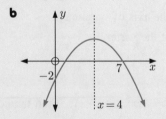
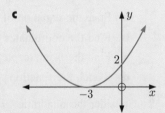

11 Draw the graph of $y = -x^2 + 2x$.

12 Find the y-intercept of the line with gradient -3 which is a tangent to the parabola $y = 2x^2 - 5x + 1$.

13 For what values of k would the graph of $y = x^2 - 2x + k$ cut the x-axis twice?

14 The graph shows the parabola $y = a(x + m)(x + n)$ where $m > n$.

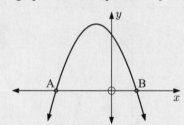

    a State the sign of:

        i the discriminant Δ **ii** a.

    b Find, in terms of m and n, the:

        i coordinates of the x-intercepts A and B

        ii equation of the axis of symmetry.

15 Find the quadratic function which cuts the x-axis at 3 and -2 and which has y-intercept 24. Give your answer in the form $y = ax^2 + bx + c$.

16 For what values of m are the lines $y = mx - 10$ tangents to the parabola $y = 3x^2 + 7x + 2$?

17 When Annie hits a softball, the height of the ball above the ground after t seconds is given by $h = -4.9t^2 + 19.6t + 1.4$ metres. Find the maximum height reached by the ball.

18 Draw a sign diagram for:

    a $(3x + 2)(4 - x)$ **b** $-x^2 + 3x + 18$

19 Solve for x:

    a $(3 - x)(x + 2) < 0$ **b** $x^2 - 4x - 5 \leqslant 0$ **c** $2x^2 + x > 10$

20 Find the values of k for which the function $f(x) = x^2 + kx + (3k - 4)$:

    a cuts the x-axis twice   **b** touches the x-axis   **c** misses the x-axis.

REVIEW SET 2B

1 Consider the quadratic $y = \frac{1}{2}(x - 2)^2 - 4$.

    a State the equation of the axis of symmetry.

    b Find the coordinates of the vertex.

    c Find the y-intercept.

    d Sketch the function.

2 Consider the quadratic $y = -3x^2 + 8x + 7$. Find the equation of the axis of symmetry, and the coordinates of the vertex.

3 Use the discriminant to find the relationship between the graph and the x-axis for:

    a $y = 2x^2 + 3x - 7$ **b** $y = -3x^2 - 7x + 4$

4 Determine whether each quadratic is positive definite, negative definite, or neither:

    a $y = -2x^2 + 3x + 2$ **b** $y = 3x^2 + x + 11$

5 Find the equation of the quadratic with vertex $(2, 25)$ and y-intercept 1.

6 Consider the quadratic $y = 2x^2 + 4x - 1$.

    a State the axis of symmetry.   **b** Find the coordinates of the vertex.

    c Find the axes intercepts.   **d** Hence sketch the function.

7   **a** Find the equation of the quadratic illustrated.

    b Hence find its vertex and axis of symmetry.

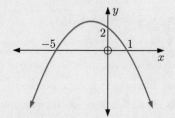

8   **a** For what values of c do the lines with equations $y = 3x + c$ intersect the parabola $y = x^2 + x - 5$ in two distinct points?

    b Choose one such value of c and find the points of intersection in this case.

9 Find the maximum or minimum value of each quadratic, and the corresponding value of x:

    a $y = 3x^2 + 4x + 7$ **b** $y = -2x^2 - 5x + 2$

10 The graph of a quadratic function cuts the x-axis at -2 and 3, and passes through $(-3, 18)$.

    a Find the equation of the function in the form $y = ax^2 + bx + c$.

    b Write down the y-intercept of the function.

    c Find the coordinates of the vertex.

11

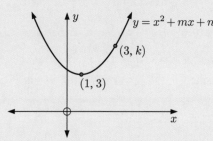

Consider the graph of $y = x^2 + mx + n$.

    a Determine the values of m and n.

    b Hence find the value of k.

12 An open square-based box has capacity 120 mL. It is made from a square piece of tinplate with 4 cm squares cut from each of its corners. Find the dimensions of the original piece of tinplate.

13 Consider $y = -x^2 - 3x + 4$ and $y = x^2 + 5x + 4$.

    a Solve for x: $\quad -x^2 - 3x + 4 = x^2 + 5x + 4$.

    b Sketch the curves on the same set of axes.

    c Hence solve for x: $\quad x^2 + 5x + 4 > -x^2 - 3x + 4$.

14

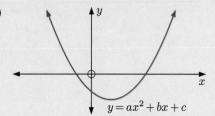

Consider the graph of $y = ax^2 + bx + c$ alongside. Determine the sign of:

    a a **b** b **c** c **d** Δ

Give reasons for your answers.

15 For each of the following quadratics:

  i Write the quadratic in completed square form.

  ii Write the quadratic in factored form.

  iii Sketch the graph of the quadratic, identifying its axes intercepts, vertex, and axis of symmetry.

  a $y = x^2 + 4x + 3$ **b** $y = x^2 + 2x - 3$

  c $y = 2x^2 - 8x - 10$ **d** $y = -x^2 + 6x + 7$

16 Two different quadratic functions of the form $y = 9x^2 - kx + 4$ both *touch* the x-axis.

  a Find the two values of k.

  b Find the point of intersection of the two quadratic functions.

17 600 m of fencing is used to construct 6 rectangular animal pens as shown.

  a Show that the area A of each pen is
  $A = x\left(\dfrac{600 - 8x}{9}\right)$ m^2.

  b Find the dimensions of each pen so that it has the maximum possible area.

  c What is the area of each pen in this case?

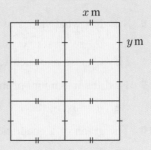

18 Draw a sign diagram for:

  a $x^2 - 3x - 10$ **b** $-(x+3)^2$

19 Solve for x:

  a $4x^2 - 3x < 0$ **b** $2x^2 - 3x - 5 \geqslant 0$ **c** $\frac{11}{3}x \leqslant 2x^2 + 1$

20 Find the values of m for which the function $y = mx^2 + 5x + (m + 12)$:

  a cuts the x-axis twice **b** touches the x-axis **c** misses the x-axis.

Chapter 3

Functions

Contents:

OPENING PROBLEM

The charges for parking a car in a short-term car park at an airport are shown in the table and graph below. The total charge is *dependent* on the length of time t the car is parked.

Car park charges	
Time t (hours)	*Charge*
$0 < t \leqslant 1$	£5.00
$1 < t \leqslant 2$	£9.00
$2 < t \leqslant 3$	£11.00
$3 < t \leqslant 6$	£13.00
$6 < t \leqslant 9$	£18.00
$9 < t \leqslant 12$	£22.00
$12 < t \leqslant 24$	£28.00

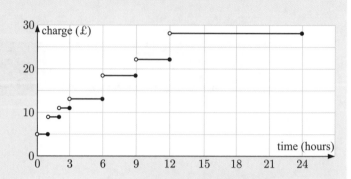

Things to think about:

a What values of *time* are illustrated in the graph?

b What are the possible charges?

c What feature of the graph ensures that there is only one charge for any given time?

In the course so far, we have studied several different relationships between variables. In particular, for two variables x and y:

- A **linear function** is a relationship which can be expressed in the form $y = ax + b$ where a, b are constants, $a \neq 0$.

- A **quadratic function** is a relationship which can be expressed in the form $y = ax^2 + bx + c$ where a, b, c are constants, $a \neq 0$.

In the **Opening Problem** we see another type of relationship, between the two variables *time* and *charge*. We call this a **piecewise function** because its graph has several sections.

In this Chapter we explore what it really means for the relationship between two variables to be called a **function**. We will then explore properties of functions which will help us work with and understand them.

A   RELATIONS AND FUNCTIONS

> A **relation** between variables x and y is any set of points in the (x, y) plane.
> We say that the points *connect* the two variables.

A relation is often expressed in the form of an **equation** connecting the **variables** x and y.

For example, $y = x + 3$ and $x = y^2$ are the equations of two relations. Each equation generates a set of ordered pairs, which we can graph:

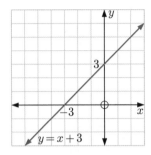 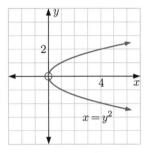

However, not all relations can be defined by an equation. Below are two examples:

(1)

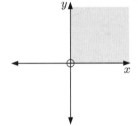

The set of all points in the first quadrant is the relation $x > 0$, $y > 0$.

(2)

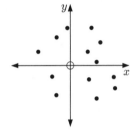

These 13 points form a relation. It can be described as a finite set of points, but not by an equation.

FUNCTIONS

> A **function** is a relation in which no two different ordered pairs have the same x-coordinate or first component.

We can see from this definition that a function is a special type of relation.

Every function is a relation, but not every relation is a function.

ALGEBRAIC TEST FOR FUNCTIONS

> Suppose a relation is given as an equation. If the substitution of any value for x results in at most one value of y, then the relation is a function.

For example:

- $y = 3x - 1$ is a function, since for any value of x there is only one corresponding value of y
- $x = y^2$ is not a function, since if $x = 4$ then $y = \pm 2$.

GEOMETRIC TEST OR VERTICAL LINE TEST FOR FUNCTIONS

> Suppose we draw all possible vertical lines on the graph of a relation.
> - If each line cuts the graph at most once, then the relation is a function.
> - If at least one line cuts the graph more than once, then the relation is not a function.

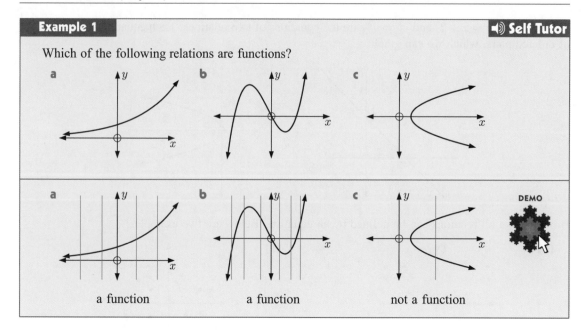

Example 1   🔊 **Self Tutor**

Which of the following relations are functions?

| a function | a function | not a function |

GRAPHICAL NOTE

- If a graph contains a small **open circle** such as ——○—— , this point is **not included**.
- If a graph contains a small **filled-in circle** such as ——●—— , this point is **included**.
- If a graph contains an **arrowhead** at an end such as ——→ , then the graph continues indefinitely in that general direction, or the shape may repeat as it has done previously.

EXERCISE 3A

1 Use algebraic methods to decide whether these relations are functions. Explain your answers.

    a $y = x^2 - 9$ **b** $x + y = 9$ **c** $x^2 + y^2 = 9$

2 Use the vertical line test to determine which of the following relations are functions:

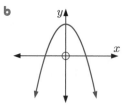

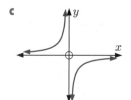

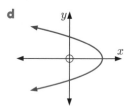

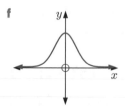

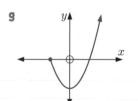

3 Is it possible for a function to have more than one y-intercept? Explain your answer.

4 Is the graph of a straight line always a function? Give evidence to support your answer.

5 The managers of a new amusement park are discussing the schedule of ticket prices. Maurice suggests the table alongside. Explain why this relation between *age* and *cost* is not a function, and discuss the problems that this will cause.

Age	Cost
0 - 2 years (infants)	$0
2 - 16 years (children)	$20
16+ years (adults)	$30

6 The graph alongside shows the curves $y = x^2$ and $y^2 = x$.

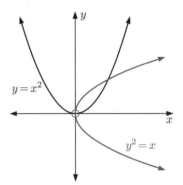

  a Discuss the similarities and differences between the curves, including whether each curve is a function.   You may also consider what transformation(s) map one curve onto the other.

  b Using $y^2 = x$, we can write $y = \pm\sqrt{x}$.

   i What part of the graph of $y^2 = x$ corresponds to $y = \sqrt{x}$?

   ii Is $y = \sqrt{x}$ a function? Explain your answer.

7 The graph alongside shows the curves $y = x^3$ and $y^3 = x$.

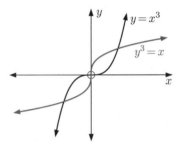

  a Explain why both of these curves are functions.

  b For the curve $y^3 = x$, write y as a function of x.

DISCUSSION

In the **Opening Problem**:

- Is the relation describing the car park charges a function?
- If we know the *time* somebody parked for, can we determine the exact *charge* they need to pay?
- If we know the *charge* somebody pays, can we determine the exact *time* they have parked for?

B   FUNCTION NOTATION

Function machines are sometimes used to illustrate how functions behave.

If 4 is the input fed into the machine, the output is $2(4) + 3 = 11$.

The above "machine" has been programmed to perform a particular function. If we use f to represent that particular function, we can write "f is the function that will convert x into $2x + 3$."

So, f would convert   2 into $2(2) + 3 = 7$ and
$\qquad\qquad\qquad\qquad$ -4 into $2(-4) + 3 = -5$.

This function can be written as:

$$f : \underset{\text{such that}}{x} \longmapsto \underbrace{2x + 3}$$

function f $\qquad$ such that $\qquad$ x is converted into $2x + 3$

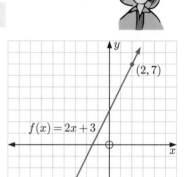

$f(x)$ is read as
"f of x".

Two other equivalent forms we use are $f(x) = 2x + 3$ and $y = 2x + 3$.

$f(x)$ is the value of y for a given value of x, so $y = f(x)$.

f is the function which converts x into $f(x)$, so we write
$f : x \longmapsto f(x)$.

$y = f(x)$ is sometimes called the **function value** or **image** of x.

For $f(x) = 2x + 3$:

- $f(2) = 2(2) + 3 = 7$

   $\therefore$ the point $(2,\ 7)$ lies on the graph of the function.

- $f(-4) = 2(-4) + 3 = -5$

   $\therefore$ the point $(-4,\ -5)$ also lies on the graph.

[graph showing line $f(x) = 2x + 3$ passing through $(2, 7)$ and $(-4, -5)$]

Example 2 $\quad$ ◀)) **Self Tutor**

If $f : x \longmapsto 2x^2 - 3x$, find the value of:

$\quad$ **a** $\ f(5)$ $\qquad\qquad\qquad$ **b** $\ f(-4)$

$f(x) = 2x^2 - 3x$

$\quad$ **a** $\ f(5) = 2(5)^2 - 3(5)$ $\qquad$ {replacing x with (5)}
$\qquad\quad = 2 \times 25 - 15$
$\qquad\quad = 35$

$\quad$ **b** $\ f(-4) = 2(-4)^2 - 3(-4)$ $\quad$ {replacing x with (-4)}
$\qquad\qquad = 2(16) + 12$
$\qquad\qquad = 44$

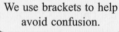

We use brackets to help
avoid confusion.

EXERCISE 3B

1 If $f : x \longmapsto 3x + 2$, find the value of:

$\quad$ **a** $\ f(0)$ $\qquad$ **b** $\ f(2)$ $\qquad$ **c** $\ f(-1)$ $\qquad$ **d** $\ f(-5)$ $\qquad$ **e** $\ f(-\frac{1}{3})$

2 If $f(x) = 3x - x^2 + 2$, find the value of:

$\quad$ **a** $\ f(0)$ $\qquad$ **b** $\ f(3)$ $\qquad$ **c** $\ f(-3)$ $\qquad$ **d** $\ f(-7)$ $\qquad$ **e** $\ f(\frac{3}{2})$

3 If $g : x \longmapsto x - \dfrac{4}{x}$, find the value of:

$\quad$ **a** $\ g(1)$ $\qquad$ **b** $\ g(4)$ $\qquad$ **c** $\ g(-1)$ $\qquad$ **d** $\ g(-4)$ $\qquad$ **e** $\ g(-\frac{1}{2})$

4 The graph of $y = f(x)$ is shown alongside.

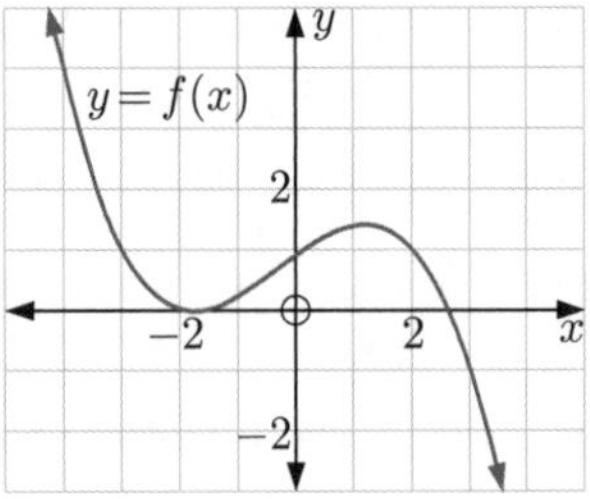

a Find:

i $f(2)$ **ii** $f(3)$

b Find the value of x such that $f(x) = 4$.

5 Suppose $G(x) = \dfrac{2x+3}{x-4}$.

a Evaluate: **i** $G(2)$ **ii** $G(0)$ **iii** $G(-\frac{1}{2})$

b Find a value of x such that $G(x)$ does not exist.

c Find x such that $G(x) = -3$.

Example 3 Self Tutor

If $f(x) = 5 - x - x^2$, find in simplest form:

a $f(-x)$ **b** $f(x+2)$ **c** $f(x-1) - 5$

a $f(-x) = 5 - (-x) - (-x)^2$ {replacing x with $(-x)$}
$= 5 + x - x^2$

b $f(x+2) = 5 - (x+2) - (x+2)^2$ {replacing x with $(x+2)$}
$= 5 - x - 2 - [x^2 + 4x + 4]$
$= 3 - x - x^2 - 4x - 4$
$= -x^2 - 5x - 1$

c $f(x-1) - 5 = (5 - (x-1) - (x-1)^2) - 5$ {replacing x with $(x-1)$}
$= 5 - x + 1 - (x^2 - 2x + 1) - 5$
$= -x^2 + x$

6 If $f(x) = 7 - 3x$, find in simplest form:

a $f(a)$ **b** $f(-a)$ **c** $f(a+3)$
d $f(2a)$ **e** $f(x+2)$ **f** $f(x+h)$

7 If $F(x) = 2x^2 + 3x - 1$, find in simplest form:

a $F(x+4)$ **b** $F(2-x)$ **c** $F(-x)$
d $F(x^2)$ **e** $F(3x)$ **f** $F(x+h)$

8 If $f(x) = x^2$, find in simplest form:

a $f(3x)$ **b** $f\left(\dfrac{x}{2}\right)$ **c** $3\,f(x)$ **d** $2\,f(x-1) + 5$

9 If $f(x) = \dfrac{1}{x}$, find in simplest form:

a $f(-x)$ **b** $f(\frac{1}{2}x)$ **c** $2\,f(x) + 3$ **d** $3\,f(x-1) + 2$

10 f represents a function. Explain the difference in meaning between f and $f(x)$.

11   On the same set of axes, draw the graphs of three different functions $f(x)$ such that $f(2) = 1$ and $f(5) = 3$.

12   Find a linear function $f(x) = ax + b$ for which $f(2) = 1$ and $f(-3) = 11$.

13   Samantha is filling her car with petrol. The amount of petrol in the tank after t minutes is given by $P(t) = 5 + 10t$ litres.

    a   Find $P(3)$, and interpret your answer.

    b   Find t when $P(t) = 50$, and explain what this represents.

    c   How many litres of petrol were in the tank when Samantha started to fill it?

14   For a hot air balloon ride, the function $H(t)$ gives the height of the balloon after t minutes. Its graph is shown alongside.

    a   Find $H(30)$, and explain what your answer means.

    b   Find the values of t such that $H(t) = 600$. Interpret your answer.

    c   For what values of t was the height of the balloon recorded?

    d   What range of heights was recorded for the balloon?

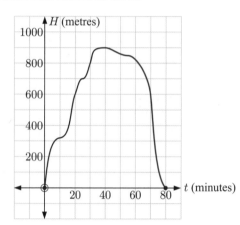

15   Given $f(x) = ax + \dfrac{b}{x}$, $f(1) = 1$, and $f(2) = 5$, find constants a and b.

16   The quadratic function $T(x) = ax^2 + bx + c$ has the values $T(0) = -4$, $T(1) = -2$, and $T(2) = 6$. Find a, b, and c.

17   The value of a photocopier t years after purchase is given by $V(t) = 9000 - 900t$ pounds.

    a   Find $V(4)$, and state what $V(4)$ means.

    b   Find t when $V(t) = 3600$, and explain what this means.

    c   Find the original purchase price of the photocopier.

    d   For what values of t is it reasonable to use this function?

C   DOMAIN AND RANGE

We have seen that a relation is a set of points which connects two variables.

The **domain** of a relation is the set of values which the variable on the horizontal axis can take. This variable is usually x.

The **range** of a relation is the set of values which the variable on the vertical axis can take. This variable is usually y.

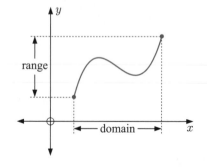

The domain and range of a relation can be described using **set notation**, **interval notation**, or a **number line graph**. For example:

Set notation	Interval notation	Number line graph	Meaning
$\{x \mid x \geqslant 3\}$	$x \geqslant 3$	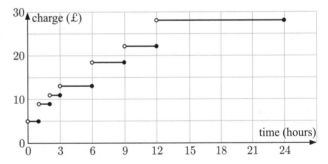	the set of all x such that x is greater than or equal to 3
$\{x \mid x < 2\}$	$x < 2$		the set of all x such that x is less than 2
$\{x \mid -2 < x \leqslant 1\}$	$-2 < x \leqslant 1$		the set of all x such that x is between -2 and 1, including 1
$\{x \mid x \leqslant 0 \ \text{ or } \ x > 4\}$	$x \leqslant 0 \ \text{ or } \ x > 4$		the set of all x such that x is less than or equal to 0, or greater than 4

DOMAIN AND RANGE OF FUNCTIONS

To find the domain and range of a function, we can observe its graph. For example:

(1) In the **Opening Problem**, the car park charges function is defined for times t such that $0 < t \leqslant 24$.

$\therefore$ the domain is $\{t \mid 0 < t \leqslant 24\}$.

The possible charges are £5, £9, £11, £13, £18, £22, and £28.

$\therefore$ the range is
$\{5, 9, 11, 13, 18, 22, 28\}$.

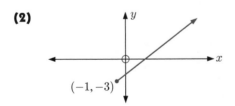

(2)

All values of $x \geqslant -1$ are included, so the domain is $\{x \mid x \geqslant -1\}$.
All values of $y \geqslant -3$ are included, so the range is $\{y \mid y \geqslant -3\}$.

(3)

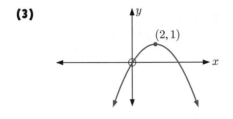

x can take any value, so the domain is $\{x \mid x \in \mathbb{R}\}$ or $x \in \mathbb{R}$.

y cannot be > 1, so the range is $\{y \mid y \leqslant 1\}$.

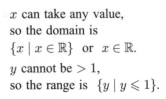

$x \in \mathbb{R}$ means "x can be any real number".

(4)

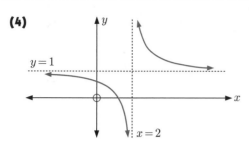

x can take all values except 2,
so the domain is $\{x \mid x \neq 2\}$ or $x \neq 2$.
y can take all values except 1,
so the range is $\{y \mid y \neq 1\}$ or $y \neq 1$.

> To fully describe a function, we need both a rule *and* a domain.

For example, we can specify $f(x) = x^2$ where $x \geqslant 0$.

If a domain is not specified, we use the **natural domain**, which is the largest part of $\mathbb{R}$ for which $f(x)$ is defined.

Some examples of natural domains are shown in the table opposite.

DOMAIN AND RANGE

Click on the icon to obtain software for finding the natural domain and range of different functions.

$f(x)$	*Natural domain*
x^2	$x \in \mathbb{R}$
$\sqrt{x}$	$x \geqslant 0$
$\dfrac{1}{x}$	$x \neq 0$
$\dfrac{1}{\sqrt{x}}$	$x > 0$

Example 4   ◀)) **Self Tutor**

For each of the following graphs, state the domain and range:

a

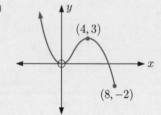

b

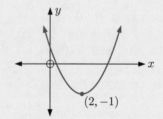

a Domain is $\{x \mid x \leqslant 8\}$
   Range is $\{y \mid y \geqslant -2\}$

b Domain is $\{x \mid x \in \mathbb{R}\}$
   Range is $\{y \mid y \geqslant -1\}$

EXERCISE 3C

1 A driver who exceeds the speed limit receives demerit points as shown in the table.

   a Draw a graph to display this information.

   b Find the domain and range of the relation.

Amount over speed limit (x km h^{-1})	*Demerit points* (y)
$0 < x < 10$	2
$10 \leqslant x < 20$	3
$20 \leqslant x < 30$	5
$30 \leqslant x < 45$	7
$x \geqslant 45$	9

2 This graph shows the temperature in Barcelona over a 30 minute period as the wind shifts.

  a Explain why a temperature graph like this must be a function.

  b Find the domain and range of the function.

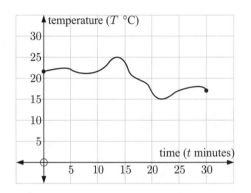

3 For each of the following graphs, find the domain and range:

a $(-1, 3)$

b $(-1, 1)$ $(5, 3)$

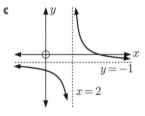

c $y = -1$ $x = 2$

d $(0, 2)$

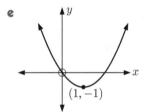

e $(1, -1)$

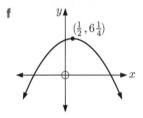

f $(\frac{1}{2}, 6\frac{1}{4})$

g $(-1, 2)$ $(2, -2)$ $(-4, -3)$

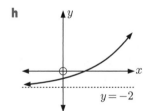

h $y = -2$

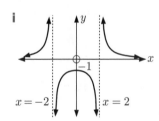

i $x = -2$ -1 $x = 2$

4 Consider the graph of $y = f(x)$ alongside. Decide whether each statement is true or false:

  a -5 is in the domain of f.

  b 2 is in the range of f.

  c 9 is in the range of f.

  d $\sqrt{2}$ is in the domain of f.

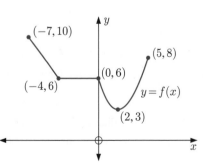

5 Use quadratic theory to find the range of each function:

    a $y = x^2$ **b** $y = -x^2$ **c** $y = x^2 + 2$

    d $y = -2(x+3)^2$ **e** $y = 1 - (x-2)^2$ **f** $y = (2x+1)^2 + 3$

    g $y = x^2 - 7x + 10$ **h** $y = -x^2 + 2x + 8$ **i** $f : x \mapsto 5x - 3x^2$

Example 5   **◄)) Self Tutor**

State the domain and range of each of the following functions:

    a $f(x) = \sqrt{x-5}$ **b** $f(x) = \dfrac{1}{x-5}$ **c** $f(x) = \dfrac{1}{\sqrt{x-5}}$

---

  a $\sqrt{x-5}$ is defined when $x - 5 \geqslant 0$

                                  $\therefore \ x \geqslant 5$

    $\therefore$ the domain is $\{x \mid x \geqslant 5\}$.

  A square root cannot be negative.

    $\therefore$ the range is $\{y \mid y \geqslant 0\}$.

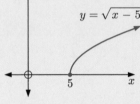

  b $\dfrac{1}{x-5}$ is defined when $x - 5 \neq 0$

                                  $\therefore \ x \neq 5$

    $\therefore$ the domain is $\{x \mid x \neq 5\}$.

  No matter how large or small x is,

  $y = f(x)$ is never zero.

    $\therefore$ the range is $\{y \mid y \neq 0\}$.

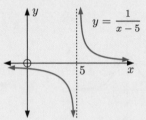

  c $\dfrac{1}{\sqrt{x-5}}$ is defined when $x - 5 > 0$

                                  $\therefore \ x > 5$

    $\therefore$ the domain is $\{x \mid x > 5\}$.

  $y = f(x)$ is always positive and never zero.

    $\therefore$ the range is $\{y \mid y > 0\}$.

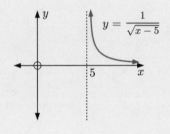

---

6 Consider the function $f(x) = \sqrt{x}$.

    a State the domain of the function.

    b Copy and complete this table of values:

                                    DOMAIN AND RANGE

x	0	1	4	9	16
$f(x)$					

    c Hence sketch the graph of the function.

    d Find the range of the function.

7 State the domain and range of each function:

    a $f(x) = \sqrt{x+6}$ **b** $f : x \mapsto \dfrac{1}{x^2}$ **c** $f(x) = \dfrac{1}{x+1}$

    d $y = -\dfrac{1}{\sqrt{x}}$ **e** $f : x \mapsto \dfrac{1}{3-x}$ **f** $f : x \mapsto \sqrt{4-x}$

| Example 6 | ◄ᴄ Self Tutor |

Use technology to help sketch these functions. Locate any turning points. Hence state the domain and range of the function.

   a $f(x) = -x^4 + 2x - 7$ **b** $f(x) = x^2 - \dfrac{1}{x}$

a

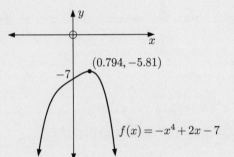

b

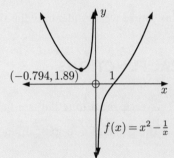

The domain is $\{x \mid x \in \mathbb{R}\}$.   The domain is $\{x \mid x \neq 0\}$.

The range is $\{y \mid y \leqslant -5.81\}$.   The range is $\{y \mid y \in \mathbb{R}\}$.

8   Use technology to help sketch these functions. Locate any turning points. Hence state the domain and range of the function.

 GRAPHING PACKAGE

    a $f(x) = x^3 - 3x^2 - 9x + 10$ **b** $f(x) = x^4 + 4x^3 - 16x + 3$

    c $f(x) = \sqrt{x^2 + 4}$ **d** $f(x) = \sqrt{x^2 - 4}$

    e $f(x) = \sqrt{9 - x^2}$ **f** $f(x) = \dfrac{x + 4}{x - 2}$

    g $f(x) = \dfrac{3x - 9}{x^2 - x - 2}$ **h** $f(x) = x + \dfrac{1}{x}$

    i $f(x) = x^2 + \dfrac{1}{x^2}$ **j** $f(x) = x^3 + \dfrac{1}{x^3}$

    k $f(x) = 3^x$ **l** $f(x) = x\,2^{-x}$

Locating any turning points is important for finding the range.

9   Use technology to sketch these functions on their given domain. Locate the points at the end(s) of the domain, as well as any turning points. Hence state the range of the function.

    a $y = -x^4 + 2x^3 + 5x^2 + x + 2, \quad 0 \leqslant x \leqslant 4$

    b $y = -2x^4 + 5x^2 + x + 2, \quad -2 \leqslant x \leqslant 2$

    c $y = \dfrac{1}{1 + 2^{-x}}, \quad x > 0$

RATIONAL FUNCTIONS

Linear and quadratic functions are the first members of a family called the **polynomials**. The polynomials can all be written in the form $y = a_0 + a_1 x + a_2 x^2 + a_3 x^3 + ...$

When a polynomial is divided by another polynomial, we call it a **rational function**.

However, in this course we consider only the simplest cases of a linear function divided by another linear function.

RECIPROCAL FUNCTIONS

> A **reciprocal function** is a function of the form $y = \dfrac{k}{x}$, $k \neq 0$.
>
> The graph of a reciprocal function is called a **rectangular hyperbola**.

The simplest example of a reciprocal function is $f(x) = \dfrac{1}{x}$. Its graph is shown below.

Notice that:

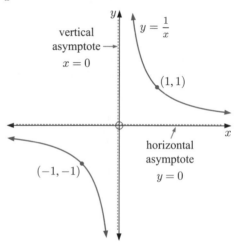

- The graph has two branches.

- $y = \dfrac{1}{x}$ is undefined when $x = 0$, so the domain is $\{x \mid x \neq 0\}$.
  On a sign diagram, we indicate this value with a dashed line.

- The graph includes two **asymptotes**, which are lines the graph approaches but never reaches.

  ▸ $x = 0$ is a **vertical asymptote**.

    We write: as $x \to 0^-$, $\dfrac{1}{x} \to -\infty$

    as $x \to 0^+$, $\dfrac{1}{x} \to \infty$

    When "as $x \to 0^+$, $\dfrac{1}{x} \to \infty$" is read out loud,

    we say "as x tends to zero from the right, $\dfrac{1}{x}$

    tends to infinity."

  ▸ $y = 0$ is a **horizontal asymptote**.

    We write: as $x \to \infty$, $\dfrac{1}{x} \to 0^+$

    as $x \to -\infty$, $\dfrac{1}{x} \to 0^-$

    When "as $x \to \infty$, $\dfrac{1}{x} \to 0^+$" is read out loud,

    we say "as x tends to infinity, $\dfrac{1}{x}$ tends to zero

    from above."

$\to$ means "approaches" or "tends to".

When sketching the graph of a reciprocal function, it is useful to determine some points which lie on the graph.

The reciprocal function $y = \dfrac{k}{x}$ passes through the points $(1, k)$, $(k, 1)$, $(-1, -k)$, and $(-k, -1)$.

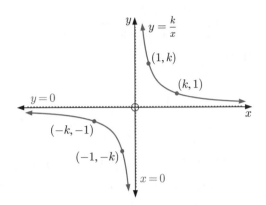

EXERCISE 3D.1

1 **a** Sketch the graphs of $y = \dfrac{1}{x}$, $y = \dfrac{2}{x}$, and $y = \dfrac{4}{x}$ on the same set of axes.

DEMO

   b For the function $y = \dfrac{k}{x}$, $k > 0$:

   i Describe the effect of varying k.

   ii State the quadrants in which the graph lies.

   iii Draw a sign diagram for the function.

2 **a** Sketch the graphs of $y = -\dfrac{1}{x}$, $y = -\dfrac{2}{x}$, and $y = -\dfrac{4}{x}$ on the same set of axes.

   b For the function $y = \dfrac{k}{x}$, $k < 0$:

   i Describe the effect of varying k.

   ii State the quadrants in which the graph lies.

   iii Draw a sign diagram for the function.

3 For the reciprocal function $y = \dfrac{k}{x}$, $k \neq 0$, state:

   a the domain

   b the range

   c the vertical asymptote

   d the horizontal asymptote.

4 Determine the equation of each reciprocal function:

a
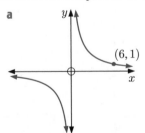

b
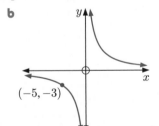

c
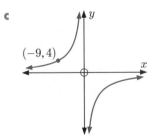

RATIONAL FUNCTIONS OF THE FORM $y = \dfrac{ax + b}{cx + d}$, $c \neq 0$

We now consider the rational functions which result when a linear function is divided by another linear function.

The graphs of these rational functions also have horizontal and vertical asymptotes.

INVESTIGATION   RATIONAL FUNCTIONS

What to do:

1   Use technology to examine graphs of the following functions. For each graph:
    GRAPHING
    PACKAGE

    i State the domain.   **ii** Write down the equations of the asymptotes.

    a $y = -1 + \dfrac{3}{x-2}$ **b** $y = \dfrac{3x+1}{x+2}$ **c** $y = \dfrac{2x-9}{3-x}$

2   Experiment with functions of the form $y = \dfrac{b}{cx+d} + a$ where $b, c \neq 0$.

    For an equation of this form, state the equation of:

    a the horizontal asymptote   **b** the vertical asymptote.

3   Experiment with functions of the form $y = \dfrac{ax+b}{cx+d}$ where $c \neq 0$.

    a For an equation of this form, state the equation of the vertical asymptote.

    b Can you see how to quickly write down the equation of the horizontal asymptote? Explain
       your answer.

- For a function written in the form $y = \dfrac{b}{cx+d} + a$ where $b, c \neq 0$:

  ▸ the vertical asymptote is $x = -\dfrac{d}{c}$ ▸ the horizontal asymptote is $y = a$.

- For a function written in the form $y = \dfrac{ax+b}{cx+d}$ where $c \neq 0$:

  ▸ the vertical asymptote is $x = -\dfrac{d}{c}$ ▸ the horizontal asymptote is $y = \dfrac{a}{c}$.

Example 7   ◀ᴺ) Self Tutor

Consider the function $y = \dfrac{6}{x-2} + 4$.

  a Find the asymptotes of the function.   **b** Find the axes intercepts.

  c Use technology to help sketch the function, including the features found in **a** and **b**.

---

a The vertical asymptote is $x = 2$.
   The horizontal asymptote is $y = 4$.

b When $y = 0$, $\dfrac{6}{x-2} = -4$

   $\therefore\ -4(x-2) = 6$

   $\therefore\ -4x + 8 = 6$

   $\therefore\ -4x = -2$

   $\therefore\ x = \tfrac{1}{2}$

When $x = 0$, $y = \dfrac{6}{-2} + 4 = 1$

So, the x-intercept is $\tfrac{1}{2}$ and the
y-intercept is 1.

c
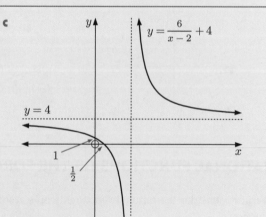

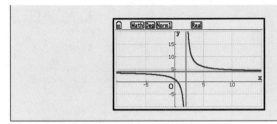 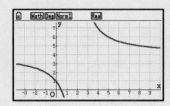

EXERCISE 3D.2

1 For each of the following functions:

    i Find the equations of the asymptotes.　　**ii** State the domain and range.

    iii Find the axes intercepts.

    iv Discuss the behaviour of the function as it approaches its asymptotes.

    v Sketch the graph of the function.

a $f(x) = \dfrac{3}{x-2}$　　　　　**b** $f : x \mapsto 2 + \dfrac{1}{x-3}$　　　　　**c** $f(x) = 2 - \dfrac{3}{x+1}$

Example 8　　　　　　　　　　　　　　　　　　　　　　　◀⧉ **Self Tutor**

Draw a sign diagram for $\dfrac{x-1}{2x+1}$.

$\dfrac{x-1}{2x+1}$ is zero when $x = 1$ and undefined when $x = -\frac{1}{2}$.

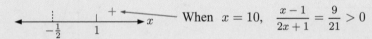　　　When $x = 10$,　$\dfrac{x-1}{2x+1} = \dfrac{9}{21} > 0$

Since $(x-1)$ and $(2x+1)$ are single factors, the signs alternate.

---

2 Draw the sign diagram for:

a
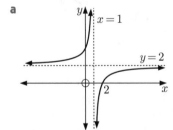　　　**b**
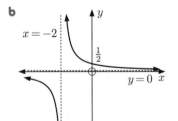　　　**c**
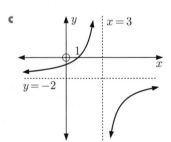

3 Draw a sign diagram for:

a $\dfrac{x+2}{x-1}$　　　　**b** $\dfrac{x}{x+3}$　　　　**c** $\dfrac{x+1}{x+5}$　　　　**d** $\dfrac{x-2}{2x+1}$

e $\dfrac{2x+3}{4-x}$　　　　**f** $\dfrac{4x-1}{2-x}$　　　　**g** $\dfrac{3x}{x-2}$　　　　**h** $\dfrac{-8x}{3-x}$

Example 9   ◀ᴴⁱ)) **Self Tutor**

Consider the function $f(x) = \dfrac{2x+1}{x-1}$.

  a Find the vertical asymptote of the function.   **b** Find the axes intercepts.

  c Rearrange the function to find the horizontal asymptote.

  d Draw a sign diagram of the function.

  e Hence discuss the behaviour of the function near the asymptotes.

  f Sketch the function, showing the features you have found.

---

  a The vertical asymptote is $x = 1$.

  b $f(0) = \dfrac{1}{-1} = -1$, so the y-intercept is -1.

     $f(x) = 0$ when $2x + 1 = 0$

                   $\therefore \ x = -\tfrac{1}{2}$

     $\therefore$ the x-intercept is $-\tfrac{1}{2}$.

  c $f(x) = \dfrac{2x+1}{x-1}$

         $= \dfrac{2(x-1)+3}{x-1}$

         $= 2 + \dfrac{3}{x-1}$

     $\therefore$ the horizontal asymptote is $y = 2$.

  d

     $\xleftarrow{\quad + \quad | \quad - \quad \vdots \quad + \quad}\to x$
            $-\tfrac{1}{2}$ 1

  f
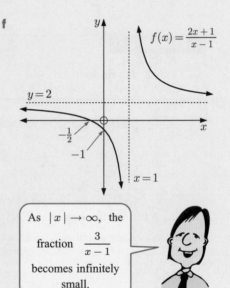

  e As $x \to 1^-$, $f(x) \to -\infty$

     As $x \to 1^+$, $f(x) \to \infty$

     As $x \to -\infty$, $f(x) \to 2^-$

     As $x \to \infty$, $f(x) \to 2^+$

As $|x| \to \infty$, the fraction $\dfrac{3}{x-1}$ becomes infinitely small.

---

4 For each of the following functions:

    i Find the equation of the vertical asymptote.

    ii Find the axes intercepts.

   iii Rearrange the function to find the horizontal asymptote.

   iv Draw a sign diagram of the function.

    v Hence discuss the behaviour of the function near its asymptotes.

   vi Sketch the graph of the function.

  a $f(x) = \dfrac{x}{x-1}$ **b** $f : x \mapsto \dfrac{x+3}{x-2}$ **c** $f(x) = \dfrac{3x-1}{x+2}$

  d $f(x) = -\dfrac{2x+1}{x-3}$ **e** $f : x \mapsto \dfrac{2x+4}{3-x}$ **f** $f(x) = \dfrac{x+3}{2x-1}$

5 Consider the function $y = \dfrac{ax + b}{cx + d}$, where a, b, c, d are constants and $c \neq 0$.

    a State the domain of the function.

    b State the equation of the vertical asymptote.

    c Find the axes intercepts.

    d Show that for $c \neq 0$, $\dfrac{ax + b}{cx + d} = \dfrac{a}{c} + \dfrac{b - \frac{ad}{c}}{cx + d}$.

    Hence explain why the horizontal asymptote is $y = \dfrac{a}{c}$.

ACTIVITY

Click on the icon to run a card game for rational functions.

GAME

E   COMPOSITE FUNCTIONS

Given $f : x \mapsto f(x)$ and $g : x \mapsto g(x)$, the **composite function** of f and g will convert x into $f(g(x))$.

$f \circ g$ is used to represent the composite function of f and g. It means "f following g".

$$(f \circ g)(x) = f(g(x)) \qquad \text{or} \qquad f \circ g : x \mapsto f(g(x)).$$

Consider $f : x \mapsto x^4$ and $g : x \mapsto 2x + 3$.

$f \circ g$ means that g converts x to $2x + 3$ and then f converts $(2x + 3)$ to $(2x + 3)^4$.

This is illustrated by the two function machines below.

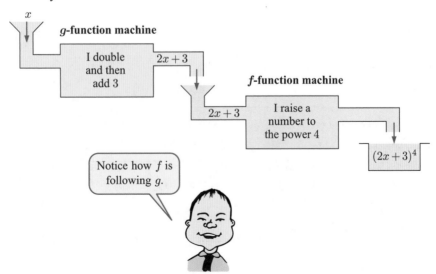

Algebraically, if $f(x) = x^4$ and $g(x) = 2x + 3$ then

$$(f \circ g)(x) = f(g(x))$$
$$= f(2x + 3) \qquad \{g \text{ operates on } x \text{ first}\}$$
$$= (2x + 3)^4 \qquad \{f \text{ operates on } g(x) \text{ next}\}$$

and $(g \circ f)(x) = g(f(x))$
$$= g(x^4) \qquad \{f \text{ operates on } x \text{ first}\}$$
$$= 2(x^4) + 3 \qquad \{g \text{ operates on } f(x) \text{ next}\}$$
$$= 2x^4 + 3$$

So, $f(g(x)) \neq g(f(x))$.

> In general, $(f \circ g)(x) \neq (g \circ f)(x)$.

Example 10 ◀) **Self Tutor**

Given $f : x \mapsto 2x + 1$ and $g : x \mapsto 3 - 4x$, find in simplest form:

a $(f \circ g)(x)$ **b** $(g \circ f)(x)$

$f(x) = 2x + 1$ and $g(x) = 3 - 4x$

a $(f \circ g)(x) = f(g(x))$
$$= f(3 - 4x)$$
$$= 2(3 - 4x) + 1$$
$$= 6 - 8x + 1$$
$$= 7 - 8x$$

b $(g \circ f)(x) = g(f(x))$
$$= g(2x + 1)$$
$$= 3 - 4(2x + 1)$$
$$= 3 - 8x - 4$$
$$= -8x - 1$$

In the previous Example you should have observed how we can substitute an expression into a function.

If $f(x) = 2x + 1$ then $\qquad f(\Delta) = 2(\Delta) + 1$
$$\text{and so} \quad f(3 - 4x) = 2(3 - 4x) + 1.$$

Example 11 ◀) **Self Tutor**

Given $f(x) = 6x - 5$ and $g(x) = x^2 + x$, find:

a $(g \circ f)(-1)$ **b** $(f \circ f)(0)$

a $(g \circ f)(-1) = g(f(-1))$
Now $f(-1) = 6(-1) - 5$
$$= -11$$
$\therefore (g \circ f)(-1) = g(-11)$
$$= (-11)^2 + (-11)$$
$$= 110$$

b $(f \circ f)(0) = f(f(0))$
Now $f(0) = 6(0) - 5$
$$= -5$$
$\therefore (f \circ f)(0) = f(-5)$
$$= 6(-5) - 5$$
$$= -35$$

You should be aware that the domain of the composite of two functions depends on the domains of the original functions.

For example, consider $f(x) = x^2$ with domain $x \in \mathbb{R}$ and $g(x) = \sqrt{x}$ with domain $x \geqslant 0$.

$$(f \circ g)(x) = f(g(x))$$
$$= (\sqrt{x})^2$$
$$= x$$

The domain of $(f \circ g)(x)$ is $x \geqslant 0$, not $\mathbb{R}$, since $(f \circ g)(x)$ is defined using function $g(x)$.

EXERCISE 3E

1 Given $f : x \mapsto 2x + 3$ and $g : x \mapsto 1 - x$, find in simplest form:
   a $(f \circ g)(x)$ b $(g \circ f)(x)$ c $(f \circ g)(-3)$ d $(g \circ f)(0)$

2 Given $f : x \mapsto -2x$ and $g : x \mapsto 1 + x^2$, find in simplest form:
   a $(f \circ g)(x)$ b $(g \circ f)(x)$ c $(f \circ g)(2)$ d $(f \circ f)(-1)$

3 Given $f(x) = 3 - x^2$ and $g(x) = 2x + 4$, find in simplest form:
   a $(f \circ g)(x)$ b $(g \circ f)(x)$ c $(g \circ g)(\frac{1}{2})$ d $(f \circ f)(-\frac{1}{2})$

4 Given $f(x) = \sqrt{6 - x}$ and $g(x) = 5x - 7$, find:
   a $(g \circ g)(x)$ b $(f \circ g)(1)$ c $(g \circ f)(6)$ d $(f \circ f)(2)$

5 Suppose $f : x \mapsto x^2 + 1$ and $g : x \mapsto 3 - x$.
   a Find in simplest form:
      i $(f \circ g)(x)$ ii $(g \circ f)(x)$
   b Find the value(s) of x such that $(g \circ f)(x) = f(x)$.

6 Suppose $f(x) = 9 - \sqrt{x}$ and $g(x) = x^2 + 4$.
   a Find $(f \circ g)(x)$ and state its domain and range.   b Find $(g \circ f)(4)$.
   c Find $(f \circ f)(x)$ and state its domain and range.

7 Suppose $f(x) = 1 - 2x$ and $g(x) = 3x + 5$.
   a Find $f(g(x))$.   b Hence solve $(f \circ g)(x) = f(x + 3)$.

8 Suppose $f : x \mapsto 2x - x^2$ and $g : x \mapsto 1 + 3x$.
   a Find in simplest form:
      i $(f \circ g)(x)$ ii $(g \circ f)(x)$
   b Find the value(s) of x such that $(f \circ g)(x) = 3(g \circ f)(x)$.

9 For each pair of functions, find $(f \circ g)(x)$ and state its domain and range:
   a $f(x) = \dfrac{1}{x}$ and $g(x) = x - 3$ b $f(x) = -\dfrac{1}{x}$ and $g(x) = x^2 + 3x + 2$

10 a If $ax + b = cx + d$ for all values of x, show that $a = c$ and $b = d$.
      Hint: If it is true for all x, it is true for $x = 0$ and $x = 1$.
   b Given $f(x) = 2x + 3$ and $g(x) = ax + b$ and that $(f \circ g)(x) = x$ for all values of x, deduce that $a = \frac{1}{2}$ and $b = -\frac{3}{2}$.
   c Is the result in b true if $(g \circ f)(x) = x$ for all x?

11 Suppose $f(x) = \sqrt{1-x}$ and $g(x) = x^2$. Find:

    a $(f \circ g)(x)$ **b** the domain and range of $(f \circ g)(x)$.

12 Suppose $f(x)$ and $g(x)$ are functions. $f(x)$ has domain D_f and range R_f. $g(x)$ has domain D_g and range R_g.

    a Under what circumstance will $(f \circ g)(x)$ be defined?

    b Assuming $(f \circ g)(x)$ is defined, find its domain.

F   INVERSE FUNCTIONS

The operations of $+$ and $-$, $\times$ and $\div$, are **inverse operations** as one "undoes" what the other does.

The function $y = 2x + 3$ can be "undone" by its *inverse* function $y = \dfrac{x - 3}{2}$.

We can think of this as two machines. If the machines are inverses then the second machine *undoes* what the first machine does.

No matter what value of x enters the first machine, it is returned as the output from the second machine.

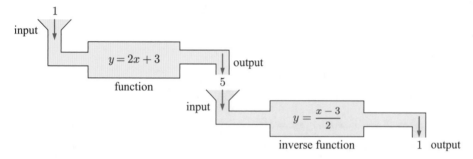

A function $y = f(x)$ *may or may not* have an inverse function. To understand which functions do have inverses, we need some more terminology.

ONE-TO-ONE AND MANY-TO-ONE FUNCTIONS

A **one-to-one** function is any function where:

- for each x there is only one value of y and
- for each y there is only one value of x.

Equivalently, a function is one-to-one if $f(a) = f(b)$ only when $a = b$.

One-to-one functions satisfy both the **vertical line test** and the **horizontal line test**.

This means that:

- no vertical line can meet the graph more than once
- no horizontal line can meet the graph more than once.

For example, $f(x) = x^3$ is one-to-one since it passes both the vertical line and horizontal line tests.

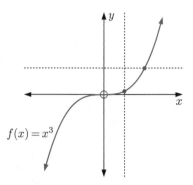

If the function $f(x)$ is **one-to-one**, it will have an inverse function which we denote $f^{-1}(x)$.

Functions that are not one-to-one are called **many-to-one**. While these functions satisfy the vertical line test, they *do not* satisfy the horizontal line test. At least one y-value has more than one corresponding x-value.

For example, $f(x) = x^2$ fails the horizontal line test, since if $f(x) = 4$ then $x = -2$ or 2.

$f(x) = x^2$ is therefore many-to-one.

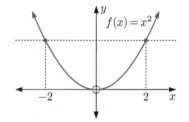

If a function $f(x)$ is **many-to-one**, it *does not* have an inverse function.

PROPERTIES OF THE INVERSE FUNCTION

If $f(x)$ has an **inverse function**, this new function:

- is denoted $f^{-1}(x)$
- must satisfy the vertical line test
- has a graph which is the reflection of $y = f(x)$ in the line $y = x$
- satisfies $(f \circ f^{-1})(x) = x$ and $(f^{-1} \circ f)(x) = x$.

The function $y = x$ is called the **identity function** because it is its own inverse, and when its inverse is found, (x, y) maps onto itself.

$f^{-1}(x)$ is the **inverse** of f. In general,
$$f^{-1}(x) \neq \frac{1}{f(x)}.$$

If (x, y) lies on f, then (y, x) must lie on f^{-1}.

Geometrically, this is achieved by *reflecting* the graph of $y = f(x)$ in the line $y = x$.

Algebraically, we find the formula for an inverse function by exchanging x and y.

For example, $f : y = 5x + 2$ becomes $f^{-1} : x = 5y + 2$,

which we rearrange to obtain $f^{-1} : y = \dfrac{x - 2}{5}$.

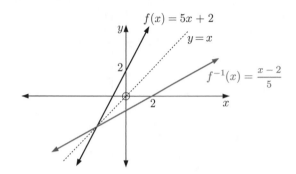

$y = f^{-1}(x)$ is the inverse of $y = f(x)$ as:

- it is also a function
- it is the reflection of $y = f(x)$ in the line $y = x$.

If $f(x)$ has an inverse function $f^{-1}(x)$, then:

The domain of f^{-1} is equal to the range of f.

The range of f^{-1} is equal to the domain of f.

Example 12   ◀)) Self Tutor

Consider $f : x \mapsto 2x + 3$.

a On the same axes, graph f and its inverse function f^{-1}.

b Find $f^{-1}(x)$ using:

   i coordinate geometry and the gradient of $y = f^{-1}(x)$ from **a**

   ii variable interchange.

c Check that $(f \circ f^{-1})(x) = (f^{-1} \circ f)(x) = x$

a $f(x) = 2x + 3$ passes through $(0, 3)$ and $(2, 7)$.

$\therefore$ $f^{-1}(x)$ passes through $(3, 0)$ and $(7, 2)$.

If f includes point (a, b) then f^{-1} includes point (b, a).

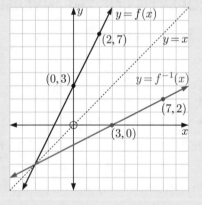

b **i** $y = f^{-1}(x)$ has gradient $\dfrac{2-0}{7-3} = \dfrac{1}{2}$

       Its equation is $\dfrac{y-0}{x-3} = \dfrac{1}{2}$

            $\therefore$ $y = \dfrac{x-3}{2}$

          $\therefore$ $f^{-1}(x) = \dfrac{x-3}{2}$

ii f is $y = 2x + 3$,

     $\therefore$ f^{-1} is $x = 2y + 3$

     $\therefore$ $x - 3 = 2y$

     $\therefore$ $\dfrac{x-3}{2} = y$

     $\therefore$ $f^{-1}(x) = \dfrac{x-3}{2}$

$$c \quad (f \circ f^{-1})(x) = f(f^{-1}(x)) \qquad \text{and} \qquad (f^{-1} \circ f)(x) = f^{-1}(f(x))$$

$$= f\left(\frac{x-3}{2}\right) \qquad\qquad\qquad\qquad = f^{-1}(2x+3)$$

$$= 2\left(\frac{x-3}{2}\right) + 3 \qquad\qquad\qquad = \frac{(2x+3)-3}{2}$$

$$= x \qquad\qquad\qquad\qquad\qquad = \frac{2x}{2}$$

$$\qquad\qquad\qquad\qquad\qquad\qquad\qquad = x$$

EXERCISE 3F

1 For each of the following functions f:

i On the same set of axes, graph $y = x$, $y = f(x)$, and $y = f^{-1}(x)$.

ii Find $f^{-1}(x)$ using coordinate geometry and the gradient of $y = f^{-1}(x)$ from **i**.

iii Find $f^{-1}(x)$ using variable interchange.

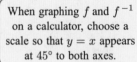

When graphing f and f^{-1} on a calculator, choose a scale so that $y = x$ appears at 45° to both axes.

a $f : x \mapsto 3x + 1$ **b** $f : x \mapsto \dfrac{x+2}{4}$

2 For each of the following functions f:

i Find $f^{-1}(x)$.

ii Sketch $y = f(x)$, $y = f^{-1}(x)$, and $y = x$ on the same set of axes.

iii Show that $(f^{-1} \circ f)(x) = (f \circ f^{-1})(x) = x$, the identity function.

a $f : x \mapsto 2x + 5$ **b** $f : x \mapsto \dfrac{3 - 2x}{4}$ **c** $f : x \mapsto x + 3$

3 Copy the graphs of the following functions and draw the graphs of $y = x$ and $y = f^{-1}(x)$ on the same set of axes. In each case, state the domain and range of both f and f^{-1}.

a
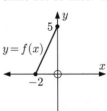

b
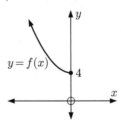

c
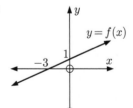

PRINTABLE GRAPHS

d
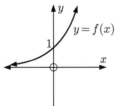

e
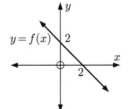

f
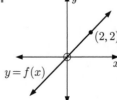

4 Given $f(x) = 2x - 5$, find $(f^{-1})^{-1}(x)$. What do you notice?

5 Show that the function $y = 3 - x$ is its own inverse.

If a function is its own inverse, we say the function is **self-inverse**.

6 Which of the following functions have inverses? Where an inverse exists, write down the inverse function.

    a $\{(1, 2), (2, 4), (3, 5)\}$ **b** $\{(-1, 3), (0, 2), (1, 3)\}$

    c $\{(2, 1), (-1, 0), (0, 2), (1, 3)\}$ **d** $\{(-1, -1), (0, 0), (1, 1)\}$

7 If the one-to-one function $H(x)$ has domain $\{x \mid -2 \leqslant x < 3\}$, find the range of its inverse $H^{-1}(x)$.

8 Sketch the graph of $f : x \mapsto x^3$ and its inverse function $f^{-1}(x)$.

9 Given $f(x) = \dfrac{1}{x}$, $x \neq 0$, show that f is self-inverse.

10 The **horizontal line test** says: *For a function to have an inverse function, no horizontal line can cut its graph more than once.*

    a Explain why this is a valid test for the existence of an inverse function.

    b Which of the following functions have an inverse function?

    i   **ii**   **iii**

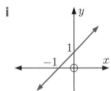 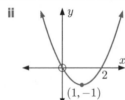 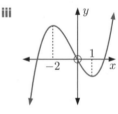

11 Explain why $f : x \mapsto x^2 - 4$ does not have an inverse.

12 Consider $f : x \mapsto x^2$, $x \leqslant 0$.

    a Find $f^{-1}(x)$.

    b Sketch $y = f(x)$, $y = x$, and $y = f^{-1}(x)$ on the same set of axes.

13 Consider the functions $f : x \mapsto 2x + 5$ and $g : x \mapsto \dfrac{8 - x}{2}$.

    a Find $g^{-1}(x)$.   **b** Hence solve $g(x) = -1$.

    c Show that $f^{-1}(-3) - g^{-1}(6) = 0$.   **d** Find x such that $(f \circ g^{-1})(x) = 9$.

14 Given $f : x \mapsto 2x$ and $g : x \mapsto 4x - 3$, show that $(f^{-1} \circ g^{-1})(x) = (g \circ f)^{-1}(x)$.

15 Find the inverse of $f : x \mapsto \dfrac{3x - 8}{x - 3}$, $x \neq 3$ by:

    a referring to its graph   **b** using algebra.

16

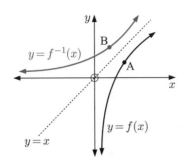

a B is the image of A under a reflection in the line $y = x$. If A is $(x, f(x))$, find the coordinates of B.

b By substituting your result from **a** into $y = f^{-1}(x)$, show that $f^{-1}(f(x)) = x$.

c Using a similar method, show that $f(f^{-1}(x)) = x$.

G   ABSOLUTE VALUE FUNCTIONS

The **absolute value** or **modulus** of a real number x is its distance from 0 on the number line. We write the absolute value of x as $|x|$.

Because the absolute value is a distance, it cannot be negative.

- If $x > 0$, $|x| = x$.

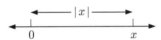

- If $x < 0$, $|x| = -x$.

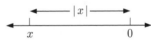

For example: $|7| = 7$ and $|-5| = 5$.

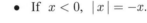

This leads us to the **algebraic definition**:

$$\text{The \textbf{absolute value of} } x \text{ is } \quad |x| = \begin{cases} x & \text{if } x \geqslant 0 \\ -x & \text{if } x < 0. \end{cases}$$

The relation $y = |x|$ is in fact a function. We call it the **absolute value function**, and it has the graph shown.

This branch is $y = -x$, $x < 0$.

This branch is $y = x$, $x \geqslant 0$.

THE GRAPH $y = |f(x)|$

The absolute value of the function $f(x)$ is $\quad |f(x)| = \begin{cases} f(x) & \text{if } f(x) \geqslant 0 \\ -f(x) & \text{if } f(x) < 0. \end{cases}$

To obtain the graph of $y = |f(x)|$ from the graph of $y = f(x)$:
- Keep the graph for $f(x) \geqslant 0$.
- Reflect the graph in the x-axis for $f(x) < 0$, discarding what was there.
- Points on the x-axis are unchanged.

Example 13   ◀) **Self Tutor**

Draw the graph of $f(x) = 3x(x-2)$ and on the same set of axes draw
the graph of $y = |f(x)|$.

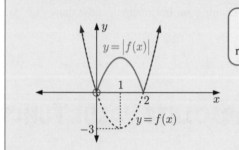

The graph of $y = f(x)$ is
unchanged for $f(x) \geqslant 0$ and
reflected in the x-axis for $f(x) < 0$.

EXERCISE 3G

1 On the same set of axes draw the graphs of:

   a $y = 2x - 4$ and $y = |2x - 4|$ **b** $y = 5 - 3x$ and $y = |5 - 3x|$

2 Copy the following graphs for $y = f(x)$ and on the same set of axes draw the graph of $y = |f(x)|$:

  a

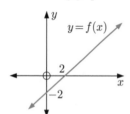

  b

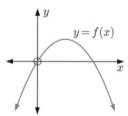

  c

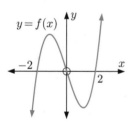

  d

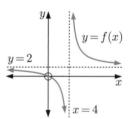

3 On the same set of axes, draw the graphs of:

   a $y = x(x+2)$ and $y = |x(x+2)|$

   b $y = -x^2 + 6x - 8$ and $y = |-x^2 + 6x - 8|$.

4 On the same set of axes, draw the graphs of:

   a $y = \dfrac{5}{x}$ and $y = \left|\dfrac{5}{x}\right|$ **b** $y = -\dfrac{3}{x}$ and $y = \left|-\dfrac{3}{x}\right|$.

THEORY OF KNOWLEDGE

The notation and terminology of mathematics has rules which tell us how to construct expressions or mathematical "sentences". This allows us to communicate mathematical ideas in a written form.

For example, the expression "$1 + 1 = 2$" tells us that "one added to one is equal to two".

> **1** What does it mean for something to be a "language"?
>
> **2** Does mathematics have a "grammar" or **syntax** in the same sense as the English language?

In computer science, **Backus-Naur form** (BNF) is commonly used to define the syntax of programming languages. BNF can also be used to describe the rules of non-programming related languages.

> **3** Research how BNF works and use it to define the syntax of mathematical function notation.
>
> **4** Mathematical expressions can also be represented with diagrams such as **abstract syntax trees** and **syntax (railroad) diagrams**. Which form is more *efficient* in conveying its information? Which form is more useful?

The fact that something is *grammatically* correct does not make it *logically* true.

For example, consider the grammatically correct but illogical English sentence: "The sun is cold."

> **5** The **syntax** of a language refers to its structure and rules. The **semantics** of a language is all about its meaning.
>
>   **a** Why is it important to distinguish between these two concepts?
>
>   **b** In mathematics, is one more important than the other?

REVIEW SET 3A

1 For each graph, state:

     i the domain   **ii** the range   **iii** whether the graph shows a function.

a
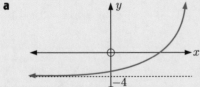

b
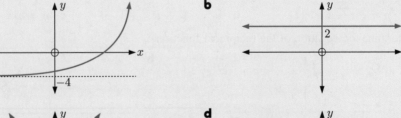

c
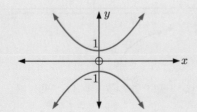

d
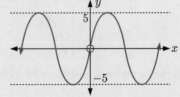

2 If $f(x) = 2x - x^2$, find:

   a $f(2)$ **b** $f(-3)$ **c** $f(-\frac{1}{2})$

3 The graph of $y = f(x)$ is shown alongside.

   a Find:

      i $f(-3)$ **ii** $f(2)$

   b Find the value of x such that $f(x) = 4$.

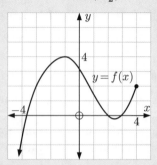

4 Suppose $f(x) = ax + b$ where a and b are constants. If $f(1) = 7$ and $f(3) = -5$, find a and b.

5 Given $h(x) = 7 - 3x$, find:

   a $h(2x - 1)$ in simplest form   **b** x such that $h(2x - 1) = -2$.

6 This graph shows the noise level at a stadium during a football match.

Find the domain and range of the function.

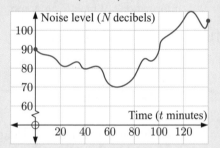

7 Consider $f(x) = \dfrac{-2}{x^2}$.

   a For what value of x is $f(x)$ undefined?   **b** Sketch the function using technology.

   c State the domain and range of the function.

8 Consider $f(x) = x^2$ and $g(x) = 1 - 6x$.

   a Show that $f(-3) = g(-\frac{4}{3})$.   **b** Find x such that $g(x) = f(5)$.

9 Find the domain and range of:

   a $y = \sqrt{x + 4}$ **b** $y = -(1 - x)^2 + 1$ **c** $y = 2x^2 - 3x + 1$

10 Determine the equation of the reciprocal functions:

   a

   b

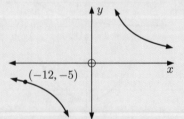

11 Sketch a rational function with domain $\{x \mid x \neq 4\}$, range $\{y \mid y \neq -1\}$, and

sign diagram x .

12 Consider the function $f : x \mapsto \dfrac{4x+1}{2-x}$.

    a Find the equations of the asymptotes.

    b State the domain and range of the function.

    c Draw a sign diagram of the function. Hence discuss the behaviour of the function as it approaches its asymptotes.

    d Find the axes intercepts.

    e Sketch the function.

13 If $f(x) = 2x - 3$ and $g(x) = x^2 + 2$, find in simplest form:

    a $(f \circ g)(x)$ **b** $(g \circ f)(x)$ **c** $(f \circ f)(2)$

14 Suppose $f(x) = 2x - 5$ and $g(x) = 3x + 1$.

    a Find $(f \circ g)(x)$.   **b** Solve $(f \circ g)(x) = f(x + 3)$.

15 If $f(x) = 1 - 2x$ and $g(x) = \sqrt{x}$, find in simplest form:

    a $(f \circ g)(x)$ **b** $(g \circ f)(x)$ **c** $(g \circ g)(81)$

16 If $f(x) = ax + b$, $f(2) = 1$, and $f^{-1}(3) = 4$, find a and b.

17 Copy the following graphs and draw the inverse function on the same set of axes:

    a 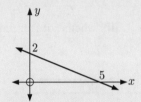   **b**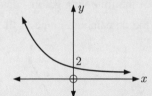

18 Find $f^{-1}(x)$ given that $f(x)$ is:

    a $4x + 2$ **b** $\dfrac{3 - 5x}{4}$

19 Given $f : x \mapsto 3x + 6$ and $h : x \mapsto \dfrac{x}{3}$, show that $(f^{-1} \circ h^{-1})(x) = (h \circ f)^{-1}(x)$.

20 The graph of the function $f(x) = -\frac{1}{2}x^2$, $0 \leqslant x \leqslant 2$ is shown alongside.

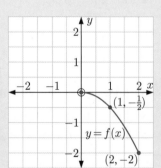

    a Sketch the graph of $y = f^{-1}(x)$.

    b State the range of f^{-1}.

    c Solve:

        i $f(x) = -\frac{3}{2}$ **ii** $f^{-1}(x) = 1$

21 Show that $f : x \mapsto \dfrac{5x - 1}{x - 5}$, $x \neq 5$ is its own inverse by:

    a referring to its graph   **b** using algebra.

22 If $f : x \mapsto \sqrt{x}$ and $g : x \mapsto 3 + x$, find:

    a $f^{-1}(2) \times g^{-1}(2)$ **b** $(f \circ g)^{-1}(2)$.

23 Draw on the same set of axes:

    a $y = -x^2 - 2x + 3$ and $y = \left| -x^2 - 2x + 3 \right|$

    b $y = -\dfrac{2}{x}$ and $y = \left| -\dfrac{2}{x} \right|$.

REVIEW SET 3B

1 State the domain and range of each function:

    a

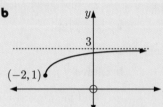

    b

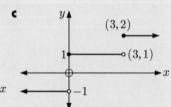

    c

2 If $g(x) = x^2 - 3x$, find in simplest form:

    a $g(x + 1)$ **b** $g(4x)$

3 For each of the following graphs, determine:

    i the domain and range   **ii** the x and y-intercepts   **iii** whether it is a function.

    a

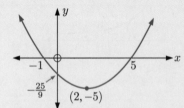

    b

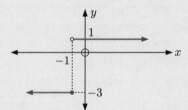

4 Use algebraic methods to determine whether these relations are functions:

    a $x + 2y = 10$ **b** $x + y^2 = 10$

5 Suppose $f(x) = \dfrac{3x - 1}{x + 2}$.

    a Evaluate:

        i $f(-1)$ **ii** $f(0)$ **iii** $f(5)$

    b Find a value of x such that $f(x)$ does not exist.

    c Find $f(x - 1)$ in simplest form.

    d Find x if $f(x) = 4$.

6 Given $f(x) = x^2 + 3$, find:

    a $f(-3)$ **b** x such that $f(x) = 4$.

7 State the domain and range of:

    a $f(x) = 10 + \dfrac{3}{2x - 1}$ **b** $f(x) = \sqrt{x + 7}$

8   a Use technology to help sketch the graph of the relation $y = \sqrt{9 - x}$.

    b Determine whether the relation is a function.

    c Find the domain and range of the relation.

9 Suppose $f(x) = ax^2 + bx + c$. Find a, b, and c if $f(0) = 5$, $f(-2) = 21$, and $f(3) = -4$.

10 Use technology to sketch $y = x^3 - 4x^2 + x$, $-1 \leqslant x \leqslant 4$. Include the points at the ends of the domain, and any turning points. Hence state the range of the function.

11 Draw a sign diagram for:

    a $\dfrac{2x - 5}{x - 4}$ **b** $\dfrac{3 - x}{x + 1}$

12 For the function $f(x) = -1 + \dfrac{3}{x + 2}$:

    a Find the equations of the asymptotes.   **b** State the domain and range.

    c Find the axes intercepts.

    d Discuss the behaviour of the function as it approaches its asymptotes.

    e Sketch the graph of the function.

13 Given $f(x) = 3 - x^2$ and $g(x) = 2x - 1$, find in simplest form:

    a $(f \circ g)(x)$ **b** $(g \circ f)(x)$ **c** $(f \circ f)(-2)$

14 Suppose $f(x) = \dfrac{1}{x^2}$ and $g(x) = x^2 - 4x + 3$. Find $(f \circ g)(x)$ and state its domain and range.

15 Suppose $f(x) = 3x + 5$ and $g(x) = 2x^2 - x$.

    a Find in simplest form:

        i $(f \circ g)(x)$ **ii** $(g \circ f)(x)$

    b Hence solve $3(f \circ g)(x) = (g \circ f)(x)$.

16 Copy the following graphs and draw the graph of each inverse function on the same set of axes:

    a 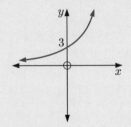   **b**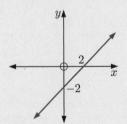

17 Find the inverse function $f^{-1}(x)$ for:

    a $f(x) = 7 - 4x$ **b** $f(x) = \dfrac{3 + 2x}{5}$

18 Consider $f : x \mapsto 2x - 7$.

    a On the same set of axes graph $y = x$, $y = f(x)$, and $y = f^{-1}(x)$.

    b Find $f^{-1}(x)$ using variable interchange.

    c Show that $(f \circ f^{-1})(x) = (f^{-1} \circ f)(x) = x$, the identity function.

19 Given $f : x \mapsto 5x - 2$ and $h : x \mapsto \dfrac{3x}{4}$, show that $(f^{-1} \circ h^{-1})(x) = (h \circ f)^{-1}(x)$.

20 Consider the functions $f(x) = 3x + 1$ and $g(x) = \dfrac{2}{x}$.

    a Find $(g \circ f)(x)$.

    b Given $(g \circ f)(x) = -4$, solve for x.

    c Let $h(x) = (g \circ f)(x)$, $x \neq -\frac{1}{3}$.

       i Write down the equations of the asymptotes of $h(x)$.

      ii Sketch the graph of $h(x)$ for $-3 \leqslant x \leqslant 2$.

     iii State the range of $h(x)$ for the domain $-3 \leqslant x \leqslant 2$.

21 Given $f(x) = 2x + 11$ and $g(x) = x^2$, find $(g \circ f^{-1})(3)$.

22 The function $f(x) = \dfrac{ax + 3}{x - b}$ has asymptotes $x = -1$ and $y = 2$.

    a Find a and b.   **b** Find the domain and range of $f^{-1}(x)$.

23 If $f : x \mapsto 2x + 1$ and $g : x \mapsto \dfrac{x + 1}{x - 2}$, find:

    a $(f \circ g)(x)$ **b** $g^{-1}(x)$.

24 Copy the graph and draw the graph of $y = |f(x)|$ on the same set of axes:

    a

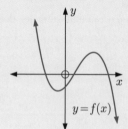

    b

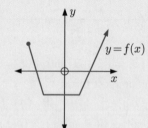

Chapter 4

Transformations of functions

Contents:

OPENING PROBLEM

In our study of quadratic functions, we saw that the completed square form $y = (x - h)^2 + k$ was extremely useful in identifying the vertex (h, k).

Things to think about:

a What transformation maps the graph $y = x^2$ onto the graph $y = (x - h)^2 + k$?

b If we let $f(x) = x^2$, what function is $f(x - h) + k$?

c In general terms, what transformation maps $y = f(x)$ onto $y = f(x - h) + k$?

In this Chapter we perform **transformations** of graphs to produce the graph of a related function.

The transformations of $y = f(x)$ we consider include:

- **translations** $y = f(x) + b$ and $y = f(x - a)$
- **stretches** $y = pf(x)$, $p > 0$ and $y = f(qx)$, $q > 0$
- **reflections** $y = -f(x)$ and $y = f(-x)$
- combinations of these transformations.

A   TRANSLATIONS

If $f(x) = x^2$ then $f(x - h) + k = (x - h)^2 + k$.

The graph $y = (x - h)^2 + k$ has the same shape as $y = x^2$.

It can be produced from $y = x^2$ by a translation h units to the right and k units upwards.

This shifts the vertex of the parabola from the origin $O(0, 0)$ to (h, k).

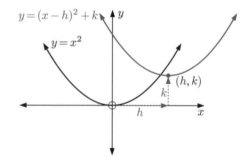

INVESTIGATION 1   TRANSLATIONS

Our observations of quadratics suggest that $y = f(x)$ can be transformed into $y = f(x - a) + b$ by a *translation*. In this Investigation we test this theory with other functions.

What to do:

1 Let $f(x) = x^3$.

GRAPHING PACKAGE

  a Write down:

    i $f(x) + 2$ **ii** $f(x) - 3$ **iii** $f(x) + 6$

    Graph $y = f(x)$ and the other three functions on the same set of axes. Record your observations.

  b Write down:

    i $f(x - 2)$ **ii** $f(x + 3)$ **iii** $f(x - 6)$

    Graph $y = f(x)$ and the other three functions on the same set of axes. Record your observations.

c Write down:

    i $f(x-1)+3$ **ii** $f(x+2)+1$ **iii** $f(x-3)-4$

    Graph $y=f(x)$ and the other three functions on the same set of axes.

2 Repeat **1** for the function $f(x)=\dfrac{1}{x}$.

3 Describe the transformation which maps $y=f(x)$ onto:

    a $y=f(x)+b$ **b** $y=f(x-a)$ **c** $y=f(x-a)+b$

4 Do any of these transformations change the *shape* of the graph?

From the **Investigation** you should have found:

- For $y=f(x)+b$, the effect of b is to **translate** the graph **vertically** through b units.
  - ▸ If $b>0$ it moves **upwards**.   ▸ If $b<0$ it moves **downwards**.
- For $y=f(x-a)$, the effect of a is to **translate** the graph **horizontally** through a units.
  - ▸ If $a>0$ it moves to the **right**.   ▸ If $a<0$ it moves to the **left**.
- For $y=f(x-a)+b$, the graph is translated horizontally a units and vertically b units.

  We say it is **translated by the vector** $\begin{pmatrix} a \\ b \end{pmatrix}$.

Example 1   ◀) **Self Tutor**

Consider the graph of $y=f(x)$ alongside.

On separate axes, draw the graphs of:

a $y=f(x)+2$ **b** $y=f(x+4)$

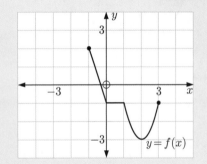

a The graph of $y=f(x)+2$ is found by translating $y=f(x)$ 2 units upwards.

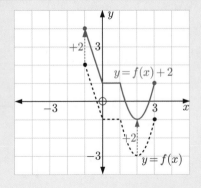

b The graph of $y = f(x+4)$ is found by translating $y = f(x)$ 4 units to the left.

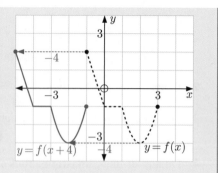

EXERCISE 4A

1 Consider the graph of $y = f(x)$ alongside. On separate axes, draw the graphs of:

    a $y = f(x) + 5$ **b** $y = f(x-3)$

    c $y = f(x-3) + 5$

PRINTABLE
GRIDS

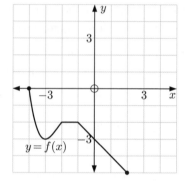

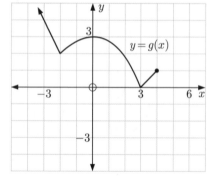

Consider the graph of $y = g(x)$ alongside. On separate axes, draw the graphs of:

    a $y = g(x) - 3$ **b** $y = g(x+1)$

    c $y = g(x+1) - 3$ **d** $y = g(x-2) - 1$

3 Write $g(x)$ in terms of $f(x)$:

a

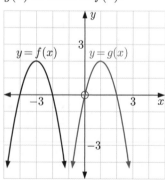

b

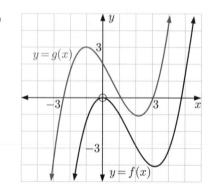

4 Find the equation of the resulting graph $g(x)$ when:

   a $f(x) = 2x + 3$ is translated 4 units downwards

   b $f(x) = 3x - 4$ is translated 2 units to the left

   c $f(x) = -x^2 + 5x - 7$ is translated 3 units upwards

   d $f(x) = x^2 + 4x - 1$ is translated 5 units to the right.

5 For each of the following functions f, sketch $y = f(x)$, $y = f(x) + 1$, and $y = f(x) - 2$ on the same set of axes.

   a $f(x) = x^2$ **b** $f(x) = x^3$ **c** $f(x) = \dfrac{1}{x}$ **d** $f(x) = (x - 1)^2 + 2$

6 For each of the following functions f, sketch $y = f(x)$, $y = f(x - 1)$, and $y = f(x + 2)$ on the same set of axes.

   a $f(x) = x^2$ **b** $f(x) = x^3$ **c** $f(x) = \dfrac{1}{x}$ **d** $f(x) = (x - 1)^2 + 2$

7 For each of the following functions f, sketch $y = f(x)$, $y = f(x - 2) + 3$, and $y = f(x + 1) - 4$ on the same set of axes.

   a $f(x) = x^2$ **b** $f(x) = x^3$ **c** $f(x) = \dfrac{1}{x}$ **d** $f(x) = (x - 1)^2 + 2$

8 The point $(-2, -5)$ lies on the graph of $y = f(x)$. Find the coordinates of the corresponding point on the graph of $g(x) = f(x - 3) - 4$.

9 Suppose the graph of $y = f(x)$ has x-intercepts -3 and 4, and y-intercept 2. What can you say about the axes intercepts of:

   a $g(x) = f(x) - 3$ **b** $h(x) = f(x - 1)$ **c** $j(x) = f(x + 2) - 4$?

10 The graph of $f(x) = x^2 - 2x + 2$ is translated 3 units to the right to form $g(x)$. Find $g(x)$ in the form $g(x) = ax^2 + bx + c$.

11 Suppose $f(x) = x^2$ is transformed to $g(x) = (x - 3)^2 + 2$.

   a Find the images of the following points on $f(x)$:

   i $(0, 0)$ **ii** $(-3, 9)$ **iii** $(2, 4)$

   b Find the points on $f(x)$ which correspond to the following points on $g(x)$:

   i $(1, 6)$ **ii** $(-2, 27)$ **iii** $(1\frac{1}{2}, 4\frac{1}{4})$

B   **STRETCHES**

In this Section we study how a function can be manipulated to *stretch* its graph.

We will consider stretches in both the horizontal and vertical directions.

A stretch can also be called a **dilation**.

In our study of quadratic functions, we saw that the coefficient a of x^2 controls the width of the parabola.

In the case of $f(x) = x^2$,

notice that $f(2x) = (2x)^2 = 4x^2$

and $4f(x) = 4x^2$

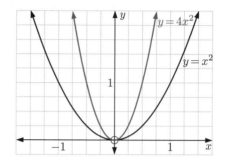

DISCUSSION

- In what ways could $y = x^2$ be *stretched* to form $y = 4x^2$?
- Will a transformation of the form $pf(x)$, $p > 0$ always be equivalent to a transformation of the form $f(qx)$, $q > 0$?

INVESTIGATION 2   STRETCHES

In this Investigation we consider transformations of the form $pf(x)$, $p > 0$, and $f(qx)$, $q > 0$.

What to do:

1 Let $f(x) = x + 2$.

    a Find, in simplest form:

        i $3f(x)$ **ii** $\frac{1}{2}f(x)$ **iii** $5f(x)$

GRAPHING
PACKAGE

    b Graph all four functions on the same set of axes.

    c Which point is *invariant* under a transformation of the form $pf(x)$, $p > 0$?

An **invariant** point does not move.

    d Copy and complete:

        For the transformation $y = pf(x)$, each point becomes ...... times its previous distance from the x-axis.

2 Let $f(x) = x + 2$.

    a Find, in simplest form:

        i $f(2x)$ **ii** $f(\frac{1}{3}x)$ **iii** $f(4x)$

    b Graph all four functions on the same set of axes.

    c Which point is *invariant* under a transformation of the form $f(qx)$, $q > 0$?

    d Copy and complete:

        For the transformation $y = f(qx)$, each point becomes ...... times its previous distance from the y-axis.

From the **Investigation** you should have found:

- $y = pf(x)$, $p > 0$ is a **vertical stretch** of $y = f(x)$ with **scale factor** p and **invariant** x-**axis**.
  - ▸ Each point becomes p times its previous distance from the x-axis.
  - ▸ If $p > 1$, points move further away from the x-axis.
  - ▸ If $0 < p < 1$, points move closer to the x-axis.
- $y = f(qx)$, $q > 0$ is a **horizontal stretch** of $y = f(x)$ with **scale factor** $\frac{1}{q}$ and **invariant** y-**axis**.
  - ▸ Each point becomes $\frac{1}{q}$ times its previous distance from the y-axis.
  - ▸ If $q > 1$, points move closer to the y-axis.
  - ▸ If $0 < q < 1$, points move further away from the y-axis.

Example 2 ◀)) **Self Tutor**

Consider the graph of $y = f(x)$ alongside.

On separate axes, draw the graphs of:

  a $y = 3f(x)$ **b** $y = f(2x)$

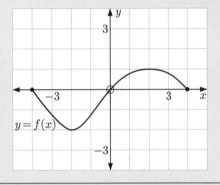

a   The graph of $y = 3f(x)$ is a vertical stretch of $y = f(x)$ with scale factor 3.

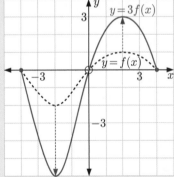

b   The graph of $y = f(2x)$ is a horizontal stretch of $y = f(x)$ with scale factor $\frac{1}{2}$.

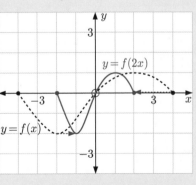

EXERCISE 4B

1 Consider the graph of $y = f(x)$ alongside.
On separate axes, draw the graphs of:

   a $y = 2f(x)$ **b** $y = f(3x)$

PRINTABLE
GRIDS

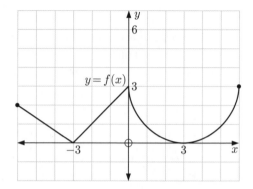

2

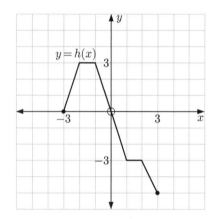

Consider the graph of $y = h(x)$ alongside.
On separate axes, draw the graphs of:

   a $y = \frac{1}{3}h(x)$ **b** $y = h\left(\frac{x}{2}\right)$

> If scale factor > 1,
> the graph is *elongated*.
> If $0 <$ scale factor < 1,
> the graph is *compressed*.

3 Write $g(x)$ in terms of $f(x)$:

  a

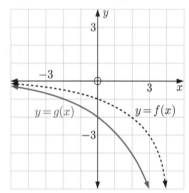

  b

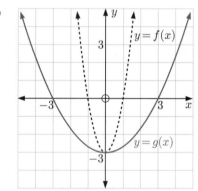

4 A linear function with gradient m is vertically stretched with scale factor c. Find the gradient of the resulting line.

5 For each of the following functions f, sketch $y = f(x)$, $y = 2f(x)$, and $y = 3f(x)$ on the same set of axes:

  a $f(x) = x - 1$ **b** $f(x) = x^2$

  c $f(x) = x^3$ **d** $f(x) = \frac{1}{x}$

6 For each of the following functions f, sketch $y = f(x)$, $y = \frac{1}{2}f(x)$, and $y = \frac{1}{4}f(x)$ on the same set of axes:

  a $f(x) = x - 1$ **b** $f(x) = x^2$ **c** $f(x) = x^3$ **d** $f(x) = \dfrac{1}{x}$

7 Sketch, on the same set of axes, the graphs of $y = f(x)$ and $y = f(2x)$ for:

  a $y = x^2$ **b** $y = (x - 1)^2$ **c** $y = (x + 3)^2$

8 Sketch, on the same set of axes, the graphs of $y = f(x)$ and $y = f(\frac{x}{2})$ for:

  a $y = x^2$ **b** $y = 2x$ **c** $y = (x + 2)^2$

9 Suppose f and g are functions such that $g(x) = f(5x)$.

  a Given that $(10,\ 25)$ lies on $y = f(x)$, find the coordinates of the corresponding point on $y = g(x)$.

  b Given that $(-5,\ -15)$ lies on $y = g(x)$, find the coordinates of the corresponding point on $y = f(x)$.

10 Find the equation of the resulting graph $g(x)$ when:

  a $f(x) = x^2 + 2$ is vertically stretched with scale factor 2

  b $f(x) = 5 - 3x$ is horizontally stretched with scale factor 3

  c $f(x) = x^3 + 8x^2 - 2$ is vertically dilated with scale factor $\frac{1}{4}$

  d $f(x) = 2x^2 + x - 3$ is horizontally dilated with scale factor $\frac{1}{2}$.

11 Graph on the same set of axes $y = x^2$, $y = 3x^2$, and $y = 3(x + 1)^2 - 2$.

Describe the combination of transformations which transform $y = x^2$ to $y = 3(x + 1)^2 - 2$.

12 Graph on the same set of axes $y = x^2$, $y = \frac{1}{2}x^2$, and $y = \frac{1}{2}(x + 1)^2 + 3$.

Describe the combination of transformations which transform $y = x^2$ to $y = \frac{1}{2}(x + 1)^2 + 3$.

13 Graph on the same set of axes $y = x^2$, $y = 2x^2$, and $y = 2(x - \frac{3}{2})^2 + 1$.

Describe the combination of transformations which transform $y = x^2$ to $y = 2(x - \frac{3}{2})^2 + 1$.

14 Describe the combination of transformations which transform $y = x^2$ to $y = 2(x + 1)^2 - 3$.
Hence sketch $y = 2(x + 1)^2 - 3$.

15 Suppose f and g are functions such that $g(x) = 3f(2x)$.

  a What transformations are needed to map $y = f(x)$ onto $y = g(x)$?

  b Find the image of each of these points on $y = f(x)$:

       i $(3, -5)$ **ii** $(1, 2)$ **iii** $(-2, 1)$

  c Find the point on $y = f(x)$ which maps onto the image point:

       i $(2, 1)$ **ii** $(-3, 2)$ **iii** $(-7, 3)$

Example 3   ◀)) **Self Tutor**

The function $g(x)$ results when $y = \dfrac{1}{x}$ is transformed by a vertical stretch with scale factor 2, followed by a translation of $\begin{pmatrix} 3 \\ -2 \end{pmatrix}$.

a Write an expression for $g(x)$ in the form $g(x) = \dfrac{ax+b}{cx+d}$.

b Find the asymptotes of $y = g(x)$.

c Sketch $y = g(x)$.

a Under a vertical stretch with scale factor 2, $f(x)$ becomes $2f(x)$.

$\therefore \quad \dfrac{1}{x}$ becomes $2\left(\dfrac{1}{x}\right) = \dfrac{2}{x}$.

Under a translation of $\begin{pmatrix} 3 \\ -2 \end{pmatrix}$, $f(x)$ becomes $f(x-3) - 2$.

$\therefore \quad \dfrac{2}{x}$ becomes $\dfrac{2}{x-3} - 2$.

So, $y = \dfrac{1}{x}$ becomes $g(x) = \dfrac{2}{x-3} - 2$

$\qquad\qquad\qquad\qquad = \dfrac{2 - 2(x-3)}{x-3}$

$\qquad\qquad\qquad\qquad = \dfrac{-2x+8}{x-3}$

$g(x)$ is a rational function which is $\dfrac{\text{linear}}{\text{linear}}$.

b The asymptotes of $y = \dfrac{1}{x}$ are $x = 0$ and $y = 0$.

These are unchanged by the stretch, and shifted $\begin{pmatrix} 3 \\ -2 \end{pmatrix}$ by the translation.

$\therefore$ the vertical asymptote is $x = 3$ and the horizontal asymptote is $y = -2$.

c

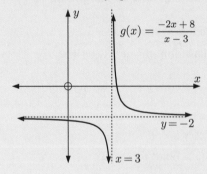

16 Write, in the form $y = \dfrac{ax+b}{cx+d}$, the function that results when $y = \dfrac{1}{x}$ is transformed by:

a a vertical dilation with scale factor $\frac{1}{2}$

b a horizontal dilation with scale factor 3

c a horizontal translation of -3

d a vertical translation of 4.

17 The function $g(x)$ results when $y = \dfrac{1}{x}$ is transformed by a vertical stretch with scale factor 3, followed by a translation of $\begin{pmatrix} 1 \\ -1 \end{pmatrix}$.

    a Write an expression for $g(x)$ in the form $g(x) = \dfrac{ax + b}{cx + d}$.

    b Find the asymptotes of $y = g(x)$.

    c State the domain and range of $g(x)$.

    d Sketch $y = g(x)$.

DISCUSSION

For a vertical stretch with scale factor p, each point on the function is moved vertically so it is p times as far from the x-axis.

1 Using this definition of a vertical stretch, does it make sense to talk about negative values of p?

2 If a function is transformed from $f(x)$ to $-f(x)$, what transformation has actually occurred?

3 What *combinations* of transformations would transform $f(x)$ to $-2f(x)$?

4 What can we say about $y = f(qx)$ for:

    a $q = -1$ **b** $q < 0,\ q \neq -1$?

C   REFLECTIONS

INVESTIGATION 3   REFLECTIONS

In this Investigation we consider **reflections** with the forms $y = -f(x)$ and $y = f(-x)$.

What to do:

GRAPHING
PACKAGE

1 Consider $f(x) = 2x + 3$.

    a Find in simplest form:

        i $-f(x)$ **ii** $f(-x)$

    b Graph $y = f(x)$, $y = -f(x)$, and $y = f(-x)$ on the same set of axes.

2 Consider $f(x) = x^3 + 1$.

    a Find in simplest form:

        i $-f(x)$ **ii** $f(-x)$

    b Graph $y = f(x)$, $y = -f(x)$, and $y = f(-x)$ on the same set of axes.

3 What transformation moves:

    a $y = f(x)$ to $y = -f(x)$ **b** $y = f(x)$ to $y = f(-x)$?

From the **Investigation** you should have discovered that:

> - For $y = -f(x)$, we **reflect** $y = f(x)$ in the **x-axis**.
> - For $y = f(-x)$, we **reflect** $y = f(x)$ in the **y-axis**.

Example 4

◆ Self Tutor

Consider the graph of $y = f(x)$ alongside.

On separate axes, draw the graphs of:

  a $y = -f(x)$ **b** $y = f(-x)$

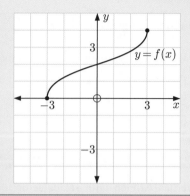

a   The graph of $y = -f(x)$ is found by reflecting $y = f(x)$ in the x-axis.

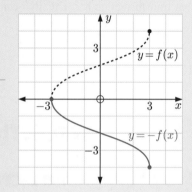

b   The graph of $y = f(-x)$ is found by reflecting $y = f(x)$ in the y-axis.

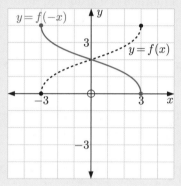

EXERCISE 4C

1   Consider the graph of $y = f(x)$ alongside.

On separate axes, draw the graphs of:

  a $y = -f(x)$ **b** $y = f(-x)$

PRINTABLE
GRIDS

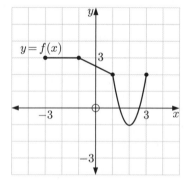

2   Copy the following graphs for $y = f(x)$ and sketch the graphs of $y = -f(x)$ on the same axes.

  a

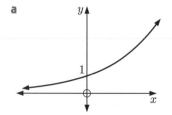

  b

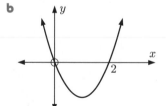

  c

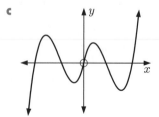

3 Copy the following graphs of $y = f(x)$ and sketch the graphs of $y = f(-x)$ on the same axes.

a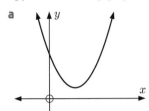

b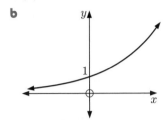

c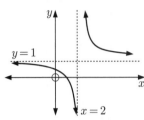

4 On the same set of axes, sketch the graphs of $y = f(x)$ and $y = -f(x)$ for:

   a $f(x) = 3x$ **b** $f(x) = x^2$ **c** $f(x) = x^3 - 2$ **d** $f(x) = 2(x + 1)^2$

5 **a** Find $f(-x)$ for:

      i $f(x) = 2x + 1$ **ii** $f(x) = x^2 + 2x + 1$ **iii** $f(x) = x^3$

   b Graph $y = f(x)$ and $y = f(-x)$ for:

      i $f(x) = 2x + 1$ **ii** $f(x) = x^2 + 2x + 1$ **iii** $f(x) = x^3$

6 The function $f(x) = x^4 - 2x^3 - 3x^2 + 5x - 7$ is reflected in the y-axis to $g(x)$. Find $g(x)$.

7 The function $y = f(x)$ is transformed to $g(x) = -f(x)$.

   a Find the image points on $y = g(x)$ corresponding to the following points on $y = f(x)$:

      i $(3, 0)$ **ii** $(2, -1)$ **iii** $(-3, 2)$

   b Find the points on $y = f(x)$ which are transformed to the following points on $y = g(x)$:

      i $(7, -1)$ **ii** $(-5, 0)$ **iii** $(-3, -2)$

8 The function $y = f(x)$ is transformed to $h(x) = f(-x)$.

   a Find the image points on $y = h(x)$ for the following points on $y = f(x)$:

      i $(2, -1)$ **ii** $(0, 3)$ **iii** $(-1, 2)$

   b Find the points on $y = f(x)$ corresponding to the following points on $y = h(x)$:

      i $(5, -4)$ **ii** $(0, 3)$ **iii** $(2, 3)$

9 A function $f(x)$ is transformed to the function $g(x) = -f(-x)$.

   a What combination of transformations has taken place?

   b If $(3, -7)$ lies on $y = f(x)$, find the transformed point on $y = g(x)$.

   c Find the point on $f(x)$ that transforms to the point $(-5, -1)$.

10 Let $f(x) = x + 2$.

   a Describe the transformation which transforms $y = f(x)$ to $y = -f(x)$.

   b Describe the transformation which transforms $y = -f(x)$ to $y = -3f(x)$.

   c Hence draw the graphs of $y = f(x)$, $y = -f(x)$, and $y = -3f(x)$ on the same set of axes.

11 Let $f(x) = (x - 1)^2 - 4$.

   a Describe the transformation which transforms $y = f(x)$ to $y = f(-x)$.

   b Describe the transformation which transforms $y = f(-x)$ to $y = f(-\frac{1}{2}x)$.

   c Hence draw the graphs of $y = f(x)$, $y = f(-x)$, and $y = f(-\frac{1}{2}x)$ on the same set of axes.

12 Graph on the same set of axes $y = x^2$, $y = -x^2$, and $y = -(x+2)^2 + 3$.

Describe the combination of transformations which transform $y = x^2$ to $y = -(x+2)^2 + 3$.

13 Graph on the same set of axes $y = \dfrac{1}{x}$, $y = -\dfrac{1}{x}$, $y = -\dfrac{1}{x-3} + 2$.

Describe the combination of transformations which transform $y = \dfrac{1}{x}$ to $y = -\dfrac{1}{x-3} + 2$.

DISCUSSION

For which combinations of two transformations on $y = f(x)$ is the order in which the transformations are performed:

- important
- not important?

D   MISCELLANEOUS TRANSFORMATIONS

A summary of all the transformations is given in the printable concept map.

CONCEPT MAP

Example 5   ◀) Self Tutor

Consider $f(x) = \frac{1}{2}x + 1$. On separate sets of axes graph:

a $y = f(x)$ and $y = f(x+2)$

b $y = f(x)$ and $y = f(x) + 2$

c $y = f(x)$ and $y = 2f(x)$

d $y = f(x)$ and $y = -f(x)$

a
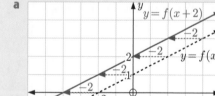

b
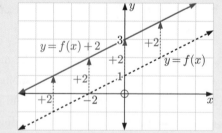

c
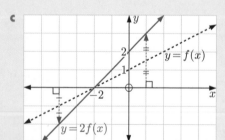

d
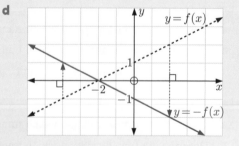

EXERCISE 4D

1 Consider $f(x) = x^2 - 1$.

    a Graph $y = f(x)$ and state its axes intercepts.

    b Graph each function and describe the transformation which has occurred:

        i $y = f(x) + 3$ **ii** $y = f(x - 1)$ **iii** $y = 2f(x)$ **iv** $y = -f(x)$

2 In each graph, $f(x)$ is transformed to $g(x)$ using a single transformation.

    i Describe the transformation.   **ii** Write $g(x)$ in terms of $f(x)$.

a

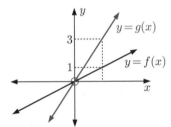

b

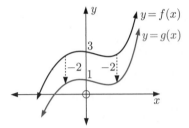

c

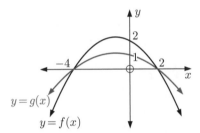

d

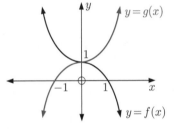

3 For the graph of $y = f(x)$ given, sketch the graph of:

    a $y = 2f(x)$ **b** $y = \frac{1}{2}f(x)$

    c $y = f(x + 2)$ **d** $y = f(2x)$

    e $y = f(\frac{1}{2}x)$

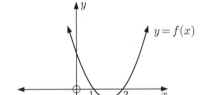

4

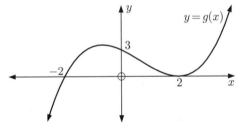

For the graph of $y = g(x)$ given, sketch the graph of:

    a $y = g(x) + 2$ **b** $y = -g(x)$

    c $y = g(-x)$ **d** $y = g(x + 1)$

5 For the graph of $y = h(x)$ given, sketch the graph of:

    a $y = h(x) + 1$ **b** $y = \frac{1}{2}h(x)$

    c $y = h(-x)$ **d** $y = h\left(\frac{x}{2}\right)$

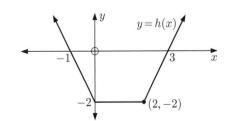

6

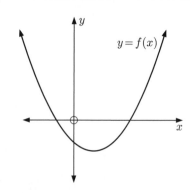

Consider the function $f(x) = (x+1)(x-\beta)$ where $\beta > 0$.
A sketch of the function is shown alongside.

  a Determine the axes intercepts of the graph of $y = f(x)$.

  b Sketch the graphs of $f(x)$ and $g(x) = -f(x-1)$ on the same set of axes.

  c Find and label the axes intercepts of $y = g(x)$.

Example 6　　　　　　　　　　　　　　　　　　　　　　　**◀⑴ Self Tutor**

Consider a function $f(x)$.

  a What function results if $y = f(x)$ is reflected in the x-axis, then translated through $\begin{pmatrix} 3 \\ -1 \end{pmatrix}$, then stretched vertically with scale factor 2?

  b Fully describe the transformations which map $y = f(x)$ onto $y = 3f(2(x-1)) - 2$.

---

a　$f(x)$ $\xrightarrow{\substack{\text{reflection} \\ \text{in } x\text{-axis}}}$ $-f(x)$ $\xrightarrow{\text{translation } \begin{pmatrix} 3 \\ -1 \end{pmatrix}}$ $-f(x-3) - 1$ $\xrightarrow{\substack{\text{vertical stretch} \\ \text{scale factor 2}}}$ $2(-f(x-3) - 1)$

The resulting function is $-2f(x-3) - 2$.

b　$f(x)$ $\xrightarrow{\substack{\text{vertical stretch} \\ \text{scale factor 3}}}$ $3f(x)$ $\xrightarrow{\substack{\text{horizontal stretch} \\ \text{scale factor } \frac{1}{2}}}$ $3f(2x)$ $\xrightarrow{\text{translation } \begin{pmatrix} 1 \\ -2 \end{pmatrix}}$ $3f(2(x-1)) - 2$

---

7 Consider a function $f(x)$. Find the function which results if $y = f(x)$ is:

  a translated through $\begin{pmatrix} 4 \\ -1 \end{pmatrix}$ then reflected in the y-axis

  b reflected in the y-axis then translated through $\begin{pmatrix} 4 \\ -1 \end{pmatrix}$

  c translated through $\begin{pmatrix} -2 \\ 1 \end{pmatrix}$ then stretched vertically with scale factor $\frac{1}{2}$

  d stretched vertically with scale factor $\frac{1}{2}$ then translated through $\begin{pmatrix} -2 \\ 1 \end{pmatrix}$.

8 Fully describe the transformations which map $y = f(x)$ onto:

  a $y = -f(x+1) + 3$　　　　　　　　**b** $y = f(\frac{1}{2}x) - 7$

  c $y = f(3(x-1))$　　　　　　　　　**d** $y = -1 + 2f(\frac{1}{4}(x-4))$

  e $y = 5 + 2f(3(x-1))$　　　　　　　**f** $y = -4f(\frac{1}{2}(x+3)) - 1$

9 The graph of $y = x^2$ is transformed into $y = a(x - h)^2 + k$ using three transformations:

- a vertical stretch with invariant x-axis

- a translation with vector $\begin{pmatrix} h \\ k \end{pmatrix}$

- a reflection in the x-axis.

Discuss what you know about:

    a the transformations   **b** the function.

REVIEW SET 4A

1 For the graph of $y = f(x)$, sketch graphs of:

  a $y = f(-x)$ **b** $y = -f(x)$

  c $y = f(x + 2)$ **d** $y = f(x) + 2$

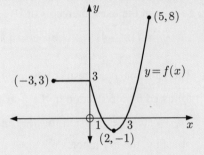

2 Consider the function $f : x \mapsto x^2$.

On the same set of axes, graph $y = f(x)$, $y = 3f(x)$, and $y = 3f(x - 1) + 2$.

3 Find the equation of the resulting graph $g(x)$ when:

  a $f(x) = 4x - 7$ is translated 3 units downwards

  b $f(x) = x^2 + 6$ is vertically stretched with scale factor 5

  c $f(x) = 7 - 3x$ is translated 4 units to the left

  d $f(x) = 2x^2 - x + 4$ is horizontally stretched with scale factor 3

  e $f(x) = x^3$ is reflected in the y-axis.

4 Sketch the graph of $f(x) = x^2 + 1$, and on the same set of axes sketch the graph of:

  a $y = -f(x)$ **b** $y = f(2x)$ **c** $y = f(x) + 3$

5 The function $f(x)$ has domain $\{x \mid -2 \leqslant x \leqslant 3\}$ and range $\{y \mid -1 \leqslant y \leqslant 7\}$.

Find the domain and range of $g(x) = f(x + 3) - 4$. Explain your answers.

6 The graph of the function $f(x) = (x + 1)^2 + 4$ is translated 2 units to the right and 4 units up.

  a Find the function $g(x)$ corresponding to the translated graph.

  b State the range of:

      i $f(x)$ **ii** $g(x)$

7 The graph of $f(x) = 3x^2 - x + 4$ is translated by the vector $\begin{pmatrix} -1 \\ 3 \end{pmatrix}$. Write the equation of the image in the form $g(x) = ax^2 + bx + c$.

8 **a** Find the equation of the line that results when the line $f(x) = 3x + 2$ is translated:

  i 2 units to the left   **ii** 6 units upwards.

  b Show that when the linear function $f(x) = ax + b$, $a > 0$ is translated k units to the left, the resulting line is the same as when $f(x)$ is translated ak units upwards.

9 Consider a function $f(x)$. Find the function which results if $y = f(x)$ is:

  a reflected in the x-axis then translated through $\begin{pmatrix} -2 \\ 3 \end{pmatrix}$

  b translated through $\begin{pmatrix} 4 \\ -1 \end{pmatrix}$ then vertically stretched with scale factor 2.

10 Suppose the graph of $y = f(x)$ has x-intercepts -5 and 1, and y-intercept -3. What can you say about the axes intercepts of:

  a $y = f(x + 4)$ **b** $y = 3f(x)$ **c** $y = f\left(\dfrac{x}{2}\right)$ **d** $y = -f(x)$?

11 The function $g(x)$ results when $y = \dfrac{1}{x}$ is transformed by a translation through $\begin{pmatrix} -1 \\ 2 \end{pmatrix}$ followed by a reflection in the y-axis.

  a Write an expression for $g(x)$ in the form $g(x) = \dfrac{ax + b}{cx + d}$.

  b Find the asymptotes of $y = g(x)$.

  c State the domain and range of $g(x)$.

  d Sketch $y = g(x)$.

12 Graph on the same set of axes $y = x^2$, $y = \frac{1}{4}x^2$, and $y = \frac{1}{4}(x - 2)^2 - 1$.

Describe the combination of transformations which transform $y = x^2$ to $y = \frac{1}{4}(x - 2)^2 - 1$.

REVIEW SET 4B

1 Consider the graph of $y = f(x)$ alongside. On separate axes, draw the graphs of:

  a $y = f(x - 1)$ **b** $y = f(2x)$

  c $y = f(x) + 3$ **d** $y = 2f(x)$

  e $y = f(-x)$ **f** $y = -f(x)$

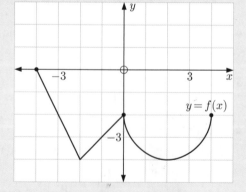

PRINTABLE GRIDS

2 Find the equation of the resulting graph $g(x)$ when:

  a $f(x) = x^2 - 3x$ is reflected in the x-axis

  b $f(x) = 14 - x$ is translated 2 units upwards

  c $f(x) = \frac{1}{3}x + 2$ is horizontally stretched with scale factor 4.

3 Consider the function $f : x \mapsto x^2$. On the same set of axes, graph $y = f(x)$, $y = 2f(x)$, and $y = 2f(x + 2) - 3$.

4 The graph of $f(x) = x^2$ is transformed to the graph of $g(x)$ by a reflection and a translation as illustrated. Find the formula for $g(x)$ in the form $g(x) = ax^2 + bx + c$.

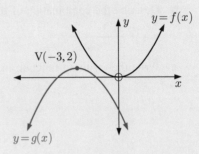

5 Given the graph of $y = f(x)$, sketch graphs of:

   a $y = f(-x)$ **b** $y = f(x + 1)$

   c $y = f(x) - 3$.

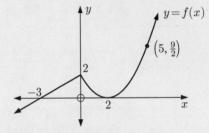

6 Sketch the graph of $f(x) = -x^2$, and on the same set of axes sketch the graph of:

   a $y = f(-x)$ **b** $y = -f(x)$ **c** $y = f(2x)$ **d** $y = f(x - 2)$

7 The graph of a cubic function $y = f(x)$ is shown alongside.

   a Sketch the graph of $g(x) = -f(x - 1)$.

   b State the coordinates of the turning points of $y = g(x)$.

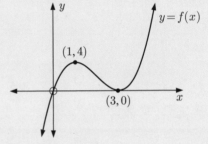

8 The graph of $f(x) = -2x^2 + x + 2$ is translated by the vector $\begin{pmatrix} 1 \\ -2 \end{pmatrix}$.

   Write the equation of the image in the form $y = ax^2 + bx + c$.

9 The graph of $y = f(x)$ is shown alongside.

   The x-axis is a tangent to $f(x)$ at $x = a$ and $f(x)$ cuts the x-axis at $x = b$.

   On the same diagram, sketch the graph of $y = f(x - c)$ where $0 < c < b - a$.

   Indicate the x-intercepts of $y = f(x - c)$.

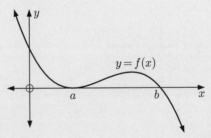

10 The point $(-1, 6)$ lies on the graph of $y = f(x)$. Find the corresponding point on the graph of $y = \frac{1}{2}f(x - 2) + 3$.

11 Fully describe the transformations which map $y = f(x)$ onto:

   a $y = 2f(x + 1) + 3$ **b** $y = -f(\frac{2}{3}x) - 6$ **c** $y = \frac{1}{3}f(-x) + 2$

12 **a** Graph on the same set of axes $y = \dfrac{1}{x}$, $y = -\dfrac{1}{x}$, $y = -\dfrac{1}{2x}$, and $y = -\dfrac{1}{2(x+1)} - 2$.

   b Describe the combination of transformations which transform $y = \dfrac{1}{x}$ into
   $y = -\dfrac{1}{2(x+1)} - 2$.

   c Write the resulting function in the form $y = \dfrac{ax+b}{cx+d}$, and state its domain and range.

Chapter 5

Exponential functions

Contents:

OPENING PROBLEM

At an antiques fair, Bernard purchases a clock for £500 and a vase for £400. The clock increases in value by 5% each year, and the vase increases in value by 7% each year.

Things to think about:

a What is the value of each item 1 year after purchase?

b Can you write a formula for the value of each item t years after purchase?

c Which item is more valuable 15 years after purchase?

d How can we determine when the items are equal in value?

We have seen previously how exponents are used to indicate when a number is raised to a power.

For a positive integer exponent, the exponent tells us how many of the base are multiplied together.

$$\begin{cases} 2^3 = 2 \times 2 \times 2 & = 8 \\ 2^2 = 2 \times 2 & = 4 \\ 2^1 = 2 & = 2 \end{cases}$$

Any non-zero base to the power 0 is defined as 1, to give consistency to the exponent laws.

$$2^0 = 1 \qquad = 1$$

For a negative integer exponent, we take the reciprocal of the corresponding positive integer power.

$$\begin{cases} 2^{-1} = \frac{1}{2} & = \frac{1}{2} \\ 2^{-2} = \frac{1}{2 \times 2} & = \frac{1}{4} \\ 2^{-3} = \frac{1}{2 \times 2 \times 2} & = \frac{1}{8} \end{cases}$$

In this Chapter we give meaning to exponents which are **rational**, allowing us to start filling in the gaps between the integer exponents. This will allow us to consider **exponential functions** for which the variable appears in an exponent.

A   RATIONAL EXPONENTS

The **laws of exponents** used previously can also be applied to **rational exponents**, or exponents $\in \mathbb{Q}$.

For any $a > 0$, notice that $\quad a^{\frac{1}{2}} \times a^{\frac{1}{2}} = a^{\frac{1}{2}+\frac{1}{2}} = a^1 = a \quad$ {exponent laws}

and $\quad \sqrt{a} \times \sqrt{a} = a \quad$ also.

Likewise, $\quad a^{\frac{1}{3}} \times a^{\frac{1}{3}} \times a^{\frac{1}{3}} = a^1 = a$

and $\quad \sqrt[3]{a} \times \sqrt[3]{a} \times \sqrt[3]{a} = a \quad$ also.

By direct comparison, we conclude that $\qquad a^{\frac{1}{2}} = \sqrt{a} \qquad$ and $\qquad a^{\frac{1}{3}} = \sqrt[3]{a}$.

In general, $\quad a^{\frac{1}{n}} = \sqrt[n]{a} \quad$ where $\sqrt[n]{a}$ reads "the nth root of a" for $n \in \mathbb{Z}^+$.

We can now determine that $\sqrt[n]{a^m} = (a^m)^{\frac{1}{n}}$

$$= a^{\frac{m}{n}}$$

$\therefore$ $\boxed{a^{\frac{m}{n}} = \sqrt[n]{a^m} \quad \text{for} \quad a > 0, \ n \in \mathbb{Z}^+, \ m \in \mathbb{Z}}$

Example 1   ◀) **Self Tutor**

Write as a single power of 2:

a $\sqrt[3]{2}$ b $\dfrac{1}{\sqrt{2}}$ c $\sqrt[5]{4}$

---

a $\sqrt[3]{2}$

$= 2^{\frac{1}{3}}$

b $\dfrac{1}{\sqrt{2}}$

$= \dfrac{1}{2^{\frac{1}{2}}}$

$= 2^{-\frac{1}{2}}$

c $\sqrt[5]{4}$

$= (2^2)^{\frac{1}{5}}$

$= 2^{2 \times \frac{1}{5}}$

$= 2^{\frac{2}{5}}$

EXERCISE 5A

1   Write as a single power of 2:

   a $\sqrt[5]{2}$ b $\dfrac{1}{\sqrt[5]{2}}$ c $2\sqrt{2}$ d $4\sqrt{2}$ e $\dfrac{1}{\sqrt[3]{2}}$

   f $2 \times \sqrt[3]{2}$ g $\dfrac{4}{\sqrt{2}}$ h $(\sqrt{2})^3$ i $\dfrac{1}{\sqrt[3]{16}}$ j $\dfrac{1}{\sqrt{8}}$

2   Write as a single power of 3:

   a $\sqrt[3]{3}$ b $\dfrac{1}{\sqrt[3]{3}}$ c $\sqrt[4]{3}$ d $3\sqrt{3}$ e $\dfrac{1}{9\sqrt{3}}$

3   Write in the form a^k, where a is a prime number and k is rational:

   a $\sqrt[3]{7}$ b $\sqrt[4]{27}$ c $\sqrt[5]{16}$ d $\sqrt[3]{32}$ e $\sqrt[7]{49}$

   f $\dfrac{1}{\sqrt[3]{7}}$ g $\dfrac{1}{\sqrt[4]{27}}$ h $\dfrac{1}{\sqrt[5]{16}}$ i $\dfrac{1}{\sqrt[3]{32}}$ j $\dfrac{1}{\sqrt[7]{49}}$

4   Write in the form x^k, where k is rational:

   a $\sqrt{x}$ b $x\sqrt{x}$ c $\dfrac{1}{\sqrt{x}}$ d $x^2\sqrt{x}$ e $\dfrac{1}{x\sqrt{x}}$

5   Use your calculator to find, correct to 3 significant figures:

   a $3^{\frac{3}{4}}$ b $4^{-\frac{3}{5}}$ c $\sqrt[4]{8}$ d $\sqrt[5]{27}$ e $\dfrac{1}{\sqrt[3]{7}}$

GRAPHICS
CALCULATOR
INSTRUCTIONS

6   Write *without* rational exponents:

   a $5^{\frac{1}{3}}$ b $3^{-\frac{1}{2}}$ c $3^{\frac{5}{2}}$ d $m^{\frac{3}{2}}$ e $x^{\frac{7}{2}}$

Example 2   ◀⦅ **Self Tutor**

Without using a calculator, write in simplest rational form:

   a $8^{\frac{4}{3}}$ **b** $27^{-\frac{2}{3}}$

a $8^{\frac{4}{3}}$

$= (2^3)^{\frac{4}{3}}$

$= 2^{3 \times \frac{4}{3}}$ $\{(a^m)^n = a^{mn}\}$

$= 2^4$

$= 16$

b $27^{-\frac{2}{3}}$

$= (3^3)^{-\frac{2}{3}}$

$= 3^{3 \times (-\frac{2}{3})}$

$= 3^{-2}$

$= \frac{1}{9}$

7 Without using a calculator, write in simplest rational form:

  a $4^{\frac{3}{2}}$ **b** $8^{\frac{5}{3}}$ **c** $16^{\frac{3}{4}}$ **d** $25^{\frac{3}{2}}$ **e** $32^{\frac{2}{5}}$

  f $4^{-\frac{1}{2}}$ **g** $9^{-\frac{3}{2}}$ **h** $8^{-\frac{4}{3}}$ **i** $27^{-\frac{4}{3}}$ **j** $125^{-\frac{2}{3}}$

B   ALGEBRAIC EXPANSION AND FACTORISATION

We can use the standard rules of algebra, together with the laws of exponents, to simplify expressions containing rational or variable exponents:

$$a(b + c) = ab + ac$$
$$(a + b)(c + d) = ac + ad + bc + bd$$
$$(a + b)(a - b) = a^2 - b^2$$
$$(a + b)^2 = a^2 + 2ab + b^2$$
$$(a - b)^2 = a^2 - 2ab + b^2$$

Example 3   ◀⦅ **Self Tutor**

Expand and simplify: $x^{-\frac{1}{2}}(x^{\frac{3}{2}} + 2x^{\frac{1}{2}} - 3x^{-\frac{1}{2}})$

$x^{-\frac{1}{2}}(x^{\frac{3}{2}} + 2x^{\frac{1}{2}} - 3x^{-\frac{1}{2}})$

$= x^{-\frac{1}{2}} \times x^{\frac{3}{2}} + x^{-\frac{1}{2}} \times 2x^{\frac{1}{2}} - x^{-\frac{1}{2}} \times 3x^{-\frac{1}{2}}$ $\{$each term is multiplied by $x^{-\frac{1}{2}}\}$

$= x^1 + 2x^0 - 3x^{-1}$ $\{$adding indices$\}$

$= x + 2 - \dfrac{3}{x}$

EXERCISE 5B

1 Simplify:

  a $x^{\frac{1}{2}} \times x^{-\frac{1}{2}}$ **b** $x^{\frac{3}{2}} \times x^{-\frac{1}{2}}$ **c** $x^2 \times x^{-\frac{3}{2}}$

2 Expand and simplify:

a $x^2(x^3 + 2x^2 + 1)$

b $2^x(2^x + 1)$

c $x^{\frac{1}{2}}(x^{\frac{1}{2}} + x^{-\frac{1}{2}})$

d $7^x(7^x + 2)$

e $3^x(2 - 3^{-x})$

f $x^{\frac{1}{2}}(x^{\frac{3}{2}} + 2x^{\frac{1}{2}} + 3x^{-\frac{1}{2}})$

g $2^{-x}(2^x + 5)$

h $5^{-x}(5^{2x} + 5^x)$

i $x^{-\frac{1}{2}}(x^2 + x + x^{\frac{1}{2}})$

j $3^x(3^x + 5 + 3^{-x})$

k $x^{-\frac{1}{2}}(2x^2 - x + 5x^{\frac{1}{2}})$

l $2^{2x}(2^x - 3 - 2^{-2x})$

Example 4 ◄)) Self Tutor

Expand and simplify:

a $(2^x + 3)(2^x + 1)$

b $(7^x + 7^{-x})^2$

a $\quad (2^x + 3)(2^x + 1)$
$= 2^x \times 2^x + 2^x + 3 \times 2^x + 3$
$= 2^{2x} + 4 \times 2^x + 3$

b $\quad (7^x + 7^{-x})^2$
$= (7^x)^2 + 2 \times 7^x \times 7^{-x} + (7^{-x})^2$
$= 7^{2x} + 2 \times 7^0 + 7^{-2x}$
$= 7^{2x} + 2 + 7^{-2x}$

---

3 Expand and simplify:

a $(2^x - 1)(2^x + 3)$

b $(3^x + 2)(3^x + 5)$

c $(5^x - 2)(5^x - 4)$

d $(2^x + 3)^2$

e $(3^x - 1)^2$

f $(4^x + 7)^2$

g $(x^{\frac{1}{2}} + 2)(x^{\frac{1}{2}} - 2)$

h $(2^x + 3)(2^x - 3)$

i $(x^{\frac{1}{2}} + x^{-\frac{1}{2}})(x^{\frac{1}{2}} - x^{-\frac{1}{2}})$

j $\left(x + \dfrac{2}{x}\right)^2$

k $(7^x - 7^{-x})^2$

l $(5 - 2^{-x})^2$

Example 5 ◄)) Self Tutor

Factorise:

a $2^{n+3} + 2^n$

b $2^{n+3} + 8$

c $2^{3n} + 2^{2n}$

a $\quad 2^{n+3} + 2^n$
$= 2^n 2^3 + 2^n$
$= 2^n(2^3 + 1)$
$= 2^n \times 9$

b $\quad 2^{n+3} + 8$
$= 2^n 2^3 + 8$
$= 8(2^n) + 8$
$= 8(2^n + 1)$

c $\quad 2^{3n} + 2^{2n}$
$= 2^{2n} 2^n + 2^{2n}$
$= 2^{2n}(2^n + 1)$

---

4 Factorise:

a $5^{2x} + 5^x$

b $3^{n+2} + 3^n$

c $7^n + 7^{3n}$

d $5^{n+1} - 5$

e $6^{n+2} - 6$

f $4^{n+2} - 16$

g $2^{2n} - 2^{n+3}$

h $2^{n+1} + 2^{n-1}$

i $4^{n+1} + 2^{2n-1}$

Example 6   ◀) **Self Tutor**

Factorise:

a $4^x - 9$ **b** $9^x + 4(3^x) + 4$

---

a $4^x - 9$
$= (2^x)^2 - 3^2$ {compare $a^2 - b^2 = (a+b)(a-b)$}
$= (2^x + 3)(2^x - 3)$

b $9^x + 4(3^x) + 4$
$= (3^x)^2 + 4(3^x) + 4$ {compare $a^2 + 4a + 4$}
$= (3^x + 2)^2$ {as $a^2 + 4a + 4 = (a+2)^2$}

---

5 Factorise:

   a $9^x - 4$ **b** $4^x - 25$ **c** $16 - 9^x$

   d $25 - 4^x$ **e** $9^x - 4^x$ **f** $4^x + 6(2^x) + 9$

   g $9^x + 10(3^x) + 25$ **h** $4^x - 14(2^x) + 49$ **i** $25^x - 4(5^x) + 4$

6 Factorise:

   a $(2^x)^2 - 2^x - 2$ **b** $(3^x)^2 + 3^x - 6$ **c** $4^x - 7(2^x) + 12$

   d $4^x + 9(2^x) + 18$ **e** $4^x - 2^x - 20$ **f** $9^x + 9(3^x) + 14$

   g $9^x + 4(3^x) - 5$ **h** $25^x + 5^x - 2$ **i** $49^x - 7^{x+1} + 12$

Example 7   ◀) **Self Tutor**

Simplify:

  a $\dfrac{6^n}{3^n}$ **b** $\dfrac{4^n}{6^n}$

---

a $\dfrac{6^n}{3^n}$ **or** $\dfrac{6^n}{3^n}$ **b** $\dfrac{4^n}{6^n}$ **or** $\dfrac{4^n}{6^n}$

     $= \dfrac{2^n 3^n}{3^n_{\ 1}}$ $= \left(\dfrac{6}{3}\right)^n$ $= \dfrac{2^n 2^n}{2^n 3^n}$ $= \left(\dfrac{4}{6}\right)^n$

     $= 2^n$ $= 2^n$ $= \dfrac{2^n}{3^n}$ $= \left(\dfrac{2}{3}\right)^n$

---

7 Simplify:

   a $\dfrac{12^n}{6^n}$ **b** $\dfrac{20^a}{2^a}$ **c** $\dfrac{6^b}{2^b}$

   d $\dfrac{4^n}{20^n}$ **e** $\dfrac{35^x}{7^x}$ **f** $\dfrac{6^a}{8^a}$

   g $\dfrac{24^k}{9^k}$ **h** $\dfrac{5^{n+1}}{5^n}$ **i** $\dfrac{5^{n+1}}{5}$

Example 8

🔊 Self Tutor

Simplify:

a $\dfrac{3^n + 6^n}{3^n}$

b $\dfrac{2^{m+2} - 2^m}{2^m}$

c $\dfrac{2^{m+3} + 2^m}{9}$

a $\dfrac{3^n + 6^n}{3^n}$

$= \dfrac{3^n + 2^n 3^n}{3^n}$

$= \dfrac{3^n(1 + 2^n)}{3^n \,_1}$

$= 1 + 2^n$

b $\dfrac{2^{m+2} - 2^m}{2^m}$

$= \dfrac{2^m 2^2 - 2^m}{2^m}$

$= \dfrac{2^m(4 - 1)}{2^m \,_1}$

$= 3$

c $\dfrac{2^{m+3} + 2^m}{9}$

$= \dfrac{2^m 2^3 + 2^m}{9}$

$= \dfrac{2^m(8 + 1)}{9 \,_1}$

$= 2^m$

8 Simplify:

a $\dfrac{6^m + 2^m}{2^m}$

b $\dfrac{2^n + 12^n}{2^n}$

c $\dfrac{8^n + 4^n}{2^n}$

d $\dfrac{12^x - 3^x}{3^x}$

e $\dfrac{6^n + 12^n}{1 + 2^n}$

f $\dfrac{5^{n+1} - 5^n}{4}$

g $\dfrac{5^{n+1} - 5^n}{5^n}$

h $\dfrac{4^n - 2^n}{2^n}$

i $\dfrac{2^n - 2^{n-1}}{2^n}$

9 Simplify:

a $2^n(n+1) + 2^n(n-1)$

b $3^n\left(\dfrac{n-1}{6}\right) - 3^n\left(\dfrac{n+1}{6}\right)$

C   EXPONENTIAL EQUATIONS

An **exponential equation** is an equation in which the unknown occurs as part of the index or exponent.

For example: $2^x = 8$ and $30 \times 3^x = 7$ are both exponential equations.

There are a number of methods we can use to solve exponential equations. These include graphing, using technology, and by using **logarithms**, which we will study in **Chapter 6**. However, in some cases we can solve the equation algebraically.

If both sides of an exponential equation are written as powers with the same base numbers, we can **equate indices**.

So, if $a^x = a^k$ then $x = k$.

For example, if $2^x = 8$ then $2^x = 2^3$. Thus $x = 3$, and this is the only solution.

Example 9   ◀)) **Self Tutor**

Solve for x:

a $2^x = 16$ b $3^{x+2} = \frac{1}{27}$

---

a $2^x = 16$ b $3^{x+2} = \frac{1}{27}$
$\therefore\ 2^x = 2^4$ $\therefore\ 3^{x+2} = 3^{-3}$
$\therefore\ x = 4$ $\therefore\ x + 2 = -3$
                                                          $\therefore\ x = -5$

Once we have the
same base, we
equate the indices.

Example 10   ◀)) **Self Tutor**

Solve for x:

a $4^x = 8$ b $9^{x-2} = \frac{1}{3}$

---

a $4^x = 8$ b $9^{x-2} = \frac{1}{3}$
$\therefore\ (2^2)^x = 2^3$ $\therefore\ (3^2)^{x-2} = 3^{-1}$
$\therefore\ 2^{2x} = 2^3$ $\therefore\ 3^{2(x-2)} = 3^{-1}$
$\therefore\ 2x = 3$ $\therefore\ 2(x-2) = -1$
$\therefore\ x = \frac{3}{2}$ $\therefore\ 2x - 4 = -1$
                                                          $\therefore\ 2x = 3$
                                                          $\therefore\ x = \frac{3}{2}$

EXERCISE 5C

1 Solve for x:

a $2^x = 32$ b $5^x = 25$ c $3^x = 81$ d $7^x = 1$

e $3^x = \frac{1}{3}$ f $2^x = \sqrt{2}$ g $5^x = \frac{1}{125}$ h $4^{x+1} = 64$

i $2^{x-2} = \frac{1}{32}$ j $3^{x+1} = \frac{1}{27}$ k $7^{x+1} = 343$ l $5^{1-2x} = \frac{1}{5}$

2 Solve for x:

a $8^x = 32$ b $4^x = \frac{1}{8}$ c $9^x = \frac{1}{27}$ d $25^x = \frac{1}{5}$

e $27^x = \frac{1}{9}$ f $16^x = \frac{1}{32}$ g $4^{x+2} = 128$ h $25^{1-x} = \frac{1}{125}$

i $4^{4x-1} = \frac{1}{2}$ j $9^{x-3} = 27$ k $\left(\frac{1}{2}\right)^{x+1} = 8$ l $\left(\frac{1}{3}\right)^{x+2} = 9$

m $81^x = 27^{-x}$ n $\left(\frac{1}{4}\right)^{1-x} = 32$ o $\left(\frac{1}{7}\right)^x = 49$ p $\left(\frac{1}{3}\right)^{x+1} = 243$

3 Solve for x, if possible:

a $4^{2x+1} = 8^{1-x}$ b $9^{2-x} = \left(\frac{1}{3}\right)^{2x+1}$ c $2^x \times 8^{1-x} = \frac{1}{4}$

4 Solve for x:

a $3 \times 2^x = 24$ b $7 \times 2^x = 28$ c $4 \times 3^{x+2} = 12$

d $12 \times 3^{-x} = \frac{4}{3}$ e $4 \times \left(\frac{1}{3}\right)^x = 36$ f $5 \times \left(\frac{1}{2}\right)^x = 20$

Example 11 ◀) **Self Tutor**

Solve for x: $4^x + 2^x - 20 = 0$

$$4^x + 2^x - 20 = 0$$
$$\therefore \ (2^x)^2 + 2^x - 20 = 0 \qquad \{\text{compare} \ \ a^2 + a - 20 = 0\}$$
$$\therefore \ (2^x - 4)(2^x + 5) = 0 \qquad \{a^2 + a - 20 = (a - 4)(a + 5)\}$$
$$\therefore \ \ 2^x = 4 \ \text{ or } \ 2^x = -5$$
$$\therefore \ \ 2^x = 2^2 \qquad \{2^x \text{ cannot be negative}\}$$
$$\therefore \ \ x = 2$$

5 Solve for x:

   a $4^x - 6(2^x) + 8 = 0$ **b** $4^x - 2^x - 2 = 0$ **c** $9^x - 12(3^x) + 27 = 0$

   d $9^x = 3^x + 6$ **e** $25^x - 23(5^x) - 50 = 0$ **f** $49^x + 1 = 2(7^x)$

Check your answers using technology.

GRAPHICS
CALCULATOR
INSTRUCTIONS

D   EXPONENTIAL FUNCTIONS

We have already seen how to evaluate a^n for any $n \in \mathbb{Q}$.

But how do we evaluate a^n when $n \in \mathbb{R}$, so n is real but not necessarily rational?

To answer this question, we can study the graphs of exponential functions.

The most simple **exponential function** has the form $y = a^x$ where $a > 0$, $a \neq 1$.

For example, $y = 2^x$ is an exponential function.

We construct a table of values from which we graph the function:

x	-3	-2	-1	0	1	2	3
y	$\frac{1}{8}$	$\frac{1}{4}$	$\frac{1}{2}$	1	2	4	8

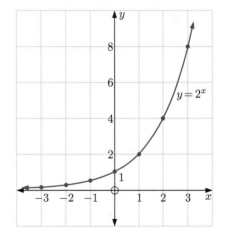

As x becomes large and negative, the graph of $y = 2^x$ approaches the x-axis from above. However, it never touches the x-axis, since 2^x becomes very small but never zero.

So, as $x \to -\infty$, $y \to 0^+$.

$y = 0$ is therefore a **horizontal asymptote**.

Plotting $y = a^x$ for $x \in \mathbb{Q}$ suggests a smooth, continuous curve. This allows us to complete the curve for all $x \in \mathbb{R}$, giving meaning to a^x for irrational values of x.

INVESTIGATION 1   GRAPHS OF EXPONENTIAL FUNCTIONS

In this Investigation we examine the graphs of various families of exponential functions.

GRAPHING
PACKAGE

You can use the **graphing package** or your calculator.

What to do:

1 **a** State the transformation which maps $y = a^x$ to $y = a^x + k$.

    b Predict the effect, if any, this transformation will have on:

      i the shape of the graph   **ii** the position of the graph

      iii the horizontal asymptote.

    c Check your predictions by graphing $y = 2^x$, $y = 2^x + 1$, and $y = 2^x - 2$ on the same set of axes.

2 **a** State the transformation which maps $y = a^x$ to $y = a^{x-h}$.

    b Predict the effect, if any, this transformation will have on:

      i the shape of the graph   **ii** the position of the graph

      iii the horizontal asymptote.

    c Check your predictions by graphing $y = 2^x$, $y = 2^{x-1}$, $y = 2^{x+2}$, and $y = 2^{x-3}$ on the same set of axes.

3 **a** State the transformation which maps $y = a^x$ to $y = p \times a^x$, $p > 0$.

    b Predict the effect, if any, this transformation will have on:

      i the shape of the graph   **ii** the position of the graph

      iii the horizontal asymptote.

    c Check your predictions by graphing $y = 2^x$, $y = 3 \times 2^x$, and $y = \frac{1}{2} \times 2^x$ on the same set of axes.

4 **a** State the transformation which maps $y = a^x$ to $y = -a^x$.

    b Predict what the graph of $y = -2^x$ will look like, and check your answer using technology.

5 **a** State the transformation which maps $y = a^x$ to $y = a^{qx}$, $q > 0$.

    b Predict the effect, if any, this transformation will have on:

      i the shape of the graph   **ii** the position of the graph

      iii the horizontal asymptote.

    c Notice that $2^{2x} = (2^2)^x = 4^x$ and $2^{3x} = (2^3)^x = 8^x$.

      Check your predictions by graphing $y = 2^x$, $y = 4^x$, and $y = 8^x$ on the same set of axes.

6 **a** State the transformation which maps $y = a^x$ to $y = a^{-x}$.

    b Notice that $2^{-x} = (2^{-1})^x = \left(\frac{1}{2}\right)^x$.

      Predict what the graph of $y = \left(\frac{1}{2}\right)^x$ will look like, and check your answer using technology.

From your **Investigation** you should have discovered that:

> For the general exponential function $y = p \times a^{x-h} + k$ where $a > 0$, $a \neq 1$, $p \neq 0$:
> - a controls how steeply the graph increases or decreases.
> - h controls horizontal translation.
> - k controls vertical translation.
> - The equation of the horizontal asymptote is $y = k$.
>
> - If $p > 0$, $a > 1$ the function is increasing.
> - If $p > 0$, $0 < a < 1$ the function is decreasing.
> - If $p < 0$, $a > 1$ the function is decreasing.
> - If $p < 0$, $0 < a < 1$ the function is increasing.

We can sketch the graphs of exponential functions using:
- the horizontal asymptote
- the y-intercept
- two other points.

All exponential graphs have a horizontal asymptote.

Example 12 ◀)) Self Tutor

Sketch the graph of $y = 2^{-x} - 3$.
Hence state the domain and range of $f(x) = 2^{-x} - 3$.

For $y = 2^{-x} - 3$,
the horizontal asymptote is $y = -3$.

When $x = 0$, $y = 2^0 - 3$
$= 1 - 3$
$= -2$

$\therefore$ the y-intercept is -2.

When $x = 2$, $y = 2^{-2} - 3$
$= \frac{1}{4} - 3$
$= -2\frac{3}{4}$

When $x = -2$, $y = 2^2 - 3 = 1$

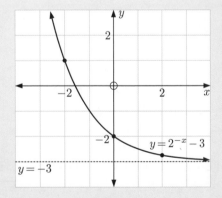

The domain is $\{x \mid x \in \mathbb{R}\}$.   The range is $\{y \mid y > -3\}$.

EXERCISE 5D

1 Consider the graph of $y = 2^x$ alongside.

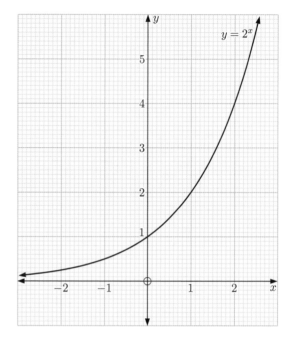

  a Use the graph to estimate the value of:

  i $2^{\frac{1}{2}}$ or $\sqrt{2}$ **ii** $2^{0.8}$

  iii $2^{1.5}$ **iv** $2^{-\sqrt{2}}$

  b Use the graph to estimate the solution to:

  i $2^x = 3$ **ii** $2^x = 0.6$

  c Use the graph to explain why $2^x = 0$ has no solutions.

  > Graphical methods can be used to solve exponential equations where we cannot equate indices.

2 Match each function with its graph:

  a $y = 2^x$ **b** $y = 10^x$

  c $y = -5^x$ **d** $y = \left(\frac{1}{3}\right)^x$

  e $y = -\left(\frac{1}{2}\right)^x$

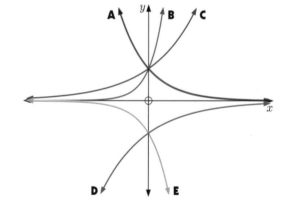

3 Use a transformation to help sketch each pair of functions on the same set of axes:

GRAPHING PACKAGE

  a $y = 2^x$ and $y = 2^x - 2$ **b** $y = 2^x$ and $y = 2^{-x}$

  c $y = 2^x$ and $y = 2^{x-2}$ **d** $y = 2^x$ and $y = 2(2^x)$

4 Draw freehand sketches of the following pairs of graphs:

  a $y = 3^x$ and $y = 3^{-x}$ **b** $y = 3^x$ and $y = 3^x + 1$

  c $y = 3^x$ and $y = -3^x$ **d** $y = 3^x$ and $y = 3^{x-1}$

5 State the equation of the horizontal asymptote of:

  a $y = 3^{-x}$ **b** $y = 2^x - 1$ **c** $y = 3 - 2^{-x}$

  d $y = 4 \times 2^x + 2$ **e** $y = 5 \times 3^{x+2}$ **f** $y = -2 \times 3^{1-x} - 4$

6 Consider the exponential function $f(x) = 3^x - 2$.

   a Find: **i** $f(0)$ **ii** $f(2)$ **iii** $f(-2)$

   b State the equation of the horizontal asymptote.

   c Sketch the graph of the function.

   d State the domain and range of the function.

7 Consider the function $g(x) = 3 \times \left(\frac{1}{2}\right)^x + 4$.

   a Find: **i** $g(0)$ **ii** $g(2)$ **iii** $g(-2)$

   b State the equation of the horizontal asymptote.

   c Sketch the graph of the function.

   d State the domain and range of the function.

8 Consider the function $h(x) = -2^{x-3} + 1$.

   a Find: **i** $h(0)$ **ii** $h(3)$ **iii** $h(6)$

   b State the equation of the horizontal asymptote.

   c Sketch the graph of the function.

   d State the domain and range of the function.

9 For each of the functions below:

   i Sketch the graph of the function.

   ii State the domain and range.

   iii Use your calculator to find the value of y when $x = \sqrt{2}$.

   iv Discuss the behaviour of y as $x \to \pm\infty$.

   v Determine the horizontal asymptote.

   a $y = 2^x + 1$ **b** $y = 2 - 2^x$ **c** $y = 2^{-x} + 3$ **d** $y = 3 - 2^{-x}$

10 The graph alongside shows the curve $y = a \times 2^x + b$, where a and b are constants.

   a Find the values of a and b.

   b Find y when $x = 6$.

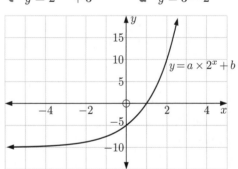

11

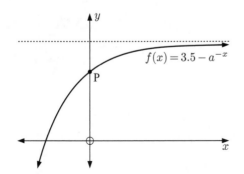

This graph shows the function $f(x) = 3.5 - a^{-x}$, where a is a positive constant.

The point $(-1,\ 2)$ lies on the graph.

   a Write down the coordinates of P.

   b Find the value of a.

   c Find the equation of the horizontal asymptote.

Example 13   ◀)) **Self Tutor**

Use technology to solve the equation $3^x = 7$.

We graph $Y_1 = 3^X$ and $Y_2 = 7$ on the same set of axes, and find their point of intersection.

Casio fx-CG50	TI-84 Plus CE	HP Prime
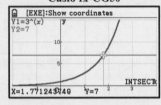		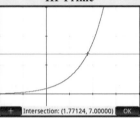

The solution is $x \approx 1.77$.

12 Use technology to solve:

    a $2^x = 11$ **b** $3^x = 15$ **c** $4^x + 5 = 10$

    d $3^{x+2} = 4$ **e** $5 \times 2^x = 18$ **f** $3^{-x} = 0.9$

    g $2 \times 3^{x-2} = 168$ **h** $26 \times (0.95)^x = 2$ **i** $2000 \times (1.03)^x = 5000$

DISCUSSION

For the exponential function $y = a^x$, why do we choose to specify $a > 0$?

What would the graph of $y = (-2)^x$ look like? What is its domain and range?

E   GROWTH AND DECAY

In this Section we will examine situations where quantities are either increasing or decreasing exponentially. These situations are known as **growth** and **decay** modelling, and occur frequently in the world around us.

Populations of animals, people, and bacteria usually *grow* in an exponential way.

Radioactive substances, cooling, and items that depreciate in value, usually *decay* exponentially.

For the exponential function $y = p \times a^{x-h} + k$ where $a, p > 0$, $a \neq 1$, we see:

- growth if $a > 1$
- decay if $a < 1$.

GROWTH

Consider a population of 100 mice which under favourable conditions is increasing by 20% each week.

To increase a quantity by 20%, we multiply it by 1.2.

If P_n is the population after n weeks, then:

$P_0 = 100$ {the *original* population}
$P_1 = P_0 \times 1.2 = 100 \times 1.2$
$P_2 = P_1 \times 1.2 = 100 \times (1.2)^2$
$P_3 = P_2 \times 1.2 = 100 \times (1.2)^3$, and so on.

From this pattern we see that $P_n = 100 \times (1.2)^n$, $n \in \mathbb{Z}$, which is a geometric sequence.

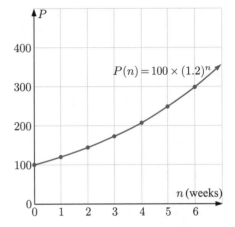

However, while the population of mice must always be an integer, we expect that the population will grow continuously throughout the year, rather than in big, discrete jumps. We therefore expect it will be well approximated by the corresponding exponential function $P(n) = 100 \times (1.2)^n$, $n \in \mathbb{R}$.

Example 14   ◀》 **Self Tutor**

A scientist monitoring a grasshopper plague notices that the area affected by the grasshoppers is given by $A(n) = 1000 \times (1.15)^n$ hectares, where n is the number of weeks after the initial observation.

a Find the original affected area.

b Find the affected area after: **i** 5 weeks   **ii** 10 weeks.

c Draw the graph of the affected area over time.

d Use your graph or technology to find how long it will take for the affected area to reach 8000 hectares.

---

a $A(0) = 1000 \times 1.15^0 = 1000$

∴   the original affected area was 1000 hectares.

b   **i** $A(5) = 1000 \times 1.15^5 \approx 2010$
The affected area is about 2010 hectares.

     ii $A(10) = 1000 \times 1.15^{10} \approx 4050$
The affected area is about 4050 hectares.

c

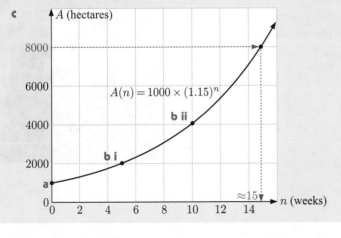

d From the graph in **c**, it appears that it would take about 15 weeks for the affected area to reach 8000 hectares.

or   Using technology, the solution is ≈ 14.9 weeks.

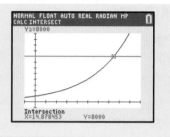

EXERCISE 5E.1

1 The weight W of bacteria in a culture t hours after establishment is given by $W(t) = 100 \times (1.07)^t$ grams.

$a > 1$ indicates growth.

a Find the initial weight.

b Find the weight after:

　i 4 hours　　　**ii** 10 hours　　　**iii** 24 hours.

c Sketch the graph of the bacteria weight over time using the results of **a** and **b** only.

Use technology to graph $Y_1 = 100 \times (1.07)^X$ and hence check your answers.

GRAPHING PACKAGE

2 A breeding program to ensure the survival of pygmy possums is established with an initial population of 50 (25 pairs). From a previous program, the expected population P in n years' time is given by $P(n) = P_0 \times (1.23)^n$.

a What is the value of P_0?

b What is the expected population after:

　i 2 years　　　**ii** 5 years　　　**iii** 10 years?

c Sketch the graph of the population over time using **a** and **b** only.

d Hence estimate the time needed for the population to reach 500.

e Use technology to graph $Y_1 = 50 \times (1.23)^X$. Hence check your answers to **d**.

3 A species of bear is introduced to a large island off Alaska where previously there were no bears. 6 pairs of bears were introduced in 1998. It is expected that the population will increase according to $B(t) = B_0 \times (1.13)^t$ where t is the time, in years, since the introduction.

a Find B_0.

b Find the expected bear population in 2018.

c Find the expected percentage increase in population from 2008 to 2018.

d How long will it take for the population to reach 200?

4 A flu virus spreads in a school. The number of people N infected after t days is given by $N = 4 \times 1.332^t$, $t \geqslant 0$.

    a Find the number of people who were initially infected.

    b Calculate the number of people who were infected after 16 days.

    c There are 1200 people in the school. Estimate the time it will take for everybody in the school to catch the flu.

5 The speed V of a chemical reaction is given by $V(t) = V_0 \times 2^{0.05t}$ where t is the temperature in °C.

    a Find the reaction speed at:

        i 0°C   **ii** 20°C.

    b Find the percentage increase in reaction speed at 20°C compared with 0°C.

    c Find $\left(\dfrac{V(50) - V(20)}{V(20)} \right) \times 100\%$ and explain what this calculation means.

6 Kayla deposited £5000 into an account. The amount in the account increases by 10% each year.

    a Write a formula for the amount $A(t)$ in the account after t years.

    b Find the amount in the account after:

        i 2 years   **ii** 5 years.

    c Sketch the graph of $A(t)$.

    d How long will it take for the amount in the account to reach £8000?

DECAY

Consider a radioactive substance with original weight 20 grams. It *decays* or reduces by 5% each year. The multiplier for this is 95% or 0.95.

If W_n is the weight after n years, then:

$W_0 = 20$ grams
$W_1 = W_0 \times 0.95 = 20 \times 0.95$ grams
$W_2 = W_1 \times 0.95 = 20 \times (0.95)^2$ grams
$W_3 = W_2 \times 0.95 = 20 \times (0.95)^3$ grams
$\vdots$
$W_{20} = 20 \times (0.95)^{20} \approx 7.2$ grams
$\vdots$
$W_{100} = 20 \times (0.95)^{100} \approx 0.1$ grams.

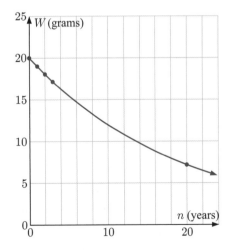

From this pattern we see that $W_n = 20 \times (0.95)^n$, $n \in \mathbb{Z}$, which is again a geometric sequence.

However, we know that radioactive decay is a continuous process, so the weight remaining will actually be given by the smooth exponential curve $W(n) = 20 \times (0.95)^n$, $n \in \mathbb{R}$.

Example 15   ◀) **Self Tutor**

When a diesel-electric generator is switched off, the current dies away according to the formula
$I(t) = 24 \times (0.25)^t$ amps, where t is the time in seconds after the power is cut.

a   Find $I(t)$ when $t = 0, 1, 2,$ and 3.

b   What current flowed in the generator at the instant it was switched off?

c   Plot the graph of $I(t)$ for $t \geqslant 0$ using the information above.

d   Use your graph or technology to find how long it takes for the current to reach 4 amps.

a $I(t) = 24 \times (0.25)^t$ amps

$I(0)$	$I(1)$	$I(2)$	$I(3)$
$= 24 \times (0.25)^0$	$= 24 \times (0.25)^1$	$= 24 \times (0.25)^2$	$= 24 \times (0.25)^3$
$= 24$ amps	$= 6$ amps	$= 1.5$ amps	$= 0.375$ amps

b $I(0) = 24$
When the generator was switched off, 24 amps of current flowed in the circuit.

c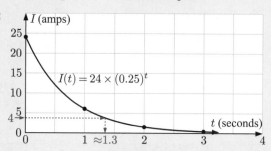

d   From the graph above, the time to reach 4 amps is about 1.3 seconds.

  or   Using technology, the solution is ≈ 1.29 seconds.

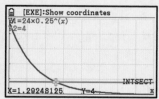

EXERCISE 5E.2

1   The weight of a radioactive substance t years after being set aside is given by $W(t) = 250 \times (0.998)^t$ grams.

   $0 < a < 1$ indicates decay.

   a   How much radioactive substance was initially set aside?

   b   Determine the weight of the substance after:

   i   400 years   ii   800 years   iii   1200 years.

   c   Sketch the graph of $W(t)$ for $t \geqslant 0$ using **a** and **b** only.

   d   Use your graph or graphics calculator to find how long it takes for the substance to decay to 125 grams.

2   The temperature T of a liquid which has been placed in a refrigerator is given by $T(t) = 100 \times (0.986)^t \ °C$ where t is the time in minutes.

   a   Find the initial temperature of the liquid.

   b   Find the temperature after:

   i   15 minutes   ii   20 minutes   iii   78 minutes.

   c   Sketch the graph of $T(t)$ for $t \geqslant 0$ using **a** and **b** only.

3 The weight W of radioactive substance remaining after t years is given by
$W(t) = 1000 \times (0.979)^t$ grams.

    a Find the initial weight of the radioactive substance.

    b Find the weight remaining after:

        i 10 years   **ii** 100 years   **iii** 1000 years.

    c Graph the weight remaining over time using **a** and **b** only.

    d Use your graph or graphics calculator to find the time when 10 grams of the substance remains.

    e Write an expression for the amount of substance that has decayed after t years.

4 An initial count of orangutans in a forest found that the forest contained 400 orangutans. Since then, the destruction of their habitat has caused the population to fall by 8% each year.

    a Write a formula for the population P of orangutans t years after the initial count.

    b Find the population of orangutans after:

        i 1 year   **ii** 5 years.

    c Sketch the graph of the population over time.

    d How long will it take for the population to fall to 200?

5 The intensity of light L diminishes below the surface of the sea according to the formula $L = L_0 \times (0.95)^d$ units, where d is the depth in metres measured from the surface of the sea.

    a If the intensity of light at the surface is 10 units, find the value of L_0.

    b Find the intensity of light 25 m below the surface.

    c A light intensity of 4 units is considered adequate for divers to be able to see clearly. Calculate the depth corresponding to this intensity of light.

    d Calculate the range of depths for which the light intensity is between 1 and 3 units.

6 The value of a car after t years is $V = 24\,000 \times r^t$ dollars, $t \geqslant 0$.

    a Write down the value of the car when it was first purchased.

    b The value of the car after 1 year was $20\,400. Find the value of r.

    c How long will it take for the value of the car to reduce to $8000? Give your answer to the nearest year.

7 The interior of a freezer has temperature $-10°C$. When a packet of peas is placed in the freezer, its temperature after t minutes is given by $T(t) = -10 + 32 \times 2^{-0.2t}$ °C.

    a What was the temperature of the packet of peas:

        i when placed in the freezer   **ii** after 5 minutes   **iii** after 10 minutes?

    b Sketch the graph of $T(t)$.

    c How long does it take for the temperature of the packet of peas to fall to $0°C$?

    d Will the temperature of the packet of peas ever reach $-10°C$? Explain your answer.

8 The weight W_t of a radioactive uranium-235 sample remaining after t years is given by the formula $W_t = W_0 \times 2^{-0.0002t}$ grams, $t \geqslant 0$.

    a Find the original weight.   **b** Find the percentage weight loss after 1000 years.

    c How long will it take until $\frac{1}{512}$ of the sample remains?

F   THE NATURAL EXPONENTIAL

We have seen that the simplest exponential functions have the form $f(x) = a^x$ where $a > 0$, $a \neq 1$.

Graphs of some of these functions are shown alongside.

We can see that for all positive values of the base a, the graph is always positive.

Hence $a^x > 0$ for all $a > 0$.

There are an infinite number of possible choices for the base number.

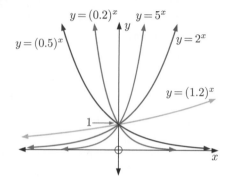

However, where exponential data is examined in science, engineering, and finance, the base $e \approx 2.7183$ is commonly used.

e is a special number in mathematics. It is irrational like π, and just as π is the ratio of a circle's circumference to its diameter, e also has a physical meaning. We explore this meaning in the following **Investigation**.

INVESTIGATION 2   CONTINUOUS COMPOUND INTEREST

A discrete formula for calculating the amount to which an investment grows under compound interest is $u_n = u_0(1 + i)^n$ where:

u_n is the final amount, u_0 is the initial amount,
 i is the interest rate per compounding period,
 n is the number of periods, or times the interest is compounded.

We will investigate the final value of an investment for various values of n, and allow n to become extremely large.

What to do:

1 Suppose $1000 is invested for one year at a fixed rate of 6% per annum. Use your calculator to find the final amount or *maturing value* if the interest is paid:

    a annually $(n = 1, \ i = 6\% = 0.06)$ **b** quarterly $(n = 4, \ i = \frac{6\%}{4} = 0.015)$

    c monthly   **d** daily

    e by the second   **f** by the millisecond.

    Comment on your answers.

2 If r is the percentage rate per year, t is the number of years, and N is the number of interest payments per year, then $i = \dfrac{r}{N}$ and $n = Nt$.

    If we let $a = \dfrac{N}{r}$, show that the growth formula becomes $u_n = u_0\left[\left(1 + \dfrac{1}{a}\right)^a\right]^{rt}$.

3 For continuous compound growth, the number of interest payments per year N gets very large.

a	$\left(1+\frac{1}{a}\right)^a$
10	
100	
1000	
10 000	
100 000	
1 000 000	
10 000 000	

    a Explain why a gets very large as N gets very large.

    b Copy and complete the table, giving your answers as accurately as technology permits.

4 You should have found that for very large values of a,

$$\left(1+\frac{1}{a}\right)^a \approx 2.718\,281\,828\,459....$$

Use the $\boxed{e^x}$ key of your calculator to find the value of e^1. What do you notice?

5 For continuous growth, $u_n = u_0 e^{rt}$ where u_0 is the initial amount, r is the annual percentage rate, and t is the number of years.

Use this formula to find the final amount if \$1000 is invested for 4 years at a fixed rate of 6% per annum, where the interest is paid continuously.

From **Investigation 2** we observe that:

If interest is paid *continuously* or *instantaneously* then the formula for calculating a compounding amount $u_n = u_0(1+i)^n$ can be replaced by $u_n = u_0 e^{rt}$, where r is the percentage rate per annum and t is the number of years.

HISTORICAL NOTE

The natural exponential e was first described in 1683 by Swiss mathematician **Jacob Bernoulli**. He discovered the number while studying compound interest, just as we did in **Investigation 2**.

The natural exponential was first called e by Swiss mathematician and physicist **Leonhard Euler** in a letter to the German mathematician **Christian Goldbach** in 1731. The number was then published with this notation in 1736.

In 1748, Euler evaluated e correct to 18 decimal places.

Leonhard Euler

Euler also discovered some patterns in **continued fraction** expansions of e. He wrote that

$$\frac{e-1}{2} = \cfrac{1}{1+\cfrac{1}{6+\cfrac{1}{10+\cfrac{1}{14+\frac{1}{18+....}}}}} \quad \text{and} \quad e-1 = 1+\cfrac{1}{1+\cfrac{1}{2+\cfrac{1}{1+\cfrac{1}{1+\cfrac{1}{4+\cfrac{1}{1+\frac{1}{1+....}}}}}}}$$

One may think that e was chosen because it was the first letter of Euler's name or for the word exponential, but it is likely that it was just the next vowel available since he had already used a in his work.

EXERCISE 5F

1 Sketch, on the same set of axes, the graphs of $y = 2^x$, $y = e^x$, and $y = 3^x$. Comment on any observations.

GRAPHING PACKAGE

2 Sketch, on the same set of axes, the graphs of $y = e^x$ and $y = e^{-x}$. What is the geometric connection between these two graphs?

3 For the general exponential function $y = pe^{qx}$, what is the y-intercept?

4 Consider $y = 2e^x$.
   a Explain why y can never be negative.
   b Find y if:
      i $x = -20$ **ii** $x = 20$.

5 Find, to 3 significant figures, the value of:
   a e^2 **b** e^3 **c** $e^{0.7}$ **d** $\sqrt{e}$ **e** e^{-1}

6 Write the following as powers of e:
   a $\sqrt{e}$ **b** $\dfrac{1}{\sqrt{e}}$ **c** $\dfrac{1}{e^2}$ **d** $e\sqrt{e}$

7 Evaluate, to five significant figures:
   a $e^{2.31}$ **b** $e^{-2.31}$ **c** $e^{4.829}$ **d** $e^{-4.829}$
   e $50e^{-0.1764}$ **f** $80e^{-0.6342}$ **g** $1000e^{1.2642}$ **h** $0.25e^{-3.6742}$

8 Expand and simplify:
   a $(e^x + 1)^2$ **b** $(1 + e^x)(1 - e^x)$ **c** $e^x(e^{-x} - 3)$

9 Factorise:
   a $e^{2x} + e^x$ **b** $e^{2x} - 16$ **c** $e^{2x} - 8e^x + 12$

10 **a** On the same set of axes, sketch and clearly label the graphs of:
      $f : x \mapsto e^x$, $g : x \mapsto e^{x-2}$, $h : x \mapsto e^x + 3$
   b State the domain and range of each function.

11 **a** On the same set of axes, sketch and clearly label the graphs of:
      $f : x \mapsto e^x$, $g : x \mapsto -e^x$, $h : x \mapsto 10 - e^x$
   b State the domain and range of each function.
   c Describe the behaviour of each function as $x \to \pm\infty$.

12 The weight of bacteria in a culture is given by $W(t) = 2e^{\frac{t}{2}}$ grams where t is the time in hours after the culture was set to grow.
   a Find the weight of the culture:
      i initially   **ii** after 30 minutes
      iii after $1\frac{1}{2}$ hours   **iv** after 6 hours.
   b Hence sketch the graph of $W(t) = 2e^{\frac{t}{2}}$.

13 Solve for x: **a** $e^x = \sqrt{e}$ **b** $e^{\frac{1}{2}x} = \dfrac{1}{e^2}$

14 The current flowing in an electrical circuit t seconds after it is switched off is given by $I(t) = 75e^{-0.15t}$ amps.

   a What current is still flowing in the circuit after:

     i 1 second   **ii** 10 seconds?

   b Use your graphics calculator to help sketch the graph of $I(t) = 75e^{-0.15t}$.

   c How long will it take for the current to fall to 1 amp?

15 Consider the function $f(x) = e^x$.

   a On the same set of axes, sketch $y = f(x)$, $y = x$, and $y = f^{-1}(x)$.

   b State the domain and range of f^{-1}.

16 It can be shown that $e^x = 1 + x + \frac{1}{2}x^2 + \frac{1}{2\times 3}x^3 + \frac{1}{2\times 3\times 4}x^4 + ... = \sum\limits_{i=0}^{\infty} \frac{1}{i!}x^i$ which is an infinite polynomial expansion.

Check this statement by finding an approximation for e^1 using its first 20 terms.

ACTIVITY

Click on the icon to run a card game for exponential functions.

CARD GAME

REVIEW SET 5A

1 Evaluate:

   a $8^{\frac{2}{3}}$ **b** $27^{-\frac{2}{3}}$ **c** $81^{-\frac{1}{4}}$

2 Solve for x:

   a $2^{x-3} = \frac{1}{32}$ **b** $9^x = 27^{2-2x}$ **c** $e^{2x} = \frac{1}{\sqrt{e}}$

3 Consider the graph of $y = 3^x$ alongside.

   a Use the graph to estimate the value of:

     i $3^{0.7}$ **ii** $3^{-0.5}$

   b Use the graph to estimate the solution to:

     i $3^x = 5$ **ii** $3^x = \frac{1}{2}$

     iii $6 \times 3^x = 20$

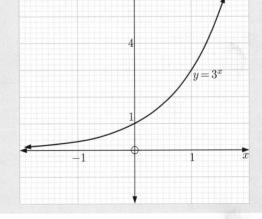

4 Expand and simplify:

   a $e^x(e^{-x} + e^x)$ **b** $(2^x + 5)^2$ **c** $(x^{\frac{1}{2}} - 7)(x^{\frac{1}{2}} + 7)$

5 Solve for x:

   a $6 \times 2^x = 192$ **b** $4 \times \left(\frac{1}{3}\right)^x = 324$

6 The point $(1, \sqrt{8})$ lies on the graph of $y = 2^{kx}$. Find the value of k.

7 If $f(x) = 3 \times 2^x$, find the value of:

   a $f(0)$ **b** $f(3)$ **c** $f(-2)$

8 On the same set of axes, draw the graphs of $y = 2^x$ and $y = 2^x - 4$. Include on your graph the y-intercept and the equation of the horizontal asymptote of each function.

9 Consider $y = 3^x - 5$.

   a Find y when $x = 0, \pm1, \pm2$.   **b** Discuss y as $x \to \pm\infty$.

   c Sketch the graph of $y = 3^x - 5$.   **d** State the equation of any asymptote.

10 Consider $y = 3 - 2^{-x}$.

   a Find y when $x = 0, \pm1, \pm2$.   **b** Discuss y as $x \to \pm\infty$.

   c Sketch the graph of $y = 3 - 2^{-x}$.   **d** State the equation of any asymptote.

11 **a** On the same set of axes, sketch and clearly label the graphs of:

      $f : x \mapsto e^x$, $g : x \mapsto e^{x-1}$, $h : x \mapsto 3 - e^x$

   b State the domain and range of each function in **a**.

   c Describe the behaviour of each function as $x \to \pm\infty$.

12 The temperature of a dish t minutes after it is removed from the microwave, is given by $T(t) = 80 \times (0.913)^t$ °C.

   a Find the initial temperature of the dish.

   b Find the temperature after:

      i 12 minutes   **ii** 24 minutes   **iii** 36 minutes.

   c Draw the graph of T against t for $t \geqslant 0$, using **a** and **b** or technology.

   d Hence find the time taken for the temperature of the dish to fall to 25°C.

13 A phycologist investigates an algal bloom in a lake. Initially it covers 10 square metres of water. Each day after it was discovered, the area covered increases by 15%.

   a Write a formula for the area $A(t)$ covered after t days.

   b Find the area covered after:

      i 2 days   **ii** 5 days.

   c Sketch the graph of $A(t)$.

   d How long will it take for the affected area to reach 300 m^2?

REVIEW SET 5B

1 Evaluate, correct to 3 significant figures:

    a $3^{\frac{5}{4}}$ **b** $27^{-\frac{1}{5}}$ **c** $\sqrt[4]{100}$

2 Expand and simplify:

    a $(3 - e^x)^2$ **b** $x^{-\frac{1}{2}}(x^{\frac{3}{2}} - 2x^{\frac{1}{2}} - x^{-\frac{1}{2}})$ **c** $2^{-x}(2^{2x} + 2^x)$

3 Factorise:

    a $3^{x+2} - 3^x$ **b** $4^x - 2^x - 12$ **c** $e^{2x} + 2e^x - 15$

4 Solve for x:

    a $2^{x+1} = 32$ **b** $3 \times \left(\frac{1}{7}\right)^{x+1} = 1029$ **c** $9^x - 10(3^x) + 9 = 0$

5 Consider the graph of $y = 4^x$ alongside.

    a Use the graph to estimate the value of:

        i $4^{0.6}$ **ii** $4^{-1.1}$

    b Use the graph to estimate the solution to $4^x = 3$.

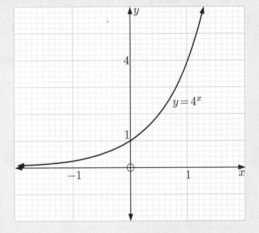

6 Suppose $f(x) = 2^{-x} + 1$.

    a Find $f\left(\frac{1}{2}\right)$.   **b** Find a such that $f(a) = 3$.

7 Consider $y = 2e^{-x} + 1$.

    a Find y when $x = 0, \pm 1, \pm 2$.   **b** Discuss y as $x \to \pm\infty$.

    c Sketch the graph of $y = 2e^{-x} + 1$.   **d** State the equation of any asymptote.

8 Match each equation to its corresponding graph:

    a $y = -e^x$ **b** $y = 3 \times 2^x$ **c** $y = e^x + 1$ **d** $y = 3^{-x}$ **e** $y = -e^{-x}$

A 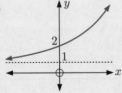   **B** 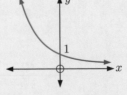   **C**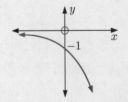

D    **E**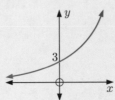

9 Let $f(x) = 3^x$.

    a Write down the value of:

        i $f(4)$ **ii** $f(-1)$

    b Find the value of k such that $f(x + 2) = k\,f(x)$, $k \in \mathbb{Z}$.

10 Suppose $y = a^x$. Express in terms of y:

    a a^{2x} **b** a^{-x} **c** $\dfrac{1}{\sqrt{a^x}}$

11 Answer the **Opening Problem** on page **120**.

12 The weight of a radioactive substance after t years is given by $W = 1500 \times (0.993)^t$ grams.

    a Find the original amount of radioactive material.

    b Find the amount of radioactive material remaining after:

        i 400 years   **ii** 800 years.

    c Sketch the graph of W against t for $t \geqslant 0$.

    d Hence find the time taken for the weight to reduce to 100 grams.

Chapter 6

Logarithms

Contents:

OPENING PROBLEM

In a plentiful springtime, a population of 1000 mice will double every week.

The population after t weeks is given by the exponential function $P(t) = 1000 \times 2^t$ mice.

Things to think about:

a What does the graph of the population over time look like?

b How long will it take for the population to reach 20 000 mice?

c Can we write a function for t in terms of P, which determines the time at which the population P is reached?

In the previous Chapter we solved exponential equations by writing both sides with the same base, and by using graphs.

In this Chapter we study a more formal solution to exponential equations in which we use the **inverse** of the exponential function. We call this a **logarithm**.

A   LOGARITHMS IN BASE 10

Consider the graph of $y = 10^x$ shown.

Notice that the range of the function is $\{y \mid y > 0\}$. This means that every positive number y can be written in the form 10^x.

For example:

- When $y = 10$, $x = 1$, so $10 = 10^1$.
- When $y = 20$, $x \approx 1.3$, so $20 \approx 10^{1.3}$.

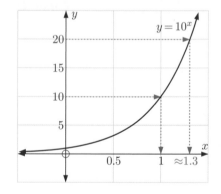

When we write a positive number y in the form 10^x, we say that x is the **logarithm in base 10**, of y.

> The **logarithm in base 10** of a positive number is the power that 10 must be raised to in order to obtain that number.

For example:

- The logarithm in base 10 of 1000 is 3, since $1000 = 10^3$.
  We write $\log_{10} 1000 = 3$ or simply $\log 1000 = 3$.

- $\log(0.01) = -2$ since $0.01 = 10^{-2}$.

If no base is indicated we assume it means base 10. $\log b$ means $\log_{10} b$.

By observing that $\log 1000 = \log(10^3) = 3$ and $\log(0.01) = \log(10^{-2}) = -2$, we conclude

that $\boldsymbol{\log 10^x = x}$ for any $x \in \mathbb{R}$.

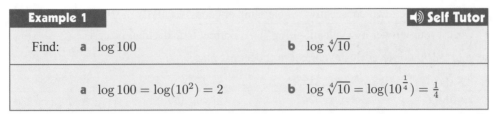

Example 1   ◀) **Self Tutor**

Find: **a** $\log 100$ **b** $\log \sqrt[4]{10}$

a $\log 100 = \log(10^2) = 2$ **b** $\log \sqrt[4]{10} = \log(10^{\frac{1}{4}}) = \frac{1}{4}$

The logarithms in **Example 1** can be found by hand because it is easy to write 100 and $\sqrt[4]{10}$ as powers of 10. The logarithms of most values, however, can only be found using a calculator.

For example, $\log 34 \approx 1.53$

so $34 \approx 10^{1.53}$

Logarithms allow us to write any number as a power of 10. In particular:

GRAPHICS
CALCULATOR
INSTRUCTIONS

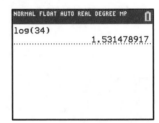

$$x = 10^{\log x} \quad \text{for any } x > 0.$$

Example 2   ◀) **Self Tutor**

Use your calculator to write the following in the form 10^x where x is correct to 4 decimal places:

a 8   **b** 800   **c** 0.08

a $8 = 10^{\log 8}$ **b** $800 = 10^{\log 800}$ **c** $0.08 = 10^{\log 0.08}$
   $\approx 10^{0.9031}$ $\approx 10^{2.9031}$ $\approx 10^{-1.0969}$

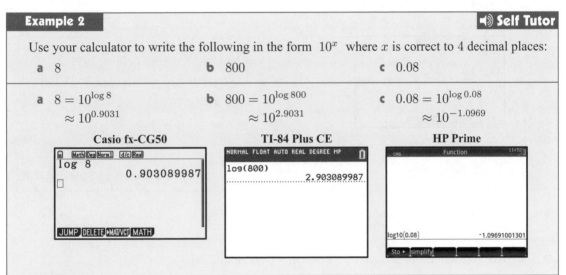

Casio fx-CG50   TI-84 Plus CE   HP Prime

EXERCISE 6A

1 Without using a calculator, find:

   a $\log 10\,000$ **b** $\log(0.001)$ **c** $\log 10$ **d** $\log 1$

   e $\log \sqrt{10}$ **f** $\log \sqrt[3]{10}$ **g** $\log\left(\dfrac{1}{\sqrt[4]{10}}\right)$ **h** $\log\left(10\sqrt{10}\right)$

   i $\log \sqrt[3]{100}$ **j** $\log\left(\dfrac{100}{\sqrt{10}}\right)$ **k** $\log\left(10 \times \sqrt[3]{10}\right)$ **l** $\log\left(1000\sqrt{10}\right)$

   Check your answers using your calculator.

2 Simplify:

   a $\log(10^n)$ **b** $\log(10^a \times 100)$ **c** $\log\left(\dfrac{10}{10^m}\right)$ **d** $\log\left(\dfrac{10^a}{10^b}\right)$

3 **a** Explain why $\log 237$ must lie between 2 and 3.

   b Use your calculator to evaluate $\log 237$ correct to 2 decimal places.

4 **a** Between which two consecutive whole numbers does $\log(0.6)$ lie?

    b Check your answer by evaluating $\log(0.6)$ correct to 2 decimal places.

5 Use your calculator to evaluate, correct to 2 decimal places:

    a $\log 76$ **b** $\log 114$ **c** $\log 3$ **d** $\log 831$

    e $\log(0.4)$ **f** $\log 3247$ **g** $\log(0.008)$ **h** $\log(-7)$

6 For what values of x is $\log x$:

    a positive   **b** zero   **c** negative   **d** undefined?

7 Use your calculator to write the following in the form 10^x where x is correct to 4 decimal places:

    a 6   **b** 60   **c** 6000   **d** 0.6   **e** 0.006

    f 15   **g** 1500   **h** 1.5   **i** 0.15   **j** 0.000 15

Example 3 🔊 **Self Tutor**

    a Use your calculator to find: **i** $\log 2$ **ii** $\log 20$

    b Explain why $\log 20 = \log 2 + 1$.

a

```
Math Deg Norm1  (d/c) Real
log 2
              0.3010299957
log 20
              1.301029996
□

JUMP DELETE MAT/VCT MATH
```

b $\log 20 = \log(2 \times 10)$

           $= \log(10^{\log 2} \times 10^1)$ $\{x = 10^{\log x}\}$

           $= \log(10^{\log 2 + 1})$ $\{$adding indices$\}$

           $= \log 2 + 1$

    i $\log 2 \approx 0.3010$

    ii $\log 20 \approx 1.3010$

---

8 **a** Use your calculator to find: **i** $\log 3$ **ii** $\log 300$

    b Explain why $\log 300 = \log 3 + 2$.

9 **a** Use your calculator to find: **i** $\log 5$ **ii** $\log(0.05)$

    b Explain why $\log(0.05) = \log 5 - 2$.

Example 4 🔊 **Self Tutor**

Find x such that:

    a $\log x = 3$ **b** $\log x \approx -0.271$

a $\log x = 3$

    $\therefore \; 10^{\log x} = 10^3$

    $\therefore \; x = 1000$

b $\log x \approx -0.271$

    $\therefore \; 10^{\log x} \approx 10^{-0.271}$

    $\therefore \; x \approx 0.536$

Remember that $10^{\log x} = x$.

---

10 Find x such that:

    a $\log x = 2$ **b** $\log x = 1$ **c** $\log x = 0$ **d** $\log x = -1$

    e $\log x = \frac{1}{2}$ **f** $\log x = -\frac{1}{2}$ **g** $\log x = 4$ **h** $\log x = -5$

    i $\log x \approx 0.8351$ **j** $\log x \approx 2.1457$ **k** $\log x \approx -1.378$ **l** $\log x \approx -3.1997$

B   LOGARITHMS IN BASE a

In the previous Section we defined the logarithm in base 10 of a number as the power that 10 must be raised to in order to obtain that number.

We can use the same principle to define logarithms in other bases:

The **logarithm in base a of b** is the power that a must be raised to in order to obtain b.

The logarithm in base a of b is written $\log_a b$.

For example, to find $\log_2 8$, we ask "What power must 2 be raised to in order to obtain 8?". We know that $2^3 = 8$, so $\log_2 8 = 3$.

$a^x = b$ and $x = \log_a b$ are *equivalent* statements.

For any $b > 0$, $\quad a^x = b \iff x = \log_a b$

Example 5   ◀) Self Tutor

a Write an equivalent exponential statement for $\log_{10} 1000 = 3$.

b Write an equivalent logarithmic statement for $3^4 = 81$.

a From $\log_{10} 1000 = 3$ we deduce that $10^3 = 1000$.

b From $3^4 = 81$ we deduce that $\log_3 81 = 4$.

EXERCISE 6B

1 Write an equivalent exponential statement for:

    a $\log_{10} 100 = 2$
    b $\log_{10} 10\,000 = 4$
    c $\log_{10}(0.1) = -1$

    d $\log_{10} \sqrt{10} = \frac{1}{2}$
    e $\log_2 8 = 3$
    f $\log_3 9 = 2$

    g $\log_2\left(\frac{1}{4}\right) = -2$
    h $\log_3 \sqrt{27} = 1.5$
    i $\log_5\left(\frac{1}{\sqrt{5}}\right) = -\frac{1}{2}$

2 Write an equivalent logarithmic statement for:

    a $4^3 = 64$
    b $5^2 = 25$
    c $7^2 = 49$
    d $2^6 = 64$

    e $2^{-3} = \frac{1}{8}$
    f $10^{-2} = 0.01$
    g $2^{-1} = \frac{1}{2}$
    h $3^{-3} = \frac{1}{27}$

Example 6   ◀) Self Tutor

Find: a $\log_2 16$
    b $\log_5(0.2)$
    c $\log_{10} \sqrt[5]{100}$
    d $\log_2\left(\frac{1}{\sqrt{2}}\right)$

a $\log_2 16$
$= \log_2(2^4)$
$= 4$

b $\log_5(0.2)$
$= \log_5\left(\frac{1}{5}\right)$
$= \log_5(5^{-1})$
$= -1$

c $\log_{10} \sqrt[5]{100}$
$= \log_{10}((10^2)^{\frac{1}{5}})$
$= \log_{10}(10^{\frac{2}{5}})$
$= \frac{2}{5}$

d $\log_2\left(\frac{1}{\sqrt{2}}\right)$
$= \log_2(2^{-\frac{1}{2}})$
$= -\frac{1}{2}$

3 Without using a calculator, find:

To find $\log_a b$ write b as a power of a.

   a $\log_{10} 100\,000$ **b** $\log_{10}(0.01)$ **c** $\log_3 \sqrt{3}$

   d $\log_2 4$ **e** $\log_2 64$ **f** $\log_2 128$

   g $\log_5 25$ **h** $\log_5 125$ **i** $\log_2(0.125)$

   j $\log_9 3$ **k** $\log_4 16$ **l** $\log_{36} 6$

   m $\log_3 243$ **n** $\log_2 \sqrt[3]{2}$ **o** $\log_8 2$

   p $\log_6\left(6\sqrt{6}\right)$ **q** $\log_4 1$ **r** $\log_9 9$

   s $\log_3\left(\frac{1}{3}\right)$ **t** $\log_{10} \sqrt[4]{1000}$ **u** $\log_7\left(\frac{1}{\sqrt{7}}\right)$

   v $\log_5\left(25\sqrt{5}\right)$ **w** $\log_3\left(\frac{1}{\sqrt{27}}\right)$ **x** $\log_4\left(\frac{1}{2\sqrt{2}}\right)$

Check your answers using technology.

GRAPHICS CALCULATOR INSTRUCTIONS

4 Simplify:

   a $\log_x(x^2)$ **b** $\log_t\left(\frac{1}{t}\right)$ **c** $\log_x \sqrt{x}$

   d $\log_m(m^3)$ **e** $\log_k \sqrt[4]{k}$ **f** $\log_x(x\sqrt{x})$

   g $\log_a\left(\frac{1}{a^2}\right)$ **h** $\log_a\left(\frac{1}{\sqrt{a}}\right)$ **i** $\log_m \sqrt{m^5}$

Example 7	◀ **Self Tutor**

Solve for x: $\log_3 x = 5$

$\log_3 x = 5$
$\therefore \;\; x = 3^5$
$\therefore \;\; x = 243$

5 Solve for x:

   a $\log_2 x = 3$ **b** $\log_4 x = \frac{1}{2}$ **c** $\log_x 81 = 4$ **d** $\log_2(x-6) = 3$

6 Suppose $\log_a b = x$, $b \neq 1$, $b > 0$. Find, in terms of x, the value of $\log_b a$.

HISTORICAL NOTE

Acharya Virasena was an 8th century Indian mathematician. Among other areas, he worked with the concept of *ardhaccheda*, which is how many times a number of the form 2^n can be divided by 2. The result is the integer n, and is the logarithm of the number 2^n in base 2.

In 1544, the German **Michael Stifel** published *Arithmetica Integra* which contains a table expressing many other integers as powers of 2. In effect, he had created an early version of a logarithmic table.

C   LAWS OF LOGARITHMS

INVESTIGATION 1   DISCOVERING THE LAWS OF LOGARITHMS

What to do:

1   **a**   Use your calculator to find:

    i $\log 2 + \log 3$ **ii** $\log 3 + \log 7$ **iii** $\log 4 + \log 20$

    iv $\log 6$ **v** $\log 21$ **vi** $\log 80$

  b   From your answers, suggest a possible simplification for $\log m + \log n$.

2   **a**   Use your calculator to find:

    i $\log 6 - \log 2$ **ii** $\log 12 - \log 3$ **iii** $\log 3 - \log 5$

    iv $\log 3$ **v** $\log 4$ **vi** $\log(0.6)$

  b   From your answers, suggest a possible simplification for $\log m - \log n$.

3   **a**   Use your calculator to find:

    i $3\log 2$ **ii** $2\log 5$ **iii** $-4\log 3$

    iv $\log(2^3)$ **v** $\log(5^2)$ **vi** $\log(3^{-4})$

  b   From your answers, suggest a possible simplification for $m\log b$.

From the **Investigation**, you should have discovered the three important **laws of logarithms**:

$$\bullet \quad \log m + \log n = \log(mn) \quad \text{for } m, n > 0$$
$$\bullet \quad \log m - \log n = \log\left(\frac{m}{n}\right) \quad \text{for } m, n > 0$$
$$\bullet \quad m\log b = \log(b^m) \quad \text{for } b > 0$$

More generally, in any base a where $a \neq 1$, $a > 0$, we have these **laws of logarithms**:

$$\bullet \quad \log_a m + \log_a n = \log_a(mn) \quad \text{for } m, n > 0$$
$$\bullet \quad \log_a m - \log_a n = \log_a\left(\frac{m}{n}\right) \quad \text{for } m, n > 0$$
$$\bullet \quad m\log_a b = \log_a(b^m) \quad \text{for } b > 0$$

Proof:

$$\bullet \quad \log_a(mn)$$
$$= \log_a\left(a^{\log_a m} \times a^{\log_a n}\right)$$
$$= \log_a\left(a^{\log_a m + \log_a n}\right)$$
$$= \log_a m + \log_a n$$

$$\bullet \quad \log_a\left(\frac{m}{n}\right)$$
$$= \log_a\left(\frac{a^{\log_a m}}{a^{\log_a n}}\right)$$
$$= \log_a\left(a^{\log_a m - \log_a n}\right)$$
$$= \log_a m - \log_a n$$

$$\bullet \quad \log_a(b^m)$$
$$= \log_a\left(\left(a^{\log_a b}\right)^m\right)$$
$$= \log_a\left(a^{m\log_a b}\right)$$
$$= m\log_a b$$

Example 8

Self Tutor

Use the laws of logarithms to write as a single logarithm or as an integer:

a $\log 5 + \log 3$ **b** $\log_3 24 - \log_3 8$ **c** $\log_2 5 - 1$

a $\quad \log 5 + \log 3$
$= \log(5 \times 3)$
$= \log 15$

b $\quad \log_3 24 - \log_3 8$
$= \log_3\left(\frac{24}{8}\right)$
$= \log_3 3$
$= 1$

c $\quad \log_2 5 - 1$
$= \log_2 5 - \log_2(2^1)$
$= \log_2\left(\frac{5}{2}\right)$

EXERCISE 6C

1 Write as a single logarithm or as an integer:

a $\log 8 + \log 2$ **b** $\log 4 + \log 5$ **c** $\log 40 - \log 5$

d $\log p - \log m$ **e** $\log_4 8 - \log_4 2$ **f** $\log 5 + \log(0.4)$

g $\log 250 + \log 4$ **h** $\log_5 100 - \log_5 4$ **i** $\log 2 + \log 3 + \log 4$

j $\log 5 + \log 4 - \log 2$ **k** $\log_3 6 - \log_3 2 - \log_3 3$ **l** $\log\left(\frac{4}{3}\right) + \log 3 + \log 7$

2 Write as a single logarithm:

a $\log 7 + 2$ **b** $\log 4 - 1$ **c** $1 + \log_2 3$

d $\log_3 5 - 2$ **e** $2 + \log 2$ **f** $\log 50 - 4$

g $t + \log w$ **h** $\log_m 40 - 2$ **i** $3 - \log_5 50$

Example 9

Self Tutor

Simplify by writing as a single logarithm or as a rational number:

a $2\log 7 - 3\log 2$ **b** $2\log 3 + 3$ **c** $\dfrac{\log 8}{\log 4}$

a $\quad 2\log 7 - 3\log 2$
$= \log(7^2) - \log(2^3)$
$= \log 49 - \log 8$
$= \log\left(\frac{49}{8}\right)$

b $\quad 2\log 3 + 3$
$= \log(3^2) + \log(10^3)$
$= \log 9 + \log 1000$
$= \log 9000$

c $\quad \dfrac{\log 8}{\log 4} = \dfrac{\log(2^3)}{\log(2^2)}$
$= \dfrac{3\log 2}{2\log 2}$
$= \dfrac{3}{2}$

3 Write as a single logarithm or integer:

a $5\log 2 + \log 3$ **b** $2\log 3 + 3\log 2$ **c** $3\log 4 - \log 8$

d $2\log_3 5 - 3\log_3 2$ **e** $\frac{1}{2}\log_6 4 + \log_6 3$ **f** $\frac{1}{3}\log\left(\frac{1}{8}\right)$

g $3 - \log 2 - 2\log 5$ **h** $1 - 3\log 2 + \log 20$ **i** $2 - \frac{1}{2}\log_n 4 - \log_n 5$

4 Simplify without using a calculator:

a $\dfrac{\log 4}{\log 2}$ **b** $\dfrac{\log_5 27}{\log_5 9}$ **c** $\dfrac{\log 8}{\log 2}$

d $\dfrac{\log 3}{\log 9}$ **e** $\dfrac{\log_3 25}{\log_3(0.2)}$ **f** $\dfrac{\log_4 8}{\log_4(0.25)}$

Example 10   ◀)) **Self Tutor**

Show that:

a $\log\left(\frac{1}{9}\right) = -2\log 3$ **b** $\log 500 = 3 - \log 2$

a $\log\left(\frac{1}{9}\right)$ **b** $\log 500$
    $= \log(3^{-2})$ $= \log\left(\frac{1000}{2}\right)$
    $= -2\log 3$ $= \log 1000 - \log 2$
                              $= \log(10^3) - \log 2$
                              $= 3 - \log 2$

5 Show that:

  a $\log 9 = 2\log 3$ **b** $\log\sqrt{2} = \frac{1}{2}\log 2$ **c** $\log\left(\frac{1}{8}\right) = -3\log 2$

  d $\log\left(\frac{1}{5}\right) = -\log 5$ **e** $\log 5 = 1 - \log 2$ **f** $\log 5000 = 4 - \log 2$

6 The number $a \times 10^k$ where $1 \leqslant a < 10$, $k \in \mathbb{Z}$ is written in standard form. Show that $\log(a \times 10^k) = \log a + k$.

7 Suppose $p = \log_b 2$, $q = \log_b 3$, and $r = \log_b 5$. Write in terms of p, q, and r:

  a $\log_b 6$ **b** $\log_b 45$ **c** $\log_b 108$

  d $\log_b\left(\frac{5\sqrt{3}}{2}\right)$ **e** $\log_b\left(\frac{5}{32}\right)$ **f** $\log_b\left(\frac{2}{9}\right)$

8 Suppose $\log_2 P = x$, $\log_2 Q = y$, and $\log_2 R = z$. Write in terms of x, y, and z:

  a $\log_2(PR)$ **b** $\log_2(RQ^2)$ **c** $\log_2\left(\dfrac{PR}{Q}\right)$

  d $\log_2\left(P^2\sqrt{Q}\right)$ **e** $\log_2\left(\dfrac{Q^3}{\sqrt{R}}\right)$ **f** $\log_2\left(\dfrac{R^2\sqrt{Q}}{P^3}\right)$

9 If $\log_t M = 1.29$ and $\log_t(N^2) = 1.72$, find:

  a $\log_t N$ **b** $\log_t(MN)$ **c** $\log_t\left(\dfrac{N^2}{\sqrt{M}}\right)$

10 Write as a single logarithm:

$\log(8!) - \log(7!) + \log(6!) - \log(5!) + \log(4!) - \log(3!) + \log(2!) - \log(1!)$

$$\boxed{n! = 1 \times 2 \times 3 \times \ldots \times n}$$

11 Write $\log_2(6!)$ in the form $a + \log_2 b$, where $a, b \in \mathbb{Z}$ and b is as small as possible.

D   NATURAL LOGARITHMS

The logarithm in base e is called the **natural logarithm**.

We use $\ln x$ to represent $\log_e x$, and call $\ln x$ the natural logarithm of x.

$$\ln e^x = x \quad \text{and} \quad e^{\ln x} = x.$$

Example 11   ◀) Self Tutor

Find: **a** $\ln e^3$ **b** $\ln \sqrt{e}$ **c** $e^{2\ln 5}$

a $\ln e^3 = 3$

b $\ln \sqrt{e} = \ln(e^{\frac{1}{2}})$
$\quad\quad\quad = \frac{1}{2}$

c $e^{2\ln 5} = (e^{\ln 5})^2$
$\quad\quad\quad = 5^2$
$\quad\quad\quad = 25$

As with base 10 logarithms, we can use our calculator to find natural logarithms.

For example, $\ln 30 \approx 3.40$, which means that $30 \approx e^{3.40}$.

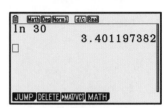

GRAPHICS CALCULATOR INSTRUCTIONS

Example 12   ◀) Self Tutor

Use your calculator to write the following in the form e^k where k is correct to 4 decimal places:

a 50   **b** 0.005

a $50 = e^{\ln 50}$ $\{x = e^{\ln x}\}$
$\quad\quad \approx e^{3.9120}$

b $0.005 = e^{\ln 0.005}$
$\quad\quad\quad \approx e^{-5.2983}$

Casio fx-CG50

TI-84 Plus CE

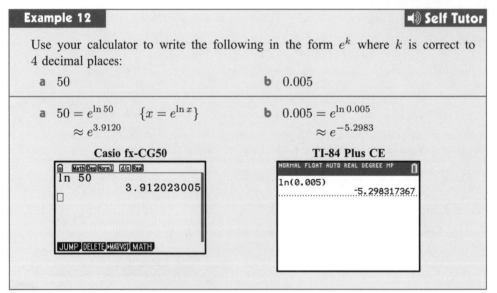

LAWS OF NATURAL LOGARITHMS

The laws for natural logarithms are the laws for logarithms written in base e:

- $\ln m + \ln n = \ln(mn)$ for $m, n > 0$
- $\ln m - \ln n = \ln\left(\dfrac{m}{n}\right)$ for $m, n > 0$
- $m \ln b = \ln(b^m)$ for $b > 0$

EXERCISE 6D

1 Without using a calculator find:

   a $\ln(e^2)$ **b** $\ln(e^4)$ **c** $\ln\left((\sqrt{e})^3\right)$ **d** $\ln 1$

   e $\ln\left(\dfrac{1}{e}\right)$ **f** $\ln \sqrt[3]{e}$ **g** $\ln\left(\dfrac{1}{e^2}\right)$ **h** $\ln\left(\dfrac{1}{\sqrt{e}}\right)$

   Check your answers using a calculator.

2 Simplify:

   a $e^{\ln 3}$ **b** $e^{2\ln 3}$ **c** $e^{-\ln 5}$ **d** $e^{-2\ln 2}$

   e $\ln e^a$ **f** $\ln(e \times e^a)$ **g** $\ln(e^a \times e^b)$ **h** $\ln\left((e^a)^b\right)$

3 Use your calculator to find, correct to 3 decimal places:

   a $\ln 12$ **b** $\ln 68$ **c** $\ln(1.4)$ **d** $\ln(0.7)$ **e** $\ln 500$

4 Explain why $\ln(-2)$ and $\ln 0$ cannot be found.

5 Use your calculator to write the following in the form e^k where k is correct to 4 decimal places:

   a 6   **b** 60   **c** 6000   **d** 0.6   **e** 0.006

   f 15   **g** 1500   **h** 1.5   **i** 0.15   **j** 0.000 15

Example 13   ◀ﬁ) **Self Tutor**

Find x if:

   a $\ln x = 2.17$ **b** $\ln x = -0.384$

   a $\ln x = 2.17$ **b** $\ln x = -0.384$

      $\therefore \; x = e^{2.17}$ $\therefore \; x = e^{-0.384}$

      $\therefore \; x \approx 8.76$ $\therefore \; x \approx 0.681$

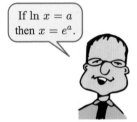

If $\ln x = a$ then $x = e^a$.

---

6 Find x if:

   a $\ln x = 3$ **b** $\ln x = 1$ **c** $\ln x = 0$ **d** $\ln x = -1$

   e $\ln x = -5$ **f** $\ln x \approx 0.835$ **g** $\ln x \approx 2.145$ **h** $\ln x \approx -3.2971$

7 **a** Write in simplest form:

      i $\ln(e^x)$ **ii** $e^{\ln x}$

   b What does this tell us about the functions $y = e^x$ and $y = \ln x$?

Example 14   ◀ﬁ) **Self Tutor**

Use the laws of logarithms to write as a single logarithm:

   a $\ln 5 + \ln 3$ **b** $\ln 24 - \ln 8$ **c** $\ln 5 - 1$

   a $\ln 5 + \ln 3$ **b** $\ln 24 - \ln 8$ **c** $\ln 5 - 1$

      $= \ln(5 \times 3)$ $= \ln\left(\dfrac{24}{8}\right)$ $= \ln 5 - \ln(e^1)$

      $= \ln 15$ $= \ln 3$ $= \ln\left(\dfrac{5}{e}\right)$

8 Write as a single logarithm or integer:

a $\ln 15 + \ln 3$

b $\ln 15 - \ln 3$

c $\ln 20 - \ln 5$

d $\ln 4 + \ln 6$

e $\ln 5 + \ln(0.2)$

f $\ln 2 + \ln 3 + \ln 5$

g $1 + \ln 4$

h $\ln 6 - 1$

i $\ln 5 + \ln 8 - \ln 2$

j $2 + \ln 4$

k $\ln 20 - 2$

l $\ln 12 - \ln 4 - \ln 3$

Example 15   🔊 **Self Tutor**

Use the laws of logarithms to simplify:

a $2 \ln 7 - 3 \ln 2$

b $2 \ln 3 + 3$

a $\quad 2 \ln 7 - 3 \ln 2$
$= \ln(7^2) - \ln(2^3)$
$= \ln 49 - \ln 8$
$= \ln\left(\frac{49}{8}\right)$

b $\quad 2 \ln 3 + 3$
$= \ln(3^2) + \ln(e^3)$
$= \ln 9 + \ln(e^3)$
$= \ln(9e^3)$

---

9 Write in the form $\ln a$, $a \in \mathbb{R}$:

a $5 \ln 3 + \ln 4$

b $3 \ln 2 + 2 \ln 5$

c $3 \ln 2 - \ln 8$

d $3 \ln 4 - 2 \ln 2$

e $\frac{1}{3} \ln 8 + \ln 3$

f $\frac{1}{3} \ln\left(\frac{1}{27}\right)$

g $-\ln 2$

h $-\ln\left(\frac{1}{2}\right)$

i $-2 \ln\left(\frac{1}{4}\right)$

j $4 \ln 2 + 2$

k $\frac{1}{2} \ln 9 - 1$

l $-3 \ln 2 + \frac{1}{2}$

10 Show that:

a $\ln 27 = 3 \ln 3$

b $\ln \sqrt{3} = \frac{1}{2} \ln 3$

c $\ln\left(\frac{1}{16}\right) = -4 \ln 2$

d $\ln\left(\frac{1}{6}\right) = -\ln 6$

e $\ln\left(\frac{1}{\sqrt{2}}\right) = -\frac{1}{2} \ln 2$

f $\ln\left(\frac{e}{5}\right) = 1 - \ln 5$

g $\ln(6e) = \ln 6 + 1$

h $\ln \sqrt[3]{5} = \frac{1}{3} \ln 5$

i $\ln\left(\frac{1}{\sqrt[5]{2}}\right) = -\frac{1}{5} \ln 2$

j $\ln\left(\frac{e^2}{8}\right) = 2 - 3 \ln 2$

k $\ln\left(\frac{\sqrt{3}}{e^4}\right) = \frac{1}{2} \ln 3 - 4$

l $\ln\left(\frac{1}{16 \times \sqrt[3]{e}}\right) = -4 \ln 2 - \frac{1}{3}$

THEORY OF KNOWLEDGE

It is easy to take modern technology, such as the electronic calculator, for granted. Until electronic computers became affordable in the 1980s, a "calculator" was a *profession*, literally someone who would spend their time performing calculations by hand. They used mechanical calculators and techniques such as logarithms. They often worked in banks, but sometimes for astronomers and other scientists.

The logarithm was invented by **John Napier** (1550 - 1617) and first published in 1614 in a Latin book which translates as a *Description of the Wonderful Canon of Logarithms*. John Napier was the 8th Lord of Merchiston, which is now part of Edinburgh, Scotland. Napier wrote a number of other books on many subjects including religion and mathematics. One of his other inventions was a device for performing long multiplication which is now called "Napier's Bones". Other calculators, such as slide rules, used logarithms as part of their design. He also popularised the use of the decimal point in mathematical notation.

Logarithms were an extremely important development, and they had an immediate effect on the seventeenth century scientific community. **Johannes Kepler** used logarithms to assist with his calculations. This helped him develop his laws of planetary motion. Without logarithms these calculations would have taken many years. Kepler published a letter congratulating and acknowledging Napier. Kepler's laws gave **Sir Isaac Newton** important evidence to support his theory of universal gravitation. 200 years later, **Laplace** said that logarithms "by shortening the labours, doubled the life of the astronomer".

Johannes Kepler

1 Can anyone claim to have *invented* logarithms?

2 Can we consider the process of mathematical discovery as an *evolution* of ideas?

3 Has modern computing effectively doubled the life of a mathematician?

Many areas of mathematics have been developed over centuries as several mathematicians have worked in a particular area, or taken the knowledge from one area and applied it to another field. Sometimes the process is held up because a method for solving a particular class of problem has not yet been found. In other cases, pure mathematicians have published research papers on seemingly useless mathematical ideas, which have then become vital in applications much later.

In *Everybody Counts: A report to the nation on the future of Mathematical Education* by the National Academy of Sciences (National Academy Press, 1989), there is an excellent section on the Nature of Mathematics. It includes:

"Even the most esoteric and abstract parts of mathematics - number theory and logic, for example - are now used routinely in applications (for example, in computer science and cryptography). Fifty years ago, the leading British mathematician G.H. Hardy could boast that number theory was the most pure and least useful part of mathematics. Today, Hardy's mathematics is studied as an essential prerequisite to many applications, including control of automated systems, data transmission from remote satellites, protection of financial records, and efficient algorithms for computation."

4 Should we only study the mathematics required to enter our chosen profession?

5 Why should we explore mathematics for its own sake, rather than to address the needs of science?

E   LOGARITHMIC EQUATIONS

We can use the laws of logarithms to write equations in a different form. This can be particularly useful if an unknown appears as an exponent.

Since the logarithmic function is one-to-one, we can take the logarithm of both sides of an equation without changing the solution. However, we can only do this if both sides are positive.

Example 16   ◀》 **Self Tutor**

Write as a logarithmic equation (in base 10):   **a** $y = a^2 b$ **b** $P = \dfrac{20}{\sqrt{n}}$

a $y = a^2 b$

∴ $\log y = \log(a^2 b)$

∴ $\log y = \log(a^2) + \log b$

∴ $\log y = 2 \log a + \log b$

b $P = \left(\dfrac{20}{\sqrt{n}} \right)$

∴ $\log P = \log \left(\dfrac{20}{n^{\frac{1}{2}}} \right)$

∴ $\log P = \log 20 - \log(n^{\frac{1}{2}})$

∴ $\log P = \log 20 - \frac{1}{2} \log n$

Example 17   ◀》 **Self Tutor**

Write without logarithms:

a $\log A = \log b + 2 \log c$ **b** $\log_2 M = 3 \log_2 a - 2$

a $\log A = \log b + 2 \log c$

∴ $\log A = \log b + \log(c^2)$

∴ $\log A = \log(bc^2)$

∴ $A = bc^2$

b $\log_2 M = 3 \log_2 a - 2$

∴ $\log_2 M = \log_2(a^3) - \log_2(2^2)$

∴ $\log_2 M = \log_2 \left(\dfrac{a^3}{4} \right)$

∴ $M = \dfrac{a^3}{4}$

EXERCISE 6E

1 Write as a logarithmic equation (in base 10), assuming all variables are positive:

a $y = 2^x$ **b** $y = 20b^3$ **c** $M = ad^4$ **d** $T = 5\sqrt{d}$

e $R = b\sqrt{l}$ **f** $Q = \dfrac{a}{b^n}$ **g** $y = ab^x$ **h** $F = \dfrac{20}{\sqrt{n}}$

i $L = \dfrac{ab}{c}$ **j** $N = \sqrt{\dfrac{a}{b}}$ **k** $S = 200 \times 2^t$ **l** $y = \dfrac{a^m}{b^n}$

2 Write without logarithms:

a $\log D = \log e + \log 2$ **b** $\log_a F = \log_a 5 - \log_a t$ **c** $\log P = \frac{1}{2} \log x$

d $\log_n M = 2 \log_n b + \log_n c$ **e** $\log B = 3 \log m - 2 \log n$ **f** $\log N = -\frac{1}{3} \log p$

g $\log P = 3 \log x + 1$ **h** $\log_a Q = 2 - \log_a x$

3 Write without logarithms:

a $\ln D = \ln x + 1$ **b** $\ln F = -\ln p + 2$ **c** $\ln P = \frac{1}{2} \ln x$

d $\ln M = 2 \ln y + 3$ **e** $\ln B = 3 \ln t - 1$ **f** $\ln N = -\frac{1}{3} \ln g$

g $\ln Q \approx 3 \ln x + 2.159$ **h** $\ln D \approx 0.4 \ln n - 0.6582$

4 **a** Write $y = 3 \times 2^x$ as a logarithmic equation in base 2.

  b Hence write x in terms of y.

  c Find the value of x when: **i** $y = 3$ **ii** $y = 12$ **iii** $y = 30$

5 Solve for x:

a $\log_3 27 + \log_3\left(\frac{1}{3}\right) = \log_3 x$

b $\log_5 x = \log_5 8 - \log_5(6-x)$

c $\log_5 125 - \log_5 \sqrt{5} = \log_5 x$

d $\log_{20} x = 1 + \log_{20} 10$

e $\log x + \log(x+1) = \log 30$

f $\log(x+2) - \log(x-2) = \log 5$

6 Let $x = \log_2 7$.

a Write the equation without logarithms.

b Take the logarithm in base 10 of both sides of your equation from **a**. Hence show that $\log_2 7 = \dfrac{\log 7}{\log 2}$, and calculate this number.

7 Consider the exponential equation $a^x = b$ where $a, b > 0$.

a Explain why $x = \log_a b$. **b** Take the logarithm in base 10 of both sides of $a^x = b$.

c Hence show that $x = \log_a b = \dfrac{\log b}{\log a}$.

F   THE CHANGE OF BASE RULE

In the previous Exercise you should have proven the base 10 case of the **change of base rule**:

$$\log_b a = \frac{\log_c a}{\log_c b} \quad \text{for } a, b, c > 0 \text{ and } b, c \neq 1.$$

Proof: If $\log_b a = x$, then $b^x = a$

$\therefore \; \log_c b^x = \log_c a$ {taking logarithms in base c}

$\therefore \; x \log_c b = \log_c a$ {power law of logarithms}

$\therefore \; x = \dfrac{\log_c a}{\log_c b}$

$\therefore \; \log_b a = \dfrac{\log_c a}{\log_c b}$

We need this rule to evaluate logarithms in bases other than 10 or e.

Example 18	◀) Self Tutor
Find $\log_2 9$ by: **a** changing to base 10 **b** changing to base e.	

a $\log_2 9 = \dfrac{\log_{10} 9}{\log_{10} 2}$ **b** $\log_2 9 = \dfrac{\ln 9}{\ln 2}$

≈ 3.17 ≈ 3.17

EXERCISE 6F

1 Use the change of base rule with base 10 to calculate:

a $\log_3 7$

b $\log_2 40$

c $\log_5 180$

d $\log_{\frac{1}{2}} 1250$

e $\log_3(0.067)$

f $\log_{0.4}(0.006\,984)$

Check your results using the change of base rule with base e.

2 Simplify $\log_m n \times \log_n (m^2)$.

3 Without using technology, show that $2^{\frac{4}{\log_5 4} + \frac{3}{\log_7 8}} = 175$.

   Hint: Use the change of base rule with base 2.

4 Solve for x:

   a $\log_4 (x^3) + \log_2 \sqrt{x} = 8$ **b** $\log_{16}(x^5) = \log_{64} 125 - \log_4 \sqrt{x}$

5 Given $x = \log_3 (y^2)$, express $\log_y 81$ in terms of x.

G | SOLVING EXPONENTIAL EQUATIONS USING LOGARITHMS

In **Chapter 5** we found solutions to simple exponential equations where we could make equal bases and then equate exponents. However, it is not always easy to make the bases the same. In these situations we can use **logarithms**.

Example 19   ◆) **Self Tutor**

   a Solve the equation $2^x = 30$ exactly.

   b Use your calculator to evaluate the solution correct to 2 decimal places.

---

   a $2^x = 30$

   $\therefore \ \log(2^x) = \log 30$ {taking the logarithm of each side}

   $\therefore \ x \log 2 = \log 30$ $\{ \log(b^m) = m \log b \}$

   $\therefore \ x = \dfrac{\log 30}{\log 2}$

   b $\dfrac{\log 30}{\log 2} \approx 4.91$, so the solution is $x \approx 4.91$.

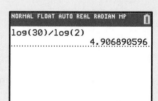

EXERCISE 6G

1 Consider the equation $2^x = 20$.

   a Explain why the solution to this equation lies between $x = 4$ and $x = 5$.

   b Find the solution exactly.

   c Use your calculator to evaluate the solution correct to 2 decimal places.

2 Consider the equation $3^x = 40$.

   a Between which two consecutive whole numbers does the solution lie?

   b Find the solution exactly.

   c Use your calculator to evaluate the solution correct to 2 decimal places.

3 Solve for x: **i** exactly   **ii** correct to 2 decimal places.

    a $2^x = 10$ **b** $3^x = 20$ **c** $4^x = 50$

    d $\left(\frac{1}{2}\right)^x = 0.0625$ **e** $\left(\frac{3}{4}\right)^x = 0.1$ **f** $10^x = 0.000\,015$

4 Solve for x, correct to 3 significant figures:

    a $5^x = 40$ **b** $3^x = 2^{x+3}$ **c** $2^{x+4} = 5^{2-x}$

Example 20   ◀)) Self Tutor

Find x exactly:

    a $e^x = 30$ **b** $3e^{\frac{x}{2}} = 21$

    a $e^x = 30$ **b** $3e^{\frac{x}{2}} = 21$

        $\therefore \ x = \ln 30$ $\therefore \ e^{\frac{x}{2}} = 7$

                                        $\therefore \ \frac{x}{2} = \ln 7$

                                        $\therefore \ x = 2\ln 7$

---

5 Solve for x, giving an exact answer:

    a $e^x = 10$ **b** $e^x = 1000$ **c** $2e^x = 0.3$

    d $e^{\frac{x}{2}} = 5$ **e** $e^{2x} = 18$ **f** $e^{-\frac{x}{2}} = 1$

6 Solve for x, giving an exact answer:

    a $3 \times 2^x = 75$ **b** $7 \times (1.5)^x = 20$ **c** $5 \times (0.8)^x = 3$

    d $4 \times 2^{-x} = 0.12$ **e** $300 \times 5^{0.1x} = 1000$ **f** $32 \times e^{-0.25x} = 4$

7 Solve for x exactly:

    a $25^x - 3 \times 5^x = 0$ **b** $8 \times 9^x - 3^x = 0$ **c** $2^x - 2 \times 4^x = 0$

Example 21   ◀)) Self Tutor

Find exactly the points of intersection of $y = e^x - 3$ and $y = 1 - 3e^{-x}$.
Check your solution using technology.

The functions meet where

$$e^x - 3 = 1 - 3e^{-x}$$

$\therefore \ e^x - 4 + 3e^{-x} = 0$

$\therefore \ e^{2x} - 4e^x + 3 = 0$ {multiplying each term by e^x}

$\therefore \ (e^x - 1)(e^x - 3) = 0$

          $\therefore \ e^x = 1$ or 3

          $\therefore \ x = \ln 1$ or $\ln 3$

          $\therefore \ x = 0$ or $\ln 3$

When $x = 0$, $y = e^0 - 3 = -2$

When $x = \ln 3$, $y = e^{\ln 3} - 3 = 0$

$\therefore$ the functions meet at $(0, -2)$ and at $(\ln 3, 0)$.

GRAPHING
PACKAGE

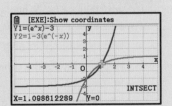

8 Solve for x:

  a $e^{2x} = 2e^x$
  b $e^x = e^{-x}$
  c $e^{2x} - 5e^x + 6 = 0$

  d $e^x + 2 = 3e^{-x}$
  e $1 + 12e^{-x} = e^x$
  f $e^x + e^{-x} = 3$

9 Find algebraically the point(s) of intersection of:

  a $y = e^x$ and $y = e^{2x} - 6$
  b $y = 2e^x + 1$ and $y = 7 - e^x$

  c $y = 3 - e^x$ and $y = 5e^{-x} - 3$

  Check your answers using technology.

Example 22   ◄)) **Self Tutor**

A farmer monitoring an insect plague finds that the area affected by the insects is given by $A(n) = 1000 \times 2^{0.7n}$ hectares, where n is the number of weeks after the initial observation.

  a Use technology to help sketch the graph of $A(n)$. Hence estimate the time taken for the affected area to reach 5000 hectares.

  b Check your answer to **a** using logarithms.

a From the graph, it appears that it will take about 3.3 weeks for the affected area to reach 5000 hectares.

b When $A(n) = 5000$,

  $1000 \times 2^{0.7n} = 5000$

  $\therefore \ 2^{0.7n} = 5$

  $\therefore \ \log(2^{0.7n}) = \log 5$

  $\therefore \ 0.7n \log 2 = \log 5$

  $\therefore \ n = \dfrac{\log 5}{0.7 \times \log 2} \approx 3.32$

  $\therefore$ it will take about 3 weeks and 2 days.

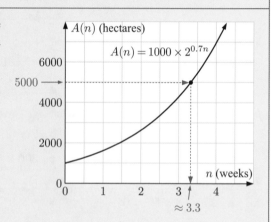

---

10 The population of turtles in an isolated colony is $P(t) = 852 \times (1.07)^t$, where t is the time in years after the colony was first recorded. How long will it take for the population to reach:

  a 1000 turtles
  b 1500 turtles?

11 The weight of bacteria in a culture t hours after establishment is given by $W(t) = 20 \times 2^{0.15t}$ grams.   Find, using logarithms, the time for the weight of the culture to reach:

  a 30 grams
  b 100 grams.

12 A biologist is modelling an infestation of fire ants. He determines that the area affected by the ants is given by $A(n) = 2000 \times e^{0.57n}$ hectares, where n is the number of weeks after the initial observation.

  a Use technology to help sketch the graph of $A(n)$.

  b Hence estimate the time taken for the infested area to reach $10\,000$ hectares.

  c Check your answer to **b** using logarithms.

13 A house is expected to increase in value at an average rate of 7.5% p.a. If the house is worth £360 000 now, when would you expect it to be worth £550 000?

14 Thabo has $10 000 to invest in an account that pays 4.8% p.a. compounded annually. How long will it take for his investment to grow to $15 000?

15 Dien invests $15 000 at 8.4% p.a. compounded *monthly*. He will withdraw his money when it reaches $25 000, at which time he plans to travel. The formula $t_n = t_0 \times r^n$ can be used to model the investment, where n is the time in months.

    a Explain why $r = 1.007$.   **b** After how many months will Dien withdraw the money?

16 The mass M_t of radioactive substance remaining after t years is given by
$M_t = 1000 \times e^{-0.04t}$ grams. Find the time taken for the mass to:

    a halve   **b** reach 25 grams   **c** reach 1% of its original value.

17 The current I flowing in a transistor radio t seconds after it is switched off, is given by
$I = I_0 \times 2^{-0.02t}$ amps. Show that it takes $\dfrac{50}{\log 2}$ seconds for the current to drop to 10% of its original value.

18 A sky diver jumps from an aeroplane. His speed of descent is given by
$V(t) = 50(1 - e^{-0.2t})$ m s^{-1}, where t is the time in seconds. Show that it will take $5\ln 5$ seconds for the sky diver's speed to reach 40 m s^{-1}.

19 Answer the **Opening Problem** on page **146**.

20 The weight of radioactive substance remaining after t years is given by
$W = 1000 \times 2^{-0.04t}$ grams.

    a Sketch the graph of W against t.   **b** Write a function for t in terms of W.

    c Hence find the time required for the weight to reach: **i** 20 grams   **ii** 0.001 grams.

21 The temperature of a liquid t minutes after it is placed in a refrigerator, is given by
$T = 4 + 96 \times e^{-0.03t}$ °C.

    a Sketch the graph of T against t.   **b** Write a function for t in terms of T.

    c Find the time required for the temperature to reach: **i** 25°C   **ii** 5°C.

22 A parachutist jumps from the basket of a stationary hot air balloon. His speed of descent is given by $V = 60(1 - 2^{-0.2t})$ m s^{-1} where t is the time in seconds. Write an expression for the time taken for his speed to reach v m s^{-1}.

23 A meteor hurtling through the atmosphere has speed of descent given by
$V(t) = 650(4 + 2 \times e^{-0.1t})$ m s^{-1} where t is the time in seconds after the meteor is sighted.

    a Is the meteor's speed increasing or decreasing?

    b Find the speed of the meteor:

        i when it was first sighted   **ii** after 2 minutes.

    c How long will it take for the meteor's speed to reach 3000 m s^{-1}?

INVESTIGATION 2   **THE "RULE OF 72"**

The "rule of 72" is used to estimate the time a quantity takes to double in value, given   RULE OF 72
the rate at which the quantity grows.

Click on the icon to view this Investigation.

H | LOGARITHMIC FUNCTIONS

We have seen that $\log_a a^x = a^{\log_a x} = x$.

Letting $f(x) = \log_a x$ and $g(x) = a^x$, we have $f \circ g = g \circ f = x$.

We can therefore say that the logarithmic function $\log_a x$ is the **inverse** of the exponential function a^x.

Algebraically, this has the effect that the logarithmic and exponential functions "undo" one another.

Geometrically, it means that the graph of $y = \log_a x$, $a > 0$, $a \neq 1$ is the *reflection* of the graph of $y = a^x$ in the line $y = x$.

We have seen previously the shape of the exponential function $y = a^x$ where $a > 0$, $a \neq 1$.

For $0 < a < 1$:
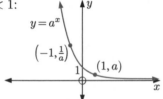

For $a > 1$:
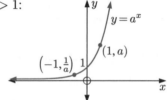

The horizontal asymptote for all of these functions is the x-axis $y = 0$.

By reflecting these graphs in the line $y = x$, we obtain the graphs for $y = \log_a x$.

For $0 < a < 1$:
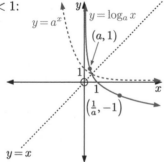

For $a > 1$:
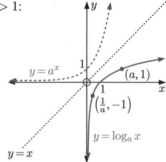

The **vertical asymptote** of $y = \log_a x$ is the y-axis $x = 0$.

For $0 < a < 1$: as $x \to \infty$, $y \to -\infty$ For $a > 1$: as $x \to \infty$, $y \to \infty$
                  as $x \to 0^+$, $y \to \infty$ as $x \to 0^+$, $y \to -\infty$

PROPERTIES OF $y = \log_a x$

Since we can only find logarithms of positive numbers, the domain of $y = \log_a x$ is $\{x \mid x > 0\}$.

We can compare the functions $y = a^x$ and $y = \log_a x$ as follows:

Function	$y = a^x$	$y = \log_a x$
Domain	$x \in \mathbb{R}$	$x > 0$
Range	$y > 0$	$y \in \mathbb{R}$
Asymptote	horizontal $y = 0$	vertical $x = 0$

TRANSFORMATIONS OF LOGARITHMIC FUNCTIONS

Click on the icon to explore the graphs of functions of the form $y = p\ln(x - h) + k$.

 LOGARITHMIC GRAPHS

Example 23 ◄)) **Self Tutor**

Consider the function $f(x) = \log_2(x - 1) + 1$.

a State the transformation which maps $y = \log_2 x$ to $y = f(x)$.

b Find the domain and range of f. **c** Find any asymptotes and axes intercepts.

d Sketch the graph of $y = f(x)$ showing all important features.

e Find the inverse function f^{-1}.

---

a $f(x)$ is a translation of $y = \log_2 x$ by $\begin{pmatrix} 1 \\ 1 \end{pmatrix}$.

b $x - 1 > 0$ when $x > 1$
So, the domain is $x > 1$ and the range is $y \in \mathbb{R}$.

c As $x \to 1^+$, $y \to -\infty$, so the vertical asymptote is $x = 1$.
As $x \to \infty$, $y \to \infty$, so there is no horizontal asymptote.
When $x = 0$, y is undefined, so there is no y-intercept.
When $y = 0$, $\log_2(x - 1) = -1$
$$\therefore \quad x - 1 = 2^{-1}$$
$$\therefore \quad x = \tfrac{3}{2} \quad \text{So, the } x\text{-intercept is } \tfrac{3}{2}.$$

d When $x = 2$, $y = \log_2(2 - 1) + 1$
$$= 1$$
When $x = 5$, $y = \log_2(5 - 1) + 1$
$$= \log_2 4 + 1$$
$$= 2 + 1$$
$$= 3$$

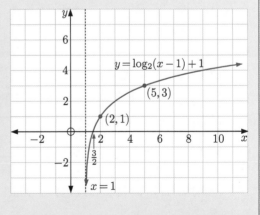

e f is defined by $y = \log_2(x - 1) + 1$
$\therefore f^{-1}$ is defined by $x = \log_2(y - 1) + 1$
$$\therefore \quad x - 1 = \log_2(y - 1)$$
$$\therefore \quad y - 1 = 2^{x-1}$$
$$\therefore \quad y = 2^{x-1} + 1$$
$$\therefore \quad f^{-1}(x) = 2^{x-1} + 1$$

EXERCISE 6H

1 For each of the following functions f:

    i Find the domain and range.   **ii** Find any asymptotes and axes intercepts.

    iii Sketch the graph of $y = f(x)$, showing all important features.

    iv Solve $f(x) = -1$ algebraically and check the solution on your graph.

    v Find the inverse function f^{-1}.

    a $f : x \mapsto \log_2 x - 2$ **b** $f : x \mapsto \log_3(x + 1)$ **c** $f : x \mapsto 1 - \log_3(x + 1)$

    d $f : x \mapsto \log_5(x - 2) - 2$ **e** $f : x \mapsto 1 - \log_5(x - 2)$ **f** $f : x \mapsto 1 - 2\log_2 x$

2 For each of the functions f:

    i State the transformation which maps $y = \ln x$ to $y = f(x)$.

    ii State the domain and range.   **iii** Find any asymptotes and intercepts.

    iv Sketch the graph of $y = f(x)$, showing all important features.

    v Find the inverse function f^{-1}.

    a $f(x) = \ln x - 4$ **b** $f(x) = \ln(x - 1) + 2$ **c** $f(x) = 3\ln x - 1$

3 Consider the curves A and B. One of them is the graph of $y = \ln x$ and the other is the graph of $y = \ln(x - 2)$.

    a Identify which curve is which, giving evidence for your answer.

    b Copy the graphs onto a new set of axes, and then draw the graph of $y = \ln(x + 2)$.

    c Find the equation of the vertical asymptote for each graph.

4 Kelly said that in order to graph $y = \ln(x^2)$, $x > 0$, you could first graph $y = \ln x$ and then double the distance of each point on the graph from the x-axis. Is Kelly correct? Explain your answer.

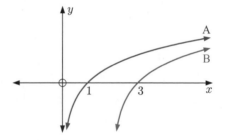

5 Draw, on the same set of axes, the graphs of:

    a $y = \ln x$ and $y = \ln(x^3)$ **b** $y = \ln x$ and $y = \ln\left(\frac{1}{x}\right)$

    c $y = \ln x$ and $y = \ln(x + e)$ **d** $y = \ln x$ and $y = \ln(x - 2) - 3$

    e $y = 2\ln x$ and $y = \ln(x^2) + 2$

6 Suppose $f(x) = be^x$ and $g(x) = \ln(bx)$. Find:

    a $(f \circ g)(x)$ **b** $(g \circ f)(x)$

    c the value of x, in terms of b, for which $(f \circ g)(x) = (g \circ f)(x)$.

7 Given $f : x \mapsto e^{2x}$ and $g : x \mapsto 2x - 1$, find:

    a $(f^{-1} \circ g)(x)$ **b** $(g \circ f)^{-1}(x)$

ACTIVITY

Click on the icon to obtain a card game for logarithmic functions.

CARD GAME

INVESTIGATION 3   LOGARITHMIC SCALES

In a **logarithmic scale**, equally spaced major tick marks correspond to integer *powers* of a base number. We often call these **orders of magnitude**.

For example, in the logarithmic scale alongside, each major tick mark represents a power of 10.

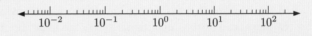

The minor tick marks correspond to integer *multiples* of each power of 10. So the minor tick marks between 10^1 and 10^2 represent 20, 30, 40, ..., and so on.

Logarithmic scales are useful when we want to represent both very large and very small numbers on the same number line. They allow us to compare real world quantities or events which are many orders of magnitude apart.

In this Investigation, we will explore the use of logarithmic scales in a variety of contexts.

What to do:

1 a For the logarithmic scale alongside, state the values of the points A, B, and C.

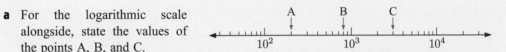

   b Explain why the minor tick marks in a logarithmic scale are not equally spaced.

   c Where is the value 0 on a logarithmic scale? Explain your answer.

2 Musical notes are named according to the frequency of their sound waves. They are labelled with letters of the alphabet. A note which has *twice* the frequency of another is said to be one **octave** higher than it. So, one C is an octave below the next C.

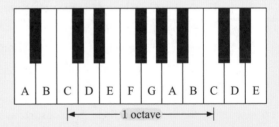

   a How many orders of magnitude apart are the frequencies of two notes separated by 3 octaves?

   b Write an expression for the frequency of a musical note f, in terms of the number of octaves n *above* middle C.

"Middle C" has the frequency $f_C = 261.6$ Hz.

   c There are 12 different notes in an octave. They are equally spaced on the logarithmic scale. Find the ratio of frequencies between two adjacent notes.

3 In some situations, the logarithm is already applied to values placed on the number line. In these cases, the major tick marks represent the *exponents* rather than the numbers themselves.

For example, suppose the scale alongside is logarithmic with base 10. The major tick mark "2" represents the value 10^2, the major tick mark "3" represents the value 10^3, and so on.

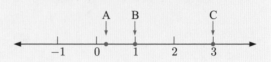

   a How many times larger is the value at C than the value at B?

   b Estimate the position on the scale representing the value:

      i 10 times smaller than A   **ii** twice as large as B.

4 Earthquakes can range from microscopic tremors to huge natural disasters. The magnitude of earthquakes is measured on the **Richter scale** which relates to the energy released by the earthquake. For this logarithmic scale, the logarithm is part of the formula. It is calculated as $M = \log\left(\dfrac{I}{I_0}\right)$, where I is the earthquake intensity and I_0 is a reference intensity level.

   a What does it mean for a tremor to have magnitude: **i** 0   **ii** 1?

   b Explain why an earthquake of magnitude 6 is *not* twice as intense as a magnitude 3 earthquake.

   c Find the magnitude of an earthquake which has half the intensity of a magnitude 4 earthquake.

5 The *acidity* of a solution is determined by the concentration of hydronium ions (H_3O^+).

The higher the concentration of H_3O^+, the more acidic it is. The opposite of acidic is *alkaline*.

   a In extremely acidic solutions, the concentration of H_3O^+ is typically more than 10^{-3} units. In very alkaline solutions, it is usually less than 10^{-12} units.

   Explain why a logarithmic scale would be useful in describing the acidity of a solution.

   b In chemistry, the **pH** scale is used to measure acidity. The pH of a solution is given by $\text{pH} = -\log C$, where C is the concentration of H_3O^+. Find:

      i the pH of a solution with H_3O^+ concentration $0.000\,234$ units

      ii the H_3O^+ concentration in a solution with pH 7.

   c Is it possible for a solution to have a negative pH? Explain what this means in terms of the concentration of H_3O^+.

6 Research the use of **decibels** in acoustics as a unit of measurement for loudness of sound. Compare the use of decibels to the scales in questions **4** and **5**.

REVIEW SET 6A

1 Find:

   a $\log \sqrt{10}$ **b** $\log\left(\dfrac{1}{\sqrt[3]{10}}\right)$ **c** $\log(10^a \times 10^{b+1})$

2 Find:

   a $\log_4 64$ **b** $\log_2 256$ **c** $\log_2(0.25)$ **d** $\log_{25} 5$

   e $\log_8 1$ **f** $\log_{81} 3$ **g** $\log_9\left(\tfrac{1}{9}\right)$ **h** $\log_k \sqrt{k}$

3 Use your calculator to evaluate, correct to 3 decimal places:

   a $\log 27$ **b** $\log(0.58)$ **c** $\log 400$ **d** $\ln 40$

4 Simplify:

   a $4\ln 2 + 2\ln 3$ **b** $\frac{1}{2}\ln 9 - \ln 2$ **c** $2\ln 5 - 1$ **d** $\frac{1}{4}\ln 81$

5 Write as a single logarithm:

   a $\log 16 + 2\log 3$ **b** $\log_2 16 - 2\log_2 3$ **c** $2 + \log_4 5$

6 Suppose $A = \log_5 2$ and $B = \log_5 3$. Write in terms of A and B:

   a $\log_5 36$ **b** $\log_5 54$ **c** $\log_5\left(8\sqrt{3}\right)$

   d $\log_5\left(\sqrt{6}\right)$ **e** $\log_5(20.25)$ **f** $\log_5\left(\frac{8}{9}\right)$

7 Write as a logarithmic equation:

   a $M = ab^n$ **b** $T = \dfrac{5}{\sqrt{l}}$ **c** $G = \dfrac{a^2 b}{c}$

8 Solve for x:

   a $3^x = 300$ **b** $30 \times 5^{1-x} = 0.15$ **c** $3^{x+2} = 2^{1-x}$

9 Solve exactly for x:

   a $e^{2x} = 3e^x$ **b** $e^{2x} - 7e^x + 12 = 0$

10 Write without logarithms:

   a $\ln P = 1.5\ln Q + \ln T$ **b** $\ln M = 1.2 - 0.5\ln N$

11 Solve for x:

   a $3e^x - 5 = -2e^{-x}$ **b** $2\ln x - 3\ln\left(\dfrac{1}{x}\right) = 10$

12 Find x if:

   a $\log_2 x = -3$ **b** $\log_5 x \approx 2.743$ **c** $\log_3 x \approx -3.145$

13 Solve for x: **i** exactly   **ii** rounded to 2 decimal places.

   a $2^x = 50$ **b** $7^x = 4$ **c** $(0.6)^x = 0.01$

14 Suppose $\log_a b = x$. Find, in terms of x, the value of $\log_a\left(\dfrac{1}{b}\right)$.

15 Show that the solution to $16^x - 5 \times 8^x = 0$ is $x = \log_2 5$.

16 Solve for x, giving exact answers:

   a $\ln x = 5$ **b** $3\ln x + 2 = 0$ **c** $e^x = 400$

   d $e^{2x+1} = 11$ **e** $25e^{\frac{x}{2}} = 750$

17 Consider $f(x) = e^{3x-4} + 1$.

   a Show that $f^{-1}(x) = \dfrac{\ln(x-1) + 4}{3}$.

   b Calculate $f^{-1}(8) - f^{-1}(3)$. Give your answer in the form $a\ln b$, where $a, b \in \mathbb{Q}^+$.

18 Consider the function $g : x \mapsto \log_3(x+2) - 2$.

    a State the transformation which maps $y = \log_3 x$ to $y = g(x)$.

    b Find the domain and range.

    c Find any asymptotes and axes intercepts for the graph of the function.

    d Find the inverse function g^{-1}.

    e Sketch the graphs of g, g^{-1}, and $y = x$ on the same set of axes.

19 The weight of a radioactive isotope remaining after t weeks is given by

$W_t = 8000 \times e^{-\frac{t}{20}}$ grams. Find the time for the weight to:

    a halve   **b** reach 1000 g   **c** reach 0.1% of its original value.

20 A population of seals is given by $P(t) = 80 \times (1.15)^t$
where t is the time in years, $t \geqslant 0$.

    a Find the time required for the population to
double in size.

    b Find the percentage increase in population during
the first 4 years.

21 For each of the following functions:

    i State the domain and range.

    ii Find any asymptotes and axes intercepts.

    iii Sketch the graph of the function, showing all important features.

    a $f(x) = \log_2(x+4) - 1$ **b** $f(x) = \ln x + 2$

22 Draw, on the same set of axes, the graphs of:

    a $y = \ln x$ and $y = \ln(x-3)$ **b** $y = \ln x$ and $y = \frac{1}{2}\ln x$

23 Consider $f(x) = e^x$ and $g(x) = \ln(x+4)$, $x > -4$. Find:

    a $(f \circ g)(5)$ **b** $(g \circ f)(0)$

REVIEW SET 6B

1 Without using a calculator, find the base 10 logarithms of:

    a $\sqrt{1000}$ **b** $\dfrac{10}{\sqrt[3]{10}}$ **c** $\dfrac{10^a}{10^{-b}}$

2 Find:

    a $\log_2 128$ **b** $\log_3\left(\frac{1}{27}\right)$ **c** $\log_5\left(\frac{1}{\sqrt{5}}\right)$

3 Write in the form 10^x, giving x correct to 4 decimal places:

    a 32   **b** 0.0013   **c** 8.963×10^{-5}

4 Find:

    a $\ln(e\sqrt{e})$ **b** $\ln\left(\frac{1}{e^3}\right)$ **c** $\ln(e^{2x})$ **d** $\ln\left(\frac{e}{e^x}\right)$

5   Simplify:

   a $\dfrac{\log_2 25}{\log_2 125}$

   b $\dfrac{\log 64}{\log 32}$

   c $\dfrac{\log_5 81}{\log_5 \sqrt{3}}$

6   Simplify:

   a $e^{4\ln x}$

   b $\ln(e^5)$

   c $\ln(\sqrt{e})$

   d $10^{\log x + \log 3}$

   e $\ln\left(\dfrac{1}{e^x}\right)$

   f $\dfrac{\log(x^2)}{\log_3 9}$

7   Write in the form e^x, where x is correct to 4 decimal places:

   a 20

   b 3000

   c 0.075

8   Solve for x: **i** exactly   **ii** rounded to 2 decimal places.

   a $5^x = 7$

   b $2^x = 0.1$

9   Write as a single logarithm:

   a $\ln 60 - \ln 20$

   b $\ln 4 + \ln 1$

   c $\ln 200 - \ln 8 + \ln 5$

10   Solve for x, giving exact answers:

   a $e^{2x} = 70$

   b $3 \times (1.3)^x = 11$

   c $5 \times 2^{0.3x} = 16$

11   What is the only value of x for which $\log x = \ln x$?

12   Write as a logarithmic equation:

   a $P = 3 \times b^x$

   b $m = \dfrac{n^3}{p^2}$

13   Show that $\log_3 7 \times 2\log_7 x = 2\log_3 x$.

14   Write the following equations without logarithms:

   a $\log T = 2\log x - \log y$

   b $\log_2 K = \log_2 n + \frac{1}{2}\log_2 t$

15   Write in the form $a\ln k$ where a and k are positive whole numbers and k is prime:

   a $\ln 32$

   b $\ln 125$

   c $\ln 729$

16   Copy and complete:

	$y = \log_2 x$	$y = \ln(x + 5)$
Domain		
Range		

17   **a** Factorise $4^x - 2^x - 20$ in the form $(2^x + a)(2^x - b)$ where $a, b \in \mathbb{Z}^+$.

   b Hence find the exact solution of $2^x(2^x - 1) = 20$.

   c Suppose $p = \log_5 2$.

     i Write the solution to **b** in terms of p.

     ii Find the solution to $8^x = 5^{1-x}$ in terms of p only.

18   Consider $g : x \mapsto 2e^x - 5$.

   a Find the inverse function g^{-1}.

   b Sketch the graphs of g and g^{-1} on the same set of axes.

   c State the domain and range of g and g^{-1}.

   d State the asymptotes and intercepts of g and g^{-1}.

172 LOGARITHMS (Chapter 6)

19 The temperature of a mug of water t minutes after it has been poured from a kettle is given by $T = 60e^{-0.1t} + 20$ °C.

Show that it will take $10 \ln 3$ minutes for the temperature of the water to fall to $40°$C.

20 The weight of a radioactive isotope after t years is given by $W(t) = 2500 \times 3^{-\frac{t}{3000}}$ grams.

  a Find the initial weight of the isotope.

  b Find the time taken for the isotope to reduce to 30% of its original weight.

  c Find the percentage of weight lost after 1500 years.

21 Solve for x, giving an exact answer:

  a $5^{\frac{x}{2}} = 9$ **b** $e^x = 30$ **c** $e^{1-3x} = 2$

22 Draw, on the same set of axes, the graphs of:

  a $y = \ln x$ and $y = \ln(x + 2)$ **b** $y = \ln x$ and $y = \ln(ex)$

23 *Hick's law* models the time taken for a person to make a selection from a number of possible options.

For a particular person, Hick's law determines that the time taken to choose between n equally probable choices is $T = 2 \ln(n + 1)$ seconds.

  a Sketch the graph of T against n for $0 \leqslant n \leqslant 50$.

  b How long will it take this person to choose between:

    i 5 possible choices   **ii** 15 possible choices?

  c If the number of possible choices increases from 20 to 40, how much longer will the person take to make a selection?

Chapter 7

The unit circle and radian measure

OPENING PROBLEM

Consider the triangles below:

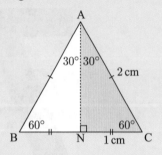 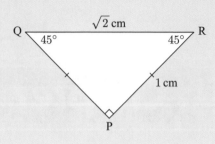

Things to think about:

a   Triangle ABC is an equilateral triangle with sides 2 cm long. Altitude [AN] bisects side [BC] and the vertical angle BAC.
   Can you use this figure to find:
     i $\sin 30°$ **ii** $\cos 60°$ **iii** $\cos 30°$ **iv** $\sin 60°$?

b   Triangle PQR is a right angled isosceles triangle with hypotenuse $\sqrt{2}$ cm long.
   Can you use this figure to find:
     i $\cos 45°$ **ii** $\sin 45°$ **iii** $\tan 45°$?

In this Chapter we build on our knowledge of angles and trigonometry. We consider:

- **radian** measure as an alternative to degrees
- the **unit circle** which helps us give meaning to the trigonometric ratios for *any* angle.

A   RADIAN MEASURE

DEGREE MEASUREMENT OF ANGLES

We have seen previously that one full revolution makes an angle of $360°$, and the angle on a straight line is $180°$. Hence, one **degree**, $1°$, can be defined as $\frac{1}{360}$th of one full revolution. This measure of angle is commonly used by surveyors and architects.

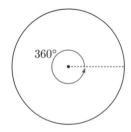

For greater accuracy we define one **minute**, $1'$, as $\frac{1}{60}$th of one degree and one **second**, $1''$, as $\frac{1}{60}$th of one minute. Obviously a minute and a second are very small angles.

Most graphics calculators can convert fractions of angles measured in degrees into minutes and seconds. This is also useful for converting fractions of hours into minutes and seconds for time measurement, as one minute is $\frac{1}{60}$th of one hour, and one second is $\frac{1}{60}$th of one minute.

GRAPHICS CALCULATOR INSTRUCTIONS

RADIAN MEASUREMENT OF ANGLES

Around 1400 AD, the Persian mathematician **Al-Kashi** began measuring angles according to the length of the arc of a circle that the angle subtends. This idea was developed into **radian** measure by the Englishman **Roger Coates** in 1714. The word "radian" is an abbreviation of "radial angle".

Suppose the arc length formed by an angle is the same length as the radius. This angle is said to have a measure of 1 **radian** (1^c).

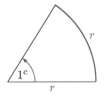

DEMO

The symbol "c" is used for radian measure but is usually omitted. By contrast, the degree symbol is *always* used when the measure of an angle is given in degrees.

From the diagram to the right, it can be seen that 1^c is slightly smaller than $60°$. In fact, $1^c \approx 57.3°$.

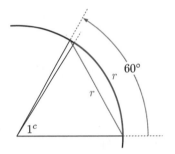

DEGREE-RADIAN CONVERSIONS

Consider a semi-circle of radius r. The arc length is πr, so there are π radians in a semi-circle.

Therefore, π radians $\equiv 180°$.

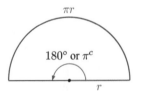

So, $1^c = \left(\frac{180}{\pi}\right)^{\circ} \approx 57.3°$ and $1° = \left(\frac{\pi}{180}\right)^{c} \approx 0.0175^c$.

To convert from degrees to radians, we multiply by $\frac{\pi}{180}$.

To convert from radians to degrees, we multiply by $\frac{180}{\pi}$.

We indicate degrees with a small $^\circ$.
To indicate radians we use a small ^{c} or else use no symbol at all.

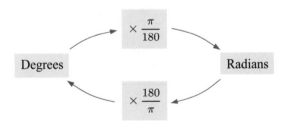

Example 1   ◀) **Self Tutor**

Convert $45°$ to radians, in terms of π.

$45° = \left(45 \times \frac{\pi}{180}\right)$ radians   *or* $180° = \pi$ radians

$\quad = \frac{\pi}{4}$ radians $\qquad\qquad\qquad \therefore \left(\frac{180}{4}\right)° = \frac{\pi}{4}$ radians

$\qquad\qquad\qquad\qquad\qquad\qquad \therefore \quad 45° = \frac{\pi}{4}$ radians

> Angles in radians may be expressed either in terms of π or as decimals.

Example 2   ◀) **Self Tutor**

Convert $126.5°$ to radians.

$\quad 126.5°$

$= \left(126.5 \times \frac{\pi}{180}\right)$ radians

≈ 2.21 radians

EXERCISE 7A

1 Convert to radians, in terms of π:

a	$90°$	**b**	$60°$	**c**	$30°$	**d**	$18°$	**e**	$9°$
f	$135°$	**g**	$225°$	**h**	$270°$	**i**	$360°$	**j**	$720°$
k	$315°$	**l**	$540°$	**m**	$36°$	**n**	$80°$	**o**	$230°$

2 Convert to radians, correct to 3 significant figures:

a	$36.7°$	**b**	$137.2°$	**c**	$317.9°$	**d**	$219.6°$	**e**	$396.7°$

Example 3   ◀) **Self Tutor**

Convert to degrees:

a $\frac{5\pi}{6}$ **b** 0.638 radians.

a $\quad \frac{5\pi}{6}$ **b** $\qquad 0.638$ radians

$\quad = \left(\frac{5\pi}{6} \times \frac{180}{\pi}\right)°$ $\quad = \left(0.638 \times \frac{180}{\pi}\right)°$

$\quad = 150°$ $\qquad\quad \approx 36.6°$

---

3 Convert to degrees:

a	$\frac{\pi}{5}$	**b**	$\frac{3\pi}{5}$	**c**	$\frac{3\pi}{4}$	**d**	$\frac{\pi}{18}$	**e**	$\frac{\pi}{9}$
f	$\frac{7\pi}{9}$	**g**	$\frac{\pi}{10}$	**h**	$\frac{3\pi}{20}$	**i**	$\frac{7\pi}{6}$	**j**	$\frac{\pi}{8}$

4 Convert to degrees, correct to 2 decimal places:

a	2	**b**	1.53	**c**	0.867	**d**	3.179	**e**	5.267

5 Match each angle measurement with the correct diagram:

   a 70°   **b** 2^c **c** $\frac{\pi}{2}$ **d** 200°   **e** 3^c **f** 0.5

A

B

C
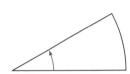

D
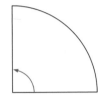

E

F

6 Copy and complete, giving answers in terms of π:

a

Degrees	0	45	90	135	180	225	270	315	360
Radians									

b

Degrees	0	30	60	90	120	150	180	210	240	270	300	330	360
Radians													

B   ARC LENGTH AND SECTOR AREA

You should have previously seen formulae for the length of an arc and the area of a sector, for an angle given in degrees.

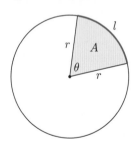

> For a sector with radius r and angle θ given in *degrees*,
>
> $$\text{arc length } \; l = \frac{\theta}{360} \times 2\pi r$$
>
> $$\text{area } \; A = \frac{\theta}{360} \times \pi r^2$$

However, if the angle θ is measured in radians, the formulae become much simpler.

- θ measures how many times longer the arc length is than the radius.

$$\therefore \; \theta = \frac{l}{r}$$

$$\therefore \; l = \theta r$$

- There are 2π radians in a circle so

$$\text{area of sector} = \frac{\theta}{2\pi} \times \text{area of circle}$$

$$\therefore \; A = \frac{\theta}{2\pi} \times \pi r^2$$

$$\therefore \; A = \tfrac{1}{2}\theta r^2$$

> For a sector with radius r and angle θ given in *radians*,
>
> $$\text{arc length } \ l = \theta r$$
> $$\text{area } \ A = \tfrac{1}{2}\theta r^2$$

Example 4   ◀)) **Self Tutor**

A sector has radius 12 cm and angle 3 radians. Find its:

a arc length   **b** area

a arc length $= \theta r$
$$= 3 \times 12$$
$$= 36 \text{ cm}$$

b area $= \tfrac{1}{2}\theta r^2$
$$= \tfrac{1}{2} \times 3 \times 12^2$$
$$= 216 \text{ cm}^2$$

EXERCISE 7B

1 Find the arc length of each sector:

a

b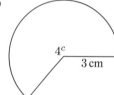

c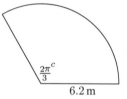

2 Find the area of each sector:

a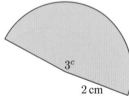

b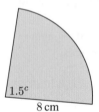

c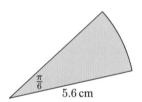

3 Find the arc length and area of a sector of a circle with:

a radius 9 cm and angle $\frac{7\pi}{4}$ **b** radius 4.93 cm and angle 4.67 radians.

Example 5   ◀)) **Self Tutor**

A sector has radius 8.2 cm and arc length 12.3 cm. Find its:

a angle   **b** area.

a $l = \theta r$ $\{\theta$ in radians$\}$
$$\therefore \ \ \theta = \frac{l}{r} = \frac{12.3}{8.2} = 1.5 \text{ radians}$$

b area $= \tfrac{1}{2}\theta r^2$
$$= \tfrac{1}{2} \times 1.5 \times 8.2^2$$
$$= 50.43 \text{ cm}^2$$

---

4 Find, in radians, the angle of a sector of:

a radius 4.3 m and arc length 2.95 m   **b** radius 10 cm and area 30 cm^2.

5   Find θ (in radians) for each of the following, and hence find the area of each figure:

a

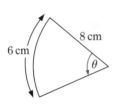

b

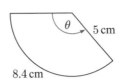

c   31.7 cm

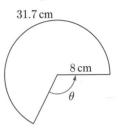

6   A sector has an angle of 1.88 radians and an arc length of 5.92 m. Find its:

   a   radius   **b**   area.

7   A sector has an angle of 1.19 radians and an area of 20.8 cm^2. Find its:

   a   radius   **b**   perimeter.

8

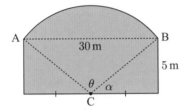

The end wall of a building has the shape illustrated, where the centre of arc AB is at C. Find:

   a α in radians to 4 significant figures

   b θ in radians to 4 significant figures

   c   the area of the wall.

9   In the given figure, the perimeter of sector OAB is $(12 + 2\pi)$ cm.

   a   Find θ.

   b   Hence state the length of the chord [AB].

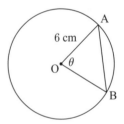

10   The cone   is made from this sector:

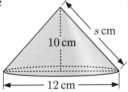

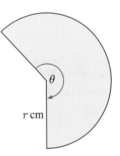

Find, correct to 3 significant figures:

   a   the slant length s cm   **b**   the value of r

   c   the arc length of the sector   **d**   the sector angle θ in radians.

11

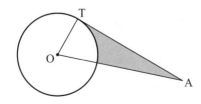

[AT] is a tangent to the given circle. OA = 13 cm and the circle has radius 5 cm. Find the perimeter of the shaded region.

12 A **nautical mile** (nmi) is the distance on the Earth's surface that subtends an angle of 1 minute (or $\frac{1}{60}$th of a degree) of the Great Circle arc measured from the centre of the Earth. A **knot** is a speed of 1 nautical mile per hour.

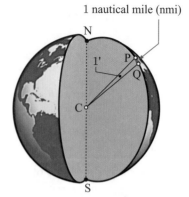

1 nautical mile (nmi)

  a Given that the radius of the Earth is 6370 km, show that 1 nmi is approximately 1.853 km.

  b Calculate how long it would take a plane to fly 2130 km from Perth to Adelaide if the plane can fly at 480 knots.

13

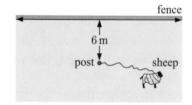

fence

6 m

post   sheep

A sheep is tethered to a post which is 6 m from a long fence. The length of the rope is 9 m. Find the area which the sheep can feed on.

14 Two semi-circles touch each other within a quarter circle as shown. P, Q, and R are collinear. The radius of the quarter circle is 12 cm.

  a Find the radius of the smaller semi-circle.

  b Calculate the area of:

   i A **ii** B.

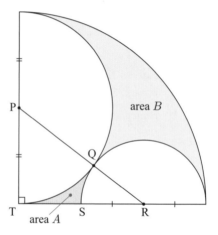

P

area B

Q

T

area A

S   R

THEORY OF KNOWLEDGE

There are several theories for why one complete turn was divided into 360 degrees:

- 360 is approximately the number of days in a year.
- The Babylonians used a counting system in base 60. If they drew 6 equilateral triangles within a circle as shown, and divided each angle into 60 subdivisions, then there were 360 subdivisions in one turn. The division of an hour into 60 minutes, and a minute into 60 seconds, is from this base 60 counting system.

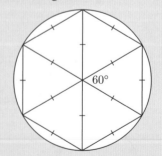

60°

- 360 has 24 divisors, including every integer from 1 to 10 except 7.

By contrast, we have seen how radians are convenient in simplifying formulae which relate angles with distances and areas.

1   Which angle measure do you think is more:

    a *practical*   **b** *natural*   **c** *mathematical?*

2   What other measures of angle are there, and for what purpose were they defined?

3   Which temperature scale, Celsius, Kelvin, or Fahrenheit, do you think is more:

    a *practical*   **b** *natural?*

4   What other measures have we defined as a way of convenience?

5   What things are done differently around the world, but would be useful to globally standardise? For example, why are there different power voltages in different countries? Why have they not been standardised?

6   What things do we measure in a particular way simply for reasons of history rather than practical purpose?

C   THE UNIT CIRCLE

When we introduced non-right angled triangle trigonometry, we used the **unit circle** to give meaning to the trigonometric ratios for obtuse angles. We now extend these definitions to include *all* angles.

The **unit circle** is the circle with centre $(0, 0)$ and radius 1 unit.

The equation of the unit circle is $x^2 + y^2 = 1$.

DEFINITION OF SINE AND COSINE

If P is any point on the unit circle such that [OP] makes an angle θ measured anticlockwise from the positive x-axis:

- $\cos \theta$ is the x-coordinate of P
- $\sin \theta$ is the y-coordinate of P

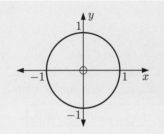

For all points on the unit circle, $-1 \leqslant x \leqslant 1$, $-1 \leqslant y \leqslant 1$, and $x^2 + y^2 = 1$. We therefore conclude:

For any angle θ:

- $-1 \leqslant \cos \theta \leqslant 1$ and $-1 \leqslant \sin \theta \leqslant 1$
- $\cos^2 \theta + \sin^2 \theta = 1$

DEFINITION OF TANGENT

Suppose we extend [OP] to meet the tangent from A$(1, 0)$.

We let the intersection between these lines be point Q.

Note that as P moves, so does Q.

The position of Q relative to A is defined as the **tangent function**.

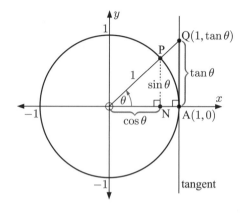

Notice that triangles ONP and OAQ are equiangular and therefore similar.

Consequently $\dfrac{\text{AQ}}{\text{OA}} = \dfrac{\text{NP}}{\text{ON}}$ and hence $\dfrac{\text{AQ}}{1} = \dfrac{\sin \theta}{\cos \theta}$.

Under the definition that $\text{AQ} = \tan \theta$, $$\tan \theta = \frac{\sin \theta}{\cos \theta}.$$

Since [OP] has gradient $\dfrac{\sin \theta}{\cos \theta}$, we can also say that $\tan \theta$ is the **gradient** of [OP].

INVESTIGATION   THE TRIGONOMETRIC RATIOS

In this Investigation we explore the signs of the trigonometric ratios in each quadrant of the unit circle.

What to do:

1 Click on the icon to run the Unit Circle software.
Drag the point P slowly around the circle.
Note the *sign* of each trigonometric ratio in each quadrant.

THE UNIT CIRCLE

Quadrant	$\cos \theta$	$\sin \theta$	$\tan \theta$
1	positive		
2			
3			
4			

2nd   1st
3rd   4th

2 Hence write down the trigonometric ratios which are *positive* for each quadrant.

From the **Investigation** you should have discovered that:

- $\sin \theta$, $\cos \theta$, and $\tan \theta$ are all positive in quadrant 1
- only $\sin \theta$ is positive in quadrant 2
- only $\tan \theta$ is positive in quadrant 3
- only $\cos \theta$ is positive in quadrant 4.

We can use a letter to show which trigonometric ratios are positive in each quadrant. The A stands for *all* of the ratios.

You might like to remember them using

   All Silly Turtles Crawl.

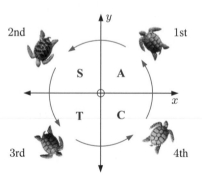

PERIODICITY OF TRIGONOMETRIC RATIOS

Since there are 2π radians in a full revolution, if we add any integer multiple of 2π to θ (in radians) then the position of P on the unit circle is unchanged.

> For θ in radians and $k \in \mathbb{Z}$,
> $$\cos(\theta + 2k\pi) = \cos\theta \quad \text{and} \quad \sin(\theta + 2k\pi) = \sin\theta.$$

We notice that for any point $(\cos\theta, \sin\theta)$ on the unit circle, the point directly opposite is $(-\cos\theta, -\sin\theta)$.

$$\therefore \quad \cos(\theta + \pi) = -\cos\theta$$
$$\sin(\theta + \pi) = -\sin\theta$$
$$\text{and} \quad \tan(\theta + \pi) = \frac{-\sin\theta}{-\cos\theta} = \tan\theta$$

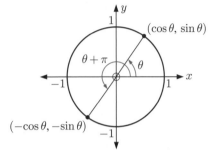

> For θ in radians and $k \in \mathbb{Z}$, $\tan(\theta + k\pi) = \tan\theta$.

CALCULATOR USE

When using your calculator to find trigonometric ratios for angles, you must make sure your calculator is correctly set to either **degree** or **radian** mode. Click on the icon for instructions.

**GRAPHICS
CALCULATOR
INSTRUCTIONS**

Example 6	◀) Self Tutor

a State the exact coordinates of P and Q in terms of sine and cosine.

b Use your calculator to give the coordinates of P and Q correct to 3 significant figures.

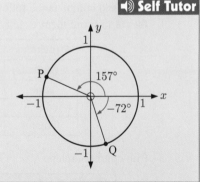

a P is $(\cos 157°, \sin 157°)$,
   Q is $(\cos(-72°), \sin(-72°))$.

b P $\approx (-0.921, 0.391)$
   Q $\approx (0.309, -0.951)$

Casio fx-CG50

```
cos 157
                -0.9205048535
sin 157
                0.3907311285
cos -72
                0.3090169944
```

θ is positive for anticlockwise rotations, and negative for clockwise rotations.

EXERCISE 7C

1 With the aid of a unit circle, complete the following table:

θ (degrees)	0°	90°	180°	270°	360°	450°
θ (radians)						
sine						
cosine						
tangent						

2 For each unit circle illustrated:

    i State the exact coordinates of points A, B, and C in terms of sine and cosine.

    ii Use your calculator to give the coordinates of A, B, and C correct to 3 significant figures.

a

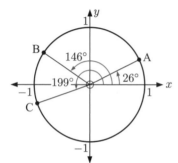

b

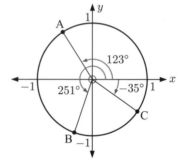

3 **a** Use your calculator to evaluate:

    i $\frac{1}{\sqrt{2}}$ **ii** $\frac{\sqrt{3}}{2}$

  b Copy and complete the following table. Use your calculator to evaluate the trigonometric ratios, then **a** to write them exactly.

θ (degrees)	30°	45°	60°	135°	150°	240°	315°
θ (radians)							
sine							
cosine							
tangent							

4 **a** Copy and complete:

Quadrant	Degree measure	Radian measure	$\cos\theta$	$\sin\theta$	$\tan\theta$
1	$0° < \theta < 90°$	$0 < \theta < \frac{\pi}{2}$	positive	positive	
2					
3					
4					

  b In which quadrants are the following true?

    i $\cos\theta$ is positive.   **ii** $\cos\theta$ is negative.

    iii $\cos\theta$ and $\sin\theta$ are both negative.   **iv** $\cos\theta$ is negative and $\sin\theta$ is positive.

5 Explain why:

  a $\cos 400° = \cos 40°$ **b** $\sin\frac{5\pi}{7} = \sin\frac{19\pi}{7}$ **c** $\tan\frac{13\pi}{8} = \tan\left(-\frac{11\pi}{8}\right)$

6 Which two of these have the same value?

    A $\tan 15°$ **B** $\tan 50°$ **C** $\tan 200°$ **D** $\tan 230°$ **E** $\tan 300°$

7 Which two of these have the same value?

    A $\sin 220°$ **B** $\sin \frac{2\pi}{9}$ **C** $\sin\left(-\frac{2\pi}{9}\right)$ **D** $\sin 120°$ **E** $\sin 40°$

8   **a** Use your calculator to evaluate:

      i $\sin 100°$ **ii** $\sin 80°$ **iii** $\sin 120°$ **iv** $\sin 60°$

      v $\sin 150°$ **vi** $\sin 30°$ **vii** $\sin 45°$ **viii** $\sin 135°$

   b Use the results from **a** to copy and complete: $\sin(180° - \theta) = \ldots\ldots$

   c Write the rule you have just found in terms of radians.

   d Justify your answer using the diagram alongside:

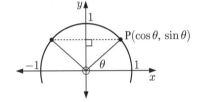

   e Find the obtuse angle with the same sine as:

      i $45°$ **ii** $51°$ **iii** $\frac{\pi}{3}$ **iv** $\frac{\pi}{6}$

9   **a** Use your calculator to evaluate:

      i $\cos 70°$ **ii** $\cos 110°$ **iii** $\cos 60°$ **iv** $\cos 120°$

      v $\cos 25°$ **vi** $\cos 155°$ **vii** $\cos 80°$ **viii** $\cos 100°$

   b Use the results from **a** to copy and complete: $\cos(180° - \theta) = \ldots\ldots$

   c Write the rule you have just found in terms of radians.

   d Justify your answer using the diagram alongside:

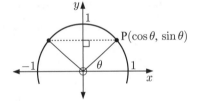

   e Find the obtuse angle which has the negative cosine of:

      i $40°$ **ii** $19°$ **iii** $\frac{\pi}{5}$ **iv** $\frac{2\pi}{5}$

10 Use the definition $\tan\theta = \dfrac{\sin\theta}{\cos\theta}$ and your results from **8** and **9** to write $\tan(\pi - \theta)$ in terms of $\tan\theta$.

11 Without using your calculator, find:

    a $\sin 137°$ if $\sin 43° \approx 0.6820$ **b** $\sin 59°$ if $\sin 121° \approx 0.8572$

    c $\cos 143°$ if $\cos 37° \approx 0.7986$ **d** $\cos 24°$ if $\cos 156° \approx -0.9135$

    e $\sin 115°$ if $\sin 65° \approx 0.9063$ **f** $\cos 132°$ if $\cos 48° \approx 0.6691$

12   **a** Copy and complete:

θ (radians)	$\sin\theta$	$\sin(-\theta)$	$\cos\theta$	$\cos(-\theta)$
0.75				
1.772				
3.414				
6.25				
-1.17				

   b What trigonometric formulae can be deduced from your results in **a**?

c The coordinates of P in the figure are $(\cos\theta,\,\sin\theta)$. By finding the coordinates of Q in terms of θ in *two different* ways, prove your formulae in **b**.

d Hence explain why

$$\cos(2\pi - \theta) = \cos\theta$$

and $\sin(2\pi - \theta) = -\sin\theta$.

e Write $\tan(2\pi - \theta)$ in terms of $\tan\theta$.

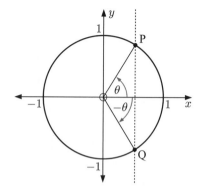

13 a Explain why P has coordinates $(\cos(\frac{\pi}{2} - \theta),\ \sin(\frac{\pi}{2} - \theta))$.

b Show that:

  i $XP = \sin\theta$ **ii** $OX = \cos\theta$

c Hence, copy and complete:

  i $\cos(\frac{\pi}{2} - \theta) = \ldots\ldots$ **ii** $\sin(\frac{\pi}{2} - \theta) = \ldots\ldots$

d Check your answer to **c** by calculating:

  i $\cos\frac{\pi}{5}$ and $\sin\frac{3\pi}{10}$ **ii** $\sin\frac{\pi}{8}$ and $\cos\frac{3\pi}{8}$.

e Write $\tan(\frac{\pi}{2} - \theta)$ in terms of $\tan\theta$.

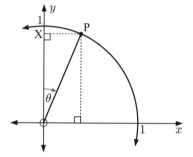

DISCUSSION   IDENTITIES

In the previous Exercise you should have proven the following trigonometric **identities**:

	Degree form	*Radian form*
Supplementary angles	$\cos(180° - \theta) = -\cos\theta$ $\sin(180° - \theta) = \sin\theta$ $\tan(180° - \theta) = -\tan\theta$	$\cos(\pi - \theta) = -\cos\theta$ $\sin(\pi - \theta) = \sin\theta$ $\tan(\pi - \theta) = -\tan\theta$
Negative angles	$\cos(-\theta) = \cos\theta$ $\sin(-\theta) = -\sin\theta$ $\tan(-\theta) = -\tan\theta$	$\cos(-\theta) = \cos\theta$ $\sin(-\theta) = -\sin\theta$ $\tan(-\theta) = -\tan\theta$
Complementary angles	$\cos(90° - \theta) = \sin\theta$ $\sin(90° - \theta) = \cos\theta$ $\tan(90° - \theta) = \dfrac{1}{\tan\theta}$	$\cos(\frac{\pi}{2} - \theta) = \sin\theta$ $\sin(\frac{\pi}{2} - \theta) = \cos\theta$ $\tan(\frac{\pi}{2} - \theta) = \dfrac{1}{\tan\theta}$

- What do we mean by the word "identity"?
- Why are identities important?
- What other identities do we use?

D   MULTIPLES OF $\frac{\pi}{6}$ AND $\frac{\pi}{4}$

Angles which are multiples of $\frac{\pi}{6}$ and $\frac{\pi}{4}$ occur frequently in geometry, so it is important for us to write their trigonometric ratios exactly.

MULTIPLES OF $\frac{\pi}{4}$ OR $45°$

Consider $\theta = 45°$.

Angle OPB also measures $45°$, so triangle OBP is isosceles.

$\therefore$ we let   OB = BP = a

Now $a^2 + a^2 = 1^2$ {Pythagoras}

$\therefore \quad a^2 = \frac{1}{2}$

$\therefore \quad a = \frac{1}{\sqrt{2}}$ {since $a > 0$}

$\therefore$ P is $\left(\frac{1}{\sqrt{2}}, \frac{1}{\sqrt{2}}\right)$ where $\frac{1}{\sqrt{2}} \approx 0.707$.

So, $\cos \frac{\pi}{4} = \frac{1}{\sqrt{2}}$ and $\sin \frac{\pi}{4} = \frac{1}{\sqrt{2}}$

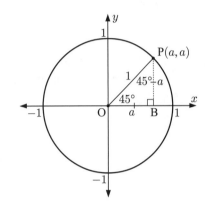

We can now find the coordinates of all points on the unit circle corresponding to multiples of $\frac{\pi}{4}$ by symmetry.

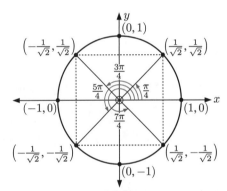

MULTIPLES OF $\frac{\pi}{6}$ OR $30°$

Consider $\theta = 60°$.

Since OA = OP, triangle OAP is isosceles.

Now $A\widehat{O}P = 60°$, so the remaining angles are therefore also $60°$. Triangle AOP is therefore equilateral.

The altitude [PN] bisects base [OA], so ON = $\frac{1}{2}$.

If P is $(\frac{1}{2}, k)$, then $(\frac{1}{2})^2 + k^2 = 1$

$\therefore \quad k^2 = \frac{3}{4}$

$\therefore \quad k = \frac{\sqrt{3}}{2}$ {since $k > 0$}

$\therefore$ P is $\left(\frac{1}{2}, \frac{\sqrt{3}}{2}\right)$ where $\frac{\sqrt{3}}{2} \approx 0.866$.

So, $\cos \frac{\pi}{3} = \frac{1}{2}$ and $\sin \frac{\pi}{3} = \frac{\sqrt{3}}{2}$

Now $N\widehat{P}O = \frac{\pi}{6} = 30°$.   Hence $\cos \frac{\pi}{6} = \frac{\sqrt{3}}{2}$ and $\sin \frac{\pi}{6} = \frac{1}{2}$

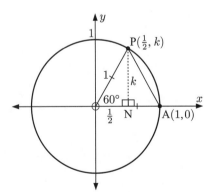

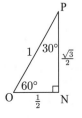

DISCUSSION

You should remember the values of cosine and sine for angles $\frac{\pi}{6}$, $\frac{\pi}{4}$, and $\frac{\pi}{3}$.

However, if you forget, you can use these diagrams to quickly generate the results.

Discuss how you can do this.

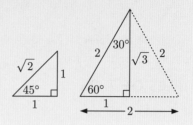

We can now find the coordinates of all points on the unit circle corresponding to multiples of $\frac{\pi}{6}$ by symmetry.

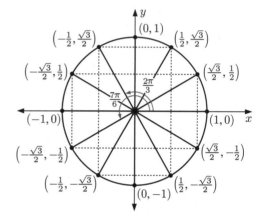

SUMMARY

- For **multiples of** $\frac{\pi}{2}$, the coordinates of the points on the unit circle involve 0 and ± 1.
- For *other* **multiples of** $\frac{\pi}{4}$, the coordinates involve $\pm\frac{1}{\sqrt{2}}$.
- For *other* **multiples of** $\frac{\pi}{6}$, the coordinates involve $\pm\frac{1}{2}$ and $\pm\frac{\sqrt{3}}{2}$.

Example 7   ◀) Self Tutor

Find the exact values of $\sin\alpha$, $\cos\alpha$, and $\tan\alpha$ for:

a $\alpha = \frac{3\pi}{4}$

b $\alpha = \frac{4\pi}{3}$

a

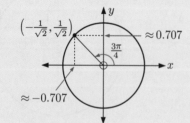

$\sin\frac{3\pi}{4} = \frac{1}{\sqrt{2}}$

$\cos\frac{3\pi}{4} = -\frac{1}{\sqrt{2}}$

$\tan\frac{3\pi}{4} = -1$

b

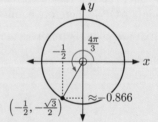

$\sin\frac{4\pi}{3} = -\frac{\sqrt{3}}{2}$

$\cos\frac{4\pi}{3} = -\frac{1}{2}$

$\tan\frac{4\pi}{3} = \dfrac{-\frac{\sqrt{3}}{2}}{-\frac{1}{2}} = \sqrt{3}$

EXERCISE 7D

1 Use a unit circle diagram to find exact values for $\sin\theta$, $\cos\theta$, and $\tan\theta$ for θ equal to:

  a $\frac{\pi}{4}$ **b** $\frac{3\pi}{4}$ **c** $\frac{7\pi}{4}$ **d** π **e** $-\frac{3\pi}{4}$

2 Use a unit circle diagram to find exact values for $\sin\beta$, $\cos\beta$, and $\tan\beta$ for β equal to:

  a $\frac{\pi}{6}$ **b** $\frac{2\pi}{3}$ **c** $\frac{7\pi}{6}$ **d** $\frac{5\pi}{3}$ **e** $\frac{11\pi}{6}$

3 Find the exact values of:

  a $\cos\frac{2\pi}{3}$, $\sin\frac{2\pi}{3}$, and $\tan\frac{2\pi}{3}$ **b** $\cos\left(-\frac{\pi}{4}\right)$, $\sin\left(-\frac{\pi}{4}\right)$, and $\tan\left(-\frac{\pi}{4}\right)$

4 **a** Find the exact values of $\cos\frac{\pi}{2}$ and $\sin\frac{\pi}{2}$.

    b What can you say about $\tan\frac{\pi}{2}$?

Example 8   ◀)) **Self Tutor**

Without using a calculator, show that $8\sin\frac{\pi}{3}\cos\frac{5\pi}{6} = -6$.

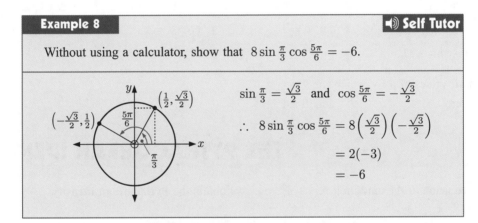

$\sin\frac{\pi}{3} = \frac{\sqrt{3}}{2}$ and $\cos\frac{5\pi}{6} = -\frac{\sqrt{3}}{2}$

$\therefore\; 8\sin\frac{\pi}{3}\cos\frac{5\pi}{6} = 8\left(\frac{\sqrt{3}}{2}\right)\left(-\frac{\sqrt{3}}{2}\right)$

$= 2(-3)$

$= -6$

---

5 Without using a calculator, evaluate:

  a $\sin^2\left(\frac{\pi}{3}\right)$ **b** $\sin\frac{\pi}{6}\cos\frac{\pi}{3}$ **c** $4\sin\frac{\pi}{3}\cos\frac{\pi}{6}$

  d $1 - \cos^2\left(\frac{\pi}{6}\right)$ **e** $\sin^2\left(\frac{2\pi}{3}\right) - 1$ **f** $\cos^2\left(\frac{\pi}{4}\right) - \sin\frac{7\pi}{6}$

  g $\sin\frac{3\pi}{4} - \cos\frac{5\pi}{4}$ **h** $1 - 2\sin^2\left(\frac{7\pi}{6}\right)$ **i** $\cos^2\left(\frac{5\pi}{6}\right) - \sin^2\left(\frac{5\pi}{6}\right)$

  j $\tan^2\left(\frac{\pi}{3}\right) - 2\sin^2\left(\frac{\pi}{4}\right)$ **k** $2\tan\left(-\frac{5\pi}{4}\right) - \sin\frac{3\pi}{2}$ **l** $\dfrac{2\tan\frac{5\pi}{6}}{1 - \tan^2\left(\frac{5\pi}{6}\right)}$

Check all answers using your calculator.

Example 9   ◀)) **Self Tutor**

Find all angles $0 \leqslant \theta \leqslant 2\pi$ with a cosine of $\frac{1}{2}$.

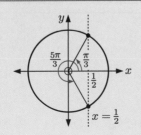

Since the cosine is $\frac{1}{2}$, we draw the vertical line $x = \frac{1}{2}$.

Because $\frac{1}{2}$ is involved, we know the required angles are multiples of $\frac{\pi}{6}$.

They are $\frac{\pi}{3}$ and $\frac{5\pi}{3}$.

6 Find all angles between 0 and 2π with:

   a a sine of $\frac{1}{2}$ **b** a sine of $\frac{\sqrt{3}}{2}$ **c** a cosine of $\frac{1}{\sqrt{2}}$

   d a cosine of $-\frac{1}{2}$ **e** a cosine of $-\frac{1}{\sqrt{2}}$ **f** a sine of $-\frac{\sqrt{3}}{2}$

7 Find all angles between 0 and 2π (inclusive) which have a tangent of:

   a 1   **b** -1 **c** $\sqrt{3}$ **d** 0   **e** $\frac{1}{\sqrt{3}}$ **f** $-\sqrt{3}$

8 Find all angles between 0 and 4π with:

   a a cosine of $\frac{\sqrt{3}}{2}$ **b** a sine of $-\frac{1}{2}$ **c** a sine of -1

9 Find θ if $0 \leqslant \theta \leqslant 2\pi$ and:

   a $\cos\theta = \frac{1}{2}$ **b** $\sin\theta = \frac{\sqrt{3}}{2}$ **c** $\cos\theta = -1$ **d** $\sin\theta = 1$

   e $\cos\theta = -\frac{1}{\sqrt{2}}$ **f** $\sin^2\theta = 1$ **g** $\cos^2\theta = 1$ **h** $\cos^2\theta = \frac{1}{2}$

   i $\tan\theta = -\frac{1}{\sqrt{3}}$ **j** $\tan^2\theta = 3$

10 Find *all* values of θ for which $\tan\theta$ is:

   a zero   **b** undefined.

E   THE PYTHAGOREAN IDENTITY

From the equation of the unit circle $x^2 + y^2 = 1$, we obtain the **Pythagorean identity**:

> For any angle θ, $\quad \cos^2\theta + \sin^2\theta = 1$.

We can use this identity to find one trigonometric ratio from another.

Example 10   ◀)) **Self Tutor**

Find the possible exact values of $\cos\theta$ for $\sin\theta = \frac{2}{3}$. Illustrate your answers.

$\cos^2\theta + \sin^2\theta = 1$

$\therefore \; \cos^2\theta + \left(\frac{2}{3}\right)^2 = 1$

$\therefore \; \cos^2\theta = \frac{5}{9}$

$\therefore \; \cos\theta = \pm\frac{\sqrt{5}}{3}$

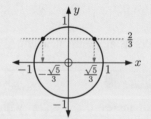

EXERCISE 7E

1 Find the possible exact values of $\cos\theta$ for:

   a $\sin\theta = \frac{1}{2}$ **b** $\sin\theta = -\frac{1}{3}$ **c** $\sin\theta = 0$ **d** $\sin\theta = -1$

2 Find the possible exact values of $\sin\theta$ for:

   a $\cos\theta = \frac{4}{5}$ **b** $\cos\theta = -\frac{3}{4}$ **c** $\cos\theta = 1$ **d** $\cos\theta = 0$

Example 11   ◀)) **Self Tutor**

If $\sin\theta = -\frac{3}{4}$ and $\pi < \theta < \frac{3\pi}{2}$, find $\cos\theta$ and $\tan\theta$. Give exact values.

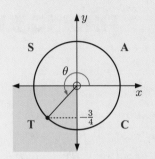

Now $\cos^2\theta + \sin^2\theta = 1$

$\therefore \cos^2\theta + \frac{9}{16} = 1$

$\therefore \cos^2\theta = \frac{7}{16}$

$\therefore \cos\theta = \pm\frac{\sqrt{7}}{4}$

But $\pi < \theta < \frac{3\pi}{2}$, so θ is a quadrant 3 angle.

$\therefore \cos\theta$ is negative.

$\therefore \cos\theta = -\frac{\sqrt{7}}{4}$ and $\tan\theta = \frac{\sin\theta}{\cos\theta} = \frac{-\frac{3}{4}}{-\frac{\sqrt{7}}{4}} = \frac{3}{\sqrt{7}}$

3 Without using a calculator, find:

a $\sin\theta$ if $\cos\theta = \frac{2}{3}$ and $0 < \theta < \frac{\pi}{2}$

b $\cos\theta$ if $\sin\theta = \frac{2}{5}$ and $\frac{\pi}{2} < \theta < \pi$

c $\cos\theta$ if $\sin\theta = -\frac{3}{5}$ and $\frac{3\pi}{2} < \theta < 2\pi$

d $\sin\theta$ if $\cos\theta = -\frac{5}{13}$ and $\pi < \theta < \frac{3\pi}{2}$.

4 Find $\tan\theta$ exactly given:

a $\sin\theta = \frac{1}{3}$ and $\frac{\pi}{2} < \theta < \pi$

b $\cos\theta = \frac{1}{5}$ and $\frac{3\pi}{2} < \theta < 2\pi$

c $\sin\theta = -\frac{1}{\sqrt{3}}$ and $\pi < \theta < \frac{3\pi}{2}$

d $\cos\theta = -\frac{3}{4}$ and $\frac{\pi}{2} < \theta < \pi$.

Example 12   ◀)) **Self Tutor**

If $\tan\theta = -2$ and $\frac{3\pi}{2} < \theta < 2\pi$, find $\sin\theta$ and $\cos\theta$. Give exact answers.

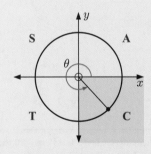

$\tan\theta = \frac{\sin\theta}{\cos\theta} = -2$

$\therefore \sin\theta = -2\cos\theta$

Now $\sin^2\theta + \cos^2\theta = 1$

$\therefore (-2\cos\theta)^2 + \cos^2\theta = 1$

$\therefore 4\cos^2\theta + \cos^2\theta = 1$

$\therefore 5\cos^2\theta = 1$

$\therefore \cos\theta = \pm\frac{1}{\sqrt{5}}$

But $\frac{3\pi}{2} < \theta < 2\pi$, so θ is a quadrant 4 angle.

$\therefore \cos\theta$ is positive and $\sin\theta$ is negative.

$\therefore \cos\theta = \frac{1}{\sqrt{5}}$ and $\sin\theta = -\frac{2}{\sqrt{5}}$.

5 Find exact values for $\sin\theta$ and $\cos\theta$ given that:

a $\tan\theta = \frac{2}{3}$ and $0 < \theta < \frac{\pi}{2}$

b $\tan\theta = -\frac{4}{3}$ and $\frac{\pi}{2} < \theta < \pi$

c $\tan\theta = \frac{\sqrt{5}}{3}$ and $\pi < \theta < \frac{3\pi}{2}$

d $\tan\theta = -\frac{12}{5}$ and $\frac{3\pi}{2} < \theta < 2\pi$

6 Suppose $\tan\theta = k$ where k is a constant and $\pi < \theta < \frac{3\pi}{2}$. Write expressions for $\sin\theta$ and $\cos\theta$ in terms of k.

F   FINDING ANGLES

In **Exercise 7C** you should have proven that:

For θ in degrees:	For θ in radians:
• $\sin(180° - \theta) = \sin\theta$	• $\sin(\pi - \theta) = \sin\theta$
• $\cos(180° - \theta) = -\cos\theta$	• $\cos(\pi - \theta) = -\cos\theta$
• $\cos(360° - \theta) = \cos\theta$	• $\cos(2\pi - \theta) = \cos\theta$
• $\sin(360° - \theta) = -\sin\theta$	• $\sin(2\pi - \theta) = -\sin\theta$

We need results such as these, and also the periodicity of the trigonometric ratios, to find angles which have a particular sine, cosine, or tangent.

Example 13   ◀◎ **Self Tutor**

Find the two angles θ on the unit circle, with $0° \leqslant \theta \leqslant 360°$, such that:

a $\cos\theta = \frac{1}{3}$ **b** $\sin\theta = \frac{3}{4}$ **c** $\tan\theta = 2$

a Using technology, $\cos^{-1}\left(\frac{1}{3}\right) \approx 70.53°$

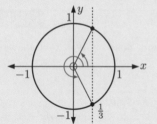

$\therefore \quad \theta \approx 70.53°$ or $360° - 70.53°$
$\therefore \quad \theta \approx 70.5°$ or $289.5°$

b Using technology, $\sin^{-1}\left(\frac{3}{4}\right) \approx 48.59°$

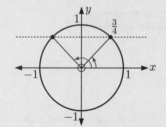

$\therefore \quad \theta \approx 48.59°$ or $180° - 48.59°$
$\therefore \quad \theta \approx 48.6°$ or $131.4°$

c Using technology, $\tan^{-1}(2) \approx 63.43°$

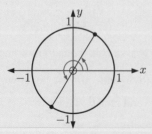

For positive $\cos\theta$, $\sin\theta$, or $\tan\theta$, your calculator will give the *acute* angle θ.

$\therefore \quad \theta \approx 63.43°$ or $180° + 63.43°$
$\therefore \quad \theta \approx 63.4°$ or $243.4°$

EXERCISE 7F

1 Find two angles θ on the unit circle, with $0° \leqslant \theta \leqslant 360°$, such that:

    a $\tan\theta = 4$ **b** $\cos\theta = 0.83$ **c** $\sin\theta = \frac{3}{5}$

    d $\cos\theta = 0$ **e** $\tan\theta = 6.67$ **f** $\cos\theta = \frac{2}{17}$

2 Find two angles θ on the unit circle, with $0 \leqslant \theta \leqslant 2\pi$, such that:

    a $\tan\theta = \frac{1}{3}$ **b** $\cos\theta = \frac{3}{7}$ **c** $\sin\theta = 0.61$

    d $\cos\theta = \frac{1}{4}$ **e** $\tan\theta = 0.114$ **f** $\sin\theta = \frac{1}{6}$

Example 14   ◀)) **Self Tutor**

Find two angles θ on the unit circle, with $0 \leqslant \theta \leqslant 2\pi$, such that:

    a $\sin\theta = -0.4$ **b** $\cos\theta = -\frac{2}{3}$ **c** $\tan\theta = -\frac{1}{3}$

a Using technology, $\sin^{-1}(-0.4) \approx -0.412$

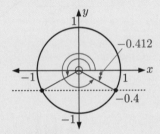

> If $\sin\theta$ or $\tan\theta$ is negative, your calculator will give θ in the domain $-\frac{\pi}{2} < \theta < 0$.
>
> If $\cos\theta$ is negative, your calculator will give the *obtuse* angle θ.
>
> The angles given by your calculator are shown in green.

But $0 \leqslant \theta \leqslant 2\pi$

$\therefore \ \theta \approx \pi + 0.412$ or $2\pi - 0.412$

$\therefore \ \theta \approx 3.55$ or 5.87

b Using technology, $\cos^{-1}\left(-\frac{2}{3}\right) \approx 2.30$

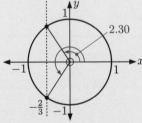

But $0 \leqslant \theta \leqslant 2\pi$

$\therefore \ \theta \approx 2.30$ or $2\pi - 2.30$

$\therefore \ \theta \approx 2.30$ or 3.98

c Using technology, $\tan^{-1}\left(-\frac{1}{3}\right) \approx -0.322$

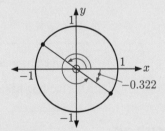

But $0 \leqslant \theta \leqslant 2\pi$

$\therefore \ \theta \approx \pi - 0.322$ or $2\pi - 0.322$

$\therefore \ \theta \approx 2.82$ or 5.96

---

3 Find two angles θ on the unit circle, with $0 \leqslant \theta \leqslant 2\pi$, such that:

    a $\cos\theta = -\frac{1}{4}$ **b** $\sin\theta = 0$ **c** $\tan\theta = -3.1$ **d** $\sin\theta = -0.421$

    e $\tan\theta = 1.2$ **f** $\cos\theta = 0.7816$ **g** $\sin\theta = \frac{1}{11}$ **h** $\cos\theta = -\frac{1}{\sqrt{3}}$

4   Find all θ such that $-180° \leqslant \theta \leqslant 180°$ and:

   a $\cos\theta = -\frac{1}{10}$ **b** $\sin\theta = \frac{4}{5}$ **c** $\tan\theta = -\frac{3}{2}$

   d $\cos\theta = 0.8$ **e** $\tan\theta = -\frac{5}{6}$ **f** $\sin\theta = -\frac{7}{11}$

G   THE EQUATION OF A STRAIGHT LINE

If a straight line makes an angle of θ with the positive x-axis then its gradient is $m = \tan\theta$.

Proof:

  • For $m \geqslant 0$:

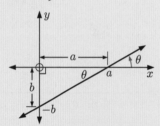

    Gradient $m = \dfrac{0 - -b}{a - 0}$

              $= \dfrac{b}{a}$

              $= \tan\theta$

  • For $m < 0$:

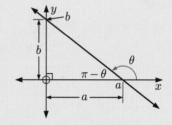

    Gradient $m = \dfrac{0 - b}{a - 0}$

              $= -\dfrac{b}{a}$

              $= -\tan(\pi - \theta)$

              $= \tan\theta$

Example 15   ◀)) **Self Tutor**

Find the equation of the given line:

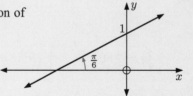

The line has gradient $m = \tan\frac{\pi}{6} = \frac{1}{\sqrt{3}}$ and y-intercept 1.

∴ the line has equation $y = \frac{1}{\sqrt{3}}x + 1$.

EXERCISE 7G

1   Find the equation of each line:

  a

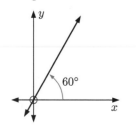

  b

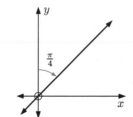

  c

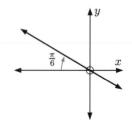

2 Find the equation of each line:

a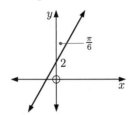 **b**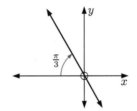 **c**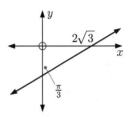

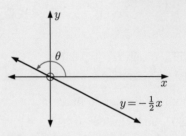

> **Example 16** ◀)) **Self Tutor**
>
> Find, in radians, the measure of θ:
>
> ---
>
> The line has gradient $-\frac{1}{2}$, so $\tan \theta = -\frac{1}{2}$.
>
> Using technology, $\tan^{-1}(-\frac{1}{2}) \approx -0.464$
>
> But $0 < \theta < \pi$, so $\theta \approx \pi - 0.464 \approx 2.68$

3 Find, in radians, the measure of θ:

a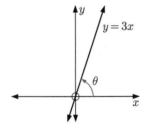 **b**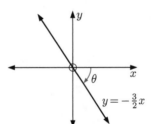 **c**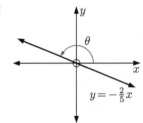

4 Find, in degrees, the measure of θ:

a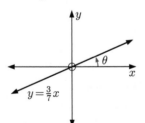 **b**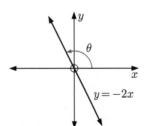 **c**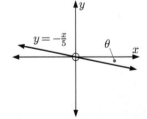

REVIEW SET 7A

1 Convert to radians in terms of π:

    a $120°$ **b** $225°$ **c** $150°$ **d** $540°$

2 Convert these radian measurements to degrees:

   a $\frac{2\pi}{5}$ **b** $\frac{5\pi}{4}$ **c** $\frac{7\pi}{9}$ **d** $\frac{11\pi}{6}$

3 Illustrate the quadrants where $\sin\theta$ and $\cos\theta$ have the same sign.

4 Determine the coordinates of the point on the unit circle corresponding to an angle of:

   a $320°$ **b** $163°$ **c** 0.68^c

5 Find the arc length of a sector with angle 1.5 radians and radius 8 cm.

6 Find the acute angles that have the same:

   a sine as $\frac{2\pi}{3}$ **b** sine as $165°$ **c** cosine as $276°$.

7 Find:

   a $\sin 159°$ if $\sin 21° \approx 0.358$ **b** $\cos 92°$ if $\cos 88° \approx 0.035$

   c $\cos 75°$ if $\cos 105° \approx -0.259$ **d** $\tan(-133°)$ if $\tan 47° \approx 1.072$.

8 Use a unit circle diagram to find:

   a $\cos 360°$ and $\sin 360°$ **b** $\cos(-\pi)$ and $\sin(-\pi)$.

9 Find exact values for $\sin\theta$, $\cos\theta$, and $\tan\theta$ for θ equal to: **a** $\frac{2\pi}{3}$ **b** $\frac{8\pi}{3}$

10

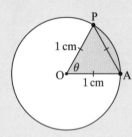

   a State the value of θ in:

     i degrees   **ii** radians.

   b State the arc length AP.

   c State the area of the minor *sector* OAP.

11 If $\sin x = -\frac{1}{4}$ and $\pi < x < \frac{3\pi}{2}$, find $\tan x$ exactly.

12 If $\cos\theta = \frac{3}{4}$, find the possible values of $\sin\theta$.

13 Evaluate:

   a $2\sin\frac{\pi}{3}\cos\frac{\pi}{3}$ **b** $\tan^2\left(\frac{\pi}{4}\right) - 1$ **c** $\cos^2\left(\frac{\pi}{6}\right) - \sin^2\left(\frac{\pi}{6}\right)$

14 Given $\tan x = -\frac{3}{2}$ and $\frac{3\pi}{2} < x < 2\pi$, find:

   a $\cos x$ **b** $\sin x$.

15

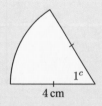

   Find the perimeter and area of the sector.

16 Suppose $\cos\theta = \frac{\sqrt{11}}{\sqrt{17}}$ and θ is acute. Find the exact value of $\tan\theta$.

17 Find two angles on the unit circle with $0 \leqslant \theta \leqslant 2\pi$, such that:

   a $\cos\theta = \frac{2}{3}$ **b** $\sin\theta = -\frac{1}{4}$ **c** $\tan\theta = 3$

18 Find the equation of each line:

a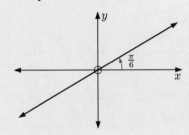

b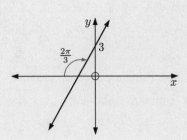

REVIEW SET 7B

1 Convert to radians, to 4 significant figures:

   a $71°$ **b** $124.6°$ **c** $-142°$

2 Convert to degrees, to 2 decimal places:

   a 3^c **b** 1.46 **c** 0.435^c **d** -5.271

3 Determine the area of a sector with angle $\frac{5\pi}{12}$ and radius 13 cm.

4 Find the coordinates of the points M, N, and P on the unit circle.

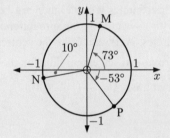

5 Find the angle [OA] makes with the positive x-axis if the x-coordinate of the point A on the unit circle is -0.222.

6 Find the radius and area of a sector of perimeter 36 cm with an angle of $\frac{2\pi}{3}$.

7 Use a unit circle diagram to find:

   a $\cos\frac{3\pi}{2}$ and $\sin\frac{3\pi}{2}$ **b** $\cos\left(-\frac{\pi}{2}\right)$ and $\sin\left(-\frac{\pi}{2}\right)$

8 Suppose $m = \sin p$, where p is acute. Write an expression in terms of m for:

   a $\sin(\pi - p)$ **b** $\sin(p + 2\pi)$ **c** $\cos p$ **d** $\tan p$

9 Find all angles between $0°$ and $360°$ which have:

   a a cosine of $-\frac{\sqrt{3}}{2}$ **b** a sine of $\frac{1}{\sqrt{2}}$ **c** a tangent of $-\sqrt{3}$

10 Find θ for $0 \leqslant \theta \leqslant 2\pi$ if:

   a $\cos\theta = -1$ **b** $\sin^2\theta = \frac{3}{4}$

11 Find the obtuse angles which have the same:

   a sine as $47°$ **b** sine as $\frac{\pi}{15}$ **c** cosine as $186°$

12 Find the perimeter and area of a sector with radius 11 cm and angle $63°$.

13 Show that $\cos\frac{3\pi}{4} - \sin\frac{3\pi}{4} = -\sqrt{2}$.

14 If $\cos\theta = -\frac{3}{4}$, $\frac{\pi}{2} < \theta < \pi$ find the exact value of:

   a $\sin\theta$ **b** $\tan\theta$ **c** $\cos(\pi-\theta)$

15 Without using a calculator, evaluate:

   a $\tan^2 60° - \sin^2 45°$ **b** $\cos^2\left(\frac{\pi}{4}\right) + \sin\frac{\pi}{2}$

   c $\cos\frac{5\pi}{3} - \tan\frac{5\pi}{4}$ **d** $\tan^2\left(\frac{2\pi}{3}\right)$

16 Explain how to use the unit circle to find θ when $\cos\theta = -\sin\theta$, $0 \leqslant \theta \leqslant 2\pi$.

17 Find, in radians, the measure of θ:

   a 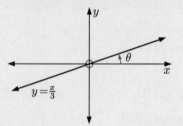   **b**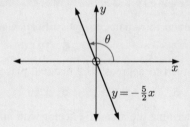

18 Three circles with radius r are drawn as shown, each with its centre on the circumference of the other two circles. A, B, and C are the centres of the three circles.

Prove that an expression for the area of the shaded region is $A = \frac{r^2}{2}(\pi - \sqrt{3})$.

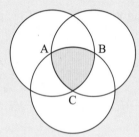

Chapter 8

Trigonometric functions

Contents:

OPENING PROBLEM

A Ferris wheel rotates anticlockwise at a constant speed. The wheel's radius is 10 m and the bottom of the wheel is 2 m above ground level. From his viewing point next to the ticket booth, Andrew is watching a green light on the perimeter of the wheel. He notices that the green light moves in a circle. It takes 100 seconds for a full revolution.

Click on the icon to visit a simulation of the Ferris wheel. You will be able to view the light from:

- in front of the wheel
- a side-on position
- above the wheel.

DEMO

You can then observe graphs of the green light's position as the wheel rotates at a constant rate.

Things to think about:

a Andrew estimates how high the light is above ground level at two second intervals. What will a graph of this data look like? Assume that the light is initially in the position shown.

b Andrew then estimates the horizontal position of the light at two second intervals. What will a graph of this data look like?

c What similarities and differences will there be between your two graphs?

d Can you write a function which will give the:
  i height of the light at any time t seconds
  ii horizontal displacement of the light at any time t seconds?

A   PERIODIC BEHAVIOUR

Periodic phenomena occur all the time in the physical world. For example, in:

- seasonal variations in our climate
- variations in average maximum and minimum monthly temperatures
- the number of daylight hours at a particular location
- tidal variations in the depth of water in a harbour
- the phases of the moon
- animal populations.

These phenomena illustrate variable behaviour which is repeated over time. The repetition may be called **periodic**, **oscillatory**, or **cyclic** in different situations.

In this Chapter we will see how trigonometric functions can be used to model periodic phenomena.

OBSERVING PERIODIC BEHAVIOUR

The table below shows the mean monthly maximum temperature for Cape Town, South Africa.

Month	Jan	Feb	Mar	Apr	May	Jun	Jul	Aug	Sep	Oct	Nov	Dec
Temperature T (°C)	28	27	$25\frac{1}{2}$	22	$18\frac{1}{2}$	16	15	16	18	$21\frac{1}{2}$	24	26

On the graph alongside we plot the temperature T on the vertical axis. We assign January as $t = 1$ month, February as $t = 2$ months, and so on for the 12 months of the year.

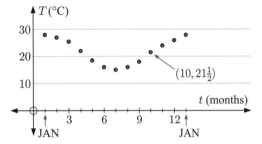

The temperature shows a variation from an average of 28°C in January through a range of values across the months. The cycle will approximately repeat itself for each subsequent 12 month period. By the end of the Chapter we will be able to establish a **periodic function** which approximately fits this set of points.

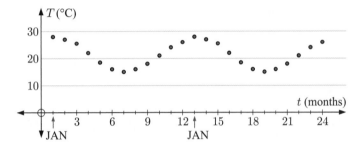

HISTORICAL NOTE

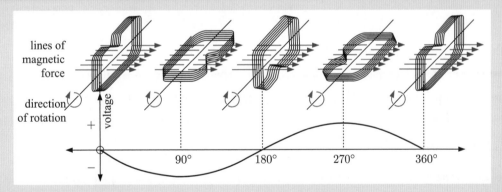

In 1831, **Michael Faraday** discovered that an electric current was generated by rotating a coil of wire at a constant speed through 360° in a magnetic field. The electric current produced showed a voltage which varied between positive and negative values in a periodic function called a **sine wave**.

TERMINOLOGY USED TO DESCRIBE PERIODICITY

A **periodic function** is one which repeats itself over and over in a horizontal direction, in intervals of the same length. The **period** of a periodic function is the length of one repetition or cycle.

$f(x)$ is a periodic function with period p if $f(x + p) = f(x)$ for all x, and p is the smallest positive value for this to be true.

A **cycloid** is an example of a periodic function. It is the curve traced out by a point on a circle as the circle rolls across a flat surface in a straight line.

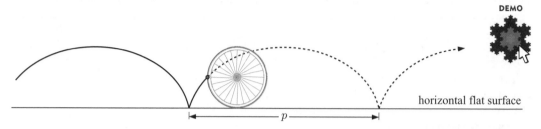

DEMO

horizontal flat surface

ACTIVITY 1   **PERIODIC FUNCTIONS**

Use a **graphing package** to examine the function $f(x) = x - \lfloor x \rfloor$ where $\lfloor x \rfloor$ is "the largest integer less than or equal to x".

GRAPHING PACKAGE

In the graphing package, you type $\lfloor x \rfloor$ as floor(x).

Is $f(x)$ periodic?   What is its period?

WAVES

In this course we are mainly concerned with periodic phenomena which show a wave pattern:

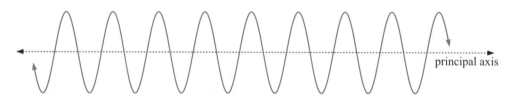

principal axis

A **wave** oscillates about a horizontal line called the **principal axis** or **mean line**.

A **maximum point** occurs at the top of a crest, and a **minimum point** at the bottom of a trough.

If the maximum and minimum values of the wave are **max** and **min** respectively, then the principal axis has equation $y = \dfrac{\mathbf{max} + \mathbf{min}}{2}$.

The **amplitude** is the distance between a maximum (or minimum) point and the principal axis.

$$\mathbf{amplitude} = \frac{\mathbf{max} - \mathbf{min}}{2}$$

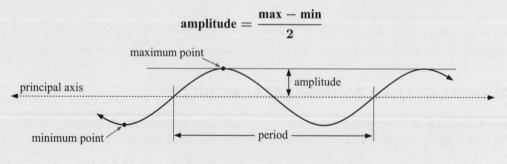

maximum point

principal axis

amplitude

minimum point

period

EXERCISE 8A

1 Which of these graphs show periodic behaviour?

a
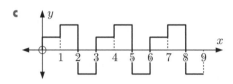

b
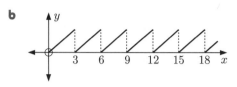

c
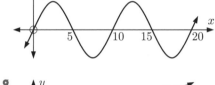

d
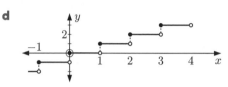

e

f
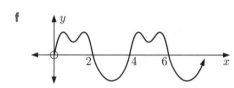

g
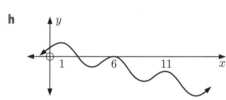

h

2 Paul spun the wheel of his bicycle. The following tabled values show the height above the ground of a point on the wheel at various times.

Time (seconds)	0	0.2	0.4	0.6	0.8	1	1.2	1.4	1.6	1.8	2
Height above ground (cm)	0	6	23	42	57	64	59	43	23	7	1

Time (seconds)	2.2	2.4	2.6	2.8	3	3.2	3.4	3.6	3.8	4
Height above ground (cm)	5	27	40	55	63	60	44	24	9	3

a Plot the graph of height against time.

b Is it reasonable to fit a curve to this data, or should we leave it as discrete points?

c Is the data periodic? If so, estimate:

   i the equation of the principal axis   **ii** the maximum value

   iii the period   **iv** the amplitude.

3 Plot the points for each data set below. Is there any evidence to suggest the data is periodic?

a

x	0	1	2	3	4	5	6	7	8	9	10	11	12
y	0	1	1.4	1	0	−1	−1.4	−1	0	1	1.4	1	0

b

x	0	2	3	4	5	6	7	8	9	10	12
y	0	4.7	3.4	1.7	2.1	5.2	8.9	10.9	10.2	8.4	10.4

GRAPHICS
CALCULATOR
INSTRUCTIONS

B | THE SINE AND COSINE FUNCTIONS

A **trigonometric function** is a function which involves one of the trigonometric ratios.

Consider the point $P(\cos\theta, \sin\theta)$ on the unit circle.

As θ increases, the point P moves around the unit circle, and the values of $\cos\theta$ and $\sin\theta$ change.

We can draw the graphs of $y = \sin\theta$ and $y = \cos\theta$ by plotting the values of $\sin\theta$ and $\cos\theta$ against θ.

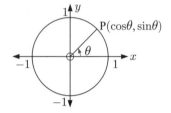

THE GRAPH OF $y = \sin\theta$

By considering the y-coordinates of the points on the unit circle at intervals of $\frac{\pi}{6}$, we can create a table of values for $\sin\theta$:

θ	0	$\frac{\pi}{6}$	$\frac{\pi}{3}$	$\frac{\pi}{2}$	$\frac{2\pi}{3}$	$\frac{5\pi}{6}$	π	$\frac{7\pi}{6}$	$\frac{4\pi}{3}$	$\frac{3\pi}{2}$	$\frac{5\pi}{3}$	$\frac{11\pi}{6}$	2π
$\sin\theta$	0	$\frac{1}{2}$	$\frac{\sqrt{3}}{2}$	1	$\frac{\sqrt{3}}{2}$	$\frac{1}{2}$	0	$-\frac{1}{2}$	$-\frac{\sqrt{3}}{2}$	-1	$-\frac{\sqrt{3}}{2}$	$-\frac{1}{2}$	0

Plotting $\sin\theta$ against θ gives:

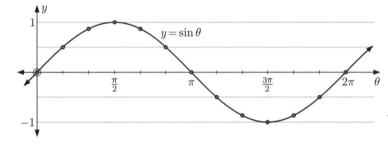
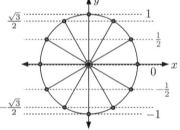

Once we reach 2π, P has completed a full revolution of the unit circle, and so this pattern repeats itself.

DEMO

THE GRAPH OF $y = \cos\theta$

By considering the x-coordinates of the points on the unit circle at intervals of $\frac{\pi}{6}$, we can create a table of values for $\cos\theta$:

θ	0	$\frac{\pi}{6}$	$\frac{\pi}{3}$	$\frac{\pi}{2}$	$\frac{2\pi}{3}$	$\frac{5\pi}{6}$	π	$\frac{7\pi}{6}$	$\frac{4\pi}{3}$	$\frac{3\pi}{2}$	$\frac{5\pi}{3}$	$\frac{11\pi}{6}$	2π
$\cos\theta$	1	$\frac{\sqrt{3}}{2}$	$\frac{1}{2}$	0	$-\frac{1}{2}$	$-\frac{\sqrt{3}}{2}$	-1	$-\frac{\sqrt{3}}{2}$	$-\frac{1}{2}$	0	$\frac{1}{2}$	$\frac{\sqrt{3}}{2}$	1

Plotting $\cos \theta$ against θ gives:

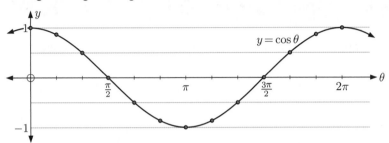

The graph of $y = \cos \theta$ shows the x-coordinate of P as P moves around the unit circle.

EXERCISE 8B

1 Below is an accurate graph of $y = \sin \theta$.

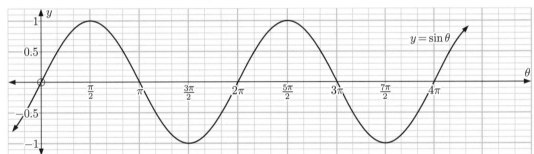

   a Find the y-intercept of the graph.

   b Find the values of θ on $0 \leqslant \theta \leqslant 4\pi$ for which:

      i $\sin \theta = 0$ **ii** $\sin \theta = -1$ **iii** $\sin \theta = \frac{1}{2}$ **iv** $\sin \theta = \frac{\sqrt{3}}{2}$

   c Find the intervals on $0 \leqslant \theta \leqslant 4\pi$ where $\sin \theta$ is:

      i positive   **ii** negative.

   d Find the range of the function.

2 Below is an accurate graph of $y = \cos \theta$.

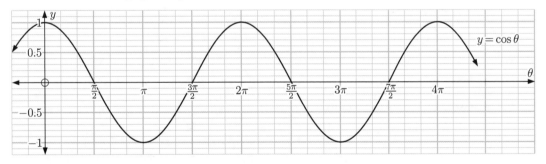

   a Find the y-intercept of the graph.

   b Find the values of θ on $0 \leqslant \theta \leqslant 4\pi$ for which:

      i $\cos \theta = 0$ **ii** $\cos \theta = 1$ **iii** $\cos \theta = -\frac{1}{2}$ **iv** $\cos \theta = -\frac{1}{\sqrt{2}}$

   c Find the intervals on $0 \leqslant \theta \leqslant 4\pi$ where $\cos \theta$ is:

      i positive   **ii** negative.

   d Find the range of the function.

C | GENERAL SINE AND COSINE FUNCTIONS

Now that we are familiar with the graphs of $y = \sin\theta$ and $y = \cos\theta$, we can use transformations to graph more complicated trigonometric functions.

Instead of using θ, we will now use x to represent the angle variable. This is just for convenience, so we are dealing with the familiar function form $y = f(x)$.

For the graphs of $y = \sin x$ and $y = \cos x$:

- the **period** is 2π
- the **amplitude** is 1
- the **principal axis** is the line $y = 0$.

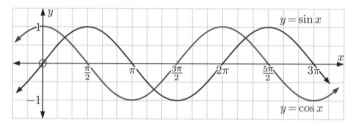

We immediately notice that $y = \sin x$ is a horizontal translation of $y = \cos x$ by $\frac{\pi}{2}$ units to the right.

$$\text{For all } x, \quad \sin x = \cos\left(x - \tfrac{\pi}{2}\right)$$
$$\text{and} \quad \cos x = \sin\left(x + \tfrac{\pi}{2}\right)$$

INVESTIGATION   FAMILIES OF TRIGONOMETRIC FUNCTIONS

What to do:

GRAPHING PACKAGE

1 **a** Use the graphing package to graph on the same set of axes:

  i $y = \sin x$ **ii** $y = 2\sin x$ **iii** $y = \frac{1}{2}\sin x$

  iv $y = -\sin x$ **v** $y = -\frac{1}{3}\sin x$ **vi** $y = -\frac{3}{2}\sin x$

  b For graphs of the form $y = a\sin x$, comment on the significance of:

  i the sign of a **ii** the size of a, or $|a|$.

2 **a** Use the graphing package to graph on the same set of axes:

  i $y = \sin x$ **ii** $y = \sin 2x$ **iii** $y = \sin\left(\frac{1}{2}x\right)$ **iv** $y = \sin 3x$

  b For graphs of the form $y = \sin bx$, $b > 0$, what is the period?

3 **a** Graph on the same set of axes:

  i $y = \sin x$ **ii** $y = \sin\left(x - \frac{\pi}{3}\right)$ **iii** $y = \sin\left(x + \frac{\pi}{6}\right)$

  b What translation moves $y = \sin x$ to $y = \sin(x - c)$?

4 **a** Graph on the same set of axes:

  i $y = \sin x$ **ii** $y = \sin x + 2$ **iii** $y = \sin x - 2$

  b What translation moves $y = \sin x$ to $y = \sin x + d$?

  c What is the principal axis of $y = \sin x + d$?

5 What sequence of transformations maps $y = \sin x$ onto $y = a\sin b(x - c) + d$?

From the **Investigation** you should have observed the following properties of the general sine function:

For the **general sine function**

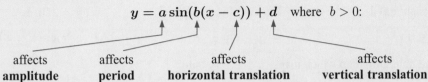

$$y = a\sin(b(x - c)) + d \quad \text{where } b > 0:$$

affects **amplitude**   affects **period**   affects **horizontal translation**   affects **vertical translation**

- the amplitude is $|a|$
- the period is $\dfrac{2\pi}{b}$
- the principal axis is $y = d$
- $y = a\sin(b(x - c)) + d$ is obtained from $y = \sin x$ by a vertical stretch with scale factor $|a|$ and a horizontal stretch with scale factor $\dfrac{1}{b}$, a reflection in the x-axis if $a < 0$, and a translation through $\begin{pmatrix} c \\ d \end{pmatrix}$.

The properties of the **general cosine function** $y = a\cos(b(x - c)) + d$ are the same as those of the general sine function.

DEMO

Example 1   ◆) **Self Tutor**

Sketch the graphs of the following on $0 \leqslant x \leqslant 2\pi$:

a $y = \sin\left(x - \frac{\pi}{3}\right)$ **b** $y = \cos 3x$ **c** $y = \cos\left(x + \frac{\pi}{6}\right) + 1$ **d** $y = -\sin x$

a We translate $y = \sin x$ horizontally $\frac{\pi}{3}$ units to the right.

b We stretch $y = \cos x$ horizontally with scale factor $\frac{1}{3}$.

$\therefore \; y = \cos 3x$ has period $\frac{2\pi}{3}$.

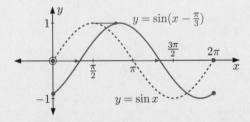

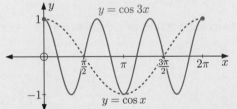

c We translate $y = \cos x$ horizontally $\frac{\pi}{6}$ units to the left, and 1 unit upwards.

d We reflect $y = \sin x$ in the x-axis.

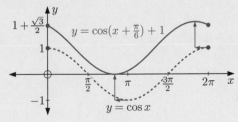

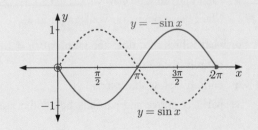

EXERCISE 8C

1 State the transformation which maps $y = \sin x$ onto:

   a $y = \sin x - 1$ **b** $y = \sin\left(x - \frac{\pi}{4}\right)$ **c** $y = 2\sin x$

   d $y = \sin 4x$ **e** $y = \sin\frac{x}{4}$ **f** $y = \sin\left(x - \frac{\pi}{3}\right) + 2$

2 State the transformation which maps $y = \cos x$ onto:

   a $y = \frac{1}{2}\cos x$ **b** $y = -\cos x$ **c** $y = \cos\left(x + \frac{\pi}{6}\right) - 2$

3 State the period of:

   a $y = \sin 5x$ **b** $y = \sin(0.6x)$ **c** $y = \sin \pi x$

   d $y = \cos 3x$ **e** $y = \cos\frac{x}{3}$ **f** $y = \cos\frac{\pi x}{50}$

4 Find b given that the function $y = \sin bx$, $b > 0$ has period:

   a 5π **b** $\frac{2\pi}{3}$ **c** 12π **d** 4 **e** 100

5 State the maximum and minimum value of:

   a $y = 4\cos 2x$ **b** $y = 3\cos x + 5$ **c** $y = -2\cos(x - 3) - 4$

6 For the function $y = 4\sin 3x + 2$, state the:

   a amplitude   **b** period   **c** range.

7 The general cosine function is $y = a\cos(b(x - c)) + d$.
   State the geometrical significance of a, b, c, and d.

8 Sketch the graphs of the following for $0 \leqslant x \leqslant 4\pi$:

   a $y = \sin x - 2$ **b** $y = \sin x + 3$ **c** $y = \sin x - 0.5$

   d $y = \sin(x - 2)$ **e** $y = \sin(x + 2)$ **f** $y = \sin\left(x - \frac{\pi}{4}\right)$

   g $y = \sin\left(x - \frac{\pi}{6}\right) + 1$ **h** $y = \sin(x - 1) - 2$ **i** $y = \sin\left(x + \frac{\pi}{4}\right) + 2$

   j $y = 3\sin x$ **k** $y = \frac{1}{2}\sin x$ **l** $y = \frac{3}{2}\sin x$

   m $y = \sin 3x$ **n** $y = \sin\frac{x}{2}$ **o** $y = \sin 4x$

9 Sketch the graphs of the following for $-2\pi \leqslant x \leqslant 2\pi$:

   a $y = \cos x + 2$ **b** $y = \cos\left(x - \frac{\pi}{4}\right)$ **c** $y = \cos\left(x + \frac{\pi}{6}\right)$

   d $y = \frac{3}{2}\cos x$ **e** $y = -\cos x$ **f** $y = \cos\left(x - \frac{\pi}{6}\right) + 1$

   g $y = \cos\left(x + \frac{\pi}{4}\right) - 1$ **h** $y = \cos 2x$ **i** $y = \cos\frac{x}{2}$

10   **a** Sketch the curve $y = 4\sin x$ for $0 \leqslant x \leqslant 2\pi$.

      b Find the value of y when: **i** $x = \frac{5\pi}{6}$ **ii** $x = \frac{7\pi}{4}$

        Mark these points on your graph in **a**.

11 For what values of d does the graph of $y = 3\cos x + d$ lie:

   a entirely above the x-axis

   b entirely below the x-axis

   c partially above and partially below the x-axis?

Example 2   ◄୬ **Self Tutor**

Sketch the graph of $y = 3\cos 2x$ for $0 \leqslant x \leqslant 2\pi$.

$a = 3$, so the amplitude is $|3| = 3$.

$b = 2$, so the period is $\dfrac{2\pi}{b} = \dfrac{2\pi}{2} = \pi$.

We stretch $y = \cos x$ vertically with scale factor 3 to give $y = 3\cos x$, then stretch $y = 3\cos x$ horizontally with scale factor $\frac{1}{2}$ to give $y = 3\cos 2x$.

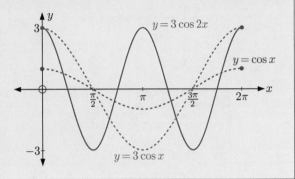

12 State the transformations which map:

    a $y = \sin x$ onto $y = 2\sin 3x$
    b $y = \cos x$ onto $y = -2\cos x$

    c $y = \sin x$ onto $y = 3\sin x - 5$
    d $y = \cos x$ onto $y = \cos\left(2\left(x + \frac{\pi}{6}\right)\right)$

13 Sketch the graphs of the following for $-2\pi \leqslant x \leqslant 2\pi$:

    a $y = -3\sin x$
    b $y = \cos 2x + 1$
    c $y = \frac{1}{2}\sin\left(x + \frac{\pi}{6}\right) - \frac{1}{3}$

    d $y = \frac{1}{3}\cos\left(x + \frac{\pi}{4}\right) + 1$
    e $y = 3\sin\left(x - \frac{\pi}{3}\right) - 1$
    f $y = -\cos\left(\frac{1}{2}\left(x - \frac{\pi}{4}\right)\right)$

14 Consider the general sine function $y = a\sin(b(x - c)) + d$, with default values $a, b = 1$, $c, d = 0$. State which of the variables a, b, c, and d can be changed to produce a change in:

    a the x-intercepts of the function
    b the y-intercept of the function

    c the range of the function.

Example 3   ◄୬ **Self Tutor**

Find the unknowns in this function:

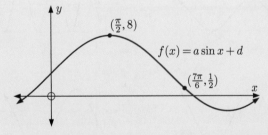

$f\left(\frac{\pi}{2}\right) = 8$, so $\quad a\sin\frac{\pi}{2} + d = 8$ $f\left(\frac{7\pi}{6}\right) = \frac{1}{2}$, so $\quad a\sin\frac{7\pi}{6} + d = \frac{1}{2}$

$\therefore\ a + d = 8$ .... (1) $\therefore\ -\frac{1}{2}a + d = \frac{1}{2}$ .... (2)

So, we have $a + d = 8 \quad \{(1)\}$

$\underline{\quad\quad\quad\ -a + 2d = 1 \quad \{2 \times (2)\}}$

Adding, $3d = 9$ and so $d = 3$

Substituting $d = 3$ into (1) gives $a + 3 = 8$

$\therefore\ a = 5$

15 Find the unknowns in each function:

a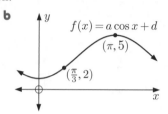

b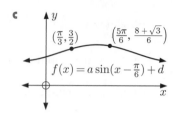

c

Example 4   ◀️) **Self Tutor**

Find the equation of this sine function.

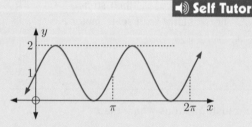

The amplitude is 1, so $a = 1$.

The period is π, so $\dfrac{2\pi}{b} = \pi$ and $\therefore\ b = 2$.

There is no horizontal translation, so $c = 0$.

The principal axis is $y = 1$, so $d = 1$.

The equation of the function is $y = \sin 2x + 1$.

---

16 Find the equation of each sine function:

a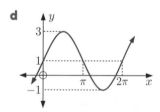

b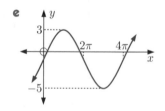

c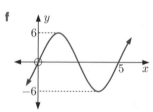

d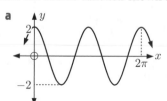

e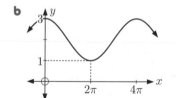

f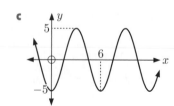

17 Find the cosine function shown in the graph:

a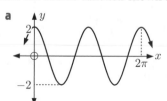

b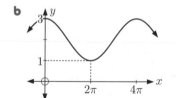

c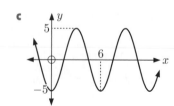

D   MODELLING PERIODIC BEHAVIOUR

The sine and cosine functions are both referred to as **sinusoidal functions**. They can be used to model many periodic phenomena in the real world. In some cases, such as the movement of the hands on a clock, the models we find will be almost exact. In other cases, such as the maximum daily temperature of a city over a year, the model will be less accurate.

Example 5   ◀) **Self Tutor**

The average daytime temperature for a city is given by the function $D(t) = 5\cos\left(\frac{\pi}{6}t\right) + 20$ °C, where t is the time in months after January.

  a Sketch the graph of D against t for $0 \leqslant t \leqslant 24$.

  b Find the average daytime temperature during May.

  c Find the minimum average daytime temperature, and the month in which it occurs.

---

  a For $D(t) = 5\cos\left(\frac{\pi}{6}t\right) + 20$:

     • the amplitude is 5

     • the period is $\dfrac{2\pi}{\left(\frac{\pi}{6}\right)} = 12$ months

     • the principal axis is $D = 20$.

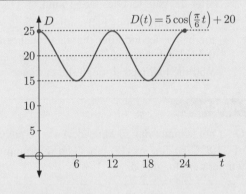

  b May is 4 months after January.

    When $t = 4$, $D = 5 \times \cos\frac{4\pi}{6} + 20$

                 $= 5 \times \left(-\frac{1}{2}\right) + 20$

                 $= 17.5$

    So, the average daytime temperature during May is 17.5°C.

  c The minimum average daytime temperature is $20 - 5 = 15$°C, which occurs when $t = 6$ or 18.

    So, the minimum average daytime temperature occurs during July.

EXERCISE 8D.1

1 The temperature inside Vanessa's house t hours after midday is given by the function
$T(t) = 6\sin\left(\frac{\pi}{12}t\right) + 26$ °C.

  a Sketch the graph of T against t for $0 \leqslant t \leqslant 24$.

  b Find the temperature inside Vanessa's house at:

    i midnight   **ii** 2 pm.

  c Find the maximum temperature inside Vanessa's house, and the time at which it occurs.

2 The depth of water in a harbour t hours after midnight is $D(t) = 4\cos\left(\frac{\pi}{6}t\right) + 6$ metres.

  a Sketch the graph of D against t for $0 \leqslant t \leqslant 24$.

  b Find the highest and lowest depths of the water, and the times at which they occur.

  c A boat requires a water depth of 5 metres to sail in. Will the boat be able to sail in the harbour at 8 pm?

3 The tip of a clock's minute hand is $H(t) = 15\cos\left(\frac{\pi}{30}t\right) + 150$ cm above ground level, where t is the time in minutes after 5 pm.

a Sketch the graph of H against t for $0 \leqslant t \leqslant 180$.

b Find the length of the minute hand.

c Find, rounded to 1 decimal place, the height of the minute hand's tip at:

  i 5:08 pm   **ii** 5:37 pm   **iii** 5:51 pm   **iv** 6:23 pm

4 On a mini-golf hole, golfers must putt the ball through a castle's entrance. The entrance is protected by a gate which moves up and down.

The height of the gate above the ground t seconds after it touches the ground is $H(t) = 4\sin\left(\frac{\pi}{4}(t-2)\right) + 4$ cm.

a Sketch the graph of H against t for $0 \leqslant t \leqslant 16$.

b Find the height of the gate above the ground 2 seconds after the gate touches the ground.

c Eric is using a golf ball with radius 2.14 cm. He putts the ball 1 second after the gate touches the ground, and the ball takes 5.3 seconds to reach the castle's entrance. Will the ball pass through the entrance?

Example 6   ◀》 **Self Tutor**

On a hot summer day in Madrid, Antonio pays careful attention to the temperature. The maximum of 41.8°C occurs at 3:30 pm. The minimum was 27.5°C. Suggest a sine function to model the temperature for that day.

The mean temperature $= \dfrac{41.8 + 27.5}{2} = 34.65°C$, so $d = 34.65$.

The amplitude $= \dfrac{41.8 - 27.5}{2} = 7.15°C$

$$\therefore \ a = 7.15$$

The period is 24 hours, so $b = \frac{2\pi}{24} = \frac{\pi}{12}$.

The maximum occurs at 3:30 pm, so we assume the temperature passed its mean value 6 hours earlier, at 9:30 am.

The day begins at midnight, so the function is shifted $9\frac{1}{2}$ hours to the right, thus $c = 9.5$.

If t is the number of hours after midnight, the temperature T is modelled by

$$T(t) = 7.15\sin\left(\frac{\pi}{12}(t - 9.5)\right) + 34.65 \ °C.$$

---

5 On a September day in Moscow, the maximum temperature 15.8°C occurred at 2 pm. The minimum was 5.4°C. Suggest a sine function to model the temperature for that day. Let T be the temperature and t be the time in hours after midnight.

6 The ferry operator at Picton, New Zealand, is studying the tides. High tides occur every 12.4 hours. The first high tide tomorrow will be at 1:30 am. The high tide will be 1.36 m and the low tide will be 0.16 m. Find a cosine function to model the tide height for the day. Let H be the tide height and t be the time in hours after midnight.

7 Answer the **Opening Problem** on page **200**.

8 Some of the largest tides in the world are observed in Canada's Bay of Fundy. The difference between high and low tides is 14 metres, and the average time difference between high tides is about 12.4 hours. On a particular day, the first high tide is 16.2 m, occurring at 9 am.

    a Find a sine model for the height of the tide H in terms of the time t.

    b Sketch the graph of the function for that day.

9 On an analogue clock, the hour hand is 6 cm long and the minute hand is 12 cm long. Let t be the time in hours after midnight.

    a Write a cosine function for the height of the tip of the hour hand relative to the centre of the clock.

    b Write a sine function for the horizontal displacement of the tip of the minute hand relative to the centre of the clock.

FITTING TRIGONOMETRIC MODELS TO DATA

Suppose we have **data** in which we observe periodic behavior. In such cases, we usually cannot fit an *exact* model. However, we can still apply the same principles to estimate the period, amplitude, and principal axis from the data.

You can check your models using your graphics calculator. Click on this icon for instructions.

GRAPHICS
CALCULATOR
INSTRUCTIONS

Example 7

◀》 **Self Tutor**

The mean monthly maximum temperatures for Cape Town, South Africa are shown below:

Month (t)	Jan	Feb	Mar	Apr	May	Jun	Jul	Aug	Sep	Oct	Nov	Dec
Temperature (T °C)	28	27	25.5	22	18.5	16	15	16	18	21.5	24	26

We want to model the data with a trigonometric function of the form $T = a\sin(b(t - c)) + d$ where Jan $\equiv 1$, Feb $\equiv 2$, and so on.

    a Draw a scatter diagram of the data.

    b Without using technology, estimate:

        i b **ii** a **iii** d **iv** c

    c Check your answers using technology.

a

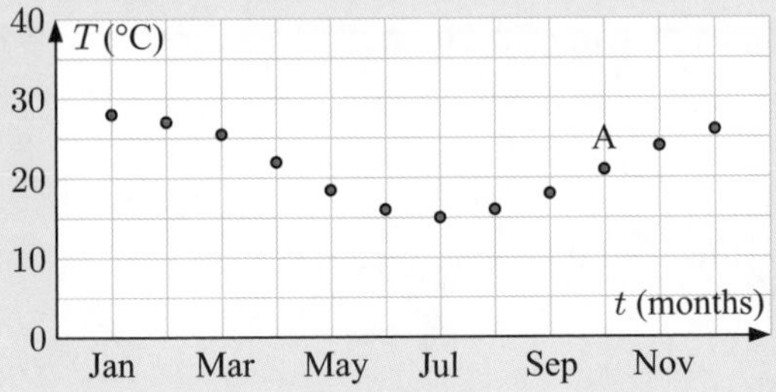

(scatter diagram: T (°C) on vertical axis from 0 to 40, t (months) on horizontal axis labelled Jan, Mar, May, Jul, Sep, Nov; point A marked near Sep)

b **i** The period is 12 months, so $\frac{2\pi}{b} = 12$ and $\therefore$ $b = \frac{\pi}{6}$.

   ii The amplitude $= \frac{\max - \min}{2} \approx \frac{28 - 15}{2} \approx 6.5$, so $a \approx 6.5$.

   iii The principal axis is midway between the maximum and minimum, so

$$d \approx \frac{28 + 15}{2} \approx 21.5.$$

   iv The model is $T \approx 6.5\sin\left(\frac{\pi}{6}(t - c)\right) + 21.5$ for some constant c.
On the original graph, point A is the first point shown at which the sine function starts a new period. Since A is at $(10, 21.5)$, $c = 10$.

c From **b**, our model is $T \approx 6.5\sin\left(\frac{\pi}{6}(t - 10)\right) + 21.5$

$$\approx 6.5\sin(0.524t - 5.24) + 21.5$$

Using technology,

$T \approx 6.29\sin(0.525t + 0.967) + 21.4$

$\approx 6.29\sin(0.525t + 0.967 - 2\pi) + 21.4$

$\approx 6.29\sin(0.525t - 5.32) + 21.4$

$\sin(x + 2k\pi) = \sin x$ for all $k \in \mathbb{Z}$.

EXERCISE 8D.2

1 Below is a table which shows the mean monthly maximum temperatures for a city in Greece.

Month	Jan	Feb	Mar	Apr	May	Jun	July	Aug	Sept	Oct	Nov	Dec
Temperature (°C)	15	14	15	18	21	25	27	26	24	20	18	16

  a Draw a scatter diagram of the data.

  b What features of the data suggest a trigonometric model is appropriate?

  c Your task is to model the data with a sine function of the form $T \approx a\sin(b(t - c)) + d$, where Jan $\equiv 1$, Feb $\equiv 2$, and so on.
Without using technology, estimate:

    i b **ii** a **iii** d **iv** c

  d Use technology to check your model. How well does your model fit?

2 The data in the table shows the mean monthly temperatures for Christchurch, New Zealand.

Month	Jan	Feb	Mar	Apr	May	Jun	July	Aug	Sept	Oct	Nov	Dec
Temperature (°C)	15	16	$14\frac{1}{2}$	12	10	$7\frac{1}{2}$	7	$7\frac{1}{2}$	$8\frac{1}{2}$	$10\frac{1}{2}$	$12\frac{1}{2}$	14

a Find a cosine model for this data in the form $T \approx a\cos(b(t-c))+d$ without using technology. Let Jan $\equiv 1$, Feb $\equiv 2$, and so on.

$$\sin x = \cos\left(x - \tfrac{\pi}{2}\right)$$

b Draw a scatter diagram of the data and sketch the graph of your model on the same set of axes.

c Use technology to check your answer to **a**.

3 At the Mawson base in Antarctica, the mean monthly temperatures for the last 30 years are:

Month	Jan	Feb	Mar	Apr	May	Jun	July	Aug	Sept	Oct	Nov	Dec
Temperature (°C)	0	0	−4	−9	−14	−17	−18	−19	−17	−13	−6	−2

a Find a sine model for this data without using technology. Use Jan $\equiv 1$, Feb $\equiv 2$, and so on.

b Draw a scatter diagram of the data and sketch the graph of your model on the same set of axes.

c How appropriate is the model?

4 An object is suspended from a spring. If the object is pulled below its resting position and then released, it will oscillate up and down. The data below shows the height of the object relative to its rest position, at different times.

Time (t seconds)	0	0.1	0.2	0.3	0.4	0.5	0.6	0.7	0.8	0.9
Height (H cm)	−15	−13	−7.5	0	7.5	13	15	13	7.5	0

Time (t seconds)	1	1.1	1.2	1.3	1.4	1.5	1.6	1.7	1.8	1.9	2.0
Height (H cm)	−7.5	−13	−15	−13	−7.5	0	7.5	13	15	13	7.5

a Draw a scatter diagram of the data.

b Find a trigonometric function which models the height of the object over time.

c Use your model to predict the height of the object after 4.25 seconds.

d What do you think is unrealistic about this model? What would happen differently in reality?

RESEARCH

1 How accurately will a trigonometric function model the phases of the moon?

2 Are there any periodic phenomena which can be modelled by the *sum* of trigonometric functions?

ACTIVITY 2   THE PENDULUM

In this Activity you will work in small groups to model the behaviour of a pendulum.

You will need: string, sticky tape, a ruler, a stopwatch, and a AA battery.

What to do:

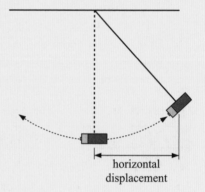

1 Cut a piece of string of length 75 cm. Attach one end of the string to the battery, and the other end to your desk.

2 Hold the battery to one side, then release it, causing the battery to swing back and forth like a pendulum.

3 Using your stopwatch and ruler, measure the maximum and minimum horizontal displacement reached by the battery, and the times at which they occurred. You may need to repeat the experiment several times, but make sure the battery is released from the same position each time.

4 Use your data to find a trigonometric function which models the horizontal displacement of the battery over time.

5 What part of the function affects the *period* of the pendulum?

6 Repeat the experiment with strings of different length. Explore the relationship between the length of the string and the period of the pendulum.

E   THE TANGENT FUNCTION

We have seen that if $P(\cos\theta,\ \sin\theta)$ is a point which is free to move around the unit circle, and if [OP] is extended to meet the tangent at $A(1, 0)$, the intersection between these lines occurs at $Q(1, \tan\theta)$.

This enables us to define the **tangent function**

$$\tan\theta = \frac{\sin\theta}{\cos\theta}.$$

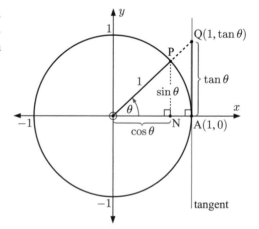

We have also seen that $\tan\theta$ is:

- positive in quadrants 1 and 3
- negative in quadrants 2 and 4
- periodic with period π.

DISCUSSION

What happens to $\tan\theta$ when P is at:

a $(1, 0)$ and $(-1, 0)$

b $(0, 1)$ and $(0, -1)$?

THE GRAPH OF $y = \tan x$

$\tan x$ is zero whenever $\sin x = 0$, so the **zeros** of $y = \tan x$ are $k\pi$, $k \in \mathbb{Z}$.

$\tan x$ is undefined whenever $\cos x = 0$, so the **vertical asymptotes** of $y = \tan x$ are $x = \frac{\pi}{2} + k\pi$ for all $k \in \mathbb{Z}$.

$\tan x$ has period $= \pi$ and range $y \in \mathbb{R}$.

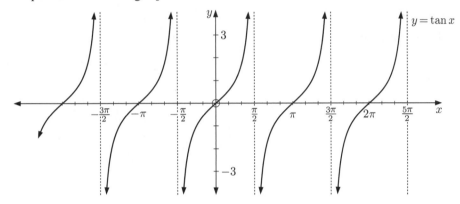

Click on the icon to explore how the tangent function is produced from the unit circle.   **TANGENT FUNCTION**

THE GENERAL TANGENT FUNCTION

The **general tangent function** is $y = a\tan(b(x - c)) + d$, $a \neq 0$, $b > 0$.

- The **principal axis** is $y = d$.
- The **period** of this function is $\frac{\pi}{b}$.   **DYNAMIC TANGENT FUNCTION**
- The **amplitude** of this function is undefined.
- There are infinitely many vertical asymptotes.

Example 8   ◀)) **Self Tutor**

Without using technology, sketch the graph of $y = \tan\left(x + \frac{\pi}{4}\right)$ for $0 \leqslant x \leqslant 3\pi$.

$y = \tan\left(x + \frac{\pi}{4}\right)$ is a horizontal translation of $y = \tan x$ to the left by $\frac{\pi}{4}$ units.

$y = \tan x$ has vertical asymptotes $x = \frac{\pi}{2}$, $x = \frac{3\pi}{2}$, $x = \frac{5\pi}{2}$, and its x-intercepts are 0, π, 2π, and 3π.

$\therefore$ $y = \tan\left(x + \frac{\pi}{4}\right)$ has vertical asymptotes $x = \frac{\pi}{4}$, $x = \frac{5\pi}{4}$, $x = \frac{9\pi}{4}$, and x-intercepts $\frac{3\pi}{4}$, $\frac{7\pi}{4}$, and $\frac{11\pi}{4}$.

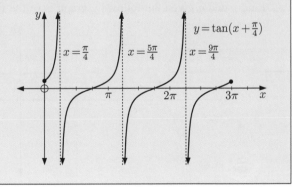

Example 9   ◀)) **Self Tutor**

Without using technology, sketch the graph of $y = \tan 2x$ for $-\pi \leqslant x \leqslant \pi$.

$y = \tan 2x$ is a horizontal stretch
of $y = \tan x$ with scale factor $\frac{1}{2}$.

Since $b = 2$, the period is $\frac{\pi}{2}$.

$y = \tan 2x$ has vertical asymptotes
$x = \pm\frac{\pi}{4}$, $x = \pm\frac{3\pi}{4}$, and
x-intercepts 0, $\pm\frac{\pi}{2}$, $\pm\pi$.

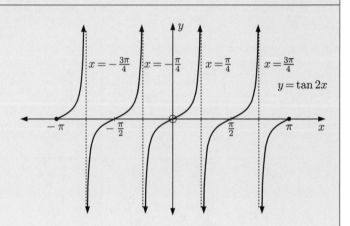

EXERCISE 8E

1   State the transformations which map $y = \tan x$ onto:

   a $y = \tan\left(x - \frac{\pi}{2}\right)$ **b** $y = 4\tan x$ **c** $y = \tan\left(\frac{\pi}{2}x\right)$

   d $y = \tan 2x - 1$ **e** $y = -\frac{1}{2}\tan x$ **f** $y = \tan(x + \pi) + 2$

2   State the period of:

   a $y = \tan 3x$ **b** $y = \tan\frac{x}{4}$ **c** $y = \tan \pi x$

   d $y = -\tan\left(\frac{\pi}{2}x\right)$ **e** $y = \tan\left(\frac{2x}{3} - \frac{\pi}{3}\right)$ **f** $y = \tan nx, \ n \neq 0$

3   For each function, write down the:

   i zeros   **ii** vertical asymptotes.

   a $y = \tan 2x$ **b** $y = \tan\left(x + \frac{\pi}{3}\right)$ **c** $y = \frac{1}{2}\tan\left(\frac{1}{2}\left(x - \frac{\pi}{6}\right)\right)$

4   Sketch the graph of the following for $-2\pi \leqslant x \leqslant 2\pi$:

   a $y = \tan\left(x - \frac{\pi}{4}\right)$ **b** $y = \frac{1}{2}\tan\frac{x}{4}$ **c** $y = 3\tan\left(x - \frac{\pi}{9}\right)$

5   Find p and q given the following graph is of the function $y = \tan pt + q$.

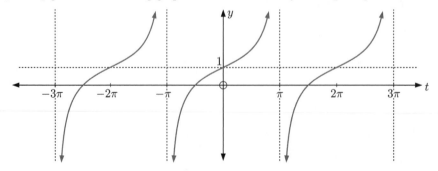

6 Find the possible values of a and b given the following graph is of the function $y = \tan a(x - b)$.

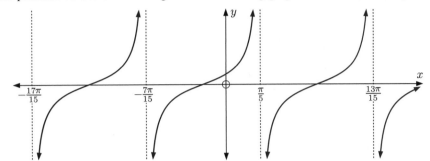

7 **a** Describe the sequence of transformations used to transform $y = \tan x$ into $y = 2\tan\left(x + \frac{\pi}{4}\right) - 1$.

  b Sketch $y = 2\tan\left(x + \frac{\pi}{4}\right) - 1$ for $-2\pi \leqslant x \leqslant 2\pi$.

8 Consider the functions $f(x) = \tan x$ and $g(x) = 2x - \frac{\pi}{2}$.

  a Find:

  i $(f \circ g)(x)$ **ii** $(g \circ f)(x)$

  b Find the value of:

  i $(f \circ g)\left(\frac{\pi}{3}\right)$ **ii** $(g \circ f)(\pi)$

  c Write down the period and vertical asymptotes of:

  i $(f \circ g)(x)$ **ii** $(g \circ f)(x)$

  d Sketch the graphs of $(f \circ g)(x)$ and $(g \circ f)(x)$ for $-2\pi \leqslant x \leqslant 2\pi$.

ACTIVITY 3

Click on the icon to run a card game for trigonometric functions.

CARD GAME

REVIEW SET 8A

1 Which of the following graphs display periodic behaviour?

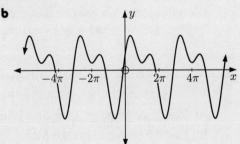

2 State the minimum and maximum values of:

  a $1 + \sin x$ **b** $-2\cos 3x$

3 State the period of:

    a $y = 4\sin\frac{x}{5}$ **b** $y = -2\cos 4x$ **c** $y = 4\cos\frac{x}{2} + 4$ **d** $y = \frac{1}{2}\tan 3x$

4 Copy and complete:

Function	Period	Amplitude	Range
$y = -3\sin\frac{x}{4} + 1$			
$y = 3\cos \pi x$			

5   **a** Draw the graph of $y = \cos 3x$ for $0 \leqslant x \leqslant 2\pi$.

    b Find the value of y when $x = \frac{3\pi}{4}$. Mark this point on your graph.

6 Sketch the graphs of the following for $-2\pi \leqslant x \leqslant 2\pi$:

    a $y = 4\sin x$ **b** $y = \sin\left(x - \frac{\pi}{3}\right) + 2$ **c** $y = \sin\frac{3x}{2}$

    d $y = \cos\left(x + \frac{\pi}{4}\right)$ **e** $y = \frac{3}{4}\cos x$ **f** $y = \cos 4x$

7 State the transformations which map:

    a $y = \sin x$ onto $y = 3\sin 2x$ **b** $y = \cos x$ onto $y = \cos\left(x - \frac{\pi}{3}\right) - 1$

8 Find the cosine function represented in each of the following graphs:

    a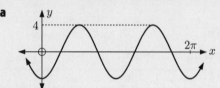   **b**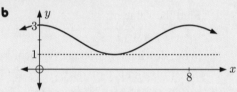

9 Sketch for $0 \leqslant x \leqslant 4\pi$:

    a $y = \tan\frac{x}{4}$ **b** $y = \frac{1}{4}\tan\frac{x}{2}$

10   **a** Describe the sequence of transformations which maps $y = \tan x$ onto $y = \tan 3x + 2$.

    b State the period of $y = \tan 3x + 2$.

    c Sketch $y = \tan 3x + 2$ for $-\pi \leqslant x \leqslant \pi$.

11 The graph of $f(x) = a\sin(b(x - c)) + d$ is shown alongside.

    a Find the values of a, b, c, and d.

    b The function $g(x)$ is obtained by translating $f(x)$ 2 units right and 3 units down, followed by a vertical stretch with scale factor 2. Find $g(x)$ in the form $g(x) = p\sin(q(x-r)) + s$.

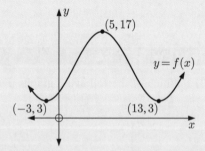

12 The proportion of the Moon which is illuminated each night is given by the function $M(t) = \frac{1}{2}\cos\left(\frac{\pi}{15}t\right) + \frac{1}{2}$, where t is the time in days after January 1st.

    a Sketch the graph of M against t for $0 \leqslant t \leqslant 60$.

    b Find the proportion of the Moon which is illuminated on the night of:

        i January 6th   **ii** January 21st   **iii** January 27th   **iv** February 19th.

    c How often does a full moon occur?

    d On what dates during January and February is the Moon not illuminated at all?

13   On an April day in Kyoto, the maximum temperature $14.1°C$ occurred at 2:30 pm. The minimum was $6.7°C$.

    a   Suggest a sine function to model the temperature for that day. Let T be the temperature and t be the time in hours after midnight.

    b   Graph $T(t)$ for $0 \leqslant t \leqslant 24$.

14   A robot on Mars records the temperature every Mars day. A summary series, showing every one hundredth Mars day, is shown in the table below.

Number of Mars days (n)	0	100	200	300	400	500	600	700	800	900	1000	1100	1200	1300
Temp. (°C)	-43	-15	-5	-21	-59	-79	-68	-50	-27	-8	-15	-70	-78	-68

    a   Find the maximum and minimum temperatures recorded by the robot.

    b   Use the data to estimate the length of a Mars year.

    c   Without using technology, find a sine model for the temperature T in terms of the number of Mars days n.

    d   Draw a scatter diagram of the data and sketch the graph of your model on the same set of axes.

    e   Check your answer to **c** using technology. How well does your model fit?

REVIEW SET 8B

1   Consider the graph alongside.

    a   Explain why this graph shows periodic behaviour.

    b   State:

       i   the period

       ii   the maximum value

       iii   the minimum value.

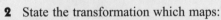

2   State the transformation which maps:

    a $y = \cos x$ onto $y = \cos\left(x + \frac{\pi}{4}\right) + 1$ **b** $y = \sin x$ onto $y = \sin 3x$

3   State the period of:

    a $y = 4\sin\frac{x}{3}$ **b** $y = \tan 4x$

4   Find b given that the function $y = \sin bx$, $b > 0$ has period: **a** 6π **b** $\frac{\pi}{12}$ **c** 9

5   State the minimum and maximum values of:

    a $y = 5\sin x - 3$ **b** $y = \frac{1}{3}\cos x + 1$

6   Find the principal axis of:

    a $y = -\frac{1}{3}\sin\left(x - \frac{\pi}{4}\right) + 5$ **b** $y = 2\cos\frac{x}{3} - 4$

7   Sketch the graphs of the following for $0 \leqslant x \leqslant 2\pi$:

    a $y = 2\cos 3x$ **b** $y = 2\sin\left(x - \frac{\pi}{3}\right) + 3$ **c** $y = -\cos\left(x + \frac{\pi}{4}\right)$

    d $y = 2\sin x - \frac{1}{2}$ **e** $y = \frac{3}{2}\tan\left(x - \frac{\pi}{6}\right)$ **f** $y = 2\tan\frac{x}{2}$

8 **a** Find the sine function shown in this graph.

   b Write down the equivalent cosine function for this graph.

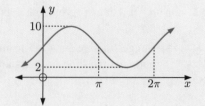

9 Draw the graph of $y = 0.6\cos(2.3x)$ for $0 \leqslant x \leqslant 5$.

10 Find a and b given the graph of $y = \tan ax + b$ shown.

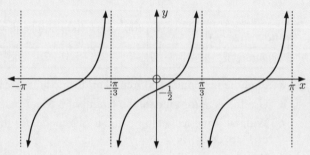

11 State the transformations which map:

   a $y = \tan x$ onto $y = -\tan 2x$

   b $y = \sin x$ onto $y = 2\sin\left(\frac{1}{2}\left(x - \frac{\pi}{2}\right)\right) + \frac{1}{2}$

12 As the tip of a windmill's blade rotates, its height above ground is given by $H(t) = 10\cos\left(\frac{\pi}{6}t\right) + 20$ metres, where t is the time in seconds.

   a Sketch the graph of H against t for $0 \leqslant t \leqslant 36$.

   b Find the height of the blade's tip after 9 seconds.

   c Find the minimum height of the blade's tip.

   d How long does the blade take to complete a full revolution?

13 A steamroller has a spot of paint on its roller. As the steamroller moves, the spot rotates around the axle. The roller has radius 1 metre and completes one full revolution every 2 seconds.

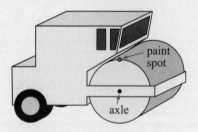

   a What does the graph of the spot's height over time look like?

   b What function gives the height of the paint spot over time?

14 The table below gives the mean monthly maximum temperature for Perth Airport in Australia.

Month (t)	Jan	Feb	Mar	Apr	May	Jun	Jul	Aug	Sep	Oct	Nov	Dec
Temperature (°C)	31.5	31.8	29.5	25.4	21.5	18.8	17.7	18.3	20.1	22.4	25.5	28.8

   a A sine function of the form $T \approx a\sin(b(t-c)) + d$ is used to model the data. Find good estimates of the constants a, b, c, and d without using technology. Use Jan $\equiv 1$, Feb $\equiv 2$, and so on.

   b Draw a scatter diagram of the data and the graph of your model on the same set of axes.

   c Check your answer to **a** using technology. How well does your model fit?

Chapter 9

Trigonometric equations and identities

Contents:

OPENING PROBLEM

Andrew is watching a Ferris wheel rotate at constant speed. There are many lights around the Ferris wheel, and Andrew watches a green light closely. The height of the green light after t seconds is given by $H(t) = 10\sin\left(\frac{\pi}{50}t\right) + 12$ metres.

Things to think about:

a At what height is the green light:
   i initially   ii after 75 seconds?
b How long does it take for the wheel to complete a full circle?
c At what times in the first three minutes is the green light 16 metres above the ground?

In this Chapter we will consider:

• **equations** involving trigonometric functions and methods for their solution
• **identities** which connect trigonometric ratios, and which are true for *all* angles.

We will see how trigonometric identities can be used to help solve more complicated equations.

A   TRIGONOMETRIC EQUATIONS

Trigonometric equations will often have infinitely many solutions unless a restricted domain such as $0 \leqslant x \leqslant 3\pi$ is given.

For example, in the **Opening Problem**, the green light will be 16 metres above the ground when $10\sin\left(\frac{\pi}{50}t\right) + 12 = 16$ metres.

This is a trigonometric equation, and it has infinitely many solutions provided the wheel keeps rotating. For this reason we would normally specify a time interval for the solution. For example, if we are interested in the first three minutes of its rotation, we specify the domain $0 \leqslant t \leqslant 180$.

We will examine solving trigonometric equations using:

• pre-prepared graphs   • technology   • algebra.

GRAPHICAL SOLUTION OF TRIGONOMETRIC EQUATIONS

If we are given a graph with sufficient accuracy, we can use it to estimate solutions.

Example 1   ◀)) Self Tutor

Solve $\cos x = 0.4$ for $0 \leqslant x \leqslant 10$ radians using the graph of $y = \cos x$.

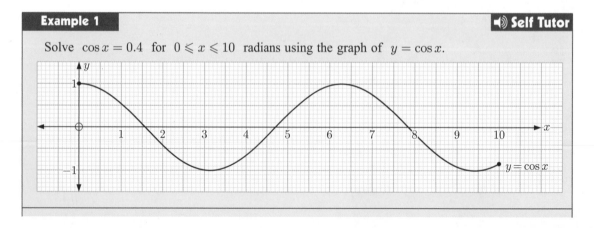

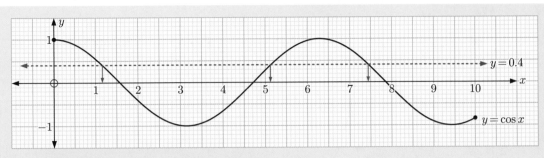

$y = 0.4$ meets $y = \cos x$ when $x \approx 1.2, 5.1,$ or 7.4.

The solutions of $\cos x = 0.4$ for $0 \leqslant x \leqslant 10$ radians are $1.2, 5.1,$ and 7.4.

EXERCISE 9A.1

1

Use the graph of $y = \sin x$ to solve, correct to 1 decimal place:

a $\sin x = 0.3$ for $0 \leqslant x \leqslant 15$

b $\sin x = -0.4$ for $5 \leqslant x \leqslant 15$

c $\sin x = 0.3$ for $0 \leqslant x \leqslant 2\pi$

d $\sin x = -0.6$ for $\pi \leqslant x \leqslant 2\pi$

2

Use the graph of $y = \cos x$ to solve, correct to 1 decimal place:

a $\cos x = 0.4$ for $0 \leqslant x \leqslant 10$

b $\cos x = -0.3$ for $4 \leqslant x \leqslant 12$

c $\cos x = 0.5$ for $\pi \leqslant x \leqslant 2\pi$

d $\cos x = -0.8$ for $\frac{\pi}{2} \leqslant x \leqslant \frac{3\pi}{2}$

3

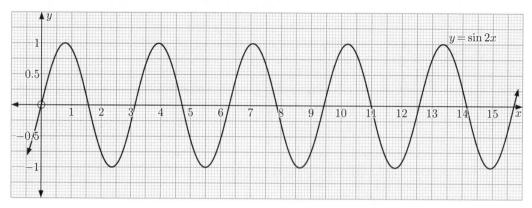

Use the graph of $y = \sin 2x$ to solve, correct to 1 decimal place:

   a $\sin 2x = 0.7$ for $0 \leqslant x \leqslant 16$ **b** $\sin 2x = -0.3$ for $0 \leqslant x \leqslant 16$

   c $\sin 2x = 0.2$ for $\pi \leqslant x \leqslant 2\pi$ **d** $\sin 2x = -0.1$ for $0 \leqslant x \leqslant 2\pi$

4

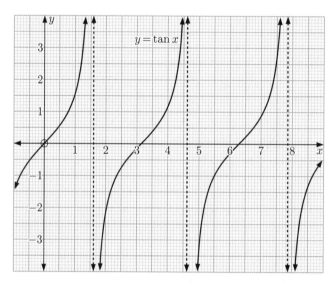

Use the graph of $y = \tan x$ to solve, correct to 1 decimal place:

   a $\tan x = 2$ for $0 \leqslant x \leqslant 8$ **b** $\tan x = -1.4$ for $2 \leqslant x \leqslant 7$

   c $\tan x = 3.5$ for $0 \leqslant x \leqslant 2\pi$ **d** $\tan x = -2.4$ for $\frac{\pi}{2} \leqslant x \leqslant \frac{3\pi}{2}$

SOLVING TRIGONOMETRIC EQUATIONS USING TECHNOLOGY

Trigonometric equations may be solved *numerically* using either a **graphing package** or a **graphics calculator**. In most cases the answers will not be exact, but rather a decimal approximation.

When using a graphics calculator, make sure that the **mode** is set to **radians**.

GRAPHING
PACKAGE

Example 2
◀)) **Self Tutor**

Solve $2\sin x - \cos x = 4 - x$ for $0 \leqslant x \leqslant 2\pi$.

We graph the functions $Y_1 = 2\sin X - \cos X$ and $Y_2 = 4 - X$ on the same set of axes.

We use **window** settings just larger than the domain:

$$X\text{min} = -\tfrac{\pi}{6} \quad X\text{max} = \tfrac{13\pi}{6} \quad X\text{scale} = \tfrac{\pi}{6}$$

GRAPHICS
CALCULATOR
INSTRUCTIONS

Casio fx-CG50	TI-84 Plus CE	TI-*n*spire
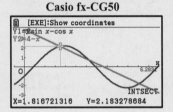	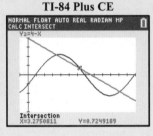	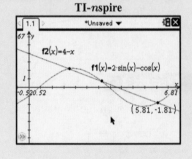

The solutions are $x \approx 1.82$, 3.28, and 5.81.

EXERCISE 9A.2

1   Solve for x on the domain $0 < x < 12$:

   a $\sin x = 0.431$ **b** $\cos x = -0.814$ **c** $3\tan x - 2 = 0$

Make sure you find *all* the solutions on the given domain.

2   Solve for x on the domain $-5 \leqslant x \leqslant 5$:

   a $5\cos x - 4 = 0$ **b** $2\tan x + 13 = 0$ **c** $8\sin x + 3 = 0$

3   Solve for $0 \leqslant x \leqslant 2\pi$:

   a $\sin(x + 2) = 0.0652$ **b** $\sin^2 x + \sin x - 1 = 0$

4   Solve for x: $\cos(x - 1) + \sin(x + 1) = 6x + 5x^2 - x^3$ for $-2 \leqslant x \leqslant 6$.

SOLVING TRIGONOMETRIC EQUATIONS USING ALGEBRA

Exact solutions obtained using algebra are called **analytic** solutions. We can find analytic solutions to *some* trigonometric equations, but only if they correspond to angles for which the trigonometric ratios can be expressed exactly.

We use the *periodicity* of the trigonometric functions to give us all solutions in the required domain. Remember that $\sin x$ and $\cos x$ both have period 2π, and $\tan x$ has period π.

When solving trigonometric equations, you must find all of the solutions in the required domain.

For an equation such as $\sin 2x = \tfrac{1}{2}$ on the domain $0 \leqslant x \leqslant 2\pi$, we need to understand that if $0 \leqslant x \leqslant 2\pi$ then $0 \leqslant 2x \leqslant 4\pi$. So, when we consider points on the unit circle with sine $\tfrac{1}{2}$, we need to consider angles from 0 to 4π.

Reminder:

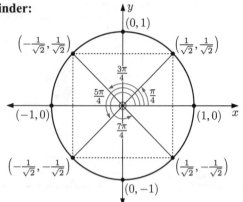 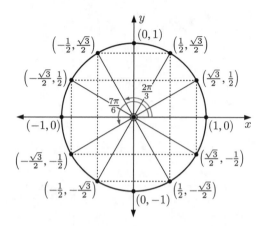

Example 3   ◀)) **Self Tutor**

Solve for x on the domain $0 \leqslant x \leqslant 2\pi$:

   a $\cos x = -\dfrac{\sqrt{3}}{2}$ **b** $2\sin x - 1 = 0$ **c** $\tan x + \sqrt{3} = 0$

---

a $\cos x = -\dfrac{\sqrt{3}}{2}$

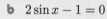

b $2\sin x - 1 = 0$

$\therefore \quad \sin x = \dfrac{1}{2}$

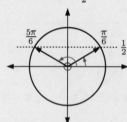

c $\tan x + \sqrt{3} = 0$

$\therefore \quad \tan x = -\sqrt{3}$

$\therefore \quad x = \dfrac{5\pi}{6}$ or $\dfrac{7\pi}{6}$ $\therefore \quad x = \dfrac{\pi}{6}$ or $\dfrac{5\pi}{6}$ $\therefore \quad x = \dfrac{2\pi}{3}$ or $\dfrac{5\pi}{3}$

EXERCISE 9A.3

1 Solve for x on the domain $0 \leqslant x \leqslant 2\pi$:

   a $\cos x = \dfrac{1}{2}$ **b** $\sin x = -\dfrac{1}{\sqrt{2}}$ **c** $\tan x = \dfrac{1}{\sqrt{3}}$

   d $\sin x = -1$ **e** $\cos x = 0$ **f** $\tan x = 0$

2 Solve for x on the domain $0 \leqslant x \leqslant 2\pi$:

   a $2\sin x = \sqrt{3}$ **b** $3\cos x + 3 = 0$ **c** $2\tan x - 2 = 0$

3 Solve for x on the domain $0 \leqslant x \leqslant 4\pi$:

   a $2\cos x + 1 = 0$ **b** $\sqrt{2}\sin x = 1$ **c** $\tan x = 1$

4 Solve for x on the domain $-2\pi \leqslant x \leqslant 2\pi$:

   a $2\sin x + \sqrt{3} = 0$ **b** $\sqrt{2}\cos x + 1 = 0$ **c** $\tan x = -1$

Example 4 ◀) **Self Tutor**

Solve $\cos^2 x = \frac{1}{2}$ on $0 \leqslant x \leqslant 2\pi$.

$\cos^2 x = \frac{1}{2}$

$\therefore \cos x = \pm \frac{1}{\sqrt{2}}$

$\therefore x = \frac{\pi}{4}, \frac{3\pi}{4}, \frac{5\pi}{4},$ or $\frac{7\pi}{4}$

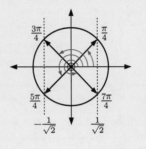

5 Solve for x on $0 \leqslant x \leqslant 2\pi$:

  a $\cos^2 x = \frac{3}{4}$ **b** $\sin^2 x = 1$ **c** $\tan^2 x = 3$

Example 5 ◀) **Self Tutor**

Solve exactly for $0 \leqslant x \leqslant 3\pi$:

  a $\sin x = -\frac{1}{2}$ **b** $\sin 2x = -\frac{1}{2}$ **c** $\sin\left(x - \frac{\pi}{6}\right) = -\frac{1}{2}$

The three equations all have the form $\sin \theta = -\frac{1}{2}$.

  a $0 \leqslant x \leqslant 3\pi$
  $\therefore x = \frac{7\pi}{6}$ or $\frac{11\pi}{6}$

  b In this case θ is $2x$.
  If $0 \leqslant x \leqslant 3\pi$ then $0 \leqslant 2x \leqslant 6\pi$.
  $\therefore 2x = \frac{7\pi}{6}, \frac{11\pi}{6}, \frac{19\pi}{6}, \frac{23\pi}{6}, \frac{31\pi}{6},$ or $\frac{35\pi}{6}$
  $\therefore x = \frac{7\pi}{12}, \frac{11\pi}{12}, \frac{19\pi}{12}, \frac{23\pi}{12}, \frac{31\pi}{12},$ or $\frac{35\pi}{12}$

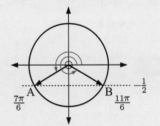

  c In this case θ is $x - \frac{\pi}{6}$.
  If $0 \leqslant x \leqslant 3\pi$ then $-\frac{\pi}{6} \leqslant x - \frac{\pi}{6} \leqslant \frac{17\pi}{6}$.
  $\therefore x - \frac{\pi}{6} = -\frac{\pi}{6}, \frac{7\pi}{6},$ or $\frac{11\pi}{6}$
  $\therefore x = 0, \frac{4\pi}{3},$ or 2π

Start at $-\frac{\pi}{6}$ and work around to $\frac{17\pi}{6}$, recording the angle every time you reach points A and B.

6 If $0 \leqslant x \leqslant 2\pi$, state the domain of:

  a $2x$ **b** $\frac{x}{4}$ **c** $x + \frac{\pi}{2}$ **d** $x - \frac{\pi}{6}$ **e** $2\left(x - \frac{\pi}{4}\right)$ **f** $-x$

7 If $-\pi \leqslant x \leqslant \pi$, state the domain of:

  a $3x$ **b** $\frac{x}{4}$ **c** $x - \frac{\pi}{2}$ **d** $2x + \frac{\pi}{2}$ **e** $-2x$ **f** $\pi - x$

8 Solve exactly for $0 \leqslant x \leqslant 3\pi$:

  a $\cos x = \frac{1}{2}$ **b** $\cos 2x = \frac{1}{2}$ **c** $\cos\left(x + \frac{\pi}{3}\right) = \frac{1}{2}$

9 Solve for x on $0 \leqslant x \leqslant 2\pi$:

a $\sin 2x = -\frac{1}{2}$

b $\cos 3x = \frac{\sqrt{3}}{2}$

c $\tan 2x - \sqrt{3} = 0$

d $\sin \frac{x}{2} = \frac{1}{\sqrt{2}}$

e $2 \cos \frac{x}{2} + 1 = 0$

f $3 \tan \frac{x}{3} - 3 = 0$

10 Solve for x on $0 \leqslant x \leqslant 2\pi$:

a $\cos^2 3x = \frac{1}{4}$

b $\sin^2 2x = 1$

c $\tan^2\left(\frac{x}{2}\right) = \frac{1}{3}$

Example 6 ◄») **Self Tutor**

Find the exact solutions of $\sqrt{3} \sin x = \cos x$ for $0 \leqslant x \leqslant 2\pi$.

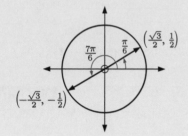

$\sqrt{3} \sin x = \cos x$

$\therefore \dfrac{\sin x}{\cos x} = \dfrac{1}{\sqrt{3}}$ {dividing both sides by $\sqrt{3} \cos x$}

$\therefore \tan x = \dfrac{1}{\sqrt{3}}$

$\therefore x = \frac{\pi}{6}$ or $\frac{7\pi}{6}$

---

11 Find the exact solutions for $0 \leqslant x \leqslant 2\pi$:

a $\sin x = -\cos x$

b $\sin 3x = \cos 3x$

c $\sin 2x = \sqrt{3} \cos 2x$

Example 7 ◄») **Self Tutor**

Solve $\sqrt{2} \cos\left(x - \frac{3\pi}{4}\right) + 1 = 0$ for $0 \leqslant x \leqslant 6\pi$.

$\sqrt{2} \cos\left(x - \frac{3\pi}{4}\right) + 1 = 0$

$\therefore \cos\left(x - \frac{3\pi}{4}\right) = -\frac{1}{\sqrt{2}}$.

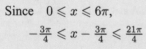

Start at $-\frac{3\pi}{4}$ and work around to $\frac{21\pi}{4}$, recording the angle every time you reach points A and B.

Since $0 \leqslant x \leqslant 6\pi$,

$-\frac{3\pi}{4} \leqslant x - \frac{3\pi}{4} \leqslant \frac{21\pi}{4}$

So, $x - \frac{3\pi}{4} = -\frac{3\pi}{4}, \frac{3\pi}{4}, \frac{5\pi}{4}, \frac{11\pi}{4}, \frac{13\pi}{4}, \frac{19\pi}{4},$ or $\frac{21\pi}{4}$

$\therefore x = 0, \frac{3\pi}{2}, 2\pi, \frac{7\pi}{2}, 4\pi, \frac{11\pi}{2},$ or 6π

---

12 Solve exactly:

a $\cos\left(x - \frac{2\pi}{3}\right) = \frac{1}{2}, \ -2\pi \leqslant x \leqslant 2\pi$

b $\sqrt{2} \sin\left(x - \frac{\pi}{4}\right) + 1 = 0, \ 0 \leqslant x \leqslant 3\pi$

c $\sin\left(4\left(x - \frac{\pi}{4}\right)\right) = 0, \ 0 \leqslant x \leqslant \pi$

d $2 \sin\left(2\left(x - \frac{\pi}{3}\right)\right) = -\sqrt{3}, \ 0 \leqslant x \leqslant 2\pi$

13 Find the unknowns in each function:

a
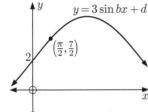

$y = 3 \sin bx + d$

$\left(\frac{\pi}{2}, \frac{7}{2}\right)$

b
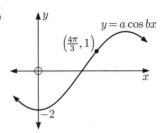

$y = a \cos bx$

$\left(\frac{4\pi}{3}, 1\right)$

c
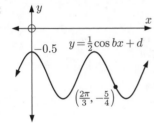

$y = \frac{1}{2} \cos bx + d$

$\left(\frac{2\pi}{3}, -\frac{5}{4}\right)$

d
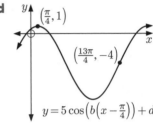

$\left(\frac{\pi}{4}, 1\right)$

$\left(\frac{13\pi}{4}, -4\right)$

$y = 5 \cos\left(b\left(x - \frac{\pi}{4}\right)\right) + d$

14 Find the exact solutions of $\tan x = \sqrt{3}$ for $0 \leqslant x \leqslant 2\pi$. Hence solve the following equations for $0 \leqslant x \leqslant 2\pi$:

a $\tan\left(x - \frac{\pi}{6}\right) = \sqrt{3}$ **b** $\tan 4x = \sqrt{3}$ **c** $\tan^2 x = 3$

Example 8   ◀)) **Self Tutor**

Solve for x on $0 \leqslant x \leqslant 2\pi$, giving your answers as exact values:

a $2 \sin^2 x + \sin x = 0$ **b** $2 \cos^2 x + \cos x - 1 = 0$

a $\quad 2 \sin^2 x + \sin x = 0$
$\therefore \ \sin x (2 \sin x + 1) = 0$
$\quad \therefore \ \sin x = 0 \text{ or } -\frac{1}{2}$

b $\quad 2 \cos^2 x + \cos x - 1 = 0$
$\therefore \ (2 \cos x - 1)(\cos x + 1) = 0$
$\quad \therefore \ \cos x = \frac{1}{2} \text{ or } -1$

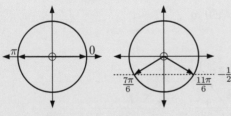

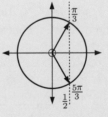

$\therefore \ x = 0, \ \pi, \ \frac{7\pi}{6}, \ \frac{11\pi}{6}, \text{ or } 2\pi.$

$\therefore \ x = \frac{\pi}{3}, \ \pi, \text{ or } \frac{5\pi}{3}.$

---

15 Solve for $0 \leqslant x \leqslant 2\pi$ giving your answers as exact values:

a $2 \sin^2 x - \sin x = 0$ **b** $2 \cos^2 x = \cos x$

c $2 \cos^2 x - \cos x - 1 = 0$ **d** $2 \sin^2 x + 3 \sin x + 1 = 0$

e $\tan^4 x - 2 \tan^2 x - 3 = 0$

B   USING TRIGONOMETRIC MODELS

Having studied trigonometric equations, we can now apply them to the trigonometric models studied in **Chapter 8**.

Example 9   ◀)) **Self Tutor**

The height of the tide above mean sea level on January 24th at Cape Town is modelled by $h(t) = 3\sin\frac{\pi t}{6}$ metres, where t is the number of hours after midnight.

a Graph $y = h(t)$ for $0 \leqslant t \leqslant 24$.

b When is high tide and what is the maximum height?

c What is the height of the tide at 2 pm?

d A ship can cross the harbour provided the tide is at least 2 m above mean sea level. When is crossing possible on January 24th?

a $h(0) = 0$

$h(t) = 3\sin\frac{\pi t}{6}$ has period $= \dfrac{2\pi}{\frac{\pi}{6}} = 2\pi \times \dfrac{6}{\pi} = 12$ hours

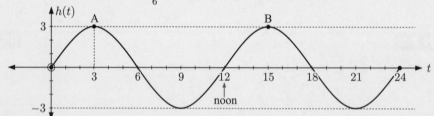

b High tide is at 3 am and 3 pm. The maximum height is 3 m above the mean as seen at points A and B.

c At 2 pm, $t = 14$ and $h(14) = 3\sin\frac{14\pi}{6} \approx 2.60$ m.

So, the tide is 2.6 m above the mean.

d

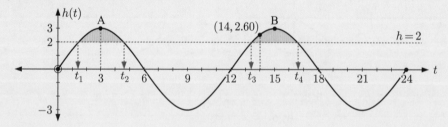

We need to solve $h(t) = 2$, so $3\sin\frac{\pi t}{6} = 2$.

Using a graphics calculator with $Y_1 = 3\sin\frac{\pi X}{6}$ and $Y_2 = 2$

we obtain $t_1 \approx 1.39$, $t_2 \approx 4.61$, $t_3 \approx 13.39$, $t_4 \approx 16.61$

Now 1.39 hours = 1 hour 23 minutes, and so on.

So, the ship can cross between 1:23 am and 4:37 am or 1:23 pm and 4:37 pm.

EXERCISE 9B

1 The population of grasshoppers after t weeks is $P(t) = 7500 + 3000 \sin \frac{\pi t}{8}$ for $0 \leqslant t \leqslant 12$.

   a Find:

      i the initial population   **ii** the population after 5 weeks.

   b What is the greatest population size over this interval and when does it occur?

   c When is the population: **i** 9000   **ii** 6000?

   d During what time interval(s) does the population size exceed 10 000?

2 Answer the **Opening Problem** on page **224**.

3 The model for the height of a passenger on a Ferris wheel is $H(t) = 20 - 19 \cos \frac{2\pi t}{3}$, where H is the height in metres above the ground, and t is in minutes.

   a Where is the passenger at time $t = 0$?

   b At what time is the passenger at the maximum height in the first revolution of the wheel?

   c How long does the wheel take to complete one revolution?

   d Sketch the graph of the function $H(t)$ over one revolution.

   e The passenger can see his friend when he is at least 13 m above the ground. During what times in the first revolution can the passenger see his friend?

4 The population of water buffalo is given by $P(t) = 400 + 250 \sin \frac{\pi t}{2}$ where t is the number of years since the first estimate was made.

   a What was the initial estimate?

   b What was the population size after:

      i 6 months   **ii** two years?

   c Find $P(1)$. What is the significance of this value?

   d Find the smallest population size and when it first occurred.

   e Find the first time when the herd exceeded 500.

5 Over a 28 day period, the cost per litre of petrol was modelled by
$C(t) = 9.2 \sin\left(\frac{\pi}{7}(t - 4)\right) + 107.8$ cents L^{-1}.

   a True or false?

      i "The cost per litre oscillates about 107.8 cents with maximum price \$1.17 per litre."

      ii "Every 14 days, the cycle repeats itself."

   b What was the cost of petrol on day 7, to the nearest tenth of a cent per litre?

   c On which days was the petrol priced at \$1.10 per litre?

   d What was the minimum cost per litre and when did it occur?

6 A paint spot X lies on the outer rim of the wheel of a paddle-steamer. The wheel has radius 3 m and rotates anticlockwise at a constant rate. X is seen entering the water every 4 seconds.

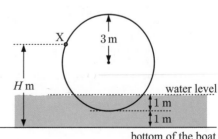

   H is the distance of X above the bottom of the boat. At time $t = 0$, X is at its highest point.

   a Find a cosine model for H in the form
$H(t) = a \cos(b(t - c)) + d$.

   b At what time t does X first enter the water?

C # TRIGONOMETRIC IDENTITIES

In mathematics, an **identity** is a result which is true for all values of a variable.

For example, we have seen that for any value of x:

- $\cos^2 x + \sin^2 x = 1$
- $\sin(-x) = -\sin x$
- $\cos(\pi - x) = -\cos x$
- $\sin(x + \frac{\pi}{2}) = \cos x$
- $\cos(x - \frac{\pi}{2}) = \sin x$
- $\tan x = \dfrac{\sin x}{\cos x}$

These equations are all examples of identities.

There are a vast number of trigonometric identities. However, we only need to remember a few because we can obtain the rest by rearrangement or substitution. This requires **trigonometric algebra**.

SIMPLIFYING TRIGONOMETRIC EXPRESSIONS

For any given angle θ, $\sin \theta$ and $\cos \theta$ are real numbers. $\tan \theta$ is also real whenever it is defined. The algebra of trigonometry is therefore identical to the algebra of real numbers.

An expression like $2 \sin \theta + 3 \sin \theta$ compares with $2x + 3x$ when we wish to do simplification, and so $2 \sin \theta + 3 \sin \theta = 5 \sin \theta$.

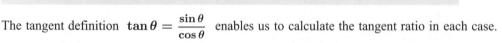

Example 10		◀)) **Self Tutor**
Simplify:	**a** $3 \cos \theta + 4 \cos \theta$	**b** $\tan \alpha - 3 \tan \alpha$
	a $3 \cos \theta + 4 \cos \theta = 7 \cos \theta$ {compare with $3x + 4x = 7x$}	**b** $\tan \alpha - 3 \tan \alpha = -2 \tan \alpha$ {compare with $x - 3x = -2x$}

ANGLE RELATIONSHIPS

The **negative angle formulae** are established by reflection in the x-axis:

$$\sin(-\theta) = -\sin \theta \qquad \cos(-\theta) = \cos \theta$$

The **supplementary angle formulae** are established by reflection in the y-axis:

$$\sin(\pi - \theta) = \sin \theta \qquad \cos(\pi - \theta) = -\cos \theta$$

The **complementary angle formulae** are established by reflection in the line $y = x$:

$$\sin(\tfrac{\pi}{2} - \theta) = \cos \theta \qquad \cos(\tfrac{\pi}{2} - \theta) = \sin \theta$$

ANGLE RELATIONSHIPS

The tangent definition $\tan \theta = \dfrac{\sin \theta}{\cos \theta}$ enables us to calculate the tangent ratio in each case.

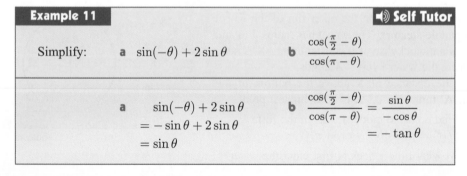

Example 11		◀)) **Self Tutor**
Simplify:	**a** $\sin(-\theta) + 2 \sin \theta$	**b** $\dfrac{\cos(\frac{\pi}{2} - \theta)}{\cos(\pi - \theta)}$
	a $\sin(-\theta) + 2 \sin \theta$ $= -\sin \theta + 2 \sin \theta$ $= \sin \theta$	**b** $\dfrac{\cos(\frac{\pi}{2} - \theta)}{\cos(\pi - \theta)} = \dfrac{\sin \theta}{-\cos \theta}$ $= -\tan \theta$

EXERCISE 9C.1

1 Simplify:

   a $\sin\theta + \sin\theta$

   b $2\cos\theta + \cos\theta$

   c $3\sin\theta - \sin\theta$

   d $3\sin\theta - 2\sin\theta$

   e $\tan\theta - 3\tan\theta$

   f $2\cos^2\theta - 5\cos^2\theta$

2 Simplify:

   a $3\tan x - \dfrac{\sin x}{\cos x}$

   b $\dfrac{\sin^2 x}{\cos^2 x}$

   c $\tan x \cos x$

   d $\dfrac{\sin x}{\tan x}$

   e $3\sin x + 2\cos x \tan x$

   f $\dfrac{2\tan x}{\sin x}$

3 Simplify:

   a $3\cos\theta - \cos(-\theta)$

   b $\tan(-\theta)$

   c $\sin(-\theta) + \cos\left(\frac{\pi}{2} - \theta\right)$

   d $\tan(\pi - \theta)$

   e $\tan\left(\frac{\pi}{2} - \theta\right)$

   f $\sin\left(\frac{\pi}{2} - \theta\right) - \cos(\pi - \theta)$

   g $\dfrac{\sin(-\theta)}{\cos(\pi - \theta)}$

   h $\dfrac{\cos(\frac{\pi}{2} - \theta)}{\cos(-\theta)}$

   i $\dfrac{\sin(\pi - \theta) - \sin(-\theta)}{\cos(-\theta)}$

THE PYTHAGOREAN IDENTITY

The **Pythagorean identity** is established by applying Pythagoras' theorem on the unit circle:

$$\sin^2\theta + \cos^2\theta = 1$$

We commonly use rearrangements of these formulae such as:

$$\sin^2\theta = 1 - \cos^2\theta \qquad\qquad \cos^2\theta = 1 - \sin^2\theta$$

Example 12   ◀) Self Tutor

Simplify:

  a $2 - 2\sin^2\theta$

  b $\cos^2\theta \sin\theta + \sin^3\theta$

  a $2 - 2\sin^2\theta$
$= 2(1 - \sin^2\theta)$
$= 2\cos^2\theta$
$\{\text{as } \cos^2\theta + \sin^2\theta = 1\}$

  b $\cos^2\theta \sin\theta + \sin^3\theta$
$= \sin\theta(\cos^2\theta + \sin^2\theta)$
$= \sin\theta \times 1$
$= \sin\theta$

EXERCISE 9C.2

1 Simplify:

   a $3\sin^2\theta + 3\cos^2\theta$

   b $-2\sin^2\theta - 2\cos^2\theta$

   c $-\cos^2\theta - \sin^2\theta$

   d $3 - 3\sin^2\theta$

   e $4 - 4\cos^2\theta$

   f $\cos^3\theta + \cos\theta \sin^2\theta$

   g $\cos^2\theta - 1$

   h $\sin^2\theta - 1$

   i $2\cos^2\theta - 2$

   j $\dfrac{1 - \sin^2\theta}{\cos^2\theta}$

   k $\dfrac{1 - \cos^2\theta}{\sin\theta}$

   l $\dfrac{\cos^2\theta - 1}{-\sin\theta}$

Example 13   ◀)) **Self Tutor**

Expand and simplify: $(\cos\theta - \sin\theta)^2$

$(\cos\theta - \sin\theta)^2$
$= \cos^2\theta - 2\cos\theta\sin\theta + \sin^2\theta$ {using $(a-b)^2 = a^2 - 2ab + b^2$}
$= \cos^2\theta + \sin^2\theta - 2\cos\theta\sin\theta$
$= 1 - 2\cos\theta\sin\theta$

---

2 Expand and simplify, if possible:

   a $(1 + \sin\theta)^2$ **b** $(\sin\alpha - 2)^2$ **c** $(\tan\alpha - 1)^2$

   d $(\sin\alpha + \cos\alpha)^2$ **e** $(\sin\beta - \cos\beta)^2$ **f** $-(2 - \cos\alpha)^2$

3 Simplify:

   a $(\sin x + \tan x)(\sin x - \tan x)$ **b** $(2\sin\theta + 3\cos\theta)^2 + (3\sin\theta - 2\cos\theta)^2$

FACTORISING TRIGONOMETRIC EXPRESSIONS

Example 14   ◀)) **Self Tutor**

Factorise:

   a $\cos^2\alpha - \sin^2\alpha$ **b** $\tan^2\theta - 3\tan\theta + 2$

   a $\cos^2\alpha - \sin^2\alpha$
      $= (\cos\alpha + \sin\alpha)(\cos\alpha - \sin\alpha)$ {using $a^2 - b^2 = (a+b)(a-b)$}

   b $\tan^2\theta - 3\tan\theta + 2$
      $= (\tan\theta - 2)(\tan\theta - 1)$ {compare with $x^2 - 3x + 2 = (x-2)(x-1)$}

Example 15   ◀)) **Self Tutor**

Simplify:

   a $\dfrac{2 - 2\cos^2\theta}{1 + \cos\theta}$ **b** $\dfrac{\cos\theta - \sin\theta}{\cos^2\theta - \sin^2\theta}$

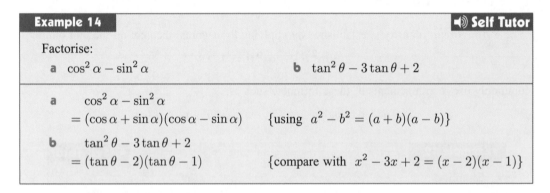

a $\dfrac{2 - 2\cos^2\theta}{1 + \cos\theta}$

    $= \dfrac{2(1 - \cos^2\theta)}{1 + \cos\theta}$

    $= \dfrac{2(1 + \cos\theta)(1 - \cos\theta)}{(1 + \cos\theta)}$

    $= 2(1 - \cos\theta)$

b $\dfrac{\cos\theta - \sin\theta}{\cos^2\theta - \sin^2\theta}$

    $= \dfrac{(\cos\theta - \sin\theta)}{(\cos\theta + \sin\theta)(\cos\theta - \sin\theta)}$

    $= \dfrac{1}{\cos\theta + \sin\theta}$

EXERCISE 9C.3

1 Factorise:

a $1 - \sin^2 \theta$

b $\sin^2 \alpha - \cos^2 \alpha$

c $\tan^2 \alpha - 1$

d $2\sin^2 \beta - \sin \beta$

e $2\cos \phi + 3\cos^2 \phi$

f $3\sin^2 \theta - 6\sin \theta$

g $\tan^2 \theta + 5\tan \theta + 6$

h $2\cos^2 \theta + 7\cos \theta + 3$

i $6\cos^2 \alpha - \cos \alpha - 1$

j $3\tan^2 \alpha - 2\tan \alpha$

k $2\sin^2 x + 7\sin x \cos x + 3\cos^2 x$

2 Solve for $0 \leqslant x \leqslant 2\pi$:

a $2\cos^2 x = \sin x + 1$

b $\sin^2 x = 2 - \cos x$

c $2\cos^2 x = 3\sin x$

3 Simplify:

a $\dfrac{1 - \sin^2 \alpha}{1 - \sin \alpha}$

b $\dfrac{\tan^2 \beta - 1}{\tan \beta + 1}$

c $\dfrac{\cos^2 \phi - \sin^2 \phi}{\cos \phi + \sin \phi}$

d $\dfrac{\cos^2 \phi - \sin^2 \phi}{\cos \phi - \sin \phi}$

e $\dfrac{\sin \alpha + \cos \alpha}{\sin^2 \alpha - \cos^2 \alpha}$

f $\dfrac{3 - 3\sin^2 \theta}{6\cos \theta}$

4 Show that:

a $(\cos \theta + \sin \theta)^2 + (\cos \theta - \sin \theta)^2 = 2$

b $(\sin \theta + 4\cos \theta)^2 + (4\sin \theta - \cos \theta)^2 = 17$

c $(1 - \cos \theta)\left(1 + \dfrac{1}{\cos \theta}\right) = \tan \theta \sin \theta$

d $\left(1 + \dfrac{1}{\sin \theta}\right)(\sin \theta - \sin^2 \theta) = \cos^2 \theta$

e $\dfrac{\cos \alpha}{1 - \tan \alpha} + \dfrac{\sin^2 \alpha}{\sin \alpha - \cos \alpha} = \sin \alpha + \cos \alpha$

f $\dfrac{\sin \theta}{1 + \cos \theta} + \dfrac{1 + \cos \theta}{\sin \theta} = \dfrac{2}{\sin \theta}$

g $\dfrac{\sin \theta}{1 - \cos \theta} - \dfrac{\sin \theta}{1 + \cos \theta} = \dfrac{2}{\tan \theta}$

h $\dfrac{1}{1 - \sin \theta} + \dfrac{1}{1 + \sin \theta} = \dfrac{2}{\cos^2 \theta}$

Check these simplifications by graphing both sides of the equations on the same set of axes.

GRAPHING PACKAGE

D   DOUBLE ANGLE IDENTITIES

INVESTIGATION 1   DOUBLE ANGLE IDENTITIES

What to do:

1 Copy and complete this table using your calculator. Include extra lines for angles of your choice.

θ	$\sin 2\theta$	$2\sin \theta$	$2\sin \theta \cos \theta$	$\cos 2\theta$	$2\cos \theta$	$\cos^2 \theta - \sin^2 \theta$
0.631						
57.81°						
−3.697						
⋮						

2 Write down any discoveries from your table of values.

3 In the diagram alongside, the semi-circle has radius
1 unit, and $\widehat{PAB} = \theta$.

$\widehat{APO} = \theta$ {$\triangle AOP$ is isosceles}

$\widehat{PON} = 2\theta$ {exterior angle of a triangle}

a Find in terms of θ, the lengths of:

  i [OM]   **ii** [AM]

  iii [ON]   **iv** [PN]

b Use $\triangle ANP$ and the lengths in **a** to show that:

  i $\cos\theta = \dfrac{\sin 2\theta}{2\sin\theta}$ **ii** $\cos\theta = \dfrac{1 + \cos 2\theta}{2\cos\theta}$

c Hence deduce that:

  i $\sin 2\theta = 2\sin\theta\cos\theta$ **ii** $\cos 2\theta = 2\cos^2\theta - 1$

d For what values of θ have we proven the results in **c**?

The formulae $\sin 2\theta = 2\sin\theta\cos\theta$ and $\cos 2\theta = 2\cos^2\theta - 1$ found in the **Investigation** are in fact true for all angles θ.

Using $\cos^2\theta = 1 - \sin^2\theta$, we find $\cos 2\theta = \cos^2\theta - \sin^2\theta$

and $\cos 2\theta = 1 - 2\sin^2\theta$.

So, the **double angle identities** for sine and cosine are:

$$\sin 2\theta = 2\sin\theta\cos\theta$$
$$\cos 2\theta = \cos^2\theta - \sin^2\theta$$
$$= 1 - 2\sin^2\theta$$
$$= 2\cos^2\theta - 1$$

GRAPHING
PACKAGE

Example 16   ◄⑴ **Self Tutor**

Given that $\sin\alpha = \frac{3}{5}$ and $\cos\alpha = -\frac{4}{5}$ find:

a $\sin 2\alpha$ **b** $\cos 2\alpha$ **c** $\tan 2\alpha$

a $\sin 2\alpha$
$= 2\sin\alpha\cos\alpha$
$= 2\left(\frac{3}{5}\right)\left(-\frac{4}{5}\right)$
$= -\frac{24}{25}$

b $\cos 2\alpha$
$= \cos^2\alpha - \sin^2\alpha$
$= \left(-\frac{4}{5}\right)^2 - \left(\frac{3}{5}\right)^2$
$= \frac{7}{25}$

c $\tan 2\alpha = \dfrac{\sin 2\alpha}{\cos 2\alpha}$
$= \dfrac{-\frac{24}{25}}{\frac{7}{25}}$ {using **a**, **b**}
$= -\frac{24}{7}$

EXERCISE 9D

1 For $\theta = 30°$, verify that:

  a $\sin 2\theta = 2\sin\theta\cos\theta$ **b** $\cos 2\theta = \cos^2\theta - \sin^2\theta$

2 If $\sin\theta = \frac{4}{5}$ and $\cos\theta = \frac{3}{5}$, find the exact values of:

  a $\sin 2\theta$ **b** $\cos 2\theta$ **c** $\tan 2\theta$

3 **a** If $\cos A = \frac{1}{3}$, find $\cos 2A$.   **b** If $\sin\phi = -\frac{2}{3}$, find $\cos 2\phi$.

Example 17   ◀)) **Self Tutor**

If $\sin \alpha = \frac{5}{13}$ where $\frac{\pi}{2} < \alpha < \pi$, find the exact value of $\sin 2\alpha$.

α is in quadrant 2, so $\cos \alpha$ is negative.

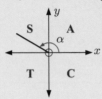

Now $\cos^2 \alpha + \sin^2 \alpha = 1$

$\therefore \ \cos^2 \alpha + \frac{25}{169} = 1$

$\therefore \ \ \cos^2 \alpha = \frac{144}{169}$

$\therefore \ \ \cos \alpha = -\frac{12}{13}$ $\{\cos \alpha < 0\}$

Using the double angle identity, $\sin 2\alpha = 2 \sin \alpha \cos \alpha$

$$= 2\left(\tfrac{5}{13}\right)\left(-\tfrac{12}{13}\right)$$

$$= -\tfrac{120}{169}$$

4 If $\sin \alpha = -\frac{2}{3}$ where $\pi < \alpha < \frac{3\pi}{2}$, find the exact value of:

   a $\cos \alpha$ **b** $\sin 2\alpha$

5 If $\cos \beta = \frac{2}{5}$ where $270° < \beta < 360°$, find the exact value of:

   a $\sin \beta$ **b** $\sin 2\beta$

Example 18   ◀)) **Self Tutor**

If α is acute and $\cos 2\alpha = \frac{3}{4}$ find the exact values of:

   a $\cos \alpha$ **b** $\sin \alpha$.

a $\cos 2\alpha = 2\cos^2 \alpha - 1$

   $\therefore \ \frac{3}{4} = 2\cos^2 \alpha - 1$

$\therefore \ \ \cos^2 \alpha = \frac{7}{8}$

$\therefore \ \ \cos \alpha = \pm \frac{\sqrt{7}}{2\sqrt{2}}$

$\therefore \ \ \cos \alpha = \frac{\sqrt{7}}{2\sqrt{2}}$

   $\{$as α is acute, $\cos \alpha > 0\}$

b $\sin \alpha = \sqrt{1 - \cos^2 \alpha}$

   $\{$as α is acute, $\sin \alpha > 0\}$

$\therefore \ \sin \alpha = \sqrt{1 - \tfrac{7}{8}}$

$\therefore \ \sin \alpha = \sqrt{\tfrac{1}{8}}$

$\therefore \ \sin \alpha = \frac{1}{2\sqrt{2}}$

6 If α is acute and $\cos 2\alpha = -\frac{7}{9}$, find without a calculator:

   a $\cos \alpha$ **b** $\sin \alpha$.

7 If θ is obtuse and $\cos 2\theta = -\frac{1}{3}$, find the exact values of:

   a $\cos \theta$ **b** $\sin \theta$.

8 Show that $\tan 2\theta = \dfrac{2 \tan \theta}{1 - \tan^2 \theta}$.

Example 19

◀⑴ **Self Tutor**

Use an appropriate double angle identity to simplify:

a $3 \sin \theta \cos \theta$ **b** $4 \cos^2 2B - 2$

a $3 \sin \theta \cos \theta$

$= \frac{3}{2}(2 \sin \theta \cos \theta)$

$= \frac{3}{2} \sin 2\theta$

b $4 \cos^2 2B - 2$

$= 2(2 \cos^2 2B - 1)$

$= 2 \cos 2(2B)$

$= 2 \cos 4B$

9 Use an appropriate double angle identity to simplify:

a $2 \sin \alpha \cos \alpha$
b $4 \cos \alpha \sin \alpha$
c $\sin \alpha \cos \alpha$

d $2 \cos^2 \beta - 1$
e $1 - 2 \cos^2 \phi$
f $1 - 2 \sin^2 N$

g $2 \sin^2 M - 1$
h $\cos^2 \alpha - \sin^2 \alpha$
i $\sin^2 \alpha - \cos^2 \alpha$

j $2 \sin 2A \cos 2A$
k $2 \cos 3\alpha \sin 3\alpha$
l $2 \cos^2 4\theta - 1$

m $1 - 2 \cos^2 3\beta$
n $1 - 2 \sin^2 5\alpha$
o $2 \sin^2 3D - 1$

p $\cos^2 2A - \sin^2 2A$
q $\cos^2\left(\frac{\alpha}{2}\right) - \sin^2\left(\frac{\alpha}{2}\right)$
r $2 \sin^2 3P - 2 \cos^2 3P$

10 Find the exact value of $\left[\cos \frac{\pi}{12} + \sin \frac{\pi}{12}\right]^2$.

11 Show that:

a $(\sin \theta + \cos \theta)^2 = 1 + \sin 2\theta$ **b** $\cos^4 \theta - \sin^4 \theta = \cos 2\theta$

GRAPHING PACKAGE

Check your answers by graphing both sides of the equations on the same set of axes.

12 Solve exactly for x where $0 \leqslant x \leqslant 2\pi$:

a $\sin 2x + \sin x = 0$ **b** $\sin 2x - 2 \cos x = 0$ **c** $\sin 2x + 3 \sin x = 0$

13 Use a double angle identity to show that:

a $\sin^2 \theta = \frac{1}{2} - \frac{1}{2} \cos 2\theta$ **b** $\cos^2 \theta = \frac{1}{2} + \frac{1}{2} \cos 2\theta$

14 Solve $\sin \theta \cos \theta = \frac{1}{4}$ for $-\pi \leqslant \theta \leqslant \pi$.

15 Solve for $0 \leqslant x \leqslant 2\pi$, giving exact answers:

a $\cos 2x - \cos x = 0$ **b** $\cos 2x + 3 \cos x = 1$ **c** $\cos 2x + \sin x = 0$

d $\sin 4x = \sin 2x$ **e** $\sin x + \cos x = \sqrt{2}$ **f** $2 \cos^2 x = 3 \sin x$

16 The curves $y = \cos x$ and $y = \cos 2x + 1$ are graphed alongside for $0 \leqslant x \leqslant 2\pi$.

a Identify each curve.

b Find the exact coordinates of A, B, C, and D.

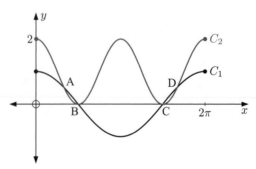

INVESTIGATION 2   PARAMETRIC EQUATIONS

Usually we write functions in the form $y = f(x)$.

For example: $y = 3x + 7$, $y = x^2 - 6x + 8$, $y = \sin x$

However, when we describe relations, it is often useful to express **both** x and y in terms of another variable t, called the **parameter**. In this case we say we have **parametric equations**.

What to do:

1   **a**   Use technology to plot
       $\{(x, y) \mid x = \cos t, \ y = \sin t, \ 0 \leqslant t \leqslant 2\pi\}$.
       Use the same scale on both axes.
       Note: Your calculator will need to be set to radians.

GRAPHICS
CALCULATOR
INSTRUCTIONS

   b   Describe the resulting graph. Is it the graph of a function?

   c   Evaluate $x^2 + y^2$. Hence determine the equation of this graph in terms of x and y only.

2   Use technology to plot:

   a $\{(x, y) \mid x = 2\cos t, \ y = \sin 2t, \ 0 \leqslant t \leqslant 2\pi\}$

   b $\{(x, y) \mid x = 2\cos t, \ y = 2\sin 3t, \ 0 \leqslant t \leqslant 2\pi\}$

   c $\{(x, y) \mid x = 2\cos t, \ y = \cos t - \sin t, \ 0 \leqslant t \leqslant 2\pi\}$

   d $\{(x, y) \mid x = \cos^2 t + \sin 2t, \ y = \cos t, \ 0 \leqslant t \leqslant 2\pi\}$

   e $\{(x, y) \mid x = \cos^3 t, \ y = \sin t, \ 0 \leqslant t \leqslant 2\pi\}$

PARAMETRIC
GRAPHING
PACKAGE

REVIEW SET 9A

1

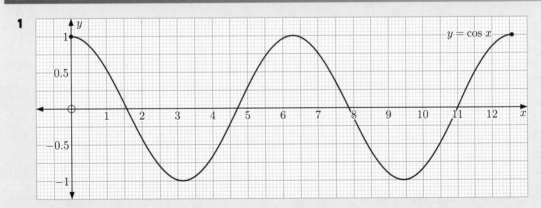

Use the graph of $y = \cos x$ on the domain $0 \leqslant x \leqslant 4\pi$ to solve, correct to 1 decimal place:

   a $\cos x = -0.4$ **b** $\cos x = 0.9$

2   Solve for $0 \leqslant x \leqslant 8$:

   a $\sin x = 0.382$ **b** $\tan \frac{x}{2} = -0.458$

3   Solve:

   a $\cos x = 0.4379$ for $0 \leqslant x \leqslant 10$ **b** $\cos(x - 2.4) = -0.6014$ for $0 \leqslant x \leqslant 6$

4 Solve for $0 \leqslant x \leqslant 2\pi$:

   a $2\sin x = -1$ **b** $\sqrt{2}\cos x - 1 = 0$ **c** $2\cos 2x + 1 = 0$

5 Solve algebraically for $0 \leqslant x \leqslant 2\pi$, giving answers in terms of π:

   a $\tan^2 2x = 1$ **b** $\sin^2 x - \sin x - 2 = 0$ **c** $4\sin^2 x = 1$

6 Find the exact solutions of:

   a $\sqrt{2}\cos\left(x + \frac{\pi}{4}\right) - 1 = 0, \ 0 \leqslant x \leqslant 4\pi$ **b** $\tan 2x - \sqrt{3} = 0, \ 0 \leqslant x \leqslant 2\pi$

7 An ecologist studying a species of water beetle estimates the population of a colony over an eight week period. If t is the number of weeks after the initial estimate is made, then the population in thousands can be modelled by $P(t) = 5 + 2\sin\frac{\pi t}{3}$ where $0 \leqslant t \leqslant 8$.

   a What was the initial population?

   b What were the smallest and largest populations?

   c During what time interval(s) did the population exceed 6000?

8 Simplify:

   a $3\cos(-\theta) - 2\cos\theta$ **b** $\cos\left(\frac{3\pi}{2} - \theta\right)$ **c** $\sin\left(\theta + \frac{\pi}{2}\right)$

   d $\dfrac{1 - \cos^2\theta}{1 + \cos\theta}$ **e** $\dfrac{\sin\alpha - \cos\alpha}{\sin^2\alpha - \cos^2\alpha}$ **f** $\dfrac{4\sin^2\alpha - 4}{8\cos\alpha}$

9 If $\sin\alpha = -\frac{3}{4}$, $\pi \leqslant \alpha \leqslant \frac{3\pi}{2}$, find the exact value of:

   a $\cos\alpha$ **b** $\sin 2\alpha$ **c** $\cos 2\alpha$

10 Show that $\dfrac{\sin 2\alpha - \sin\alpha}{\cos 2\alpha - \cos\alpha + 1} = \tan\alpha$.

11 Suppose $f(x) = \cos x$ and $g(x) = 2x$. Solve for $0 \leqslant x \leqslant 2\pi$:

   a $(f \circ g)(x) = 1$ **b** $(g \circ f)(x) = 1$

12 Consider triangle ABC shown.

   a Show that $\cos\alpha = \frac{5}{6}$.

   b Show that x is a solution of $3x^2 - 25x + 48 = 0$.

   c Find x by solving the equation in **b**.

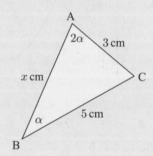

REVIEW SET 9B

1 Consider $y = \sin \frac{x}{3}$ on the domain $-7 \leqslant x \leqslant 7$. Use the graph to solve, correct to 1 decimal place:

    a $\sin \frac{x}{3} = -0.9$ **b** $\sin \frac{x}{3} = \frac{1}{4}$

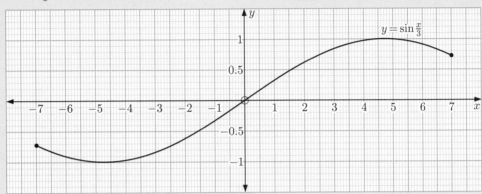

2 Solve for $0 \leqslant x \leqslant 2\pi$:

    a $\cos x = 0.3$ **b** $43 + 8\sin x = 50.1$

3 Solve for $0 \leqslant x \leqslant 10$:

    a $\tan x = 4$ **b** $\tan \frac{x}{4} = 4$ **c** $\tan(x - 1.5) = 4$

4 Solve for $0 \leqslant x \leqslant 2\pi$:

    a $2\sin 3x = -\sqrt{3}$ **b** $\sqrt{3}\tan \frac{x}{2} = -1$ **c** $\cos 2x = \sqrt{3}\sin 2x$

5 Find exact solutions for x given $-\pi \leqslant x \leqslant \pi$:

    a $\tan\left(x + \frac{\pi}{6}\right) = -\sqrt{3}$ **b** $\tan 2x = -\sqrt{3}$ **c** $\tan^2 x - 3 = 0$

6 Find the x-intercepts of:

    a $y = 2\sin 3x + \sqrt{3}$ for $0 \leqslant x \leqslant 2\pi$ **b** $y = \sqrt{2}\sin\left(x + \frac{\pi}{4}\right)$ for $0 \leqslant x \leqslant 3\pi$

7 In an industrial city, the amount of pollution in the air becomes greater during the working week when factories are operating, and lessens over the weekend. The number of milligrams of pollutants in a cubic metre of air is given by $P(t) = 40 + 12\sin\left(\frac{2\pi}{7}\left(t - \frac{37}{12}\right)\right)$ where t is the number of days after midnight on Saturday night.

    a What is the minimum level of pollution?

    b At what time during the week does this minimum level occur?

8 Simplify:

    a $\cos^3 \theta + \sin^2 \theta \cos \theta$ **b** $\dfrac{\cos^2 \theta - 1}{\sin \theta}$

    c $5 - 5\sin^2 \theta$ **d** $\dfrac{\sin^2 \theta - 1}{\cos \theta}$

9 If $\sin A = \frac{5}{13}$ and $\cos A = \frac{12}{13}$, find:

    a $\sin 2A$ **b** $\cos 2A$

10 Show that:

    a $\dfrac{\cos \theta}{1 + \sin \theta} + \dfrac{1 + \sin \theta}{\cos \theta} = \dfrac{2}{\cos \theta}$ **b** $\left(1 + \dfrac{1}{\cos \theta}\right)\left(\cos \theta - \cos^2 \theta\right) = \sin^2 \theta$

11 Solve $\dfrac{1 - \cos 2\theta}{\sin 2\theta} = \sqrt{3}$ for $0 < \theta < \frac{\pi}{2}$.

12 Find exactly the length of [BC].

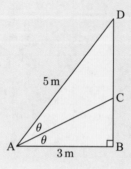

Chapter 10

Reasoning and proof

OPENING PROBLEM

A group of people are involved in a business meeting. Alice looks at Bob and Bob looks at Clare. Alice is married but Clare is not.

Things to think about:

a Do we know whether Bob is married?

b Can we *prove* that a married person looks at an unmarried person?

c What is necessary for a mathematical argument to be convincing and complete?

Greek mathematicians more than 2000 years ago realised that progress in mathematical thinking could be brought about by conscious formulation of the methods of **abstraction** and **proof**.

By considering a few examples, we might notice a certain common quality or pattern from which we could predict a rule or formula for the general case. In mathematics this prediction is known as a **conjecture**. Mathematicians love to find patterns, and try to understand why they occur.

Experiments and further examples might help to convince you that the conjecture is true. However, problems will often contain extra information which can sometimes obscure the essential detail, particularly in applied mathematics. Stripping this away is the process of **abstraction**.

For example, by considering the given table of values we may conjecture:

"If a and b are real numbers, then $a < b$ implies that $a^2 < b^2$."

However, on observing that $-2 < 1$ but $(-2)^2 \not< 1^2$ we have a **counter example**.

a	b	a^2	b^2
1	2	1	4
3	5	9	25
4	5	16	25
5	7	25	49
6	9	36	81

In the light of this we reformulate and refine our conjecture:

"If a and b are *positive* real numbers then $a < b$ implies $a^2 < b^2$."

The difficulty is that this process might continue with reformulations, counter examples, and revised conjectures indefinitely. We can only be certain that the conjecture is true if it is **proven**.

WHAT IS PROOF?

Science relies on experimental evidence. Mathematics relies on logic and reasoning.

A **mathematical proof** is a correct argument which establishes the truth of a mathematical statement.

A mathematical proof:

- starts with assumptions called **hypotheses**
- is a sequence of correct mathematical steps
- ends in a **conclusion**.

A mathematical proof can include logic, calculation, or a combination of the two. We will discuss both of these during the Chapter.

In the **Opening Problem**, we do not know whether or not Bob is married, so we need to consider both cases. We could write the following proof:

Proof:

Bob is either married or he is not married.

- If Bob is married, then when Bob looks at Clare, a married person looks at an unmarried person.
- If Bob is *not* married, then when Alice looks at Bob, a married person looks at an unmarried person.

In both cases, a married person looks at an unmarried person.

These cases exhaust all possibilities, so a married person always looks at an unmarried person.

In this proof, notice that:

- "Alice is married" is a *hypothesis*.
- The *conclusion* is that a married person looks at an unmarried person.
- This *style* of proof is called *proof by exhaustion*, because we have considered all possible cases: Bob is married, and Bob is not married.
- This proof contains logic only. There is no calculation.

THE PURPOSES OF PROOF

Mathematical proof is important:

- **to convince**
  Proofs help you decide if and why a statement is true or false. This is important when the result seems strange.
- **to understand**
  Proofs help you understand how and why all the different assumptions play a part in the result.
- **to communicate**
  Mathematicians use proofs to communicate and debate ideas with each other.
- **to organise**
  Proofs help you organise your thoughts.
- **to discover new mathematics**
  By carefully examining each step of a proof, mathematicians discover new mathematics.

ADVICE ON WRITING PROOFS

- State what you are proving. Make it clear when you have reached your conclusion.
- Include enough detail to make your proof easy to check.
- Your proof should be written in good English, including simple, complete, correct sentences.
- Present your calculations on the page in a manner which makes them easy to follow. Use your layout to clearly separate the parts or different cases considered in your proof.
- Use diagrams when appropriate to give a visual representation of the situation.
- It is often useful to use examples when exploring a problem. However, a single example is usually not sufficient to complete a proof.
- Check to see where you have used each hypothesis. If you have not used a particular hypothesis then either:
  - ► you did not need it, or
  - ► your proof should have made use of it, and is incorrect!
- Do not expect to write a complete proof the first time. Expect to use rough working first, and then write a neat version.

LOGICAL CONNECTIVES

Mathematical language uses **logical connectives** to link mathematical statements together:

Connective	Symbol	Formal name
and	$\wedge$	conjunction
or	$\vee$	disjunction
not	$\neg$	negation
if .... then	$\Rightarrow$	implication
if, and only if	$\Leftrightarrow$	equivalence

We can illustrate the use of these connectives using *variables* such as A, B, C, ...

For example, $(A \wedge B) \Rightarrow C$ means "A and B implies C". The two arguments $(A \wedge B)$ and C are connected by the connective $\Rightarrow$. The argument $(A \wedge B)$ is itself made up of arguments A and B, connected by the connective $\wedge$. It is therefore helpful to think of statements as mathematical trees, connected by the logical connectives.

NEGATION

The negation of a variable A is its opposite. If A is true then $\neg A$ is false, and vice versa.

For example:

- the negation of "Today is Wednesday" is "Today is not Wednesday"
- if we know $x \in \mathbb{Z}$, the negation of "x is an even integer" is "x is an odd integer"
- if we know $x \in \mathbb{R}$, the negation of "x is an even integer" is "x is not an even integer", since x might be an odd integer, or it might also be a non-integer.

IMPLICATIONS

Implications commonly arise when we deduce one thing from another.

For the implication $A \Rightarrow B$, we start with the statement A, and from it we deduce the statement B. The statement A is called the **hypothesis**, and B is called the **conclusion**.

In English there are many words we can use to show an implication.

For example:

$$A \left\{ \begin{array}{c} \text{implies} \\ \text{so} \\ \text{hence} \\ \text{thus} \\ \text{therefore} \end{array} \right\} B.$$

We use $\therefore$ to mean "therefore".

The **converse** of the implication $A \Rightarrow B$ is the statement $B \Rightarrow A$.

It is important to recognise that while the implication $A \Rightarrow B$ may be true, its converse may not be true.

For example, the statement "If $x = 2$ then $x^2 = 4$" is true. However, its converse "If $x^2 = 4$ then $x = 2$" is false, since x may be -2.

EQUIVALENCE

Two statements A and B are **equivalent** if both $A \Rightarrow B$ *and* $B \Rightarrow A$. In this case we can say A is true if and only if B is true.

For example, the statement "If $x = -2$ or 2, then $x^2 = 4$" is true. The statement "If $x^2 = 4$ then $x = -2$ or 2" is also true. Therefore, $x = -2$ or $2 \Leftrightarrow x^2 = 4$.

EXERCISE 10A

1 For each statement, state its negation:

   a The cat is black.   b x is prime.   c The tree is deciduous.

2 State, with justification, whether each statement is true or false:

   a If $x^2 = 9$ then $x = 3$.   b If $x = 3$ then $x^2 = 9$.   c $x = 3$ if and only if $x^2 = 9$.

3 State, with justification, whether each statement is true or false:

   a If x is positive then $\sqrt{x} \in \mathbb{R}$.   b If $\sqrt{x} \in \mathbb{R}$ then x is positive.

   c x is positive if and only if $\sqrt{x} \in \mathbb{R}$.

4 a Write the converse of the statement "If Socrates is a cat then Socrates is an animal".

   b Is this converse true or false?

5 Determine whether A and B are equivalent:

   a A: $xyz = 0$, B: $(x = 0) \lor (y = 0) \lor (z = 0)$

   b A: x is even, B: x^2 is even

6 There are four cards on a table. Every card has a letter on one side and a number on the other. With the cards placed, you see:

> This problem is a well studied logic test, devised in 1966 by Peter Wason.

Identify precisely which cards you need to turn over, and which you do not, to establish the truth of the statement: "Every card which has a D on one side has a 7 on the other".

B   PROOF BY DEDUCTION

Throughout the course already, we have used algebra to show different results. In cases where we are given some information (the hypothesis) and are asked to prove something, we use a chain of implications. This is called **proof by deduction**.

We have mostly used the therefore symbol "∴" to indicate our implications, but we could have also used the implication symbol "$\Rightarrow$".

Since these arguments only need to go from the starting information to the conclusion, we also call this type of proof a "left-to-right" proof.

INVESTIGATION   **PYTHAGORAS' THEOREM**

Pythagoras' Theorem is one of the most famous results in mathematics:

> If a right angled triangle has sides a, b, and hypotenuse c, then $a^2 + b^2 = c^2$.

Proof by pictures:

The pictures below each show four copies of the original triangle, in different arrangements.

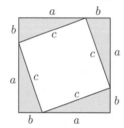   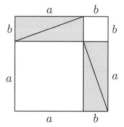

In each figure, the total area is $(a + b)^2$, and the shaded area is $4 \times \frac{1}{2}ab = 2ab$.

$\therefore$ the unshaded areas are equal

$\therefore$ $c^2 = a^2 + b^2$

In 1968, E. Loomis collected around 365 different proofs in his book *The Pythagorean Proposition* (National Council of Teachers of Mathematics, Washington). It might seem strange to have so many different proofs of the same thing, given that just one correct proof establishes the theorem. However, one purpose of proof is to help us understand the result, and different proofs can help develop this understanding.

What to do:

1 The sequence of pictures below shows shears and translations of parallelograms. Explain how the sequence proves Pythagoras' Theorem.

2 The sequence of pictures below shows shears and rotations of triangles. Explain how the sequence proves Pythagoras' Theorem.

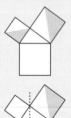

3 The figure below shows a jigsaw made from three pieces, in two arrangements. Explain how these prove Pythagoras' Theorem.

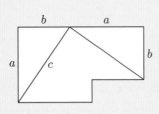 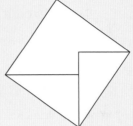

In a numerical or algebraic argument, we perform operations at each deductive step. For a proof by deduction to be valid, only a correct **implication** is required, rather than equivalence.

Example 1 🔊 **Self Tutor**

a Prove by deduction: "If $x < -5$ then $x^2 > 25$."

b Explain why the converse is *not* true.

---

a If $x < -5$ then $|x| > 5$ {geometric definition of absolute value}

$\therefore \ |x|^2 > 5^2$ {squaring both sides}

$\therefore \ x^2 > 25$ {$|x|^2 = x^2$}

b The converse would be: "If $x^2 > 25$ then $x < -5$."

This is not necessarily true because $6^2 > 25$, but $6 > -5$.

EXERCISE 10B

1 **a** Prove by deduction: "If $x = -2$ then $x^2 - x - 6 = 0$."

    b Explain why the converse is *not* true.

2 In the diagram alongside, three semi-circles have been constructed using the sides of a right angled triangle as diameters. The areas of the semi-circles are A, B, and C as shown. Prove that $A + B = C$.

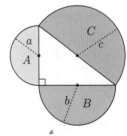

3 Suppose $a, b \in \mathbb{N}$. Let $x = a^2 - b^2$, $y = 2ab$, and $z = a^2 + b^2$. Prove that $x^2 + y^2 = z^2$.

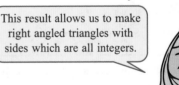

This result allows us to make right angled triangles with sides which are all integers.

4 Prove that the sum of three consecutive integers is divisible by 3.

5 The product of three consecutive integers is increased by the middle integer. Prove that the result is a perfect cube.

Hint: Let the middle number be x.

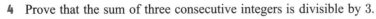

6 Prove that $\dfrac{a^2 + b^2}{2} \geqslant ab$ for all $a, b \in \mathbb{R}$.

7 Prove by deduction that $\sin 2\theta \tan \theta = 2 \sin^2 \theta$.

8 Consider a 3-digit number "abc", $a \neq c$. Written backwards, it is "cba". Let S be the result when the smaller of the two numbers is subtracted from the larger. When S is written backwards and the result is added to S, prove that the sum is always 1089.

For example: 276 backwards is 672, so $S = 396$ and $396 + 693 = 1089$.

9 The following "proofs" by deduction are incorrect. Identify the incorrect step(s) in each case:

a $4x^2 = 3x$

$\therefore \ 4x = 3$

$\therefore \ x = \frac{3}{4}$

b $(x + 3)(2 - x) = 4$

$\therefore \ x + 3 = 4 \ \text{ or } \ 2 - x = 4$

$\therefore \ x = 1 \ \text{ or } \ x = -2$

HISTORICAL NOTE

Charles Lutwidge Dodgson (1832 - 1898) was a lecturer of mathematics at Christ Church college, Oxford. A curious and controversial figure, he is best known by his pen name, **Lewis Carroll**, under which he wrote a number of books including *Alice's Adventures in Wonderland* (1865) and *Through the Looking-Glass and What Alice Found There* (1871).

In his latter years, Carroll wrote several more mathematical books, including *The Game of Logic* (1886) and *Symbolic Logic* (1896). These books include numerous "nonsense" statements written to challenge the reader as to what, if anything, could be deduced from them.

Charles Lutwidge Dodgson

For example, consider these statements from *The Game of Logic*:

- "No bald person needs a hair-brush; No lizards have hair."
  We can deduce that since lizards do not have hair, they do not need a hair-brush.

- "Some oysters are silent; No silent creatures are amusing."
  We can deduce that silent oysters are not amusing, but we cannot say anything about oysters which are not silent.

- "No riddles interest me that can be solved; All these riddles are insoluble."
  We can deduce nothing from these statements, because no comment is made about whether insoluble riddles interest him.

Think about these for yourself:

- Toothache is never pleasant; Warmth is never unpleasant.
- All uneducated men are shallow; All these students are educated.
- No lobsters are unreasonable; No reasonable creatures expect impossibilities.
- No misers are generous; Some old men are not generous.
- Sugar is sweet; Some sweet things are liked by children.
- "I saw it in a newspaper; All newspapers tell lies."
- All wasps are unfriendly; No puppies are unfriendly.

PROOF BY EQUIVALENCE

In proof by deduction, we were only concerned with moving in one direction.

This means that if we want to show that two statements A and B are *equivalent*, then we would need to prove both $A \Rightarrow B$ and $B \Rightarrow A$ separately.

However, if we can construct an argument so that each deductive step is an equivalence, then we will prove $A \Rightarrow B$ and $B \Rightarrow A$ at the same time.

For example, to deduce the solutions of $(x+1)^3 = x^3 + 1$ we can write the following series of equivalent statements:

Reasoning by equivalence is stronger than deduction because the converse must also be true in every step.

$$(x + 1)^3 = x^3 + 1$$
$$\Leftrightarrow \quad x^3 + 3x^2 + 3x + 1 = x^3 + 1$$
$$\Leftrightarrow \quad 3x^2 + 3x = 0$$
$$\Leftrightarrow \quad 3x(x + 1) = 0$$
$$\Leftrightarrow \quad x = 0 \text{ or } x = -1$$

This chain of reasoning relies on the facts that:

- two equations are equivalent if they have precisely the same solutions
- two functions $p(x)$ and $q(x)$ are equivalent if $p(x) = q(x)$ for all $x \in \mathbb{R}$.

> To maintain mathematical equivalence, we can:
> - add or subtract the same term from both sides of an equation
> - multiply or divide both sides of an equation by a non-zero term
> - substitute for an equivalent sub-term, for example by replacing a term by its factored or expanded form.

There are some other operations which maintain equivalence, for example some of the rules of logarithms with positive terms.

However, squaring or taking square roots of both sides of an equation does not maintain equivalence!

Given $a^2 = b^2$, taking the square root of both sides gives $a = b$. However, in doing this we have ignored the possibility that $a = -b$.

Instead, we use the difference between two squares result as follows:

$$a^2 = b^2$$
$$\Leftrightarrow \quad a^2 - b^2 = 0$$
$$\Leftrightarrow \quad (a - b)(a + b) = 0 \qquad \text{\{difference between two squares\}}$$
$$\Leftrightarrow \quad a - b = 0 \text{ or } a + b = 0 \quad \text{\{null factor law\}}$$
$$\Leftrightarrow \quad a = b \text{ or } a = -b$$
$$\Leftrightarrow \quad a = \pm b$$

Using this procedure, equivalence is maintained. With experience, mathematicians *compress* this working into a single step.

Example 2   ◀ **Self Tutor**

Find the smallest positive integer a for which $x^2 + (a-2)x + a = 0$ has real solutions.

$$x^2 + (a-2)x + a = 0$$

$$\Leftrightarrow \quad \left(x + \frac{a-2}{2}\right)^2 - \left(\frac{a-2}{2}\right)^2 + a = 0 \qquad \{\text{completing the square}\}$$

$$\Leftrightarrow \qquad\qquad \left(x + \frac{a-2}{2}\right)^2 = \frac{(a-2)^2}{4} - a$$

The equation has real solutions if and only if

$$\frac{(a-2)^2}{4} - a \geqslant 0$$

$$\Leftrightarrow \qquad (a-2)^2 - 4a \geqslant 0$$

$$\Leftrightarrow \qquad a^2 - 8a + 4 \geqslant 0$$

$$\Leftrightarrow \quad (a-4)^2 - 16 + 4 \geqslant 0$$

$$\Leftrightarrow \qquad (a-4)^2 \geqslant 12$$

$$\Leftrightarrow \qquad a - 4 \geqslant \sqrt{12} \ \text{ or } \ a - 4 \leqslant -\sqrt{12}$$

$$\Leftrightarrow \qquad a \geqslant 4 + \sqrt{12} \approx 7.46 \ \text{ or } \ a \leqslant 4 - \sqrt{12} \approx 0.536$$

$\therefore$ the smallest positive integer a for which the equation has real solutions is $a = 8$.

EXERCISE 10C

1 Prove that:

    a $(a+b)^2 - (a-b)^2 = 4ab$ **b** $(a+b)^2 - 4(a-b)^2 = (3b-a)(3a-b)$

2 Find the smallest positive integer a for which $x^2 + (a-3)x + 2a = 0$ has real solutions.

3 Prove that $(x-y)^5 + (x-y)^3 = 0$ if and only if $x = y$.

4   **a** Expand and collect like terms: $(n^2 - 2n + 2)(n^2 + 2n + 2)$

    b Hence find all integers n such that $n^4 + 4$ is prime.

5   **a** Prove that $(k+1)^2 - (k-1)^2 = 4k$.

    b Hence find two square numbers that have difference:

        i 40   **ii** 100.

6 The following "proofs" end in nonsensical results. Identify the incorrect step(s) in each case:

a
$$a = b$$
$$\Leftrightarrow \qquad a^2 = ab$$
$$\Leftrightarrow \qquad a^2 - b^2 = ab - b^2$$
$$\Leftrightarrow \quad (a-b)(a+b) = b(a-b)$$
$$\Leftrightarrow \qquad a + b = b$$
$$\Leftrightarrow \qquad 2a = a$$
$$\Leftrightarrow \qquad 2 = 1$$

b
$$\frac{x+10}{x-6} - 5 = \frac{4x-40}{13-x}$$
$$\Leftrightarrow \quad \frac{x+10 - 5(x-6)}{x-6} = \frac{4x-40}{13-x}$$
$$\Leftrightarrow \qquad \frac{4x-40}{6-x} = \frac{4x-40}{13-x}$$
$$\Leftrightarrow \qquad 6 - x = 13 - x$$
$$\Leftrightarrow \qquad 6 = 13$$

7 The following "proofs" give correct results but their methods are incorrect. Identify the incorrect step(s) in each case:

a
$$6x - 12 = 3(x - 2)$$
$$\Leftrightarrow \quad 6x - 12 + 3(x - 2) = 0$$
$$\Leftrightarrow \quad 12x - 24 = 0$$
$$\Leftrightarrow \quad x = 2$$

b
$$x^2 - 6x + 9 = 0$$
$$\Leftrightarrow \quad x^2 - 6x = -9$$
$$\Leftrightarrow \quad x(x - 6) = 3(-3)$$
$$\Leftrightarrow \quad x = 3 \ \text{ or } \ x - 6 = -3$$
$$\Leftrightarrow \quad x = 3$$

8 The sum of fractions $\frac{1}{4} + \frac{1}{12} = \frac{1}{3}$ has the form $\dfrac{1}{m} + \dfrac{1}{3m} = \dfrac{4}{3m}$ where $m = 4$, or alternatively the form $\dfrac{1}{n + 1} + \dfrac{1}{n^2 + n} = \dfrac{1}{n}$ where $n = 3$.

a Prove by equivalence: **i** $\dfrac{1}{m} + \dfrac{1}{3m} = \dfrac{4}{3m}$ **ii** $\dfrac{1}{n + 1} + \dfrac{1}{n^2 + n} = \dfrac{1}{n}$ for $n \neq 0, -1$.

b Is it accurate to say that $\dfrac{1}{n + 1} + \dfrac{1}{n^2 + n}$ is equivalent to $\dfrac{1}{n}$? Explain your answer.

DISCUSSION   DIRECT AND INDIRECT PROOFS

In a **direct proof** we start with the hypothesis and work forward to the conclusion.

For example, here is a direct proof that if $a < b$ then $a < \dfrac{a + b}{2}$:

> **Proof:** $\qquad\qquad a < b$
>
> $\Rightarrow \qquad\qquad \dfrac{a}{2} < \dfrac{b}{2} \qquad\qquad$ {dividing by 2 which is > 0}
>
> $\Rightarrow \qquad \dfrac{a}{2} + \dfrac{a}{2} < \dfrac{a}{2} + \dfrac{b}{2} \qquad$ {adding $\dfrac{a}{2}$ to both sides}
>
> $\Rightarrow \qquad\qquad a < \dfrac{a + b}{2}$

In **proof by contradiction** we deliberately assume the opposite to what we are trying to prove. By a series of correct steps we show that this is impossible, hence our assumption must be false, and so its opposite is true. We call this an **indirect proof** because we do not start with the hypothesis.

For example, here is a proof by contradiction that if $a < b$ then $a < \dfrac{a + b}{2}$:

> **Proof (by contradiction):**
>
> For $a < b$, suppose that $\quad a \geqslant \dfrac{a + b}{2}$
>
> $\Rightarrow \quad 2a \geqslant 2\left(\dfrac{a + b}{2}\right) \qquad$ {multiplying both sides by 2}
>
> $\Rightarrow \quad 2a \geqslant a + b$
>
> $\Rightarrow \quad a \geqslant b \qquad\qquad$ {subtracting a from both sides}
>
> This is a contradiction to our assumption, so the supposition must be false and the alternative, $a < \dfrac{a + b}{2}$ must be true.

1 Can a proof by contradiction be considered a proof by deduction or proof by equivalence?

2 Is an indirect proof "cheating"?

D   DEFINITIONS

THEORY OF KNOWLEDGE

In mathematics we clearly *define* terms so there is no misunderstanding of their exact meaning.

For example:

- A **rational number** is a number which can be written in the form $\frac{p}{q}$ where $p, q \in \mathbb{Z}$, $q \neq 0$.
- An integer n is **even** if $n = 2k$ for some integer k.
- An integer n is **odd** if $n = 2k + 1$ for some integer k.

We can understand the need for specific definitions by considering integers and rational numbers:

- 2 is an integer, and is also a rational number since $2 = \frac{4}{2}$.
- $\frac{4}{2}$ is a rational number, and is also an integer since $\frac{4}{2} = 2$.
- $\frac{4}{3}$ is a rational number, but is *not* an integer.

1 Why is it important that mathematicians use the same definitions?

2 Words such as *similar, or, function, domain, range, period,* and *wave* are common words in English, but also have different or more specific mathematical definitions.

   For each of these words, discuss the difference between their mathematical definition and their common use in English.

3 What is the difference between *equal, equivalent,* and *the same*? Why is it important to distinguish between these terms?

4 Are there any words which we use only in mathematics? What does this tell us about the nature of mathematics and the world around us?

Example 3   ◀ **Self Tutor**

Prove that $0.\overline{13} \in \mathbb{Q}$.

> Let $x = 0.\overline{13} = 0.1313131313....$
> $\Rightarrow \quad 100x = 13.13131313....$
> $\Rightarrow \quad 100x = 13 + x$
> $\Rightarrow \quad 99x = 13$
> $\Rightarrow \quad x = \frac{13}{99}$
> $\Rightarrow \quad x \in \mathbb{Q}$
> $\Rightarrow \quad 0.\overline{13} \in \mathbb{Q}$

This Example requires the definition of rational numbers.

Example 4   ◀ **Self Tutor**

Prove that the sum of any two rational numbers is also a rational number.

Proof:

Let x and y be two rational numbers.

By definition, there exists $p, q \in \mathbb{Z}$, $q \neq 0$ so that $x = \frac{p}{q}$.

By definition, there exists $r, s \in \mathbb{Z}$, $s \neq 0$ so that $y = \frac{r}{s}$.

So, $x + y = \dfrac{p}{q} + \dfrac{r}{s} = \dfrac{ps + rq}{qs}$

Since p, q, r, s are all integers, $ps + rq$ is an integer which we call P.

Since q, s are non-zero integers, qs is a non-zero integer which we call Q.

$\therefore \quad x + y = \dfrac{ps + rq}{qs} = \dfrac{P}{Q}$ where $P, Q \in \mathbb{Z}$, $Q \neq 0$

$\therefore$ by definition, $x + y$ is a rational number.

We have written this proof in great detail. However, the whole point of a proof is that you should be able to check each step easily.

Mathematicians sometimes choose to leave out steps to make the argument shorter and easier to read. If the reader trusts the writer this is fine. However, it should always be possible to fill in the missing steps.

Learning which steps to include is part of learning how to write a mathematical proof.

Try to include steps of about the same "size". Sudden large jumps in the proof make people suspicious!

EXERCISE 10D

1 Prove that $0.\overline{9} \in \mathbb{Z}$.

2 Prove that:

    a $0.\overline{4} \in \mathbb{Q}$ **b** $0.\overline{23} \in \mathbb{Q}$ **c** $0.0\overline{79} \in \mathbb{Q}$

3 Prove that the infinite geometric series $\left(4 - \sqrt{2}\right) + \dfrac{4 - \sqrt{2}}{3 - \sqrt{2}} + \dfrac{4 - \sqrt{2}}{(3 - \sqrt{2})^2} + \dfrac{4 - \sqrt{2}}{(3 - \sqrt{2})^3} + \ldots \in \mathbb{Z}$.

4 Prove that the difference between any two rational numbers is also a rational number.

5 Prove that the product of any two rational numbers is also a rational number.

6 Prove that the product of two odd integers is odd.

7 Prove that if p and q are odd integers then $p^2 - q^2$ is divisible by 8.

8 Prove that if p and q are consecutive odd integers, $p > q$, then $p^3 - q^3 - 2$ is divisible by 24.

9 If a, b, c are integers and $ax^2 + bx + c = 0$ has rational root $\dfrac{r}{s}$ in lowest terms, prove that s is a factor of a, and r is a factor of c.

DISCUSSION

Mathematical definitions are very difficult to write. They are often the result of careful thought by many experienced mathematicians. Once commonly accepted, they rarely change, because if they did it would cause great confusion.

Definitions collect similar examples together. When attempting to understand something, it is always worth building up a collection of examples which do and do not satisfy the definition.

Discuss how you could define a *chair*.

THEORY OF KNOWLEDGE

An **axiom** is a statement that is taken to always be true. Axioms form the foundation for proofs of all results and theorems in mathematics.

For example, these are the axioms for addition and multiplication on the real numbers:

Axiom 1:   Associativity: $a + (b + c) = (a + b) + c$ and $a \times (b \times c) = (a \times b) \times c$

Axiom 2:   Commutativity: $a + b = b + a$ and $a \times b = b \times a$

Axiom 3:   Distributivity: $a \times (b + c) = a \times b + a \times c$

Axiom 4:   Additive identity: $a + 0 = a$ and Multiplicative identity: $a \times 1 = a$

Axiom 5:   Additive inverse: $a + (-a) = 0$ and Multiplicative inverse: $a \times a^{-1} = 1$.

Using only these axioms, we can prove that $0 \times x = x \times 0 = 0$ for all $x \in \mathbb{R}$.

Proof:

$$0 = 0 + 0$$
$$\therefore \ 0 \times x = (0 + 0) \times x \qquad \text{\{multiplying both sides by } x\}$$
$$\therefore \ 0 \times x = 0 \times x + 0 \times x \qquad \text{\{Axiom 3\}}$$
$$\therefore \ 0 \times x + (-(0 \times x)) = (0 \times x + 0 \times x) + (-(0 \times x)) \qquad \text{\{adding the additive inverse}$$
$$\text{of } 0 \times x\}$$
$$\therefore \ 0 \times x + (-(0 \times x)) = (0 \times x) + [0 \times x + (-(0 \times x))] \qquad \text{\{Axiom 1\}}$$
$$\therefore \ 0 = 0 \times x + 0$$
$$\therefore \ 0 = 0 \times x \qquad \text{\{Axiom 4\}}$$
$$\therefore \ 0 \times x = 0 = x \times 0 \qquad \text{\{Axiom 2\}}$$

1 Is an axiom a definition, an assumption, both, or neither?

2 Is it necessarily practical to *only* use axioms to prove results?

Axioms are important because they cannot be proven. In some ways, they are similar to the fundamental Laws of Physics and other sciences.

3 Some fundamental laws of physics, such as Newton's Laws, have been verified via strong experimental evidence and therefore are generally accepted. Why does this not work for mathematical axioms?

In 1939, Austrian mathematician **Kurt Gödel** proved that there does not exist any set of consistent axioms that is able to prove everything. In other words, there will be results that cannot be proved. This result is known as **Gödel's incompleteness theorem**.

4 Does this mean that we must accept unprovable results as axioms?

5 Are there an infinite number of axioms?

Kurt Gödel

In 1637, French mathematician **Pierre de Fermat** famously claimed that the equation $a^n + b^n = c^n$ where $n > 2$, $n \in \mathbb{N}$ has no integer solutions for a, b, and c. He scrawled this in the margin of a copy of *Arithmetica*, claiming that his proof was too large for the margin to contain.

This statement became known as **Fermat's Last Theorem**. It remained unproved for 350 years until British mathematician **Andrew Wiles** proved it in 1994. Whether or not Fermat's supposed proof was valid is debatable, as Wiles required modern mathematical methods from after Fermat's time.

6 Are we *discovering* mathematics or *inventing* it?

7 Can two people "discover" the same thing?

REVIEW SET 10A

1 The roots of $f(x) = x^2 + px + q$ are a and b. Prove that $q = ab$ and $p = -(a+b)$.

2 Prove that:
   a $2.\overline{9} \in \mathbb{Z}$
   b $0.\overline{38} \in \mathbb{Q}$

3 State the negation of each statement:
   a The boy has blue eyes.
   b x is larger than 4.

4 State, with justification, whether each statement is true or false.
   a If a function f is periodic with period p, then $f(x+p) = f(x)$ for all x.
   b If $f(x+p) = f(x)$ for all x, then f is periodic with period p.
   c f is periodic with period p if and only if $f(x+p) = f(x)$ for all x.

5 Prove that $9a^2 + b^2 \geqslant 6ab$ for all $a, b \in \mathbb{R}$.

6 **a** Prove by equivalence that $\tan^2 \theta - \sin^2 \theta = \tan^2 \theta \sin^2 \theta$.

   b **i** Prove by deduction that $\dfrac{1 - \sin^2 \theta}{\cos \theta} = \cos \theta$.

   ii Explain why the argument in **i** cannot be strengthened to equivalence for all θ.

7 Prove that the quotient of two non-zero rational numbers is also a rational number.

8 **a** Evaluate the following, and state whether the result is prime or composite:
   i $1^3 + 2^3$ **ii** $2^3 + 3^3$ **iii** $3^3 + 4^3$ **iv** $4^3 + 5^3$
   b Prove that $k^3 + (k+1)^3 = (2k+1)(k^2 + k + 1)$.
   c Hence prove that the sum of two consecutive positive cubes is always composite.

REVIEW SET 10B

1 Let $p(x) = x^2 + 2bx + c$ and define $q(x) = p(x - b)$. Prove that $q(x) = q(-x)$ for all x.

2 Prove that $\dfrac{a+b}{2} \geqslant \sqrt{ab}$ for all $a, b \in \mathbb{R}^+$.

3 Consider the statement: "If x is acute then $\sin x$ is positive".

    a Is the statement true or false?   **b** Write the converse of the statement.

    c Is the converse true or false?

4 Determine whether A and B are equivalent:

    a A: x is not prime, B: x is composite

    b A: x and y are both odd integers, B: xy is odd

5 Prove that if k is an odd integer then $k^3 + k^2 - k - 1$ is divisible by 8.

6 Prove that, in an equilateral triangle, the sum of the distances from any point in the triangle to the three sides is a constant.

7 Prove that the difference between the two digit numbers "ab" and "ba" is always divisible by 9.

8 Identify the incorrect step in the following "proof":

$$-6 = -6$$
$$\Leftrightarrow \quad 9 - 15 = 4 - 10$$
$$\Leftrightarrow \quad 3^2 - 3 \times 5 = 2^2 - 2 \times 5$$
$$\Leftrightarrow \quad 3^2 - 2 \times 3 \times \tfrac{5}{2} + \left(\tfrac{5}{2}\right)^2 = 2^2 - 2 \times 2 \times \tfrac{5}{2} + \left(\tfrac{5}{2}\right)^2$$
$$\Leftrightarrow \quad \left(3 - \tfrac{5}{2}\right)^2 = \left(2 - \tfrac{5}{2}\right)^2$$
$$\Leftrightarrow \quad 3 - \tfrac{5}{2} = 2 - \tfrac{5}{2}$$
$$\Leftrightarrow \quad 3 = 2$$

Chapter 11

Introduction to differential calculus

OPENING PROBLEM

Suppose we add water to a container at a constant rate. The depth of the water increases over time.

Things to think about:

a Think about the graph of the *volume of water added* against *time*.

   i Can you explain why this graph is a straight line passing through the origin?

   ii What does the *gradient* of the straight line tell us?

b Think about the graph of the *depth of water* against *time*.

   i Can you explain why this graph is a straight line for a cylindrical container?

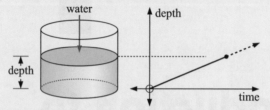

   ii Can you explain why this graph is *not* a straight line for the container shown?

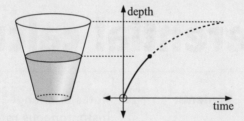

c By examining the shape of each container, can you predict the depth-time graph when water is added at a constant rate?

   i   **ii**   **iii**   **iv**   **v**

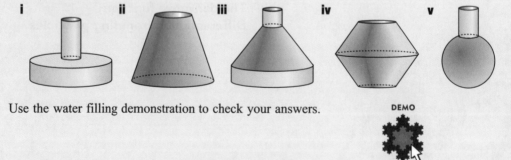

Use the water filling demonstration to check your answers.   **DEMO**

d Consider the depth-time graph alongside.

   i How can we measure the *average rate* at which the depth increases from $t = 5$ to $t = 10$ seconds?

   ii How can we measure the *instantaneous rate* at which the depth is increasing at the instant when $t = 8$ seconds?

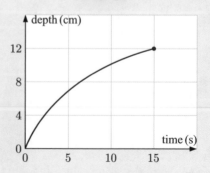

If the relationship between two variables is a straight line, the gradient of the line tells us the rate at which one variable changes with respect to the other.

For example, in a travel graph showing distance against time, the gradient of a straight line segment tells us the *speed* of the object.

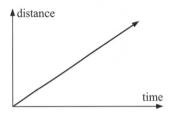

In the real world, rates such as speed are constantly changing. Their travel graphs are curves rather than straight lines. In order to calculate the instantaneous speed of an object, we need a branch of mathematics called **differential calculus**.

Differential calculus deals with **rates of change**. It has widespread applications in science, engineering, and finance.

A   RATES OF CHANGE

> A **rate** is a comparison between two quantities with different units.

We often judge performances by rates. For example:

- Sir Donald Bradman's average batting rate at Test cricket level was 99.94 runs per innings.
- Michael Jordan's average basketball scoring rate was 30.1 points per game.
- Rangi's average typing rate is 63 words per minute with an error rate of 2.3 errors per page.

CONSTANT RATES OF CHANGE

Suppose water from a hose is used to fill a swimming pool. The volume of water in the pool is recorded at 1 minute intervals in the table alongside.

Time (minutes)	0	1	2	3	4	5
Volume (litres)	0	15	30	45	60	75

+15 +15 +15 +15 +15

Notice that the volume of water increases by the same amount each time interval. The rate of change in volume is constant, so the graph of *volume* against *time* is a straight line.

The **gradient** of the line gives the rate of change:

$$\text{rate of flow} = \frac{15 - 0}{1 - 0}$$

$$= 15 \text{ litres per minute}$$

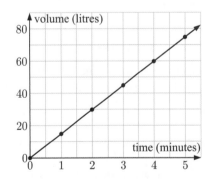

EXERCISE 11A.1

1 The table alongside shows the distance travelled by a jogger at 30-second intervals.

Time (seconds)	0	30	60	90	120	150
Distance (metres)	0	90	180	270	360	450

   a Is the jogger travelling at a constant speed? Explain your answer.

   b Draw the graph of distance against time.

   c Find the speed of the jogger in metres per second.

2 This graph shows the height of a seedling during its first 10 weeks.

  a Is the height changing at a constant rate? Explain your answer.

  b Find the rate of change in height.

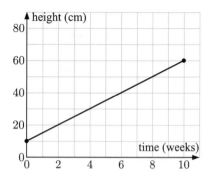

3 Find the rate of change for each function. Do not include units in your answer.

  a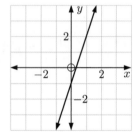

  b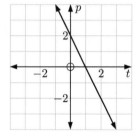

  c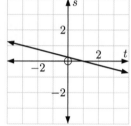

4 Find the rate of change for the function $f(x) = \frac{5}{2}x - 3$.

AVERAGE RATES OF CHANGE

In most real-world situations, rates of change are not constant. They vary over time.

For example, this graph shows the temperature of a glass of water which is left in the sun. The graph is not a straight line, which means the rate of change in temperature is not constant. The temperature increases quickly at first, and then more slowly as time goes by.

In such cases, we can find an **average rate of change** over a particular time interval.

For example, from time $t = 0$ to $t = 2$ minutes, the temperature increases from 5°C to 20°C. So, the average rate of change is $\dfrac{20 - 5}{2 - 0} = 7.5°\text{C}$ per minute.

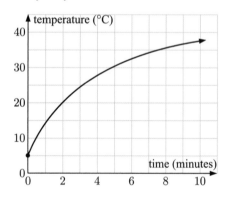

In the context of functions, we say that:

The **average rate of change** in $f(x)$ from $x = a$ to $x = b$ is $\dfrac{f(b) - f(a)}{b - a}$.

This is the **gradient of the chord [AB]**.

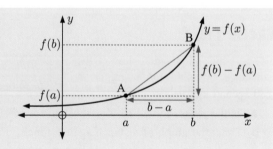

EXERCISE 11A.2

1   Aileen is driving from Amsterdam to Zurich. This graph shows the distance travelled against time.

   a   Did Aileen travel at constant speed? Explain your answer.

   b   Find Aileen's average speed for:

   i   the first 5 hours   **ii**   the final 5 hours.

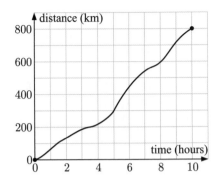

2   Chris went hiking in the mountains. His elevation above sea level is shown on this graph.

   Find Chris' average rate of change in elevation from:

   a $t = 1$ hour to $t = 2.5$ hours

   b $t = 3.5$ hours to $t = 6$ hours.

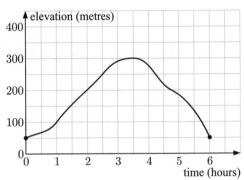

3   For each function, find the average rate of change in $f(x)$ from A to B:

   a
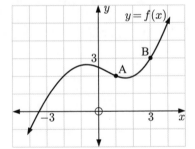

   b
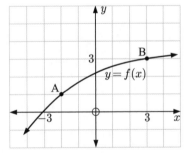

   c
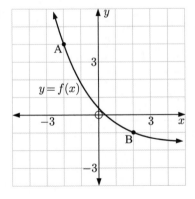

   d
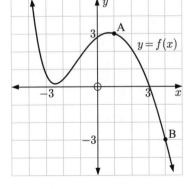

4 Consider the graph of $f(x) = x^2$.

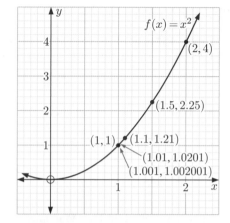

    a Find the average rate of change in $f(x)$ from:

        i $x = 1$ to $x = 2$

        ii $x = 1$ to $x = 1.5$

        iii $x = 1$ to $x = 1.1$

        iv $x = 1$ to $x = 1.01$

        v $x = 1$ to $x = 1.001$

    b Comment on your answers in **a**.

B   INSTANTANEOUS RATES OF CHANGE

Suppose the speedometer in a car indicates that you are travelling at 60 km per hour. This is not an average speed, but an *instantaneous speed*. It is the speed at which you are travelling at that particular instant.

INVESTIGATION 1   INSTANTANEOUS SPEED

A ball bearing is dropped from the top of a tall building. The distance D it has fallen after t seconds is recorded, and the following graph of distance against time is obtained.

Consider a fixed point F on the curve when $t = 2$ seconds. We now choose another point M on the curve, and draw the line segment or **chord** [FM] between the two points. To start with, let M be the point when $t = 4$ seconds.

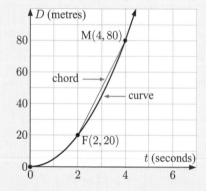

The *average* speed of the ball bearing over the time interval $2 \leqslant t \leqslant 4$

$$= \frac{\text{distance travelled}}{\text{time taken}}$$

$$= \frac{(80 - 20)\,\text{m}}{(4 - 2)\,\text{s}}$$

$$= \tfrac{60}{2}\,\text{m s}^{-1}$$

$$= 30\,\text{m s}^{-1}$$

In this Investigation we will try to measure the *instantaneous* speed of the ball bearing when $t = 2$ seconds.

What to do:

DEMO

1 Click on the icon to start the demonstration.

The gradient of the chord [FM] is shown. This is the *average speed* of the ball bearing in the interval from F to M. For M at $t = 4$ seconds, you should see that the average speed is 30 m s^{-1}.

2 Click on M and drag it slowly towards F. Copy and complete the table alongside, where M corresponds to the given value of t.

t	gradient of [FM]
4	30
3	
2.5	
2.1	
2.01	

3 Observe what happens as M reaches F. Explain why this is so.

4 What do you suspect is the instantaneous speed of the ball bearing when $t = 2$ seconds? Explain your answer.

5 Move M to the origin, and then slide it towards F from the left. Copy and complete the table, where M again corresponds to the given value of t.

t	gradient of [FM]
0	
1.5	
1.9	
1.99	

6 Do your results agree with those in **4**?

If A and B are two points on a function, the gradient of the chord [AB] is the average rate of change between these points.

From the **Investigation**, if we let B get closer and closer to A, then the average rate of change from A to B will approach the *instantaneous* rate of change at A.

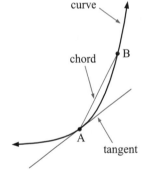

However, as B gets closer to A, the chord [AB] approaches the line which *touches* the curve at A. This line is called the **tangent** to the curve at A.

DEMO

In particular, as B approaches A, the gradient of [AB] approaches the gradient of the tangent at A.

The **instantaneous rate of change** in $f(x)$ at any point A on the curve is the **gradient of the tangent** at A.

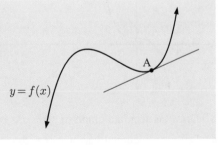

$y = f(x)$

Example 1   ◀)) **Self Tutor**

Use the tangents drawn to find the instantaneous rate of change in $y = f(x)$ at:

    a A   **b** B

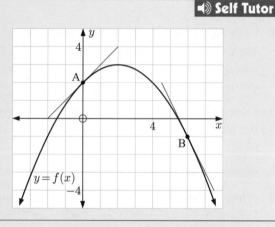

a The tangent at A has gradient 1.
   ∴ the instantaneous rate of change at A is 1.

b The tangent at B has gradient -2.
   ∴ the instantaneous rate of change at B is -2.

EXERCISE 11B

1 This graph shows the distance travelled by a swimmer in a pool.

Use the tangents drawn to find the swimmer's instantaneous speed after:

    a 30 seconds   **b** 90 seconds.

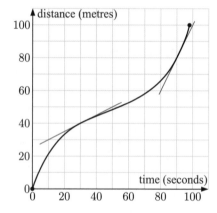

2

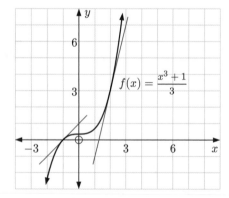

The graph of $f(x) = \dfrac{x^3 + 1}{3}$ is shown alongside.

Use the tangents drawn to find the instantaneous rate of change in $f(x)$ at:

    a $x = -1$ **b** $x = 2$.

3   **a** Draw an accurate graph of $y = x^2$ on a fine grid.

    b Draw, as accurately as possible, the tangent to $y = x^2$ at $x = -1$.

    c Hence find the instantaneous rate of change in $y = x^2$ when $x = -1$.

PRINTABLE GRAPH

C   LIMITS

Drawing a tangent on a graph and measuring its gradient can be time-consuming and inaccurate. We therefore seek a more efficient and accurate method for finding the gradient of a tangent.

We cannot find the gradient of the tangent at point A by direct calculation, because we only know one point on the tangent. However, if B is another point on the function $y = f(x)$, the gradient of the chord [AB] is $\dfrac{f(a + h) - f(a)}{h}$.

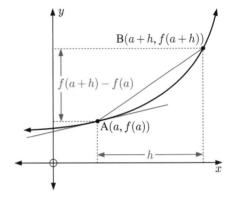

To calculate the gradient of the tangent at A, we let the point B get closer and closer to A. This means that the horizontal step h becomes infinitely small.

To understand what happens when this occurs, we use a mathematical principle called **limits**.

The following definition of a limit is informal but adequate for the purposes of this course:

> If $f(x)$ is as close as we like to some real number A for all x sufficiently close to (but not equal to) a, then we say that $f(x)$ has a **limit** of A as x approaches a, and we write $\lim\limits_{x \to a} f(x) = A$.
>
> In this case, $f(x)$ is said to **converge** to A as x approaches a.

Notice that the limit is defined for x close to but *not equal to* a. Whether the function f is defined or not at $x = a$ is not important to the definition of the limit of f as x approaches a. What *is* important is the behaviour of the function as x gets *very close to* a.

For example, suppose we wish to find the limit of $f(x) = \dfrac{5x + x^2}{x}$ as $x \to 0$.

It is tempting for us to simply substitute $x = 0$ into $f(x)$. However, in doing this, not only do we get the meaningless value of $\frac{0}{0}$, but also we ignore the basic limit definition.

Instead, observe that if $f(x) = \dfrac{5x + x^2}{x} = \dfrac{x(5 + x)}{x}$

then $f(x) = \begin{cases} 5 + x & \text{if } x \neq 0 \\ \text{is undefined if } x = 0. \end{cases}$

The graph of $y = f(x)$ is therefore the straight line $y = x + 5$ with the point $(0, 5)$ missing, called a **point of discontinuity** of the function.

However, even though this point is missing, the *limit* of $f(x)$ as x approaches 0 does exist. In particular, as $x \to 0$ from either direction, $f(x) \to 5$.

We write $\lim\limits_{x \to 0} \dfrac{5x + x^2}{x} = 5$ which reads:

"the limit as x approaches 0, of $\dfrac{5x + x^2}{x}$, is 5".

In practice we do not need to graph functions each time to determine limits, and most can be found algebraically.

Example 2   ◀)) **Self Tutor**

Evaluate:

a $\displaystyle\lim_{x\to 2} x^2$ **b** $\displaystyle\lim_{x\to 0} \frac{x^2 + 3x}{x}$ **c** $\displaystyle\lim_{x\to 3} \frac{x^2 - 9}{x - 3}$

a x^2 can be made as close as we like to 4 by making x sufficiently close to 2.

$\therefore \displaystyle\lim_{x\to 2} x^2 = 4.$

b $\displaystyle\lim_{x\to 0} \frac{x^2 + 3x}{x}$

$= \displaystyle\lim_{x\to 0} \frac{\cancel{x}(x + 3)}{\cancel{x}}$

$= \displaystyle\lim_{x\to 0} (x + 3)$ {since $x \neq 0$}

$= 3$ {as $x \to 0$, $x + 3 \to 3$}

c $\displaystyle\lim_{x\to 3} \frac{x^2 - 9}{x - 3}$

$= \displaystyle\lim_{x\to 3} \frac{(x + 3)\cancel{(x - 3)}}{\cancel{x - 3}}$

$= \displaystyle\lim_{x\to 3} (x + 3)$ {since $x \neq 3$}

$= 6$ {as $x \to 3$, $x + 3 \to 6$}

EXERCISE 11C.1

1 Evaluate:

a $\displaystyle\lim_{x\to 3} (x + 4)$ **b** $\displaystyle\lim_{x\to -1} (5 - 2x)$ **c** $\displaystyle\lim_{x\to 4} (3x - 1)$

d $\displaystyle\lim_{x\to 2} (5x^2 - 3x + 2)$ **e** $\displaystyle\lim_{h\to 0} h^2(1 - h)$ **f** $\displaystyle\lim_{x\to 0} (x^2 + 5)$

2 Evaluate:

a $\displaystyle\lim_{x\to 0} 5$ **b** $\displaystyle\lim_{h\to 2} 7$ **c** $\displaystyle\lim_{x\to 0} c, \quad c$ a constant

3 Evaluate:

a $\displaystyle\lim_{x\to 1} \frac{x^2 - 3x}{x}$ **b** $\displaystyle\lim_{h\to 2} \frac{h^2 + 5h}{h}$ **c** $\displaystyle\lim_{x\to 0} \frac{x - 1}{x + 1}$

4 Explain why $\displaystyle\lim_{x\to 0} \frac{x}{x} = 1$, even though $\frac{0}{0}$ is meaningless.

5 **a** Copy and complete the tables of values alongside.

b Hence predict the value of $\displaystyle\lim_{x\to 2} \frac{x^2 - 4}{x - 2}$.

c Prove your result by evaluating $\displaystyle\lim_{x\to 2} \frac{x^2 - 4}{x - 2}$ directly.

x	$\dfrac{x^2 - 4}{x - 2}$
1.9	
1.99	
1.999	
1.9999	
1.99999	

x	$\dfrac{x^2 - 4}{x - 2}$
2.1	
2.01	
2.001	
2.0001	
2.00001	

6 Evaluate:

a $\displaystyle\lim_{x\to 0} \frac{x^2 - 3x}{x}$ **b** $\displaystyle\lim_{x\to 0} \frac{x^2 + 5x}{x}$ **c** $\displaystyle\lim_{x\to 0} \frac{2x^2 - x}{x}$

d $\displaystyle\lim_{h\to 0} \frac{2h^2 + 6h}{h}$ **e** $\displaystyle\lim_{h\to 0} \frac{3h^2 - 4h}{h}$ **f** $\displaystyle\lim_{h\to 0} \frac{h^3 - 8h}{h}$

g $\displaystyle\lim_{x\to 1} \frac{x^2 - x}{x - 1}$ **h** $\displaystyle\lim_{x\to 2} \frac{x^2 - 2x}{x - 2}$ **i** $\displaystyle\lim_{x\to 3} \frac{x^2 - x - 6}{x - 3}$

DISCUSSION

1 Do limits always exist?

2 Consider the graph of $f(x) = \dfrac{1}{x}$.

    a What happens to the graph as $x \to 0$ from the:
       i left   **ii** right?

    b Does $f(x) = \dfrac{1}{x}$ have a limit as $x \to 0$?

THEORY OF KNOWLEDGE

The Greek philosopher Zeno of Elea lived in what is now southern Italy, in the 5th century BC. He is most famous for his paradoxes, which were recorded in Aristotle's work *Physics*.

The arrow paradox

"If everything when it occupies an equal space is at rest, and if that which is in locomotion is always occupying such a space at any moment, the flying arrow is therefore motionless."

This argument says that if we choose any particular instant in time, the arrow is motionless. Therefore, how does the arrow actually move?

The dichotomy paradox

"That which is in locomotion must arrive at the half-way stage before it arrives at the goal."

If an object is to move a fixed distance then it must travel half that distance. Before it can travel a half the distance, it must travel a half *that* distance. With this process continuing indefinitely, motion is impossible.

Achilles and the tortoise

"In a race, the quickest runner can never overtake the slowest, since the pursuer must first reach the point from which the pursued started, and so the slower must always hold a lead."

According to this principle, the athlete Achilles will never be able to catch the slow tortoise!

1 A paradox is a logical argument that leads to a contradiction or a situation which defies logic or reason. Can a paradox be the truth?

2 Are Zeno's paradoxes really paradoxes?

3 Are the three paradoxes essentially the same?

4 We know from experience that things *do* move, and that Achilles *would* catch the tortoise. Does that mean that logic has failed?

5 What do Zeno's paradoxes have to do with limits?

LIMITS AT INFINITY

We can use the idea of limits to discuss the behaviour of functions for extreme values of x.

We write $x \to \infty$ to mean "x tends to plus infinity" and $x \to -\infty$ to mean "x tends to minus infinity".

Notice that as $x \to \infty$, the value of $\frac{1}{x}$ gets very small. In fact, we can make $\frac{1}{x}$ as close to 0 as we like by making x large enough. This means that $\lim\limits_{x \to \infty} \frac{1}{x} = 0$ even though $\frac{1}{x}$ never actually reaches 0.

We observe this on the graph of $y = \frac{1}{x}$ as the function tends towards its asymptote $y = 0$.

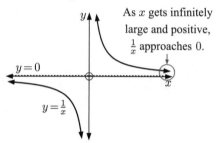

As x gets infinitely large and positive, $\frac{1}{x}$ approaches 0.

A function has a limit as $x \to \infty$ or as $x \to -\infty$ if the function is either a constant, or if it approaches a constant value. In the latter case, we observe this as a horizontal asymptote.

Example 3　　　　　　　　　　　　　　　　　　　🔊 **Self Tutor**

a Discuss the behaviour of $f(x) = \frac{2 - x}{1 + x}$ near its asymptotes, and hence deduce their equations.

b If they exist, state the values of $\lim\limits_{x \to -\infty} f(x)$ and $\lim\limits_{x \to \infty} f(x)$.

---

a As $x \to -1^-$,　$f(x) \to -\infty$

As $x \to -1^+$,　$f(x) \to \infty$

As $x \to -\infty$,　$f(x) \to -1^-$

As $x \to \infty$,　　$f(x) \to -1^+$

The vertical asymptote is $x = -1$.

The horizontal asymptote is $y = -1$.

b $\lim\limits_{x \to -\infty} f(x) = -1$ and $\lim\limits_{x \to \infty} f(x) = -1$.

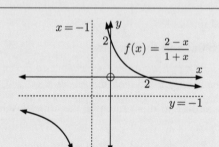

Example 4　　　　　　　　　　　　　　　　　　　🔊 **Self Tutor**

Find, if possible:　　**a** $\lim\limits_{x \to -\infty} (3 - e^{-x})$　　**b** $\lim\limits_{x \to \infty} (3 - e^{-x})$.

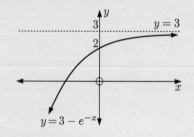

a As $x \to -\infty$, $3 - e^{-x} \to -\infty$.

Since $3 - e^{-x}$ does not approach a finite value, $\lim\limits_{x \to -\infty} (3 - e^{-x})$ does not exist.

b As $x \to \infty$, $3 - e^{-x} \to 3^-$

$\therefore \lim\limits_{x \to \infty} (3 - e^{-x}) = 3$

EXERCISE 11C.2

1 For each of the following functions:

  i Discuss the behaviour near its asymptotes, and hence deduce their equations.

  ii If they exist, state the values of $\lim\limits_{x\to-\infty} f(x)$ and $\lim\limits_{x\to\infty} f(x)$.

  a $f(x) = \dfrac{1}{x}$ **b** $f(x) = \dfrac{3x-2}{x+3}$ **c** $f(x) = \dfrac{1-2x}{3x+2}$ **d** $f(x) = \dfrac{x}{1-x}$

2 **a** Sketch the graph of $y = e^x - 6$.

  b Hence discuss the value and geometric interpretation of:

  i $\lim\limits_{x\to-\infty} (e^x - 6)$ **ii** $\lim\limits_{x\to\infty} (e^x - 6)$

3 Find, if possible:

  a $\lim\limits_{x\to-\infty} (2e^{-x} - 3)$ **b** $\lim\limits_{x\to\infty} (2e^{-x} - 3)$.

4 **a** Copy and complete this table of values:

x	xe^{-x}
10	
50	
100	
200	

  b Hence predict the value of $\lim\limits_{x\to\infty} xe^{-x}$.

  c Graph $y = xe^{-x}$ using technology. Does your graph support your prediction in **b**?

INVESTIGATION 2   LIMITS IN NUMBER SEQUENCES

The sequence 0.3, 0.33, 0.333, ... can be defined by the general term $x_n = 0.333....3$ where there are n 3s after the decimal point, $n \in \mathbb{Z}^+$.

What to do:

1 Copy and complete the table alongside:

n	x_n	$3x_n$	$1 - 3x_n$
1			
2			
3			
4			
5			
10			

2 Consider x_{100} which contains 100 3s. In the number $(1-3x_{100})$, how many 0s are there between the decimal point and the 1?

3 In the limit as n tends to infinity, x_n contains an increasingly large number of 3s. In the number $(1 - 3x_n)$, how many 0s are there between the decimal point and the 1?

4 Using your answer to **3**, state $\lim\limits_{n\to\infty} (1 - 3x_n)$.

5 Hence state $\lim\limits_{n\to\infty} x_n$, which is the exact value of $0.\overline{3}$.

D   THE GRADIENT OF A TANGENT

We have seen that for two points $A(a, f(a))$ and $B(a + h, f(a + h))$ on a function, the gradient of the chord [AB] is $\dfrac{f(a + h) - f(a)}{h}$.

Letting B get infinitely close to A is equivalent to taking the limit as $h \to 0$.

The **gradient of the tangent** to the curve $y = f(x)$ at the point where $x = a$ is

$$\lim_{h \to 0} \frac{f(a + h) - f(a)}{h}.$$

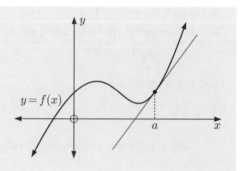

Example 5   ◀) **Self Tutor**

Find the gradient of the tangent to $f(x) = x^2$ at the point $(2, 4)$.

Let F be the point $(2, 4)$. Suppose M has x-coordinate $2 + h$ and also lies on the graph, so M is $(2 + h, (2 + h)^2)$.

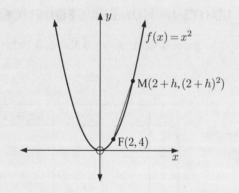

The gradient of the tangent at F

$= \lim\limits_{h \to 0} \dfrac{f(2 + h) - f(2)}{h}$

$= \lim\limits_{h \to 0} \dfrac{(2 + h)^2 - 4}{h}$

$= \lim\limits_{h \to 0} \dfrac{\cancel{4} + 4h + h^2 - \cancel{4}}{h}$

$= \lim\limits_{h \to 0} \dfrac{\cancel{h}(4 + h)}{\cancel{h}}$

$= \lim\limits_{h \to 0} (4 + h) \qquad \{\text{as } h \neq 0\}$

$= 4$

You can use technology to find the gradient of the tangent to a function at a given point, and hence check your answers.

GRAPHING
PACKAGE

GRAPHICS
CALCULATOR
INSTRUCTIONS

EXERCISE 11D

1 F(3, 9) lies on the graph of $f(x) = x^2$. M also lies on the graph, and has x-coordinate $3 + h$.

   a State the y-coordinate of M.

   b Show that the gradient of the line segment [FM] is $6 + h$.

   c *Hence* find the gradient of [FM] if M has coordinates:

      i (4, 16)   **ii** (3.5, 12.25)

      iii (3.1, 9.61)   **iv** (3.01, 9.0601)

   d Use limits to find the gradient of the tangent to $f(x) = x^2$ at the point (3, 9).

2 **a** Find the gradient of the tangent to $f(x) = x^2$ at the point where:

      i $x = 1$ **ii** $x = 4$

   b Use **a** and other results from this Section to complete the table alongside for $f(x) = x^2$.

x-coordinate	Gradient of tangent to $f(x) = x^2$
1	
2	
3	
4	

   c Predict the gradient of the tangent to $f(x) = x^2$ at the point where $x = a$.

3 Find the gradient of the tangent to:

   a $f(x) = x^2 + x$ at the point (2, 6)   **b** $f(x) = x^3$ at the point where $x = 1$

   c $f(x) = \dfrac{4}{x}$ at the point where $x = 2$ **d** $f(x) = x^4$ at the point where $x = 1$.

HISTORICAL NOTE

The word "calculus" is a Latin word referring to the small pebbles the ancient Romans used for counting.

The first known description of calculus is found on the **Egyptian Moscow papyrus** from about 1850 BC. Here, it was used to calculate areas and volumes.

Ancient Greek mathematicians such as **Democritus** and **Eudoxus** developed these ideas further by dividing objects into an infinite number of sections. This led to the study of **infinitesimals**, and allowed **Archimedes of Syracuse** to find the tangent to a curve other than a circle.

The methods of Archimedes were the foundation for modern calculus developed almost 2000 years later by mathematicians such as **Johann Bernoulli** and **Isaac Barrow**.

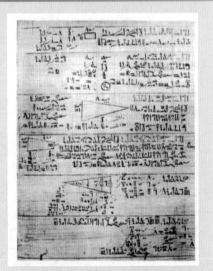

Egyptian Moscow papyrus

E | THE DERIVATIVE FUNCTION

For a non-linear function $y = f(x)$, the gradient of the tangent changes as we move along the curve.

We can therefore write a **gradient function** which gives the gradient of the tangent for any given value of x.

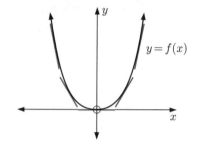

> The gradient function of $y = f(x)$ is called its **derivative function** and is labelled $f'(x)$.

For example, in question **2** of the previous Exercise, you should have observed that for $f(x) = x^2$, the gradient of the tangent is always double the x-coordinate.

$f'(x)$ is read "eff dashed of x".

So, for $f(x) = x^2$ we write $f'(x) = 2x$.

Since $f'(3) = 6$, the gradient of the tangent to $f(x) = x^2$ at the point where $x = 3$, is 6.

| **Example 6** | ◀)) **Self Tutor** |

For the given graph, find $f'(4)$.

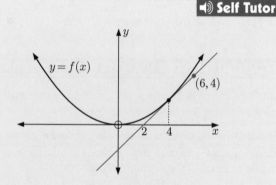

The graph shows the tangent to the curve $y = f(x)$ at the point where $x = 4$.

The tangent passes through $(2, 0)$ and $(6, 4)$.

$\therefore\ f'(4) = $ gradient of the tangent

$= \dfrac{4 - 0}{6 - 2}$

$= 1$

If we are given y written as a function of x, we often write the derivative function as $\dfrac{dy}{dx}$. This is called "the derivative of y with respect to x", and is read "dee y by dee x".

For example, for $y = x^2$ we have $\dfrac{dy}{dx} = 2x$.

EXERCISE 11E

1 Using the graph below, find:

   a $f(0)$ **b** $f'(0)$

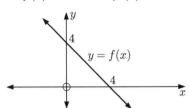

2 Use the graph below to find $f'(2)$.

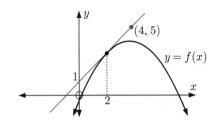

3 For the graph of $y = f(x)$ alongside, decide whether the following are positive or negative:

   a $f(3)$ **b** $f'(1)$

   c $f(-4)$ **d** $f'(-2)$

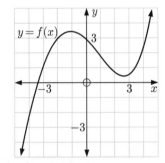

4

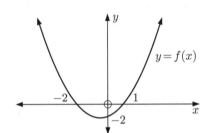

For the graph of $y = f(x)$ alongside, the derivative function is $f'(x) = 2x + 1$.

   a Find and interpret: **i** $f'(-2)$ **ii** $f'(0)$

   b Copy the graph, and include the information in **a**.

5 Consider the graph of $y = x^3$.

Which of the functions below could be the derivative function $\dfrac{dy}{dx}$? Explain your answer.

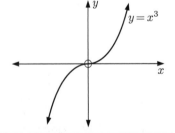

  A $\dfrac{dy}{dx} = -x^2$ **B** $\dfrac{dy}{dx} = 4x$ **C** $\dfrac{dy}{dx} = 3x^2$

  D $\dfrac{dy}{dx} = 3$ **E** $\dfrac{dy}{dx} = 3(x - 2)^2$

INVESTIGATION 3   GRADIENT FUNCTIONS

The software, accessible using the icon alongside, can be used to find the gradient of the tangent to a function $f(x)$ at any point. By sliding the point along the graph, we observe the changing gradient of the tangent and hence generate the gradient function $f'(x)$.

GRADIENT FUNCTIONS

What to do:

  1 Consider the functions $f(x) = 0$, $f(x) = 2$, and $f(x) = 4$.

    a For each of these functions, what is the gradient?

    b Is the gradient constant for all values of x?

2 Consider the function $f(x) = mx + c$.

    a State the gradient of the function.

    b Is the gradient constant for all values of x?

    c Use the software to graph the following functions and observe the gradient function $f'(x)$. Hence verify your answer to **b**.

        i $f(x) = x - 1$ **ii** $f(x) = 3x + 2$ **iii** $f(x) = -2x + 1$

3 **a** Observe the function $f(x) = x^2$ using the software. What *type* of function is the gradient function $f'(x)$?

    b Observe the following quadratic functions using the software:

        i $f(x) = x^2 + x - 2$ **ii** $f(x) = 2x^2 - 3$

        iii $f(x) = -x^2 + 2x - 1$ **iv** $f(x) = -3x^2 - 3x + 6$

    c What *type* of function are each of the gradient functions $f'(x)$ in **b**?

4 **a** Observe the function $f(x) = e^x$ using the software.

    b What is the gradient function $f'(x)$?

F   DIFFERENTIATION FROM FIRST PRINCIPLES

To find the derivative function $f'(x)$ for a function $f(x)$, we use limit theory to find the gradient of the tangent to the curve at a general point $(x, f(x))$.

Let A$(x, f(x))$ and B$(x + h, f(x + h))$ be two points on the curve.

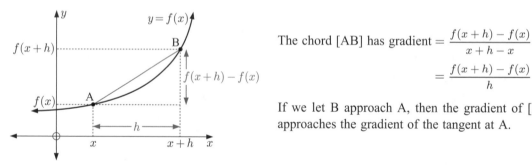

The chord [AB] has gradient $= \dfrac{f(x + h) - f(x)}{x + h - x}$

$$= \dfrac{f(x + h) - f(x)}{h}$$

If we let B approach A, then the gradient of [AB] approaches the gradient of the tangent at A.

So, the gradient of the tangent at the general point $(x, f(x))$ is $\lim\limits_{h \to 0} \dfrac{f(x + h) - f(x)}{h}$.

Since there is at most one value of the gradient for each value of x, the formula is actually a function.

> The **derivative function** or simply **derivative** of $y = f(x)$ is defined as
>
> $$f'(x) \text{ or } \frac{dy}{dx} = \lim_{h \to 0} \frac{f(x + h) - f(x)}{h}$$
>
> The domain of $f'(x)$ is the set of values for which this limit exists.

When we evaluate this limit to find a derivative function, we say we are **differentiating from first principles**.

Example 7   ◀ Self Tutor

Use first principles to find the gradient function $f'(x)$ of $f(x) = x^2$.

$$f'(x) = \lim_{h \to 0} \frac{f(x+h) - f(x)}{h}$$

$$= \lim_{h \to 0} \frac{(x+h)^2 - x^2}{h}$$

$$= \lim_{h \to 0} \frac{\cancel{x^2} + 2hx + h^2 - \cancel{x^2}}{h}$$

$$= \lim_{h \to 0} \frac{\cancel{h}(2x + h)}{\cancel{h}}$$

$$= \lim_{h \to 0} (2x + h) \qquad \{\text{as } h \neq 0\}$$

$$= 2x$$

THE DERIVATIVE WHEN $x = a$

The derivative at the point where $x = a$, denoted $f'(a)$, can be found using $f'(a) = \lim_{h \to 0} \frac{f(a+h) - f(a)}{h}$.
We did this in **Section D** on page **274**.

Alternatively, we can find the derivative function $f'(x)$, and then substitute $x = a$ to find $f'(a)$.

Example 8   ◀ Self Tutor

a Given $f(x) = x^4$, find $f'(x)$.

b Find $f'(-1)$, and interpret your answer.

a $f'(x) = \lim_{h \to 0} \frac{f(x+h) - f(x)}{h}$

$$= \lim_{h \to 0} \frac{(x+h)^4 - x^4}{h}$$

$$= \lim_{h \to 0} \frac{\cancel{x^4} + 4x^3h + 6x^2h^2 + 4xh^3 + h^4 - \cancel{x^4}}{h} \qquad \{\text{binomial expansion}\}$$

$$= \lim_{h \to 0} \frac{\cancel{h}(4x^3 + 6x^2h + 4xh^2 + h^3)}{\cancel{h}}$$

$$= \lim_{h \to 0} (4x^3 + 6x^2h + 4xh^2 + h^3) \qquad \{\text{since } h \neq 0\}$$

$$= 4x^3$$

b $f'(-1) = 4(-1)^3$

$$= -4$$

The tangent to $f(x) = x^4$ at the point
where $x = -1$, has gradient -4.

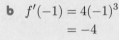

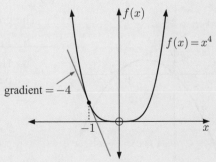

gradient $= -4$

EXERCISE 11F

1 Find, from first principles, the gradient function of $f(x)$ where $f(x)$ is:

    a x
        b 1
        c x^3

2 Find $f'(x)$ from first principles, given that $f(x)$ is:

    a $2x + 5$
        b $x^2 - 3x$
        c $-x^2 + 5x - 3$

3 Find $\dfrac{dy}{dx}$ from first principles given:

    a $y = 4 - x$
        b $y = 2x^2 + x - 1$
        c $y = x^3 - 2x^2 + 3$

4 Use the first principles formula $f'(a) = \lim\limits_{h \to 0} \dfrac{f(a+h) - f(a)}{h}$ to find:

    a $f'(2)$ for $f(x) = x^3$
        b $f'(3)$ for $f(x) = x^4$.

5 **a** Find $f'(x)$ given $f(x) = \dfrac{1}{x}$.

    b Find $f'(-1)$ and $f'(3)$, and interpret your answers.

6 The graph of $f(x) = -x^2 + 3x$ is shown alongside.

    a Use the graph to estimate the gradient of the tangent to the curve at the point where:

        i $x = 0$
        ii $x = 2$.

    b Find $f'(x)$ from first principles.

    c Find $f'(0)$ and $f'(2)$, and hence check your estimates in **a**.

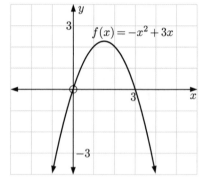

7 **a** Given $y = x^3 - 3x$, find $\dfrac{dy}{dx}$ from first principles.

    b Hence find the points on the graph at which the tangent has zero gradient.

8 Consider the function $f(x) = 2x^2 + 2x - 12$.

    a Find $f'(x)$.

    b Hence find the point where the tangent has gradient -2.

    c Draw the graph of $f(x) = 2x^2 + 2x - 12$, and include the information from **b**.

9

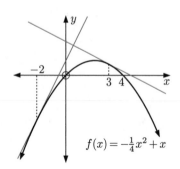

The graph of $f(x) = -\frac{1}{4}x^2 + x$ is shown alongside.

    a Find $f'(x)$.

    b Hence show that the illustrated tangents are perpendicular.

10 **a** Use the previous results to copy and complete the table alongside.

$f(x)$	$f'(x)$
x^1	
x^2	
x^3	
x^4	
x^{-1}	
x^0	

  b Copy and complete:

  If $f(x) = x^n$, then $f'(x) = $ ......

DISCUSSION

1 Does a function always have a derivative function?

2 Are the domains of a function and its derivative always the same?

REVIEW SET 11A

1 Find the average rate of change in $f(x)$ from A to B.

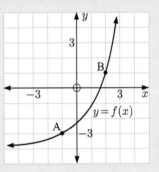

2 Chantelle is riding in a ski-lift. Her height above the base of the mountain is shown on the graph below.

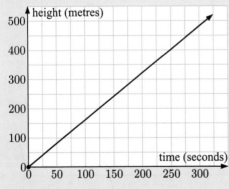

  a Is the ski-lift increasing in height at a constant rate? Explain your answer.

  b Find the rate at which the ski-lift is increasing in height.

3 Evaluate:

  a $\displaystyle\lim_{x \to 1} (6x - 7)$

  b $\displaystyle\lim_{h \to 0} \frac{2h^2 - h}{h}$

  c $\displaystyle\lim_{x \to 4} \frac{x^2 - 16}{x - 4}$

4 **a** Sketch the graph of $y = \dfrac{2+x}{x-4}$.

   b Discuss the behaviour of the graph near its asymptotes, and hence deduce their equations.

   c State the values of $\displaystyle\lim_{x\to-\infty} \dfrac{2+x}{x-4}$ and $\displaystyle\lim_{x\to\infty} \dfrac{2+x}{x-4}$.

5 Consider $f(x) = 2x^2$.

   a Show that $\dfrac{f(x+h) - f(x)}{h} = 4x + 2h$ provided $h \neq 0$.

   b Hence evaluate $\dfrac{f(3+h) - f(3)}{h}$ for each value of h in the table:

h	$\dfrac{f(3+h) - f(3)}{h}$
0.1	
0.01	
0.001	
0.0001	

   c Evaluate $\displaystyle\lim_{h\to0} \dfrac{f(3+h) - f(3)}{h}$. Give a geometric interpretation of your result.

6 Use the graph alongside to find $f'(3)$.

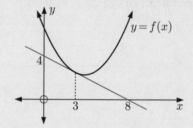

7 Find, from first principles, the derivative of:

   a $f(x) = x^2 + 2x$ **b** $y = 4 - 3x^2$

8 **a** Given $y = 2x^2 - 1$, find $\dfrac{dy}{dx}$ from first principles.

   b Hence state the gradient of the tangent to $y = 2x^2 - 1$ at the point where $x = 4$.

   c For what value of x is the gradient of the tangent to $y = 2x^2 - 1$ equal to -12?

9 The graph of $f(x) = x^3 - 3x^2$ is shown alongside.

   a Find $f'(x)$.

   b Hence show that the illustrated tangents are parallel.

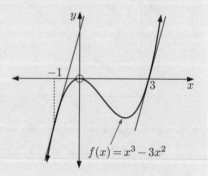

REVIEW SET 11B

1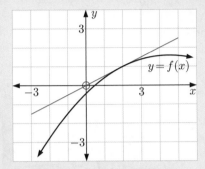

Use the tangent drawn to find the instantaneous rate of change in $f(x)$ at $x = 2$.

2 This graph shows the temperature in Berlin from 6 am to 6 pm on a particular day.

Find the average rate of change in temperature from:

a 7 am to noon

b 3 pm to 5 pm.

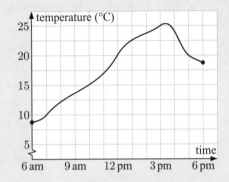

3 Evaluate the limits:

a $\displaystyle\lim_{h \to 0} \frac{h^3 - 3h}{h}$

b $\displaystyle\lim_{x \to 1} \frac{3x^2 - 3x}{x - 1}$

c $\displaystyle\lim_{x \to 2} \frac{x^2 - 3x + 2}{2 - x}$

4 **a** Sketch the graph of $y = e^{x-2} - 3$.

b Hence find, if possible:

i $\displaystyle\lim_{x \to -\infty} (e^{x-2} - 3)$

ii $\displaystyle\lim_{x \to \infty} (e^{x-2} - 3)$.

5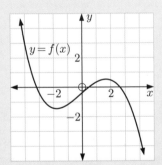

Decide whether the following are positive or negative:

a $f(-1)$

b $f'(0)$

c $f(2)$

d $f'(3)$

6 **a** Draw an accurate graph of $f(x) = x^2 - 2$.

b Draw, as accurately as possible, the tangent to $f(x) = x^2 - 2$ at $x = 2$.

c Hence find the instantaneous rate of change in $f(x) = x^2 - 2$ when $x = 2$.

d Check your answer using $f'(a) = \displaystyle\lim_{h \to 0} \frac{f(a+h) - f(a)}{h}$.

7   **a**   Find $f'(x)$ given $f(x) = x^4 - 2x$.

    b   Find $f'(-2)$ and interpret your answer.

8   **a**   Given $y = x^2 + 5x - 2$, find $\dfrac{dy}{dx}$ from first principles.

    b   Hence find the point on the graph at which the tangent has gradient -3.

9   In a BASE jumping competition from the Petronas
Towers in Kuala Lumpur, the altitude of a
professional jumper in the first 3 seconds is
given by $f(t) = 452 - 4.8t^2$ metres, where
$0 \leqslant t \leqslant 3$ seconds.

    a   Find the height of the jumper after:

        i   1 second   **ii**   2 seconds.

    b   Find $f'(t)$ from first principles.

    c   Find the speed of the jumper after:

        i   1 second   **ii**   2 seconds.

Chapter 12

Rules of differentiation

Contents:

OPENING PROBLEM

Consider the curve $y = x^2$.

In the previous Chapter we found that the gradient function of this curve is $\dfrac{dy}{dx} = 2x$.

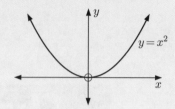

Things to think about:

a At which point on the graph of $y = x^2$ is the tangent to the curve horizontal? How do we observe this from the derivative function $\dfrac{dy}{dx}$?

b Consider the transformation of $y = x^2$ onto $y = x^2 + 3$.
   i What transformation has taken place?
   ii For a given value of x, has the gradient of the tangent to the function changed?
   iii What is the gradient function of $y = x^2 + 3$?

c Consider the transformation of $y = x^2$ onto $y = (x - 2)^2$.
   i What transformation has taken place?
   ii How does the gradient function of $y = (x - 2)^2$ relate to the gradient function of $y = x^2$?
   iii Can you write down the gradient function of $y = (x - 2)^2$?

d Consider the transformation of $y = x^2$ onto $y = 2x^2$.
   i What transformation has taken place?
   ii How does the gradient function of $y = 2x^2$ relate to the gradient function of $y = x^2$? If necessary, use the software to help you.

DEMO

In this Chapter we will discover rules which make it easier to find derivative functions.

A   SIMPLE RULES OF DIFFERENTIATION

Differentiation is the process of finding a derivative or gradient function.

Given a function $f(x)$, we obtain $f'(x)$ by **differentiating with respect to** the variable x.

There are a number of rules associated with differentiation. These rules can be used to differentiate more complicated functions without having to use first principles.

INVESTIGATION 1   SIMPLE RULES OF DIFFERENTIATION

In **Chapter 11** we used first principles to find the derivative of $f(x) = x^n$ for various values of n.

In this Investigation we generalise this derivative for any $n \in \mathbb{N}$, then consider rules which allow us to differentiate functions which are the sum or difference of polynomial terms.

What to do:

1 Use the binomial expansion $(x+h)^n = \sum_{r=0}^{n} \binom{n}{r} x^{n-r}h^r$

$$= \binom{n}{0}x^n + \binom{n}{1}x^{n-1}h + \binom{n}{2}x^{n-2}h^2 + ... + \binom{n}{n}h^n$$

and the first principles formula $f'(x) = \lim_{h\to 0} \dfrac{f(x+h)-f(x)}{h}$ to find the derivative of $f(x) = x^n$ for $x \in \mathbb{N}$.

2 **a** Differentiate using first principles:
   i $4x^2$ **ii** $2x^3$ **iii** $7x^4$

   b Copy and complete: "If $f(x) = cx^n$, then $f'(x) = ...$"

3 **a** Use first principles to find $f'(x)$ for:
   i $f(x) = x^2 + 3x$ **ii** $f(x) = x^3 - 2x^2$

   b Copy and complete: "If $f(x) = u(x) + v(x)$, then $f'(x) = ...$"

The rules you found in the **Investigation** can actually be used much more widely than the cases you just considered.

For example, the rule "if $f(x) = x^n$ then $f'(x) = nx^{n-1}$" is true not just for all $n \in \mathbb{N}$, but actually for all $n \in \mathbb{R}$.

We can summarise the following rules:

$f(x)$	$f'(x)$	Name of rule
c (a constant)	0	**differentiating a constant**
x^n	nx^{n-1}	**differentiating x^n**
$c\,u(x)$	$c\,u'(x)$	**constant times a function**
$u(x) + v(x)$	$u'(x) + v'(x)$	**addition rule**

The last two rules can be proved using the first principles definition of $f'(x)$.

- If $f(x) = c\,u(x)$, then $f'(x) = c\,u'(x)$.

  Proof:

  $f'(x)$
  $= \lim_{h\to 0} \dfrac{f(x+h)-f(x)}{h}$
  $= \lim_{h\to 0} \dfrac{c\,u(x+h) - c\,u(x)}{h}$
  $= \lim_{h\to 0} c\left[\dfrac{u(x+h)-u(x)}{h}\right]$
  $= c\lim_{h\to 0} \dfrac{u(x+h)-u(x)}{h}$
  $= c\,u'(x)$

- If $f(x) = u(x) + v(x)$, then $f'(x) = u'(x) + v'(x)$

  Proof:

  $f'(x)$
  $= \lim_{h\to 0} \dfrac{f(x+h)-f(x)}{h}$
  $= \lim_{h\to 0} \left(\dfrac{u(x+h)+v(x+h) - [u(x)+v(x)]}{h}\right)$
  $= \lim_{h\to 0} \left(\dfrac{u(x+h)-u(x)+v(x+h)-v(x)}{h}\right)$
  $= \lim_{h\to 0} \dfrac{u(x+h)-u(x)}{h} + \lim_{h\to 0} \dfrac{v(x+h)-v(x)}{h}$
  $= u'(x) + v'(x)$

Using the rules we have now developed, we can differentiate sums of powers of x.

For example,   if $f(x) = 3x^4 + 2x^3 - 5x^2 + 7x + 6$ then
$$f'(x) = 3(4x^3) + 2(3x^2) - 5(2x) + 7(1) + 0$$
$$= 12x^3 + 6x^2 - 10x + 7$$

Example 1   ◀) **Self Tutor**

Find $f'(x)$ for $f(x)$ equal to:

a $5x^3 + 6x^2 - 3x + 2$

b $7x - \dfrac{4}{x} + \dfrac{3}{x^3}$

a $f(x) = 5x^3 + 6x^2 - 3x + 2$
$\therefore\ f'(x) = 5(3x^2) + 6(2x) - 3(1)$
$= 15x^2 + 12x - 3$

b $f(x) = 7x - \dfrac{4}{x} + \dfrac{3}{x^3}$
$= 7x - 4x^{-1} + 3x^{-3}$
$\therefore\ f'(x) = 7(1) - 4(-1x^{-2}) + 3(-3x^{-4})$
$= 7 + 4x^{-2} - 9x^{-4}$
$= 7 + \dfrac{4}{x^2} - \dfrac{9}{x^4}$

Example 2   ◀) **Self Tutor**

Find the gradient function for:

a $f(x) = 3\sqrt{x} + \dfrac{2}{x}$

b $g(x) = x^2 - \dfrac{4}{\sqrt{x}}$

a $f(x) = 3\sqrt{x} + \dfrac{2}{x}$
$= 3x^{\frac{1}{2}} + 2x^{-1}$
$\therefore\ f'(x) = 3(\tfrac{1}{2}x^{-\frac{1}{2}}) + 2(-1x^{-2})$
$= \tfrac{3}{2}x^{-\frac{1}{2}} - 2x^{-2}$
$= \dfrac{3}{2\sqrt{x}} - \dfrac{2}{x^2}$

b $g(x) = x^2 - \dfrac{4}{\sqrt{x}}$
$= x^2 - 4x^{-\frac{1}{2}}$
$\therefore\ g'(x) = 2x - 4(-\tfrac{1}{2}x^{-\frac{3}{2}})$
$= 2x + 2x^{-\frac{3}{2}}$
$= 2x + \dfrac{2}{x\sqrt{x}}$

EXERCISE 12A

1   Find $f'(x)$ given that $f(x)$ is:

a x^3 b x^8 c x^{11} d $6x$
e $2x^3$ f $7x^2$ g $3x^5$ h $5x^6$
i $5x - 2$ j $x^2 - 3$ k $x^2 + x$ l $x^2 + 3x - 5$
m $2x^2 + x - 1$ n $3x^2 - 7x + 8$ o $4 - 2x^2$ p $\tfrac{1}{2}x^4 - 6x^2$
q $x^3 - 4x^2 + 6x$ r $2x^3 + x - 1$ s $7 - x - 4x^3$ t $\tfrac{1}{5}x^3 - \tfrac{7}{2}x^2 - 2$

2 Differentiate with respect to x:

a $\dfrac{1}{x^2}$

b $\dfrac{1}{x^5}$

c $\dfrac{3}{x}$

d $\dfrac{4}{x^3}$

e $-\dfrac{7}{x^4}$

f $2x + \dfrac{3}{x^2}$

g $x^2 - \dfrac{6}{x}$

h $9 - \dfrac{2}{x^3}$

i $\dfrac{2}{x^2} + \dfrac{9}{x^4}$

j $3x - \dfrac{1}{x} + \dfrac{2}{x^2}$

k $5 - \dfrac{8}{x^2} + \dfrac{4}{x^3}$

l $\dfrac{1}{5x^2}$

m $4x - \dfrac{1}{4x}$

n $\dfrac{x^3 + 4}{x}$

o $\dfrac{2x - 5}{x^2}$

Remember that $\dfrac{1}{x^n} = x^{-n}$.

3 Find the gradient function for $f(x)$ where $f(x)$ is:

a $\sqrt{x}$

b $\sqrt[3]{x}$

c $\dfrac{1}{\sqrt{x}}$

d $x^3 - \tfrac{1}{2}\sqrt{x}$

e $\dfrac{1}{x^2} + 6\sqrt{x}$

f $2x - \sqrt{x}$

g $x\sqrt{x}$

h $\dfrac{1}{x\sqrt{x}}$

i $2x^2 - \dfrac{3}{\sqrt{x}}$

j $\dfrac{\sqrt{x} - 4}{x}$

k $\dfrac{x + 5}{\sqrt{x}}$

l $\dfrac{7 - x^2}{\sqrt{x}}$

m $3x^2 - x\sqrt{x}$

n $\dfrac{4}{x^2\sqrt{x}}$

o $2x - \dfrac{3}{x\sqrt{x}}$

p $\dfrac{x^2 - x + 2}{\sqrt[3]{x}}$

4 Find $\dfrac{dy}{dx}$ for:

a $y = \pi x^2$

b $y = 3x^2 - \dfrac{8}{x^2}$

c $y = 6\sqrt{x} + \dfrac{5}{x}$

d $y = 4\pi x^3$

e $y = 2.5x^3 - 1.4x^2 - 1.3$

f $y = 10(x + 1)$

g $y = (x + 1)(x - 2)$

h $y = (2x + 1)(3x - 2)$

i $y = (5 - x)^2$

j $(2x - 1)^2$

k $y = x(x + 1)(2x - 5)$

l $y = \dfrac{(x - 3)^2}{\sqrt{x}}$

5 Find:

a $\dfrac{dy}{dt}$ for $y = \tfrac{1}{2}t^4 - \tfrac{1}{3}t$

b $\dfrac{dy}{dt}$ for $y = 7 - \dfrac{6}{\sqrt{t}}$

c $\dfrac{dT}{dt}$ for $T = \sqrt[3]{t} - \dfrac{2}{t^2}$

d $\dfrac{dP}{du}$ for $P = \dfrac{5}{u} - 10u\sqrt{u}$

Example 3 ◀) **Self Tutor**

Find the gradient of the tangent to $y = x^2 - \dfrac{4}{x}$ at the point where $x = 2$.

$y = x^2 - \dfrac{4}{x}$ $\therefore \dfrac{dy}{dx} = 2x - 4(-1x^{-2})$

$ = x^2 - 4x^{-1}$ $\phantom{\therefore \dfrac{dy}{dx}} = 2x + 4x^{-2}$

$\phantom{\therefore \dfrac{dy}{dx} = 2x} = 2x + \dfrac{4}{x^2}$

When $x = 2$, $\dfrac{dy}{dx} = 4 + 1 = 5$. So, the tangent has gradient 5.

6 Find the gradient of the tangent to:

   a $y = x^2$ at $x = 2$

   b $y = x^3 - 5x + 2$ at the point $(3, 14)$

   c $y = \dfrac{8}{x^2}$ at the point $\left(9, \frac{8}{81}\right)$

   d $y = 2x^2 - 3x + 7$ at $x = -1$

   e $y = 3\sqrt{x}$ at the point $(1, 3)$

   f $y = 2x - \dfrac{5}{x}$ at the point $\left(2, \frac{3}{2}\right)$

   g $y = \dfrac{x^2 - 4}{x^2}$ at the point $\left(4, \frac{3}{4}\right)$

   h $y = \dfrac{x^3 - 4x - 8}{x^2}$ at $x = -1$

7 Find constants b and c such that:

   a $f(x) = x^2 + (b+1)x + 2c$, $f(2) = 4$, and $f'(-1) = 2$

   b $f(x) = bx + \dfrac{c}{x}$, $f(3) = 5$, and $f'(1) = 5$.

Example 4   ◀ **Self Tutor**

If $y = 3x^2 - 4x$, find $\dfrac{dy}{dx}$ and interpret its meaning.

As $y = 3x^2 - 4x$, $\dfrac{dy}{dx} = 6x - 4$.

$\dfrac{dy}{dx}$ is the gradient function or derivative of $y = 3x^2 - 4x$ from which the gradient of the tangent at any point on the curve can be found. It is also the instantaneous rate of change of y with respect to x.

---

8 If $y = 4x - \dfrac{3}{x}$, find $\dfrac{dy}{dx}$ and interpret its meaning.

9 Consider the function $f(x) = \sqrt{x} - \dfrac{4}{\sqrt{x}}$.

   a State the domain of $f(x)$.

   b Find the derivative function $f'(x)$.

   c State the domain of $f'(x)$.

   d Find $f'(1)$ and interpret your answer.

10 The position of a car moving along a straight road is given by $S = 2t^2 + 4t$ metres where t is the time in seconds.

   a Find $\dfrac{dS}{dt}$ and interpret its meaning.

   b Find the value of $\dfrac{dS}{dt}$ when $t = 3$, and interpret your answer.

11 The cost of producing x toasters each week is given by $C = 1785 + 3x + 0.002x^2$ pounds. Find the value of $\dfrac{dC}{dx}$ when $x = 1000$, and interpret its meaning.

ACTIVITY   **THE INCREMENTS FORMULA**

For a function y expressed in terms of x, the **increments formula** can be used to estimate the change in y for a given change in x.

The increments formula states that the change in y, δy, can be estimated by

$$\delta y \approx \dfrac{dy}{dx} \times \delta x, \text{ where } \delta x \text{ is the change in } x.$$

For example, suppose $y = x^5$, and therefore $\dfrac{dy}{dx} = 5x^4$.

To estimate the value of 2.01^5, we let $x = 2$ and $\delta x = 0.01$.

Now $\delta y \approx \dfrac{dy}{dx} \times \delta x$

$\qquad \approx 5x^4 \times \delta x$

$\qquad \approx 5 \times 2^4 \times 0.01$

$\qquad \approx 0.8$

Since $2^5 = 32$, we estimate that $2.01^5 \approx 32 + 0.8 \approx 32.8$.

What to do:

1 Use the increments formula to estimate the value of:

    a 5.01^2 **b** 2.01^6 **c** 2.98^3 **d** 1.95^4

    Use your calculator to check your estimates.

2   **a** Use the diagram to explain what is actually calculated when we use the increments formula to estimate δy.

    b Explain why the formula only provides accurate estimates for small values of δx.

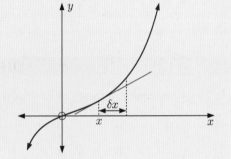

B   THE CHAIN RULE

In **Chapter 3** we saw that the **composite** of two functions g and f is $(g \circ f)(x)$ or $g(f(x))$.

We can often write complicated functions as the composite of two or more simpler functions.

For example $y = (x^2 + 3x)^4$ could be rewritten as $y = u^4$ where $u = x^2 + 3x$, or as $y = g(f(x))$ where $g(x) = x^4$ and $f(x) = x^2 + 3x$.

Example 5   ◆) **Self Tutor**

Find:

    a $g(f(x))$ if $g(x) = \sqrt{x}$ and $f(x) = 2 - 3x$

    b $g(x)$ and $f(x)$ such that $g(f(x)) = \dfrac{1}{x - x^2}$.

> There are several possible answers for **b**.

    a $g(f(x)) = g(2 - 3x)$ **b** If we let $f(x) = x - x^2$ then

               $= \sqrt{2 - 3x}$ $g(f(x)) = \dfrac{1}{f(x)}$

                                   $\therefore \ g(x) = \dfrac{1}{x}$ and $f(x) = x - x^2$

EXERCISE 12B.1

1 Find $g(f(x))$ if:

    a $g(x) = x^2$ and $f(x) = 2x + 7$ **b** $g(x) = 2x + 7$ and $f(x) = x^2$

    c $g(x) = \sqrt{x}$ and $f(x) = 3 - 4x$ **d** $g(x) = 3 - 4x$ and $f(x) = \sqrt{x}$

    e $g(x) = \dfrac{2}{x}$ and $f(x) = x^2 + 3$ **f** $g(x) = x^2 + 3$ and $f(x) = \dfrac{2}{x}$

2 Find $g(x)$ and $f(x)$ such that $g(f(x))$ is:

    a $(3x + 10)^3$ **b** $(7 - 2x)^5$ **c** $\dfrac{1}{2x + 4}$

    d $\sqrt{x^2 - 3x}$ **e** $\dfrac{1}{(5x - 1)^4}$ **f** $\dfrac{10}{(3x - x^2)^3}$

DERIVATIVES OF COMPOSITE FUNCTIONS

The reason we are interested in writing complicated functions as composite functions is to make finding derivatives easier.

INVESTIGATION 2   DIFFERENTIATING COMPOSITE FUNCTIONS

In this Investigation we want to learn how to differentiate composite functions.

Based on the rule "if $y = x^n$ then $\dfrac{dy}{dx} = nx^{n-1}$", we might suspect that if $y = (2x + 1)^2$ then $\dfrac{dy}{dx} = 2(2x + 1)^1$. But is this so?

What to do:

1 Expand $y = (2x + 1)^2$, and hence find $\dfrac{dy}{dx}$. How does this compare with $2(2x + 1)^1$?

2 Expand $y = (3x + 1)^2$, and hence find $\dfrac{dy}{dx}$. How does this compare with $2(3x + 1)^1$?

3 Expand $y = (ax + 1)^2$ where a is a constant, and hence find $\dfrac{dy}{dx}$. How does this compare with $2(ax + 1)^1$?

4 Suppose $y = u^2$.

    a Find $\dfrac{dy}{du}$.

    b Now suppose $u = ax + 1$, so $y = (ax + 1)^2$.

        i Find $\dfrac{du}{dx}$.   **ii** Write $\dfrac{dy}{du}$ from **a** in terms of x.

        iii Hence find $\dfrac{dy}{du} \times \dfrac{du}{dx}$.   **iv** Compare your answer to the result in **3**.

    c If $y = u^2$ where u is a function of x, what do you suspect $\dfrac{dy}{dx}$ will be equal to?

5 Expand $y = (x^2 + 3x)^2$ and hence find $\dfrac{dy}{dx}$.

    Does your answer agree with the rule you suggested in **4 c**?

6 Consider $y = (2x + 1)^3$.

  a Expand the brackets and hence find $\dfrac{dy}{dx}$.

  b If we let $u = 2x + 1$, then $y = u^3$.

   i Find $\dfrac{du}{dx}$.

   ii Find $\dfrac{dy}{du}$, and write it in terms of x.

   iii Hence find $\dfrac{dy}{du} \times \dfrac{du}{dx}$.

   iv Compare your answer to the result in **a**.

7 Copy and complete: "If y is a function of u, and u is a function of x, then $\dfrac{dy}{dx} = \ldots\ldots$"

THE CHAIN RULE

If $y = g(u)$ where $u = f(x)$ then $\dfrac{dy}{dx} = \dfrac{dy}{du}\dfrac{du}{dx}$.

This rule is extremely important and allows us to differentiate complicated functions much faster.

For example, for any function $f(x)$:

If $y = [f(x)]^n$ then $\dfrac{dy}{dx} = n[f(x)]^{n-1} \times f'(x)$.

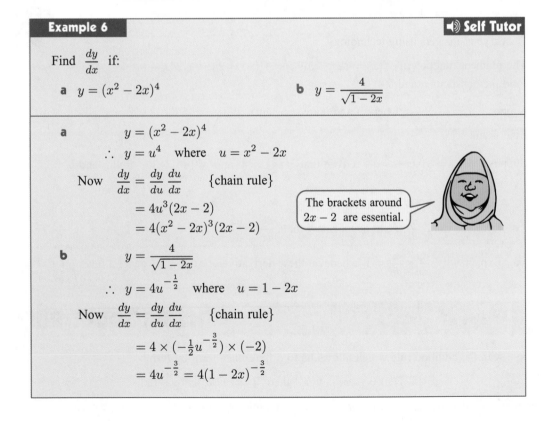

Example 6   ◀)) **Self Tutor**

Find $\dfrac{dy}{dx}$ if:

a $y = (x^2 - 2x)^4$

b $y = \dfrac{4}{\sqrt{1 - 2x}}$

a $y = (x^2 - 2x)^4$

$\therefore\ y = u^4$ where $u = x^2 - 2x$

Now $\dfrac{dy}{dx} = \dfrac{dy}{du}\dfrac{du}{dx}$ {chain rule}

$= 4u^3(2x - 2)$

$= 4(x^2 - 2x)^3(2x - 2)$

The brackets around $2x - 2$ are essential.

b $y = \dfrac{4}{\sqrt{1 - 2x}}$

$\therefore\ y = 4u^{-\frac{1}{2}}$ where $u = 1 - 2x$

Now $\dfrac{dy}{dx} = \dfrac{dy}{du}\dfrac{du}{dx}$ {chain rule}

$= 4 \times (-\tfrac{1}{2}u^{-\frac{3}{2}}) \times (-2)$

$= 4u^{-\frac{3}{2}} = 4(1 - 2x)^{-\frac{3}{2}}$

EXERCISE 12B.2

1 Write in the form au^n, clearly stating what u is:

   a $\dfrac{1}{(2x-1)^2}$
      b $\sqrt{x^2-3x}$
      c $\dfrac{2}{\sqrt{2-x^2}}$

   d $\sqrt[3]{x^3-x^2}$
      e $\dfrac{4}{(3-x)^3}$
      f $\dfrac{10}{x^2-3}$

2 Differentiate $y=(2x+3)^2$ by:

   a using the chain rule with $u=2x+3$

   b expanding $y=(2x+3)^2$ then differentiating term-by-term.

3 Find the derivative function $\dfrac{dy}{dx}$ for:

   a $y=(4x-5)^2$
      b $y=\dfrac{1}{5-2x}$
      c $y=\sqrt{3x-x^2}$

   d $y=(1-3x)^4$
      e $y=6(5-x)^3$
      f $y=\sqrt[3]{2x^3-x^2}$

   g $y=\dfrac{6}{(5x-4)^2}$
      h $y=(x^2-5x+8)^5$
      i $y=2\left(x^2-\dfrac{2}{x}\right)^3$

4 Find the gradient of the tangent to:

   a $y=\sqrt{1-x^2}$ at $x=\frac{1}{2}$
      b $y=(3x+2)^6$ at $x=-1$

   c $y=\dfrac{1}{(2x-1)^4}$ at $x=1$
      d $y=6\times\sqrt[3]{1-2x}$ at $x=0$

   e $y=\dfrac{4}{x+2\sqrt{x}}$ at $x=4$
      f $y=\left(x+\dfrac{1}{x}\right)^3$ at $x=1$.

GRAPHING PACKAGE

   Check your answers using technology.

5 The gradient function of $f(x)=(2x-b)^a$ is $f'(x)=24x^2-24x+6$.
   Find the constants a and b.

6 Suppose $y=\dfrac{a}{\sqrt{1+bx}}$ where a and b are constants. When $x=3$, $y=1$ and $\dfrac{dy}{dx}=-\frac{1}{8}$.
   Find a and b.

7 Suppose $f(x)=3\left(ax-\dfrac{b}{x}\right)^3$. Given that $f(\frac{3}{2})=3$ and $f'(\frac{3}{2})=30$, find a and b.

8 If $y=x^3$ then $x=y^{\frac{1}{3}}$.

   a Find $\dfrac{dy}{dx}$ and $\dfrac{dx}{dy}$, and hence show that $\dfrac{dy}{dx}\times\dfrac{dx}{dy}=1$.

   b Explain why $\dfrac{dy}{dx}\times\dfrac{dx}{dy}=1$ whenever these derivatives exist for any general function $y=f(x)$.

C   THE PRODUCT RULE

We have seen the addition rule which allows us to differentiate term-by-term:

$$\text{If } f(x)=u(x)+v(x) \text{ then } f'(x)=u'(x)+v'(x).$$

If we now consider the case $f(x)=u(x)\,v(x)$, we might wonder if $f'(x)=u'(x)\,v'(x)$.

In other words, does the derivative of a product of two functions equal the product of their derivatives?

INVESTIGATION 3   THE PRODUCT RULE

Suppose $u(x)$ and $v(x)$ are two functions of x, and that $f(x) = u(x)\,v(x)$ is the product of these functions. In this Investigation we attempt to find a rule for determining $f'(x)$.

What to do:

1 Suppose $u(x) = x$ and $v(x) = x$, so $f(x) = x^2$.

   a Find $f'(x)$ by direct differentiation.   **b** Find $u'(x)$ and $v'(x)$.

   c Does $f'(x) = u'(x)\,v'(x)$?

2 Suppose $u(x) = x$ and $v(x) = \sqrt{x}$, so $f(x) = x\sqrt{x} = x^{\frac{3}{2}}$.

   a Find $f'(x)$ by direct differentiation.   **b** Find $u'(x)$ and $v'(x)$.

   c Does $f'(x) = u'(x)\,v'(x)$?

3 Copy and complete the following table, finding $f'(x)$ by direct differentiation.

$f(x)$	$f'(x)$	$u(x)$	$v(x)$	$u'(x)$	$v'(x)$	$u'(x)\,v(x) + u(x)\,v'(x)$
x^2		x	x			
$x^{\frac{3}{2}}$		x	$\sqrt{x}$			
$x(x+1)$		x	$x+1$			
$(x-1)(2-x^2)$		$x-1$	$2-x^2$			

4 Copy and complete: "If $f(x) = u(x)\,v(x)$ then $f'(x) = \ldots\ldots$"

THE PRODUCT RULE

If $f(x) = u(x)\,v(x)$ then $f'(x) = u'(x)\,v(x) + u(x)\,v'(x)$.

Alternatively, if $y = uv$ where u and v are functions of x, then

$$\frac{dy}{dx} = u'v + uv' = \frac{du}{dx}v + u\frac{dv}{dx}.$$

Example 7   ◀》 **Self Tutor**

If $y = x^2(x^2 - 2x)^4$, find $\dfrac{dy}{dx}$.

$y = x^2(x^2 - 2x)^4$ is the product of

   $u = x^2$ and $v = (x^2 - 2x)^4$

$\therefore\ u' = 2x$ and $v' = 4(x^2 - 2x)^3(2x - 2)$ {chain rule}

Now $\dfrac{dy}{dx} = u'v + uv'$ {product rule}

      $= 2x(x^2 - 2x)^4 + x^2 \times 4(x^2 - 2x)^3(2x - 2)$

      $= 2x(x^2 - 2x)^4 + 4x^2(x^2 - 2x)^3(2x - 2)$

> Used together, the product rule and chain rule are extremely powerful.

Example 8   ◀) **Self Tutor**

Find $\dfrac{dy}{dx}$ given $y = \sqrt{x}(2x+1)^3$.

$y = \sqrt{x}(2x+1)^3$ is the product of $u = x^{\frac{1}{2}}$ and $v = (2x+1)^3$

$\therefore \ u' = \tfrac{1}{2}x^{-\frac{1}{2}}$ and $v' = 3(2x+1)^2 \times 2$ {chain rule}

$\qquad\qquad\qquad\qquad\qquad\qquad\qquad\quad = 6(2x+1)^2$

Now $\dfrac{dy}{dx} = u'v + uv'$ {product rule}

$\qquad = \tfrac{1}{2}x^{-\frac{1}{2}}(2x+1)^3 + x^{\frac{1}{2}} \times 6(2x+1)^2$

$\qquad = \tfrac{1}{2}x^{-\frac{1}{2}}(2x+1)^3 + 6x^{\frac{1}{2}}(2x+1)^2$

EXERCISE 12C

1   Use the product rule to differentiate:

    a $f(x) = x(x-1)$ **b** $f(x) = 2x(x+1)$ **c** $f(x) = x^2\sqrt{x+1}$

    d $f(x) = (x+3)(x-1)$ **e** $f(x) = x\sqrt{x^2-1}$ **f** $f(x) = x(x+1)^2$

2   Find $\dfrac{dy}{dx}$ using the product rule:

    a $y = x^2(2x-1)$ **b** $y = 4x(2x+1)^3$ **c** $y = x^2\sqrt{3-x}$

    d $y = \sqrt{x}(x-3)^2$ **e** $y = 5x^2(3x^2-1)^2$ **f** $y = \sqrt{x}(x-x^2)^3$

3   Find the gradient of the tangent to:

    a $y = x^4(1-2x)^2$ at $x = -1$ **b** $y = \sqrt{x}(x^2-x+1)^2$ at $x = 4$

    c $y = x\sqrt{1-2x}$ at $x = -4$ **d** $y = x^3\sqrt{5-x^2}$ at $x = 1$.

4   Consider $y = \sqrt{x}(3-x)^2$.

    a Show that $\dfrac{dy}{dx} = \dfrac{(3-x)(3-5x)}{2\sqrt{x}}$.

    b Find the x-coordinates of all points on $y = \sqrt{x}(3-x)^2$ where the tangent is horizontal.

    c State the domain of $\dfrac{dy}{dx}$. Discuss how it differs from the domain of the original function.

5   Suppose $y = -2x^2(x+4)$. For what values of x does $\dfrac{dy}{dx} = 10$?

6   Suppose $y = (x+3)(x-2)^2$. For what values of x does $\dfrac{dy}{dx} = -7$?

7   Find the value of x for which the tangent to $f(x) = ax\sqrt{1-x}$, $a \neq 0$ has gradient:

    a 0   **b** a.

8   Find the values of a such that $f(x) = x^2\sqrt{x^2+a}$ and $f'(-2) = -\tfrac{34}{3}$.

D   THE QUOTIENT RULE

Expressions like $\dfrac{x^2 + 1}{2x - 5}$, $\dfrac{\sqrt{x}}{1 - 3x}$, and $\dfrac{x^3}{(x - x^2)^4}$ are **quotients** because they represent the division of one expression by another.

Quotient functions have the form $Q(x) = \dfrac{u(x)}{v(x)}$.

$$\text{Notice that} \quad u(x) = Q(x)\, v(x)$$
$$\therefore \quad u'(x) = Q'(x)\, v(x) + Q(x)\, v'(x) \qquad \{\text{product rule}\}$$
$$\therefore \quad u'(x) - Q(x)\, v'(x) = Q'(x)\, v(x)$$
$$\therefore \quad Q'(x)\, v(x) = u'(x) - \frac{u(x)}{v(x)}\, v'(x)$$
$$\therefore \quad Q'(x)\, v(x) = \frac{u'(x)\, v(x) - u(x)\, v'(x)}{v(x)}$$
$$\therefore \quad Q'(x) = \frac{u'(x)\, v(x) - u(x)\, v'(x)}{[v(x)]^2} \qquad \text{when this exists.}$$

THE QUOTIENT RULE

If $Q(x) = \dfrac{u(x)}{v(x)}$ then $Q'(x) = \dfrac{u'(x)\, v(x) - u(x)\, v'(x)}{[v(x)]^2}$.

Alternatively, if $y = \dfrac{u}{v}$ where u and v are functions of x, then

$$\frac{dy}{dx} = \frac{u'v - uv'}{v^2} = \frac{\dfrac{du}{dx}\, v - u\, \dfrac{dv}{dx}}{v^2}$$

Example 9   ◀ɴ Self Tutor

Use the quotient rule to find $\dfrac{dy}{dx}$ given $y = \dfrac{1 + 3x}{x^2 + 1}$.

$y = \dfrac{1 + 3x}{x^2 + 1}$ is a quotient with $u = 1 + 3x$ and $v = x^2 + 1$
$$\therefore \quad u' = 3 \qquad \text{and} \quad v' = 2x$$

Now $\dfrac{dy}{dx} = \dfrac{u'v - uv'}{v^2}$ $\{$quotient rule$\}$

$$= \frac{3(x^2 + 1) - (1 + 3x)2x}{(x^2 + 1)^2}$$
$$= \frac{3x^2 + 3 - 2x - 6x^2}{(x^2 + 1)^2}$$
$$= \frac{3 - 2x - 3x^2}{(x^2 + 1)^2}$$

Example 10

Find $\dfrac{dy}{dx}$ given $y = \dfrac{\sqrt{x}}{(1-2x)^2}$.

$y = \dfrac{\sqrt{x}}{(1-2x)^2}$ is a quotient with

$u = x^{\frac{1}{2}}$ and $v = (1-2x)^2$

$\therefore\ u' = \frac{1}{2}x^{-\frac{1}{2}}$ and $v' = 2(1-2x)^1 \times (-2)$ {chain rule}

$\qquad\qquad\qquad\qquad = -4(1-2x)$

Now $\dfrac{dy}{dx} = \dfrac{u'v - uv'}{v^2}$ {quotient rule}

$= \dfrac{\frac{1}{2}x^{-\frac{1}{2}}(1-2x)^2 - x^{\frac{1}{2}} \times (-4(1-2x))}{(1-2x)^4}$

$= \dfrac{\frac{1}{2}x^{-\frac{1}{2}}(1-2x)^2 + 4x^{\frac{1}{2}}(1-2x)}{(1-2x)^4}$

$= \dfrac{\cancel{(1-2x)}\left[\frac{1-2x}{2\sqrt{x}} + 4\sqrt{x}\left(\frac{2\sqrt{x}}{2\sqrt{x}}\right)\right]}{(1-2x)^{\cancel{4}\,3}}$

$= \dfrac{1 - 2x + 8x}{2\sqrt{x}(1-2x)^3}$

$= \dfrac{6x + 1}{2\sqrt{x}(1-2x)^3}$

If you only need the gradient of a tangent at a given point, you will not need to simplify $\dfrac{dy}{dx}$.

In such cases, substitute the value for x into the derivative function immediately.

EXERCISE 12D

1 Use the quotient rule to find $\dfrac{dy}{dx}$ if:

   a $y = \dfrac{1 + 3x}{2 - x}$
   b $y = \dfrac{x^2}{2x + 1}$
   c $y = \dfrac{x}{x^2 - 3}$

   d $y = \dfrac{\sqrt{x}}{1 - 2x}$
   e $y = \dfrac{x^2 - 3}{3x - x^2}$
   f $y = \dfrac{x}{\sqrt{1 - 3x}}$

2 Find:

   a $\dfrac{d}{dx}\left(\dfrac{x + 1}{3 - x}\right)$
   b $\dfrac{d}{dx}\left(\dfrac{3x}{x^2 - 1}\right)$

   c $\dfrac{d}{dx}\left(\dfrac{x^3}{2x - 1}\right)$
   d $\dfrac{d}{dx}\left(\dfrac{4x}{\sqrt{x - 5}}\right)$

   e $\dfrac{d}{dx}\left(\dfrac{\sqrt{x}}{3 - x^2}\right)$
   f $\dfrac{d}{dx}\left(-\dfrac{x^2}{\sqrt{x^2 + 3}}\right)$

$\dfrac{d}{dx}(....)$ reads "the derivative of $(....)$ with respect to x".

3 Find the gradient of the tangent to:

   a $y = \dfrac{x}{1 - 2x}$ at $x = 1$
       b $y = \dfrac{x^3}{x^2 + 1}$ at $x = -1$

   c $y = \dfrac{\sqrt{x}}{2x + 1}$ at $x = 4$
       d $y = \dfrac{x^2}{\sqrt{x^2 + 5}}$ at $x = -2$.

4 Suppose $f(x) = \dfrac{x}{\sqrt{x-1}}$.   Find $f'(x)$ using the quotient rule.

Check your answer by writing $f(x) = \dfrac{x-1}{\sqrt{x-1}} + \dfrac{1}{\sqrt{x-1}}$ and then differentiating.

5 Consider the graph of $y = \dfrac{2x+3}{x+1}$ alongside.

   a Find $\dfrac{dy}{dx}$.

   b Hence show that the illustrated tangents are parallel.

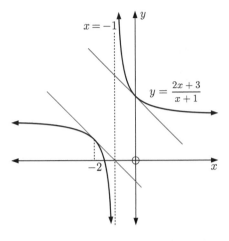

6 **a** If $y = \dfrac{2\sqrt{x}}{1-x}$, show that $\dfrac{dy}{dx} = \dfrac{x+1}{\sqrt{x}(1-x)^2}$.

   b For what values of x is $\dfrac{dy}{dx}$:   **i** zero   **ii** undefined?

7 **a** If $y = \dfrac{x^2+6}{2x+1}$, show that $\dfrac{dy}{dx} = \dfrac{2x^2+2x-12}{(2x+1)^2}$.

   b For what values of x is $\dfrac{dy}{dx}$:   **i** zero   **ii** undefined?

8 **a** If $y = \dfrac{x^2-3x+1}{x+2}$, show that $\dfrac{dy}{dx} = \dfrac{x^2+4x-7}{(x+2)^2}$.

   b For what values of x is $\dfrac{dy}{dx}$:   **i** zero   **ii** undefined?

E   DERIVATIVES OF EXPONENTIAL FUNCTIONS

We have seen previously that the simplest **exponential functions** have the form $f(x) = b^x$ where b is any positive constant, $b \neq 1$.

The graphs of all members of the exponential family $f(x) = b^x$:

- pass through the point $(0, 1)$
- are asymptotic to the x-axis at one end
- lie above the x-axis for all x.

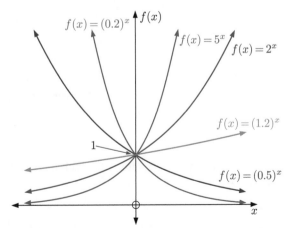

INVESTIGATION 4   THE DERIVATIVE OF b^x

The purpose of this Investigation is to observe the nature of the derivatives of $f(x) = b^x$ for various values of b.

What to do:

1 Use the software provided to help fill in the table for $y = 2^x$:

CALCULUS DEMO

x	y	$\dfrac{dy}{dx}$	$\dfrac{dy}{dx} \div y$
0			
0.5			
1			
1.5			
2			

2 Repeat **1** for the following functions:

   a $y = 3^x$ **b** $y = 5^x$ **c** $y = (0.5)^x$

3 Use your observations from **1** and **2** to write a statement about the derivative of the general exponential $y = b^x$ for $b > 0$, $b \neq 1$.

From the **Investigation** you should have found that:

$$\text{If } f(x) = b^x \text{ then } f'(x) = f'(0) \times b^x.$$

Proof:

    If $f(x) = b^x$,

then $f'(x) = \lim_{h \to 0} \dfrac{b^{x+h} - b^x}{h}$ {definition of the derivative}

$\qquad\qquad = \lim_{h \to 0} \dfrac{b^x(b^h - 1)}{h}$

$\qquad\qquad = b^x \times \left(\lim_{h \to 0} \dfrac{b^h - 1}{h} \right)$ {as b^x is independent of h}

But $f'(0) = \lim_{h \to 0} \dfrac{f(0+h) - f(0)}{h}$

$\qquad\qquad = \lim_{h \to 0} \dfrac{b^h - 1}{h}$

$\therefore \; f'(x) = b^x \times f'(0)$

gradient $= f'(0)$

$f(x) = b^x$

Given this result, if we can find a value of b such that $f'(0) = 1$, then we will have found *a function which is its own derivative*!

INVESTIGATION 5   SOLVING FOR b IF $f(x) = b^x$ AND $f'(x) = b^x$

Click on the icon to graph $f(x) = b^x$ and its derivative function $y = f'(x)$.

DEMO

Experiment with different values of b until the graphs of $f(x) = b^x$ and $y = f'(x)$ appear the same.

Estimate the corresponding value of b to 3 decimal places.

You should have discovered that $f(x) = f'(x) = b^x$ when $b \approx 2.718$.

To find this value of b more accurately we return to the algebraic approach:

We have already shown that if $f(x) = b^x$ then $f'(x) = b^x \left(\lim\limits_{h \to 0} \dfrac{b^h - 1}{h} \right)$.

So, to find the value of b such that $f'(x) = b^x$, we require

$$\lim_{h \to 0} \frac{b^h - 1}{h} = 1$$

Now $\dfrac{b^h - 1}{h} = 1 \iff b = (1 + h)^{\frac{1}{h}}$,   so taking the limit on both sides gives

$$b = \lim_{h \to 0} (1 + h)^{\frac{1}{h}}$$

Letting $h = \dfrac{1}{n}$, we notice that $h \to 0$ as $n \to \infty$.

$\therefore \quad b = \lim\limits_{n \to \infty} \left(1 + \dfrac{1}{n} \right)^n$ if this limit exists.

We have in fact already seen this limit previously in an **Investigation** on continuously compounding interest.

We found that as $n \to \infty$,

$$\left(1 + \frac{1}{n} \right)^n \to 2.718\,281\,828\,459\,045\,235\,....$$

and this irrational number is the natural exponential e.

Check this for yourself by evaluating

$\left(1 + \dfrac{1}{n} \right)^n$

for very large values of n.

We therefore conclude: If $f(x) = e^x$ then $f'(x) = e^x$.

THE DERIVATIVE OF $e^{f(x)}$

The functions e^{-x}, e^{2x+3}, and e^{-x^2} all have the form $e^{f(x)}$.

Suppose $y = e^{f(x)} = e^u$ where $u = f(x)$.

Now $\dfrac{dy}{dx} = \dfrac{dy}{du} \dfrac{du}{dx}$ {chain rule}

$\qquad = e^u \dfrac{du}{dx}$

$\qquad = e^{f(x)} \times f'(x)$

Function	Derivative
e^x	e^x
$e^{f(x)}$	$e^{f(x)} \times f'(x)$

Example 11   ◀)) **Self Tutor**

Find the gradient function for y equal to:

a $2e^x + e^{-3x}$ b $x^2 e^{-x}$ c $\dfrac{e^{2x}}{x}$

a If $y = 2e^x + e^{-3x}$ then $\dfrac{dy}{dx} = 2e^x + e^{-3x}(-3)$ {addition rule}

$\qquad\qquad\qquad\qquad\qquad\; = 2e^x - 3e^{-3x}$

b If $y = x^2 e^{-x}$ then $\dfrac{dy}{dx} = 2xe^{-x} + x^2 e^{-x}(-1)$ {product rule}

$\qquad\qquad\qquad\qquad\quad\; = 2xe^{-x} - x^2 e^{-x}$

c If $y = \dfrac{e^{2x}}{x}$ then $\dfrac{dy}{dx} = \dfrac{e^{2x}(2)x - e^{2x}(1)}{x^2}$ {quotient rule}

$\qquad\qquad\qquad\qquad\;\; = \dfrac{e^{2x}(2x - 1)}{x^2}$

EXERCISE 12E

1 Find the gradient function for $f(x)$ equal to:

a e^{4x}

b $e^x + 3$

c e^{-2x}

d $e^{\frac{x}{2}}$

e $2e^{-\frac{x}{2}}$

f $1 - 2e^{-x}$

g $4e^{\frac{x}{2}} - 3e^{-x}$

h $\dfrac{e^x + e^{-x}}{2}$

i e^{-x^2}

j $e^{\frac{1}{x}}$

k $10(1 + e^{2x})$

l $20(1 - e^{-2x})$

m e^{2x+1}

n $e^{\frac{x}{4}}$

o e^{1-2x^2}

p $e^{-0.02x}$

2 Find the derivative of:

a xe^x

b $x^3 e^{-x}$

c $\dfrac{e^x}{x}$

d $\dfrac{x}{e^x}$

e $x^2 e^{3x}$

f $\dfrac{e^x}{\sqrt{x}}$

g $20xe^{-0.5x}$

h $\dfrac{e^x + 2}{e^{-x} + 1}$

Example 12   ◀)) **Self Tutor**

Find the gradient function for y equal to:

a $(e^x - 1)^3$ b $\dfrac{1}{\sqrt{2e^{-x} + 1}}$

a $y = (e^x - 1)^3$

$\quad = u^3$ where $u = e^x - 1$

$\dfrac{dy}{dx} = \dfrac{dy}{du}\dfrac{du}{dx}$ {chain rule}

$\qquad = 3u^2 \dfrac{du}{dx}$

$\qquad = 3(e^x - 1)^2 \times e^x$

$\qquad = 3e^x(e^x - 1)^2$

b $y = (2e^{-x} + 1)^{-\frac{1}{2}}$

$\quad = u^{-\frac{1}{2}}$ where $u = 2e^{-x} + 1$

$\dfrac{dy}{dx} = \dfrac{dy}{du}\dfrac{du}{dx}$ {chain rule}

$\qquad = -\tfrac{1}{2}u^{-\frac{3}{2}} \dfrac{du}{dx}$

$\qquad = -\tfrac{1}{2}(2e^{-x} + 1)^{-\frac{3}{2}} \times 2e^{-x}(-1)$

$\qquad = e^{-x}(2e^{-x} + 1)^{-\frac{3}{2}}$

3 Find the gradient function for y equal to:

   a $(2 + e^x)^4$
   b $\sqrt{e^x - 1}$
   c $(e^x + e^{-x})^{\frac{3}{2}}$
   d $\dfrac{1}{\sqrt{e^{2x} + 2}}$

4 Find the gradient of the tangent to:

   a $y = (e^x + 2)^4$ at $x = 0$
   b $y = \dfrac{1}{2 - e^{-x}}$ at $x = 0$

   c $y = \sqrt{e^{2x} + 10}$ at $x = \ln 3$
   d $y = \dfrac{2 - x}{e^{3x}}$ at $x = 1$.

5 The graph of $f(x) = \sqrt{6 - e^x}$ is shown alongside.

   a State the domain of the function.

   b The point P has y-coordinate 2. Find exactly:

   i the coordinates of P

   ii the gradient of the tangent at P.

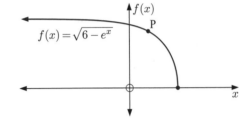

6 Given $f(x) = e^{kx} + x$ and $f'(0) = -8$, find k.

7 **a** By substituting $e^{\ln 2}$ for 2 in $y = 2^x$, find $\dfrac{dy}{dx}$.

   b Show that if $y = b^x$ where $b > 0$, $b \neq 1$, then $\dfrac{dy}{dx} = b^x \times \ln b$.

   c Find $\dfrac{dy}{dx}$ for: **i** $y = 5^x$ **ii** $y = 8 \times 10^x$

8 The tangent to $f(x) = x^2 e^{-x}$ at point P is horizontal. Find the possible coordinates of P.

9 Suppose $S(x) = \frac{1}{2}(e^x - e^{-x})$ and $C(x) = \frac{1}{2}(e^x + e^{-x})$.

   a Show that $[C(x)]^2 - [S(x)]^2 = 1$.
   b Show that $\dfrac{d}{dx}[S(x)] = C(x)$.

   c Find $\dfrac{d}{dx}[C(x)]$ in terms of $S(x)$.

   d If $T(x) = \dfrac{S(x)}{C(x)}$, find $\dfrac{d}{dx}[T(x)]$ in terms of $C(x)$.

F   DERIVATIVES OF LOGARITHMIC FUNCTIONS

INVESTIGATION 6   THE DERIVATIVE OF $\ln x$

What to do:

1 Click on the icon to see the graph of $y = \ln x$. Observe the gradient function being drawn as the point moves from left to right along the graph.

CALCULUS
DEMO

2 Predict a formula for the gradient function of $y = \ln x$.

3 Find the gradient of the tangent to $y = \ln x$ for $x = 0.25, 0.5, 1, 2, 3, 4,$ and 5.
Do your results confirm your prediction in **2**?

From the **Investigation** you should have observed:

$$\text{If } y = \ln x \text{ then } \frac{dy}{dx} = \frac{1}{x}, \quad x > 0.$$

THE DERIVATIVE OF $\ln f(x)$

Suppose $y = \ln f(x)$

$\quad \therefore \quad y = \ln u$ where $u = f(x)$.

Now $\dfrac{dy}{dx} = \dfrac{dy}{du}\dfrac{du}{dx}$ {chain rule}

$\therefore \quad \dfrac{dy}{dx} = \dfrac{1}{u}\dfrac{du}{dx}$

$\qquad = \dfrac{f'(x)}{f(x)}$

Function	Derivative
$\ln x$	$\dfrac{1}{x}, \quad x > 0$
$\ln f(x)$	$\dfrac{f'(x)}{f(x)}$

Example 13
🔊 **Self Tutor**

Find the gradient function of:

a $y = \ln(1 - 3x)$

b $y = x^3 \ln x$

a $\qquad y = \ln(1 - 3x)$

$\therefore \quad \dfrac{dy}{dx} = \dfrac{-3}{1 - 3x}$

$\qquad\quad = \dfrac{3}{3x - 1}$

b $\qquad y = x^3 \ln x$

$\therefore \quad \dfrac{dy}{dx} = 3x^2 \ln x + x^3\left(\dfrac{1}{x}\right)$ {product rule}

$\qquad\quad = 3x^2 \ln x + x^2$

$\qquad\quad = x^2(3 \ln x + 1)$

The laws of logarithms can help us to differentiate some logarithmic functions more easily.

$$\text{For } a > 0, \ b > 0, \ n \in \mathbb{R}: \quad \ln(ab) = \ln a + \ln b$$

$$\ln\left(\frac{a}{b}\right) = \ln a - \ln b$$

$$\ln(a^n) = n \ln a$$

EXERCISE 12F

1 Find the gradient function of:

a $y = \ln(7x)$

b $y = \ln(2x + 1)$

c $y = \ln(x - x^2)$

d $y = 3 - 2 \ln x$

e $y = x^2 \ln x$

f $y = \dfrac{\ln x}{2x}$

g $y = e^x \ln x$

h $y = (\ln x)^2$

i $y = \sqrt{\ln x}$

j $y = e^{-x} \ln x$

k $y = \sqrt{x} \ln(2x)$

l $y = \dfrac{2\sqrt{x}}{\ln x}$

m $y = 3 - 4 \ln(1 - x)$

n $y = x \ln(x^2 + 1)$

o $y = \dfrac{\ln x}{x^2}$

2 Given $f(x) = \ln(kx)$ where $k \neq 0$, find $f'(x)$.

Use the laws of logarithms to explain why this derivative does not depend on the value of k.

3 Find $\dfrac{dy}{dx}$ for:

   a $y = x \ln 5$ **b** $y = \ln(x^3)$ **c** $y = \ln(x^4 + x)$

   d $y = \ln(10 - 5x)$ **e** $y = [\ln(2x + 1)]^3$ **f** $y = \dfrac{\ln(4x)}{x}$

   g $y = \ln\left(\dfrac{1}{x}\right)$ **h** $y = \ln(\ln x)$ **i** $y = \dfrac{1}{\ln x}$

Example 14   ◀) **Self Tutor**

Differentiate with respect to x:

  a $y = \ln(xe^{-x})$ **b** $y = \ln\left[\dfrac{x^2}{(x+2)(x-3)}\right]$

---

  a $y = \ln(xe^{-x})$

         $= \ln x + \ln e^{-x}$ $\{\ln(ab) = \ln a + \ln b\}$

         $= \ln x - x$ $\{\ln e^a = a\}$

    $\therefore \quad \dfrac{dy}{dx} = \dfrac{1}{x} - 1$

A derivative function will only be valid on *at most* the domain of the original function.

  b $y = \ln\left[\dfrac{x^2}{(x+2)(x-3)}\right]$

         $= \ln x^2 - \ln[(x+2)(x-3)]$ $\left\{\ln\left(\dfrac{a}{b}\right) = \ln a - \ln b\right\}$

         $= 2\ln x - [\ln(x+2) + \ln(x-3)]$

         $= 2\ln x - \ln(x+2) - \ln(x-3)$

    $\therefore \quad \dfrac{dy}{dx} = \dfrac{2}{x} - \dfrac{1}{x+2} - \dfrac{1}{x-3}$

---

4 Use the laws of logarithms to help differentiate with respect to x:

   a $y = \ln\sqrt{1 - 2x}$ **b** $y = \ln\left(\dfrac{1}{2x + 3}\right)$

   c $y = \ln(e^x \sqrt{x})$ **d** $y = \ln(x\sqrt{2 - x})$

   e $y = \ln\left(\dfrac{x + 3}{x - 1}\right)$ **f** $y = \ln\left(\dfrac{x^2}{3 - x}\right)$

5 Differentiate with respect to x:

   a $f(x) = \ln((3x - 4)^3)$ **b** $f(x) = \ln(x(x^2 + 1))$

   c $f(x) = \ln\left(\dfrac{x^2 + 2x}{x - 5}\right)$ **d** $f(x) = \ln\left(\dfrac{x^3}{(x + 4)(x - 1)}\right)$

6 Find the gradient of the tangent to $y = x\ln x$ at the point where $x = e$.

7 Suppose $f(x) = a\ln(bx^2)$ where $f(e) = 3$ and $f'(1) = 6$. Find the constants a and b.

8 Suppose $f(x) = ax\ln(bx)$ where $f(1) = 12$ and $f'(1) = 16$. Find the constants a and b.

9 Find the point(s) at which the tangent to $y = \ln(15 - x^2)$ has gradient 1.

G   DERIVATIVES OF TRIGONOMETRIC FUNCTIONS

We have seen that the sine and cosine curves naturally arise from circular motion.

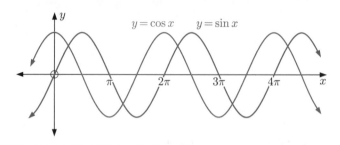

INVESTIGATION 7   DERIVATIVES OF $\sin x$ AND $\cos x$

What to do:

1 Click on the icon to observe the graph of $y = \sin x$. A tangent with x-step of length 1 unit moves across the curve, and its y-step is translated onto the gradient graph. Predict the derivative of the function $y = \sin x$.

DERIVATIVES DEMO

2 Repeat the process in **1** for the graph of $y = \cos x$. Hence predict the derivative of the function $y = \cos x$.

3

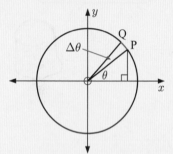

Suppose P and Q are points on the unit circle corresponding to angles θ and $\theta + \Delta\theta$ respectively from the positive x-axis.

a Explain why $PR = \sin(\theta + \Delta\theta) - \sin\theta$.

b If P and Q are close together then $\Delta\theta$ is very small.
Explain why as Q approaches P:

   i   the arc PQ resembles line segment [PQ]

   ii the length of the line segment $PQ \approx \Delta\theta$

   iii $Q\hat{P}O$ approaches a right angle

   iv $Q\hat{P}R \approx \theta$.

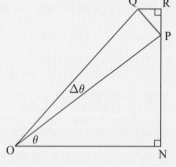

c Use right angled triangle trigonometry in $\triangle QRP$ to show that $\cos\theta \approx \dfrac{\sin(\theta + \Delta\theta) - \sin\theta}{\Delta\theta}$.

Hence explain why in the limit as $\Delta\theta \to 0$, $\cos\theta = \dfrac{d}{d\theta}(\sin\theta)$.

From the **Investigation** you should have deduced that:

> For x in radians: If $f(x) = \sin x$ then $f'(x) = \cos x$.
>
>   If $f(x) = \cos x$ then $f'(x) = -\sin x$.

THE DERIVATIVES OF $\sin[f(x)]$ AND $\cos[f(x)]$

Suppose $y = \sin[f(x)]$

If we let $u = f(x)$, then $y = \sin u$.

But $\dfrac{dy}{dx} = \dfrac{dy}{du}\dfrac{du}{dx}$ {chain rule}

$\therefore \ \dfrac{dy}{dx} = \cos u \times f'(x)$

$\qquad = \cos[f(x)] \times f'(x)$

We can perform a similar procedure for $\cos[f(x)]$.

Function	Derivative
$\sin[f(x)]$	$\cos[f(x)]\,f'(x)$
$\cos[f(x)]$	$-\sin[f(x)]\,f'(x)$

Example 15   ◀)) Self Tutor

Differentiate with respect to x:

a $x\sin x$ **b** $4\cos^2 3x$

a $\qquad y = x\sin x$

$\therefore \ \dfrac{dy}{dx} = (1)\sin x + (x)\cos x$

$\qquad\qquad$ {product rule}

$\qquad = \sin x + x\cos x$

b $\qquad y = 4\cos^2 3x$

$\qquad = 4u^2$ where $u = \cos 3x$

$\dfrac{dy}{dx} = \dfrac{dy}{du}\dfrac{du}{dx}$ {chain rule}

$\therefore \ \dfrac{dy}{dx} = 8u \times \dfrac{du}{dx}$

$\qquad = 8\cos 3x \times (-3\sin 3x)$

$\qquad = -24\cos 3x \sin 3x$

$\qquad = -12\sin 6x$

EXERCISE 12G

1 Find $\dfrac{dy}{dx}$ for:

a $y = \sin 2x$ **b** $y = \sin x + \cos x$ **c** $y = \cos 3x - \sin x$

d $y = \sin(x+1)$ **e** $y = \cos(3-2x)$ **f** $y = 3 - 2\cos 3x$

g $y = \sin\frac{x}{2} - 3\cos x$ **h** $y = 4\sin x - \cos 2x$ **i** $y = \frac{1}{2}\cos 6x - 5\sin 4x$

2 Differentiate with respect to x:

a $x^2 + \cos x$ **b** $e^x \cos x$ **c** $e^{-x}\sin x$ **d** $\ln(\sin x)$

e $e^{\cos 5x}$ **f** $\cos\frac{x}{2}$ **g** $x\cos x$ **h** $\dfrac{\sin x}{x}$

3 Differentiate with respect to x:

a $\sin(x^2)$ **b** $\cos(\sqrt{x})$ **c** $\sqrt{\cos x}$ **d** $\sin^2 x$

e $\cos^3 x$ **f** $\cos x \sin 2x$ **g** $\cos^3 4x$ **h** $\dfrac{2}{\sin^2 2x}$

4 **a** Use the quotient rule to find the derivative of $\tan x$.

b *Hence* find $\dfrac{dy}{dx}$ for:

i $y = \tan 5x$ **ii** $y = \tan x - 3\sin x$ **iii** $y = e^{2x}\tan x$ **iv** $y = x\tan x$

5 Find the gradient of the tangent to:

    a $f(x) = \sin^3 x$ at the point where $x = \frac{2\pi}{3}$

    b $f(x) = \cos x \sin x$ at the point where $x = \frac{\pi}{4}$.

6 Consider the function $f(x) = 2\cos^2 x + 2\sin^2 x + 1$.

    a Find $f'(x)$.   **b** Explain your answer to **a**.

7 The graph of $y = \cos x + 2\sin 2x$ is shown alongside.

    a Which tangent appears to have the steeper gradient?

    b Find $\dfrac{dy}{dx}$, and hence check your answer to **a**.

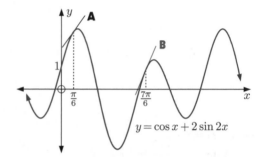

$y = \cos x + 2\sin 2x$

H   SECOND DERIVATIVES

Given a function $f(x)$, the derivative $f'(x)$ is known as the **first derivative**.

The **second derivative** of $f(x)$ is the derivative of $f'(x)$, or **the derivative of the first derivative**.

We use $f''(x)$, y'', or $\dfrac{d^2y}{dx^2}$ to represent the second derivative.

$f''(x)$ reads "*f double dashed x*".

$\dfrac{d^2y}{dx^2} = \dfrac{d}{dx}\left(\dfrac{dy}{dx}\right)$ reads "*dee two y by dee x squared*".

$f''(x)$ is the rate of change of $f'(x)$ with respect to x.

Example 16	◀) **Self Tutor**

Find $f''(x)$ given:

    a $f(x) = x^3 - \dfrac{3}{x}$ **b** $f(x) = x\cos x + \dfrac{1}{x}$

a $f(x) = x^3 - 3x^{-1}$

    $\therefore \ f'(x) = 3x^2 + 3x^{-2}$

    $\therefore \ f''(x) = 6x - 6x^{-3}$

           $= 6x - \dfrac{6}{x^3}$

b $f(x) = x\cos x + x^{-1}$

    $\therefore \ f'(x) = (1)\cos x + (x)(-\sin x) - x^{-2}$

           $= \cos x - x\sin x - x^{-2}$

    $\therefore \ f''(x) = -\sin x - (1)\sin x - (x)\cos x + 2x^{-3}$

           $= -2\sin x - x\cos x + \dfrac{2}{x^3}$

EXERCISE 12H

1 Find $f''(x)$ given that:

    a $f(x) = 3x^2 - 6x + 2$ **b** $f(x) = \dfrac{2}{\sqrt{x}} - 1$ **c** $f(x) = 2x^3 - 3x^2 - x + 5$

    d $f(x) = \dfrac{2 - 3x}{x^2}$ **e** $f(x) = (1 - 2x)^2$ **f** $f(x) = \dfrac{x + 2}{2x - 1}$

2 Find $\dfrac{d^2y}{dx^2}$ given that:

    a $y = x - x^3$ **b** $y = x^2 - \dfrac{5}{x^2}$ **c** $y = 2 - \dfrac{3}{\sqrt{x}}$

    d $y = \dfrac{4 - x}{x}$ **e** $y = (x^2 - 3x)^2$ **f** $y = x^2 - x + \dfrac{1}{1 - x}$

    g $y = e^{3x} + 2x$ **h** $y = \dfrac{1 - e^{-x}}{x}$ **i** $y = \dfrac{3 - x}{xe^x}$

3 Given $f(x) = x^3 - 2x + 5$, find:

    a $f(2)$ **b** $f'(2)$ **c** $f''(2)$

4 Find the value(s) of x such that $f''(x) = 0$, given:

    a $f(x) = 2x^3 - 6x^2 + 5x + 1$ **b** $f(x) = x^4 - 10x^3 + 36x^2 - 72x + 108$

5 Consider the function $f(x) = 2x^3 - x$.

Copy and complete the table alongside by indicating whether $f(x)$, $f'(x)$, and $f''(x)$ are positive (+), negative (−), or zero (0) at the given values of x.

x	−1	0	1
$f(x)$	−		
$f'(x)$			
$f''(x)$			

6 Given $f(x) = x^2 - \dfrac{1}{x}$, find:

    a $f(1)$ **b** $f'(1)$ **c** $f''(1)$

7 Given $f(x) = 3e^x - 2x$, find:

    a $f(1)$ **b** $f'(1)$ **c** $f''(1)$

8 Find $\dfrac{d^2y}{dx^2}$ given that:

    a $y = x \sin x$ **b** $y = \dfrac{\cos^2 x - x}{x^2}$ **c** $y = e^{-x} \sin x$

9 Suppose $y = Ae^{kx}$ where A and k are constants. Show that:

    a $\dfrac{dy}{dx} = ky$ **b** $\dfrac{d^2y}{dx^2} = k^2y$

10 Suppose $f(x) = 2\sin^3 x - 3\sin x$.

    a Show that $f'(x) = -3\cos x \cos 2x$.   **b** Find $f''(x)$.

11 Given $f(x) = \frac{2}{3}\sin 3x$, find $f''\left(\frac{2\pi}{9}\right)$.

12 Find $\dfrac{d^2y}{dx^2}$ given:

    a $y = -\ln x$ **b** $y = x \ln x$ **c** $y = (\ln x)^2$

13 If $y = 2e^{3x} + 5e^{4x}$, show that $\dfrac{d^2y}{dx^2} - 7\dfrac{dy}{dx} + 12y = 0$.

14 If $y = \sin(2x + 3)$, show that $\dfrac{d^2y}{dx^2} + 4y = 0$.

15 If $y = 2\sin x + 3\cos x$, show that $\dfrac{d^2y}{dx^2} + y = 0$.

REVIEW SET 12A

1 Find $f'(x)$ given that $f(x)$ is:

   a $5x^3$ **b** $x^6 - 5x$ **c** $7x^2 - \dfrac{3}{x}$

   d $3x - \dfrac{4}{x^2}$ **e** $2x\sqrt{x}$ **f** $4\sqrt{x} - \dfrac{1}{\sqrt{x}}$

2 Find $\dfrac{dy}{dx}$ for:

   a $y = 3x^2 - x^4$ **b** $y = \dfrac{x^3 - x}{x^2}$ **c** $y = x^2\sqrt{x - 2}$

3 **a** Find $f'(x)$ given $f(x) = \dfrac{x}{\sqrt{x^2 + 1}}$.

   b At what point on the curve $f(x) = \dfrac{x}{\sqrt{x^2 + 1}}$ does the tangent have gradient 1?

4 Find $\dfrac{dy}{dx}$ if:

   a $y = e^{x^3 + 2}$ **b** $y = \ln\left(\dfrac{x + 3}{x^2}\right)$ **c** $y = x^3 e^{2x}$

5 Find the gradient of the tangent to:

   a $f(x) = -x^2 + 4x - 2$ at $(-3, -23)$ **b** $y = (2 - 3x)^5$ at $x = 1$.

6 Differentiate with respect to x:

   a $5x - 3x^{-1}$ **b** $(3x^2 + \sqrt{x})^4$ **c** $(x^2 + 1)(1 - x^2)^3$

7 Find all points on the curve $y = 2x^3 + 3x^2 - 10x + 3$ where the gradient of the tangent is 2.

8 Differentiate with respect to x:

   a $\sin 5x \ln x$ **b** $\sin x \cos 2x$ **c** $e^{-x} \cos x$

9 Find the gradient of the tangent to $y = \sin^2 x$ at the point where $x = \frac{\pi}{3}$.

10 Given $y = 3e^x - e^{-x}$, show that $\dfrac{d^2y}{dx^2} = y$.

11 Consider the function $f(x) = \dfrac{x^2 - 4x - 1}{e^x}$.

   a Find $f'(x)$.

   b Find the gradient of the tangent to $y = f(x)$ at $x = 1$.

   c For what values of x is the tangent to $y = f(x)$ horizontal?

12 Find the derivative with respect to x of:

   a $f(x) = (x^2 + 3)^4$ **b** $g(x) = \dfrac{\sqrt{x + 5}}{x^2}$ **c** $h(x) = \dfrac{e^{4x}}{1 - 2x}$

13 The graph of $y = \sin x \cos x$ is shown alongside.

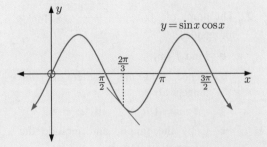

$y = \sin x \cos x$

a Find $\dfrac{dy}{dx}$.

b Show that $y = \frac{1}{2} \sin 2x$ has the same derivative.

c Find the gradient of the illustrated tangent.

14 For $f(x) = 2 \sin x + \cos 2x$, find:

a $f(\frac{\pi}{2})$
b $f'(\frac{\pi}{2})$
c $f''(\frac{\pi}{2})$

15 Find $\dfrac{d^2 y}{dx^2}$ for:

a $y = \frac{1}{8}x^4 + \frac{1}{6}x^3 - \frac{1}{4}x^2$
b $y = xe^{-x}$

16 For the function $f(x) = \sqrt{x} \cos 4x$:

a Find $f'(x)$ and $f''(x)$.

b Hence find: **i** $f'(\frac{\pi}{16})$ **ii** $f''(\frac{\pi}{8})$

17 Consider the curves $y = e^{x-1} + 1$ and $y = 3 - e^{1-x}$.

a Sketch the curves on the same set of axes.

b Find the point of intersection of the two curves.

c Show that the tangents to each curve at this point have the same gradient. Comment on the significance of this result.

REVIEW SET 12B

1 Find $f'(x)$ given that $f(x)$ is:

a $3x^2 - 7x + 4$
b $(x + 5)^2$
c $2\sqrt{x} - \dfrac{3}{x}$
d $6x^2 \sqrt{x}$

2 Find $\dfrac{dy}{dx}$ for:

a $y = 2x^3 - 6x^2 + 7x - 4$
b $y = \dfrac{3}{x} - \dfrac{5}{x^3}$
c $y = \dfrac{15}{\sqrt[3]{x}}$

3 If $f(x) = 7 + x - 3x^2$, find:

a $f(3)$
b $f'(3)$
c $f''(3)$

4 Differentiate with respect to x:

a $y = x^3 \sqrt{1 - x^2}$
b $y = \dfrac{x^2 - 3x}{\sqrt{x + 1}}$

5 **a** Find $\dfrac{dy}{dx}$ for $y = xe^x$.

b Find all points on the curve $y = xe^x$ where the gradient of the tangent is $2e$.

6 Differentiate with respect to x:

a $f(x) = \ln(e^x + 3)$
b $f(x) = \ln \left[\dfrac{(x + 2)^3}{x} \right]$

7 The graph of $f(x) = \dfrac{x^2 + 2}{x}$ is shown alongside.

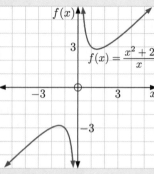

PRINTABLE GRAPH

a Find $f'(x)$.

b Hence find the gradient of the tangent at:

    i $x = 1$ **ii** $x = -2$

c Copy the graph, and include the information from **b**.

8 Suppose $y = \left(x - \dfrac{1}{x}\right)^4$. Find $\dfrac{dy}{dx}$ at the point where $x = 1$.

9 Find $\dfrac{dy}{dx}$ if:

    a $y = \ln(x^3 - 3x)$ **b** $y = \dfrac{e^x}{x^2}$ **c** $y = e^{2x} \sin x$

10 Suppose $f(x) = 2x^4 - 4x^3 - 9x^2 + 4x + 7$.

    a Find $f''(x)$.   **b** Find x such that $f''(x) = 0$.

11 Differentiate with respect to x:

    a $10x - \sin 10x$ **b** $\ln\left(\dfrac{1}{\cos x}\right)$ **c** $\sin 5x \ln(2x)$

12 Find the gradient of the tangent to $y = \dfrac{x^3}{x + 1}$ at $x = 2$.

13 Suppose $f(x) = a\ln(bx)$ where $f(e) = 12$ and $f'(2) = 2$. Find the constants a and b.

14 The graph of $y = \dfrac{\cos x}{\sin x + 2}$ is shown alongside.

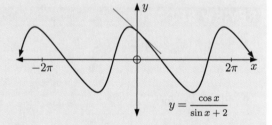

a Find the gradient of the illustrated tangent.

b Show that it is impossible to draw a tangent to the graph with gradient $-\frac{1}{2}$.

15 **a** If $y = \dfrac{e^x}{\sqrt{x}}$, show that $\dfrac{dy}{dx} = \dfrac{e^x(2x - 1)}{2x\sqrt{x}}$.

    b For what values of x is $\dfrac{dy}{dx}$:   **i** zero   **ii** undefined?

16 Find $\dfrac{d^2y}{dx^2}$ for:

    a $y = \dfrac{3x^2 - 2}{1 - 2x}$ **b** $y = x^3 - x + \dfrac{1}{\sqrt{x}}$

17 Suppose $y = 3\sin 2x + 2\cos 2x$. Show that $4y + \dfrac{d^2y}{dx^2} = 0$.

18 Let $f(x) = \dfrac{6x}{3 + x^2}$. Find the value(s) of x such that:

    a $f(x) = -\frac{1}{2}$ **b** $f'(x) = 0$ **c** $f''(x) = 0$

Chapter 13

Properties of curves

Contents:

OPENING PROBLEM

The curve $y = x^3 - 4x$ is shown alongside.

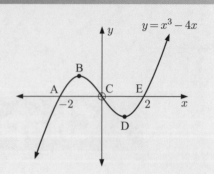

Things to think about:

a What features of this curve could you describe to someone?

b How can we use calculus to help identify important features?

c How would you describe the *shape* of a curve? What rules would you use to identify a curve's shape?

In the previous Chapter we saw how to differentiate many types of functions.

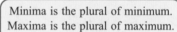

Minima is the plural of minimum.
Maxima is the plural of maximum.

In this Chapter we will use derivatives to find:

- tangents and normals to curves
- turning points, which are local minima and maxima
- inflection points where the curve changes shape.

A   TANGENTS

> The **tangent** to a curve at point A is the best approximating straight line to the curve at A.

In cases we have seen already, the tangent *touches* the curve.

For example, consider the tangents to the circle and parabola shown.

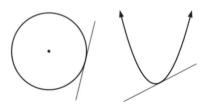

However, we note that for some functions:

- The tangent may intersect the curve again somewhere else.
- It is possible for the tangent to pass through the curve at the point of tangency. If this happens, we call it a **point of inflection**.

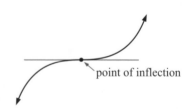

point of inflection

Consider a curve $y = f(x)$.

If A is the point with x-coordinate a, then the gradient of the tangent to the curve at this point is $f'(a)$.

The equation of the tangent is

$$y - f(a) = f'(a)(x - a)$$

or $$y = f'(a)(x - a) + f(a).$$

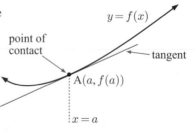

Example 1 ◄⏵ **Self Tutor**

Find the equation of the tangent to $f(x) = x^2 + 1$ at the point where $x = 1$.

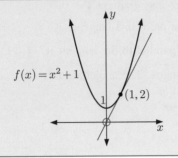

Since $f(1) = 1^2 + 1 = 2$, the point of contact is $(1, 2)$.

Now $f'(x) = 2x$, so at $x = 1$ the tangent has gradient $f'(1) = 2$.

$\therefore$ the tangent has equation $y = 2(x - 1) + 2$

which is $y = 2x$.

EXERCISE 13A

1 The graph of $f(x) = x^2 - 4x$ is shown alongside.

   a Find $f'(x)$.

   b Hence find the equation of the illustrated tangent.

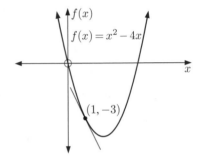

2 Find the equation of the tangent to:

   a $y = x - 2x^2 + 3$ at $x = 2$

   b $y = \sqrt{x} + 1$ at $x = 4$

   c $y = x^3 - 5x$ at $x = 1$

   d $y = \dfrac{4}{\sqrt{x}}$ at $(1, 4)$

   e $y = \dfrac{3}{x} - \dfrac{1}{x^2}$ at $(-1, -4)$

   f $y = 3x^2 - \dfrac{1}{x}$ at $x = -1$.

GRAPHING PACKAGE

Check your answers using technology.

Example 2 ◄⏵ **Self Tutor**

Find the equations of any horizontal tangents to $y = x^3 - 12x + 2$.

Since $y = x^3 - 12x + 2$, $\dfrac{dy}{dx} = 3x^2 - 12$

Horizontal tangents have gradient 0,

so $3x^2 - 12 = 0$

$\therefore 3(x^2 - 4) = 0$

$\therefore 3(x + 2)(x - 2) = 0$

$\therefore x = -2$ or 2

When $x = 2$, $y = 8 - 24 + 2 = -14$

When $x = -2$, $y = -8 + 24 + 2 = 18$

$\therefore$ the points of contact are $(2, -14)$ and $(-2, 18)$

$\therefore$ the tangents are $y = -14$ and $y = 18$.

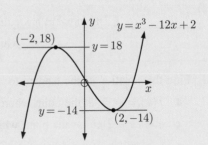

3   Find the equations of any horizontal tangents to:

   a $y = 2x^3 + 3x^2 - 12x + 1$ **b** $y = -x^3 + 3x^2 + 9x - 4$ **c** $y = \sqrt{x} + \dfrac{1}{\sqrt{x}}$

4   The tangent to $y = 2x^3 + kx^2 - 3$ at the point where $x = 2$ has gradient 4.

   a   Find k.   **b**   Hence find the equation of this tangent.

5   Find another tangent to $y = 1 - 3x + 12x^2 - 8x^3$ which is parallel to the tangent at $(1, 2)$.

6   Consider the curve $y = x^2 + ax + b$ where a and b are constants. The tangent to this curve at the point where $x = 1$ is $2x + y = 6$. Find the values of a and b.

7   Find the values of a and b.

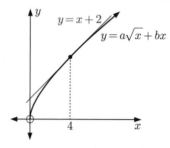

8   Show that the equation of the tangent to $y = 2x^2 - 1$ at the point where $x = a$, is $4ax - y = 2a^2 + 1$.

9   Consider the function $f(x) = x^2 + \dfrac{4}{x^2}$.

   a   Find $f'(x)$.

   b   Find the values of x at which the tangent to the curve is horizontal.

   c   Show that the tangents at these points are the same line.

10   Consider the curve $y = a\sqrt{1 - bx}$ where a and b are constants. The tangent to this curve at the point where $x = -1$ is $3x + y = 5$. Find the values of a and b.

Example 3   ◀)) **Self Tutor**

Show that the equation of the tangent to $y = \ln x$ at the point where $y = -1$ is $y = ex - 2$.

When $y = -1$, $\ln x = -1$
$$\therefore \quad x = e^{-1} = \tfrac{1}{e}$$

$\therefore$ the point of contact is $\left(\tfrac{1}{e}, -1\right)$.

Now $f(x) = \ln x$ has derivative $f'(x) = \dfrac{1}{x}$

$\therefore$ the tangent at $\left(\tfrac{1}{e}, -1\right)$ has gradient $\dfrac{1}{\frac{1}{e}} = e$

$\qquad\qquad\therefore$ the tangent has equation $y = e\left(x - \tfrac{1}{e}\right) - 1$

$\qquad\qquad\qquad$ which is $y = ex - 2$

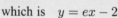

---

11   Find the equation of the tangent to:

   a $f(x) = e^{-x}$ at the point where $x = 2$ **b** $y = \ln(2 - x)$ at the point where $x = -1$

   c $y = (x + 2)e^x$ at the point where $x = 1$ **d** $y = \ln \sqrt{x}$ at the point where $y = -1$

   e $y = e^{3x-5}$ at the point where $y = e$.

12 Consider $f(x) = \ln(x(x-2))$.

    a State the domain of $f(x)$.   **b** Find $f'(x)$.

    c Find the equation of the tangent to $y = f(x)$ at the point where $x = 3$.

13 Find the axes intercepts of the tangent to $y = x^2 e^x$ at $x = 1$.

14 Find the exact area of the shaded triangle.

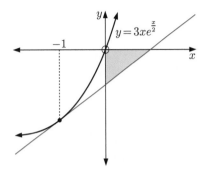

15 Find the equation of the tangent to:

    a $y = \sin x$ at the origin   **b** $y = \cos x$ at the point where $x = \frac{\pi}{6}$

    c $y = \dfrac{1}{\sin 2x}$ at the point where $x = \frac{\pi}{4}$

    d $y = \cos 2x + 3\sin x$ at the point where $x = \frac{\pi}{2}$.

16 Show that the curve with equation $y = \dfrac{\cos x}{1 + \sin x}$ does not have any horizontal tangents.

Example 4   **◄) Self Tutor**

Find where the tangent to $y = x^3 + x + 2$ at $(1, 4)$ meets the curve again.

Let $f(x) = x^3 + x + 2$

$\therefore\; f'(x) = 3x^2 + 1$ and $\therefore\; f'(1) = 3 + 1 = 4$

$\therefore\;$ the equation of the tangent at $(1, 4)$ is $4x - y = 4(1) - 4$

                           or $y = 4x$.

> $(x-1)^2$ must be a factor of $x^3 - 3x + 2 = 0$ since we are considering the *tangent* at $x = 1$.

The curve meets the tangent again when $x^3 + x + 2 = 4x$

                         $\therefore\; x^3 - 3x + 2 = 0$

                     $\therefore\; (x-1)^2(x+2) = 0$

When $x = -2$, $y = (-2)^3 + (-2) + 2 = -8$

$\therefore\;$ the tangent meets the curve again at $(-2, -8)$.

Casio fx-CG50	TI-84 Plus CE	HP Prime
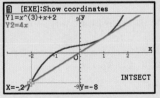	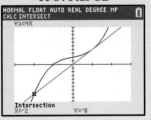	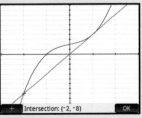

17 Find where the tangent to the curve $y = x^3$ at the point where $x = 2$, meets the curve again.

18 Find where the tangent to the curve $y = -x^3 + 2x^2 + 1$ at the point where $x = -1$, meets the curve again.

19 Find where the tangent to the curve $y = \dfrac{1}{x} - \dfrac{1}{x^2}$ at the point where $x = 1$, meets the curve again.

Example 5   ◀) **Self Tutor**

Find the equations of the tangents to $y = x^2$ from the external point $(2, 3)$.

Let (a, a^2) be a general point on $f(x) = x^2$.

Now $f'(x) = 2x$, so $f'(a) = 2a$

$\therefore$ the equation of the tangent at (a, a^2) is
$y = 2a(x - a) + a^2$ which is $y = 2ax - a^2$.

Thus the tangents which pass through $(2, 3)$ satisfy
$$3 = 2a(2) - a^2$$
$$\therefore \ a^2 - 4a + 3 = 0$$
$$\therefore \ (a - 1)(a - 3) = 0$$
$$\therefore \ a = 1 \text{ or } 3$$

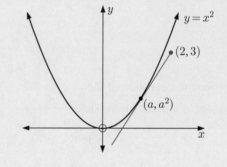

$\therefore$ two tangents pass through the external point $(2, 3)$.

If $a = 1$, the tangent has equation $y = 2x - 1$ with point of contact $(1, 1)$.

If $a = 3$, the tangent has equation $y = 6x - 9$ with point of contact $(3, 9)$.

---

20 **a** Find the equation of the tangent to $y = x^2 - x + 9$ at the point where $x = a$.
   b Hence find the equations of the two tangents from $(0, 0)$ to the curve. State the coordinates of the points of contact.

21 **a** Find the equation of the tangent to $y = x^2 + 4x$ at the point where $x = a$.
   b Hence find the equations of the tangents to $y = x^2 + 4x$ which pass through the external point $(1, -4)$. State the coordinates of the points of contact.

22 Find the equations of the tangents to $y = x^2 - 3x + 1$ which pass through $(1, -10)$.

23 **a** Find the equation of the tangent to $y = e^x$ at the point where $x = a$.
   b Hence find the equation of the tangent to $y = e^x$ which passes through the origin.

24 Consider the function $y = 2x^2$.
   a Find the equations of the tangents to the function from the external point $(1, -6)$.
   b Find the points of contact for the tangents.
   c Show that no tangents to the function pass through the point $(1, 4)$.
   d Draw a graph of $y = 2x^2$ showing the information above.

25 Consider $f(x) = \dfrac{8}{x^2}$.

    a Sketch the graph of the function.

    b Find the equation of the tangent at the point where $x = a$.

    c If the tangent in **b** cuts the x-axis at A and the y-axis at B, find the coordinates of A and B.

    d Find the area of triangle OAB and discuss the area of the triangle as $a \to \infty$.

26 Find, correct to 2 decimal places, the angle between the tangents to $y = 3e^{-x}$ and $y = 2 + e^x$ at their point of intersection.

27 A quadratic of the form $y = ax^2$, $a > 0$, touches the logarithmic function $y = \ln x$ as shown.

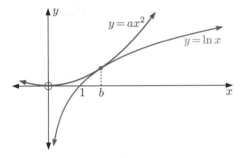

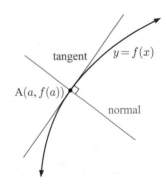

If two curves *touch* then they share a common tangent at that point.

    a If the x-coordinate of the point of contact is b, explain why $ab^2 = \ln b$ and $2ab = \dfrac{1}{b}$.

    b Deduce that the point of contact is $(\sqrt{e}, \frac{1}{2})$.

    c Find the value of a.

    d Find the equation of the common tangent.

28 Let $p(x) = ax^2$, $a \neq 0$.

    a Find the equations of the tangents to the curve at $x = s$ and $x = t$.

    b Prove that the two tangent lines intersect at $x = \dfrac{s+t}{2}$.

    c Prove that if the tangent lines are perpendicular then they intersect at $y = -\dfrac{1}{4a}$.

B   NORMALS

A **normal** to a curve is a line which is perpendicular to the tangent at the point of contact.

The gradients of perpendicular lines are negative reciprocals of each other, so:

The gradient of the normal to the curve at $x = a$ is $-\dfrac{1}{f'(a)}$.

The equation of the normal to the curve at $x = a$ is

$$y = -\frac{1}{f'(a)}(x - a) + f(a).$$

Example 6   ◀)) **Self Tutor**

Find the equation of the normal to $y = \dfrac{8}{\sqrt{x}}$ at the point where $x = 4$.

When $x = 4$, $y = \dfrac{8}{\sqrt{4}} = \dfrac{8}{2} = 4$.   So, the point of contact is $(4, 4)$.

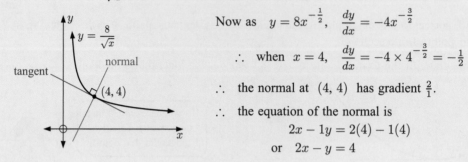

Now as $y = 8x^{-\frac{1}{2}}$, $\dfrac{dy}{dx} = -4x^{-\frac{3}{2}}$

∴ when $x = 4$, $\dfrac{dy}{dx} = -4 \times 4^{-\frac{3}{2}} = -\dfrac{1}{2}$

∴ the normal at $(4, 4)$ has gradient $\dfrac{2}{1}$.

∴ the equation of the normal is
$$2x - 1y = 2(4) - 1(4)$$
or $\quad 2x - y = 4$

EXERCISE 13B

1 Find the equation of the normal to:

a $y = x^2$ at the point $(4, 16)$

b $y = x^3 - 5x + 2$ at $x = -2$

c $y = \dfrac{5}{\sqrt{x}} - \sqrt{x}$ at the point $(1, 4)$

d $y = 8\sqrt{x} - \dfrac{1}{x^2}$ at $x = 1$

e $f(x) = \dfrac{x}{1 - 3x}$ at $(-1, -\tfrac{1}{4})$

f $f(x) = \dfrac{x^2}{1 - x}$ at $(2, -4)$.

2 Suppose $f(x) = x^2 - \dfrac{8}{x}$.

a Find the equation of the tangent to $y = f(x)$ at $x = -2$.

b Find the equation of the normal to $y = f(x)$ at $x = 3$.

Example 7   ◀)) **Self Tutor**

Find the equation of the normal to $y = e^{x-2}$ at the point where $x = 3$.

When $x = 3$, $y = e^{3-2} = e$. So, the point of contact is $(3, e)$.

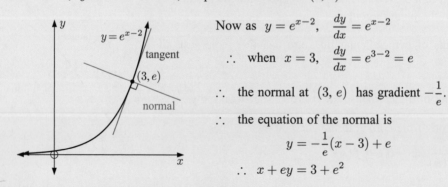

Now as $y = e^{x-2}$, $\dfrac{dy}{dx} = e^{x-2}$

∴ when $x = 3$, $\dfrac{dy}{dx} = e^{3-2} = e$

∴ the normal at $(3, e)$ has gradient $-\dfrac{1}{e}$.

∴ the equation of the normal is
$$y = -\dfrac{1}{e}(x - 3) + e$$
$$\therefore \quad x + ey = 3 + e^2$$

3 Find the equation of the normal to:

   a $y = e^{-x}$ at $x = 0$ **b** $y = \ln x$ at $x = e$

   c $y = e^{2x-1}$ at $x = 1$ **d** $y = \sin x$ at $x = \frac{\pi}{3}$.

4 Consider the curve $y = a\sqrt{x} + \dfrac{b}{\sqrt{x}}$ where a and b are constants. The normal to this curve at the point where $x = 4$ is $4x + y = 22$. Find the values of a and b.

5 Find the points where the normal to $y = x^3 - 2x^2 + 1$ at $x = 1$, meets the curve again.

6 Find the equation of the normal to $f(x) = \cos x$ which passes through the origin.

7 Find the equation of the normal to $y = \sqrt{x}$ from the external point $(4, 0)$.

   Hint: There is no normal at the point where $x = 0$, as this is the end point of the function.

C   INCREASING AND DECREASING

When we draw a graph of a function, we may notice that the function is **increasing** or **decreasing** over particular intervals.

> Suppose S is an interval in the domain of $f(x)$, so $f(x)$ is defined for all x in S.
>
> - $f(x)$ is **increasing** on S $\Leftrightarrow$ $f(a) \leqslant f(b)$ for all $a, b \in S$ such that $a < b$.
> - $f(x)$ is **decreasing** on S $\Leftrightarrow$ $f(a) \geqslant f(b)$ for all $a, b \in S$ such that $a < b$.

For example, $y = x^2$ is decreasing for $x \leqslant 0$ and increasing for $x \geqslant 0$.

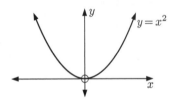

Important: In this example, people often get confused about the point $x = 0$. They wonder how the curve can be both increasing and decreasing at this point. The answer is that the notion of increasing and decreasing is associated with *intervals*, not particular values for x. $y = x^2$ is decreasing *on the interval* $x \leqslant 0$ and increasing *on the interval* $x \geqslant 0$.

Example 8   ◀) **Self Tutor**

Find intervals where $f(x)$ is:

   a increasing

   b decreasing.

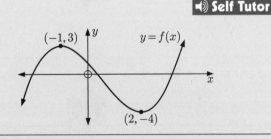

---

   a $f(x)$ is increasing for $x \leqslant -1$ and for $x \geqslant 2$.

   b $f(x)$ is decreasing for $-1 \leqslant x \leqslant 2$.

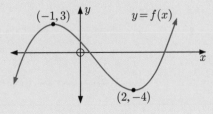

We can determine intervals where a curve $y = f(x)$ is increasing or decreasing by considering a **sign diagram** of the derivative function $f'(x)$.

For most functions that we deal with in this course:

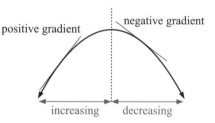

- $f(x)$ is **increasing** on S $\Leftrightarrow$ $f'(x) \geqslant 0$ for all x in S
- $f(x)$ is **decreasing** on S $\Leftrightarrow$ $f'(x) \leqslant 0$ for all x in S.

positive gradient   negative gradient

increasing   decreasing

Sign diagrams for the derivative are extremely useful for determining intervals where a function is increasing or decreasing. Consider the following examples:

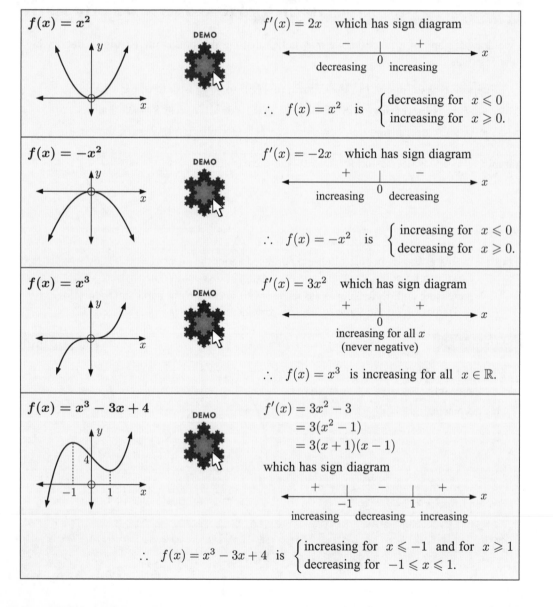

$f(x) = x^2$

DEMO

$f'(x) = 2x$ which has sign diagram

$$\begin{array}{ccc} - & | & + \\ & 0 & \\ \text{decreasing} & & \text{increasing} \end{array} \longrightarrow x$$

$\therefore$ $f(x) = x^2$ is $\begin{cases} \text{decreasing for } x \leqslant 0 \\ \text{increasing for } x \geqslant 0. \end{cases}$

$f(x) = -x^2$

DEMO

$f'(x) = -2x$ which has sign diagram

$$\begin{array}{ccc} + & | & - \\ & 0 & \\ \text{increasing} & & \text{decreasing} \end{array} \longrightarrow x$$

$\therefore$ $f(x) = -x^2$ is $\begin{cases} \text{increasing for } x \leqslant 0 \\ \text{decreasing for } x \geqslant 0. \end{cases}$

$f(x) = x^3$

DEMO

$f'(x) = 3x^2$ which has sign diagram

$$\begin{array}{ccc} + & | & + \\ & 0 & \end{array} \longrightarrow x$$
increasing for all x
(never negative)

$\therefore$ $f(x) = x^3$ is increasing for all $x \in \mathbb{R}$.

$f(x) = x^3 - 3x + 4$

DEMO

$f'(x) = 3x^2 - 3$
$ = 3(x^2 - 1)$
$ = 3(x + 1)(x - 1)$

which has sign diagram

$$\begin{array}{ccccc} + & | & - & | & + \\ & -1 & & 1 & \end{array} \longrightarrow x$$
increasing   decreasing   increasing

$\therefore$ $f(x) = x^3 - 3x + 4$ is $\begin{cases} \text{increasing for } x \leqslant -1 \text{ and for } x \geqslant 1 \\ \text{decreasing for } -1 \leqslant x \leqslant 1. \end{cases}$

Example 9   ◀) **Self Tutor**

Find the intervals where the following functions are increasing or decreasing:

  a $f(x) = -x^3 + 3x^2 + 5$ **b** $f(x) = 3x^4 - 8x^3 + 2$

a $f(x) = -x^3 + 3x^2 + 5$

  $\therefore \ f'(x) = -3x^2 + 6x$

  $\qquad = -3x(x - 2)$

which has sign diagram:

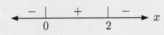

TI-84 Plus CE

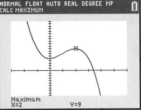

So, $f(x)$ is decreasing for $x \leqslant 0$ and for $x \geqslant 2$, and increasing for $0 \leqslant x \leqslant 2$.

b $f(x) = 3x^4 - 8x^3 + 2$

  $\therefore \ f'(x) = 12x^3 - 24x^2$

  $\qquad = 12x^2(x - 2)$

which has sign diagram:

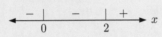

Casio fx-CG50

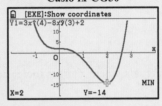

So, $f(x)$ is decreasing for $x \leqslant 2$, and increasing for $x \geqslant 2$.

Remember that $f(x)$ must be defined for all x on an interval before we can classify the function as increasing or decreasing on that interval. We need to take care with vertical asymptotes and other values for x where the function is not defined.

EXERCISE 13C

1 Write down the intervals where the graphs are:

  i increasing   **ii** decreasing.

  a   **b**   **c**

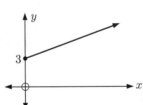   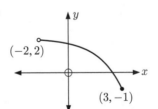   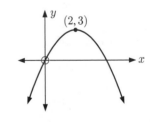

  d   **e**   **f**

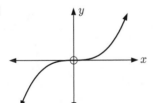   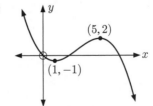   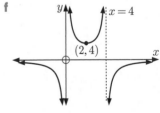

2 The graph of $f(x) = x^3 - 6x^2 + 9x + 2$ is shown alongside.

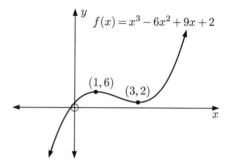

   a Use the graph to write down the intervals where the function is:

   i increasing   **ii** decreasing.

   b Check your answer by finding $f'(x)$ and constructing its sign diagram.

3 The graph of $f(x) = x^3 - 6x^2 + 10$ is shown alongside.

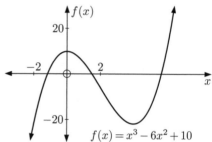

   a Find $f'(x)$, and draw its sign diagram.

   b Find the intervals where $f(x)$ is increasing or decreasing.

4 Find the intervals where $f(x)$ is increasing or decreasing:

   a $f(x) = x^2$

   b $f(x) = -x^3$

   c $f(x) = 2x^2 + 3x - 4$

   d $f(x) = \dfrac{1}{x}$

   e $f(x) = \dfrac{2}{\sqrt{x}}$

   f $f(x) = x^3 - 6x^2$

   g $f(x) = -2x^3 + 4x$

   h $f(x) = -4x^3 + 15x^2 + 18x + 3$

   i $f(x) = 3x^4 - 16x^3 + 24x^2 - 2$

   j $f(x) = x^3 - 6x^2 + 3x - 1$

5 Consider the function $f(x) = x^3 - 3x^2 + 5x + 2$.

   a Find $f'(x)$.

   b Show that $f'(x) > 0$ for all x, and explain the significance of this result.

   c Use technology to sketch $y = f(x)$, and check your answer to **b**.

Example 10   ◀) **Self Tutor**

Consider $f(x) = \dfrac{2x - 3}{x^2 + 2x - 3}$.

   a Show that $f'(x) = \dfrac{-2x(x - 3)}{(x - 1)^2(x + 3)^2}$, and draw its sign diagram.

   b Hence find the intervals where $y = f(x)$ is increasing or decreasing.

---

a $f(x) = \dfrac{2x - 3}{x^2 + 2x - 3}$

$\therefore \ f'(x) = \dfrac{2(x^2 + 2x - 3) - (2x - 3)(2x + 2)}{(x^2 + 2x - 3)^2}$ {quotient rule}

$\qquad = \dfrac{2x^2 + 4x - 6 - (4x^2 - 2x - 6)}{((x - 1)(x + 3))^2}$

$$= \frac{-2x^2 + 6x}{(x-1)^2(x+3)^2}$$

$$= \frac{-2x(x-3)}{(x-1)^2(x+3)^2} \quad \text{which has sign diagram:}$$

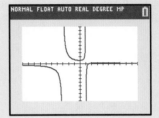

b $f(x)$ is increasing for $0 \leqslant x < 1$
and for $1 < x \leqslant 3$.

$f(x)$ is decreasing for $x < -3$
and for $-3 < x \leqslant 0$
and for $x \geqslant 3$.

6 Let $f(x) = x + \dfrac{9}{x}$.

a Show that $f'(x) = \dfrac{(x+3)(x-3)}{x^2}$ and draw its sign diagram.

b Hence find intervals where $y = f(x)$ is increasing or decreasing.

7 Consider $f(x) = \dfrac{4x}{x^2 + 1}$.

a Show that $f'(x) = \dfrac{-4(x+1)(x-1)}{(x^2+1)^2}$ and draw its sign diagram.

b Hence find intervals where $y = f(x)$ is increasing or decreasing.

8 Consider $f(x) = \dfrac{4x}{(x-1)^2}$.

a Show that $f'(x) = \dfrac{-4(x+1)}{(x-1)^3}$ and draw its sign diagram.

b Hence find intervals where $y = f(x)$ is increasing or decreasing.

9 Consider $f(x) = \dfrac{-x^2 + 4x - 7}{x - 1}$.

a Show that $f'(x) = \dfrac{-(x+1)(x-3)}{(x-1)^2}$ and draw its sign diagram.

b Hence find intervals where $y = f(x)$ is increasing or decreasing.

10 To find the intervals where $f(x) = \ln x$ is increasing or decreasing, Kenneth states that $f'(x) = \dfrac{1}{x}$, which has sign diagram $\underset{\substack{\\0x}}{\xleftarrow{\quad - \quad\vdots\quad + \quad}}{}^{f'(x)}$. He therefore concludes that $f(x) = \ln x$ is increasing for $x > 0$, and decreasing for $x < 0$. Explain the mistake Kenneth has made.

11 Find the intervals where $f(x)$ is increasing or decreasing:

a $f(x) = e^x$

b $f(x) = \ln(x+2)$

c $f(x) = 3 + e^{-x}$

d $f(x) = xe^x$

e $f(x) = x - 2\sqrt{x}$

f $f(x) = x^3 \ln x$

g $f(x) = \dfrac{x^3}{x^2 - 1}$

h $f(x) = e^{-x^2}$

i $f(x) = (3x^2 + 1)^4$

j $f(x) = x^2 + \dfrac{4}{x-1}$

k $f(x) = \ln(x^2 + 4)$

l $f(x) = \dfrac{e^{-x}}{x}$

D STATIONARY POINTS

A **stationary point** of a function is a point where $f'(x) = 0$.

It could be a **local maximum** or **local minimum**, or else a **stationary inflection**.

At a stationary point, the tangent is horizontal.

TURNING POINTS (MAXIMA AND MINIMA)

The graph shown has the restricted domain $-5 \leqslant x \leqslant 6$.

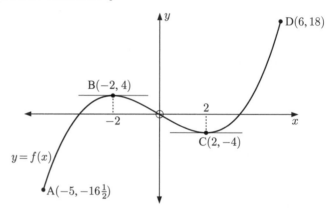

A is a **global minimum** as it has the minimum value of y on the entire domain.

B is a **local maximum** as it is a turning point where $f'(x) = 0$ and the curve has shape ⌢ .

C is a **local minimum** as it is a turning point where $f'(x) = 0$ and the curve has shape ⌣ .

D is a **global maximum** as it is the maximum value of y on the entire domain.

For many functions, a local maximum or minimum is also the global maximum or minimum.

For example, for $y = x^2$ the point $(0, 0)$ is a local minimum and is also the global minimum.

STATIONARY POINTS OF INFLECTION

It is not always true that whenever we find a value of x where $f'(x) = 0$, we have a local maximum or minimum.

For example, $f(x) = x^3$ has $f'(x) = 3x^2$, so $f'(x) = 0$ when $x = 0$.

The tangent to the curve crosses over the curve at $O(0, 0)$. This tangent is horizontal, but $O(0, 0)$ is neither a local maximum nor a local minimum.

Rather, this point is called a **stationary inflection** (or **inflexion**) as the curve changes its curvature or shape.

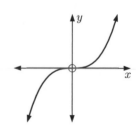

SIGN DIAGRAMS

In calculus we commonly use sign diagrams of the derivative function $f'(x)$ to determine the nature of a stationary point.

Consider the graph alongside.

The sign diagram of its gradient function is shown directly beneath it.

The signs on the sign diagram of $f'(x)$ indicate whether the gradient of $y = f(x)$ is positive or negative on that interval.

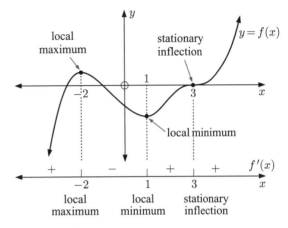

DEMO

We observe the following properties:

Stationary point where $f'(a) = 0$	Sign diagram of $f'(x)$ near $x = a$	Shape of curve near $x = a$
local maximum	$\xleftarrow{\quad + \ \mid \ - \quad} f'(x) \atop a \qquad x$	$x = a$
local minimum	$\xleftarrow{\quad - \ \mid \ + \quad} f'(x) \atop a \qquad x$	$x = a$
stationary inflection	$\xleftarrow{\ + \ \mid \ + \ } f'(x) \atop a \quad x$ $\qquad \xleftarrow{\ - \ \mid \ - \ } f'(x) \atop a \quad x$	$x = a \qquad x = a$

To find the stationary points of a function $f(x)$, we find the values of x for which $f'(x) = 0$. The sign diagram of $f'(x)$ tells us whether each stationary point is a local maximum, local minimum, or stationary inflection.

Example 11   ◀⧏ **Self Tutor**

Find and classify all stationary points of $f(x) = x^3 - 3x^2 - 9x + 5$.

$f(x) = x^3 - 3x^2 - 9x + 5$
$\therefore \ f'(x) = 3x^2 - 6x - 9$
$\qquad\quad = 3(x^2 - 2x - 3)$
$\qquad\quad = 3(x - 3)(x + 1)$

which has sign diagram

$\xleftarrow{\quad + \quad\frown\quad - \quad\smile\quad + \quad} f'(x) \atop \qquad -1 \qquad 3 \qquad\quad x$

So, we have a local maximum at $x = -1$ and a local minimum at $x = 3$.

$$f(-1) = (-1)^3 - 3(-1)^2 - 9(-1) + 5 \qquad f(3) = 3^3 - 3 \times 3^2 - 9 \times 3 + 5$$
$$= 10 \qquad\qquad\qquad\qquad\qquad = -22$$

TI-84 Plus CE

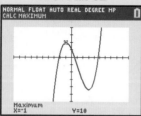

Casio fx-CG50

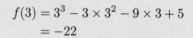
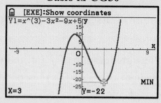

There is a local maximum at $(-1, \, 10)$.   There is a local minimum at $(3, \, -22)$.

EXERCISE 13D

1   The tangents at points A, O, and B are horizontal.

   a   Classify points A, O, and B.

   b   Draw a sign diagram for the gradient function $f'(x)$ for all x.

   c   State intervals where $y = f(x)$ is:

      i   increasing   **ii**   decreasing.

   d   Draw a sign diagram for $f(x)$ for all x.

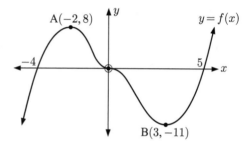

2

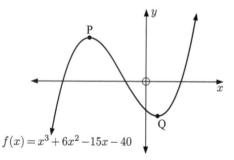

$f(x) = x^3 + 6x^2 - 15x - 40$

The graph of $f(x) = x^3 + 6x^2 - 15x - 40$ is shown alongside. P and Q are stationary points.

   a   Classify points P and Q.

   b   Find $f'(x)$.

   c   Find the coordinates of P and Q.

3   Consider the function $f(x) = \frac{1}{3}x^3 - 9x + 4$.

   a   Find $f'(x)$, and draw its sign diagram.

   b   Find intervals where the function is increasing and decreasing.

   c   Find and classify any stationary points.

   d   Describe the behaviour of the function as $x \to \infty$ and as $x \to -\infty$.

   e   Sketch the graph of $y = f(x)$, showing the features you have found.

4   Consider the function $g(x) = -2x^3 + 6x^2 + 18x - 7$.

   a   Find $g'(x)$, and draw its sign diagram.

   b   Find intervals where the function is increasing and decreasing.

   c   Find and classify any stationary points.

   d   Describe the behaviour of the function as $x \to \infty$ and as $x \to -\infty$.

   e   Sketch the graph of $y = g(x)$, showing the features you have found.

5 For each of the following functions, find and classify any stationary points. Sketch the function, showing all important features.

    a $f(x) = x^2 - 2$ **b** $f(x) = x^3 + 1$

    c $f(x) = x^3 - 3x + 2$ **d** $f(x) = x^4 - 2x^2$

    e $f(x) = x^3 - 6x^2 + 12x + 1$ **f** $f(x) = \sqrt{x} + 2$

    g $f(x) = x - \sqrt{x}$ **h** $f(x) = x^4 - 6x^2 + 8x - 3$

    i $f(x) = 1 - x\sqrt{x}$ **j** $f(x) = x^4 - 2x^2 - 8$

6   **a** For what value of x does the quadratic function $f(x) = ax^2 + bx + c$, $a \neq 0$, have a stationary point?

    b Under what conditions is the stationary point a local maximum or a local minimum?

Example 12   ◀) **Self Tutor**

Find the exact position and nature of the stationary point of $y = (x - 2)e^{-x}$.

$\dfrac{dy}{dx} = (1)e^{-x} + (x - 2)e^{-x}(-1)$ {product rule}

$\phantom{\dfrac{dy}{dx}} = e^{-x}(1 - (x - 2))$

$\phantom{\dfrac{dy}{dx}} = \dfrac{3 - x}{e^x}$ where e^x is positive for all x.

So, $\dfrac{dy}{dx} = 0$ when $x = 3$.

The sign diagram of $\dfrac{dy}{dx}$ is

$\therefore$ at $x = 3$ we have a local maximum.

When $x = 3$, $y = (1)e^{-3} = \dfrac{1}{e^3}$ $\therefore$ the local maximum is at $\left(3, \dfrac{1}{e^3}\right)$.

---

7 Find the position and nature of the stationary point(s) of:

    a $y = xe^{-x}$ **b** $y = x^2 e^x$ **c** $y = \dfrac{e^x}{x}$ **d** $y = e^{-x}(x + 2)$

8 $f(x) = 2x^3 + ax^2 - 24x + 1$ has a local maximum at $x = -4$.

    a Find a.   **b** Find the coordinates of the local maximum.

9 $f(x) = x^3 + ax + b$ has a stationary point at $(-2, 3)$.

    a Find the values of a and b.

    b Find the position and nature of all stationary points.

10 $y = \dfrac{e^{ax}}{bx}$ has a stationary point at $\left(\dfrac{1}{3}, \dfrac{e}{2}\right)$.

    a Find the values of a and b.   **b** State the nature of the stationary point.

11 Consider $f(x) = x \ln x$.

    a For what values of x is $f(x)$ defined?

    b Show that the minimum value of $f(x)$ is $-\dfrac{1}{e}$.

12 For each of the following, determine the position and nature of the stationary points on the interval $0 \leqslant x \leqslant 2\pi$, then show them on a graph of the function.

    a $f(x) = \sin x$ **b** $f(x) = \cos 2x$

    c $f(x) = \sin^2 x$ **d** $f(x) = e^{\sin x}$

    e $f(x) = \cos x - \sin x$ **f** $f(x) = \sin 2x + 2\cos x$

13 The cubic polynomial $P(x) = ax^3 + bx^2 + cx + d$ touches the line with equation $y = 9x + 2$ at the point $(0, 2)$, and has a stationary point at $(-1, -7)$. Find $P(x)$.

Example 13   ◀) **Self Tutor**

Find the greatest and least value of $y = x^3 - 6x^2 + 5$ on the interval $-2 \leqslant x \leqslant 5$.

Now $\dfrac{dy}{dx} = 3x^2 - 12x$

            $= 3x(x - 4)$

$\therefore \dfrac{dy}{dx} = 0$ when $x = 0$ or 4.

The sign diagram of $\dfrac{dy}{dx}$ is:

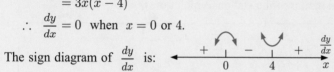

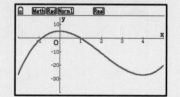

$\therefore$ there is a local maximum at $x = 0$, and a local minimum at $x = 4$.

Critical value (x)	y
-2 (end point)	-27
0 (local maximum)	5
4 (local minimum)	-27
5 (end point)	-20

> If an interval is given, we must also check the value of the function at the end points.

The greatest of these values is 5 when $x = 0$.

The least of these values is -27 when $x = -2$ and when $x = 4$.

---

14 Find the greatest and least value of:

    a $x^3 - 12x - 2$ for $-3 \leqslant x \leqslant 5$ **b** $4 - 3x^2 + x^3$ for $-2 \leqslant x \leqslant 3$

    c $x^2 + \dfrac{16}{x}$ for $1 \leqslant x \leqslant 4$ **d** $x - 4\sqrt{x}$ for $0 \leqslant x \leqslant 5$.

15 Show that $y = 4e^{-x}\sin x$ has a local maximum when $x = \frac{\pi}{4}$.

16 Consider $f(x) = \sin x \cos 2x$ for $0 \leqslant x \leqslant \pi$.

    a Find $f'(x)$ in terms of $\cos x$ only.

    b Show that $f'(x) = 0$ when $\cos x = 0$ or $\pm\sqrt{\frac{5}{6}}$.

    c Hence find the position and nature of the turning points of $y = f(x)$.

    d Graph $y = f(x)$, showing the features you have found.

17 $f(t) = ate^{bt^2}$ has a maximum value of 1 when $t = 2$. Find constants a and b.

18 Prove that $\dfrac{\ln x}{x} \leqslant \dfrac{1}{e}$ for all $x > 0$.

19 Consider the function $f(x) = x - \ln x$.

  a Show that $y = f(x)$ has a local minimum and that this is the only turning point.

  b Hence prove that $\ln x \leqslant x - 1$ for all $x > 0$.

E   SHAPE

We have seen that the first derivative $f'(x)$ gives the gradient of the curve $y = f(x)$ for any value of x.

The second derivative $f''(x)$ tells us the rate of change of the gradient $f'(x)$. It therefore gives us information about the **shape** or **curvature** of the curve $y = f(x)$.

When a curve, or part of a curve, has shape:

    we say that the curve is **concave downwards**

            we say that the curve is **concave upwards**.

For example:

  • the curve $f(x) = -x^2$ is concave downwards

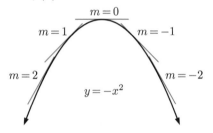

Wherever we are on the curve, as x increases, the gradient of the tangent decreases.

$\therefore$ $f'(x)$ is decreasing

$\therefore$ $f''(x) < 0$.

  • the curve $f(x) = x^2$ is concave upwards.

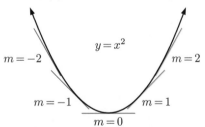

Wherever we are on the curve, as x increases, the gradient of the tangent increases.

$\therefore$ $f'(x)$ is increasing

$\therefore$ $f''(x) > 0$.

We conclude that:

  • A curve is **concave downwards** on an interval $S \Leftrightarrow f''(x) \leqslant 0$ for all $x \in S$.

  • A curve is **concave upwards** on an interval $S \Leftrightarrow f''(x) \geqslant 0$ for all $x \in S$.

Example 14   ◀) **Self Tutor**

Find intervals where the curve is concave up or concave down:

a $y = 2x^3 - 3x^2 + 4x - 6$

b $f(x) = \dfrac{x+1}{x-3}$

a $\qquad y = 2x^3 - 3x^2 + 4x - 6$

$\therefore \dfrac{dy}{dx} = 6x^2 - 6x + 4$

$\therefore \dfrac{d^2y}{dx^2} = 12x - 6$

$\qquad = 6(2x - 1)$

$$\xleftarrow{\quad - \quad\Big|\quad + \quad} \begin{array}{c} \frac{d^2y}{dx^2} \\ x \end{array}$$
$$\frac{1}{2}$$

The curve is concave up for $x \geqslant \frac{1}{2}$ and concave down for $x \leqslant \frac{1}{2}$.

b $\qquad f(x) = \dfrac{x+1}{x-3}$

$\therefore f'(x) = \dfrac{(1)(x-3) - (x+1)(1)}{(x-3)^2}$

$\qquad = \dfrac{x - 3 - x - 1}{(x-3)^2}$

$\qquad = -4(x-3)^{-2}$

$\therefore f''(x) = 8(x-3)^{-3}$

$$\xleftarrow{\quad - \quad\vdots\quad + \quad} \begin{array}{c} f''(x) \\ x \end{array}$$
$$3$$

The curve is concave up for $x > 3$ and concave down for $x < 3$.

EXERCISE 13E

1 **a** Complete the table by indicating whether each value is zero, positive, or negative:

Point	$f(x)$	$f'(x)$	$f''(x)$
A	+		
B			
C			
D		0	
E			

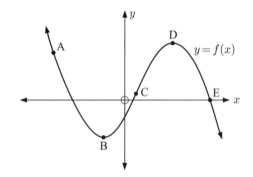

b Describe the turning points of $y = f(x)$.

c At which point does the shape of $y = f(x)$ change?

2 The graph of $f(x) = x^3 + 3x^2 - 5x + 2$ is shown alongside.

a Find $f'(x)$ and $f''(x)$.

b Draw the sign diagram of $f''(x)$.

c State the interval on which the function is:

    i concave up   **ii** concave down.

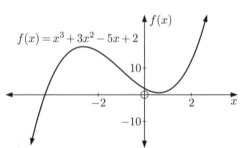

3 Determine the shape of each quadratic function:

a $y = 2x^2 - 3x + 4$

b $y = -2(x-3)(x+1)$

c $y = -4 - x^2 + 6x$

d $y = (5-x)(1-2x)$

4 For each of the following functions, determine the interval(s) on which the function is:

    i increasing   **ii** decreasing   **iii** concave upwards   **iv** concave downwards.

  a $f(x) = x^2 + 1$ **b** $f(x) = -x^3$ **c** $f(x) = e^x$

  d $f(x) = \sqrt{x} - 2$ **e** $f(x) = -\dfrac{1}{\sqrt{x}}$ **f** $f(x) = x^4 - 12x^2$

5 Consider $f(x) = \ln(2x - 1) - 3$.

  a Find the x-intercept.

  b Can $f(0)$ be found? What is the significance of this result?

  c Find the domain of f.

  d Find the gradient of the tangent to the curve at $x = 1$.

  e Find $f''(x)$, and hence explain why $f(x)$ is concave down for all x in the domain of f.

  f Graph the function, showing the features you have found.

6 Consider $f(x) = \ln x$.

  a For what values of x is $f(x)$ defined?

  b Draw the sign diagrams of $f'(x)$ and $f''(x)$, and give a geometrical interpretation of each.

  c Find the equation of the normal to $y = f(x)$ at the point where $y = 1$.

7 Consider the function $f(x) = \dfrac{e^x}{x}$.

  a Does the graph of $y = f(x)$ have any x or y-intercepts?

  b Discuss $f(x)$ as $x \to \infty$ and as $x \to -\infty$.

  c Find and classify any stationary points of $y = f(x)$.

  d Find the intervals where $f(x)$ is: **i** concave up   **ii** concave down.

  e Sketch the graph of $y = f(x)$, showing all important features.

  f Find the equation of the tangent to $f(x) = \dfrac{e^x}{x}$ at the point where $x = -1$.

F   INFLECTION POINTS

A **point of inflection** is a point at which the tangent to the curve crosses the curve.

At a point of inflection, $f''(x) = 0$.

DEMO

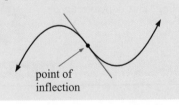   or   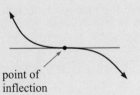

point of inflection   point of inflection

If the tangent at a point of inflection is horizontal, then this is a **stationary inflection point**.

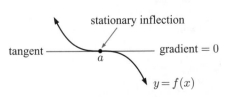

$f'(x)$ has sign diagram

$f''(x)$ has sign diagram

If the tangent at a point of inflection is *not* horizontal, then this is a **non-stationary inflection point**.

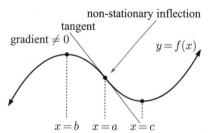

$f'(x)$ has sign diagram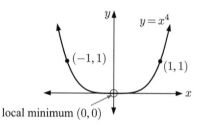

$f''(x)$ has sign diagram

The tangent at the point of inflection, also called the **inflecting tangent**, crosses the curve at that point.

> There is a **point of inflection** at $x = a$ if $f''(a) = 0$ **and** the sign of $f''(x)$ changes at $x = a$.
> The point of inflection is a:
> - **stationary inflection** if $f'(a) = 0$ • **non-stationary inflection** if $f'(a) \neq 0$.

Notice that if $f(x) = x^4$ then $f'(x) = 4x^3$
                   and $f''(x) = 12x^2$.

$f''(x)$ has sign diagram

Although $f''(0) = 0$ we do not have a point of inflection at $(0, 0)$ because the sign of $f''(x)$ does not change at $x = 0$.

SUMMARY

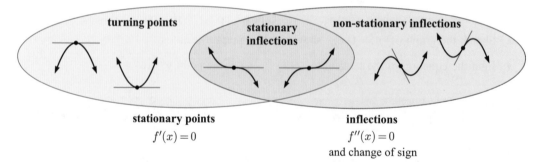

Click on the demo icon to examine some common functions for turning points, points of inflection, and intervals where the function is increasing, decreasing, and concave up or down.

DEMO

Example 15   ◀) **Self Tutor**

Consider $f(x) = 3x^4 - 16x^3 + 24x^2 - 9$.
  a   Find and classify all points where $f'(x) = 0$.
  b   Find and classify all points of inflection.
  c   Find intervals where the function is increasing or decreasing.
  d   Find intervals where the function is concave up or down.
  e   Sketch the function showing the features you have found.

a $f(x) = 3x^4 - 16x^3 + 24x^2 - 9$

$\therefore\ f'(x) = 12x^3 - 48x^2 + 48x$ $\therefore\ f'(x)$ has sign diagram:

$\qquad = 12x(x^2 - 4x + 4)$

$\qquad = 12x(x - 2)^2$

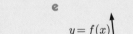

Now $f(0) = -9$ and $f(2) = 7$

$\therefore\ (0, -9)$ is a local minimum and $(2, 7)$ is a stationary inflection.

b $f''(x) = 36x^2 - 96x + 48$ $\therefore\ f''(x)$ has sign diagram:

$\qquad = 12(3x^2 - 8x + 4)$

$\qquad = 12(x - 2)(3x - 2)$

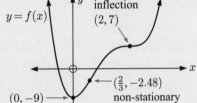

Now $f(\frac{2}{3}) \approx -2.48$

$\therefore\ (2, 7)$ is a stationary inflection and $(\frac{2}{3}, -2.48)$ is a non-stationary inflection.

c $f(x)$ is decreasing for $x \leqslant 0$

$f(x)$ is increasing for $x \geqslant 0$.

d $f(x)$ is concave up for $x \leqslant \frac{2}{3}$ and $x \geqslant 2$

$f(x)$ is concave down for $\frac{2}{3} \leqslant x \leqslant 2$.

e

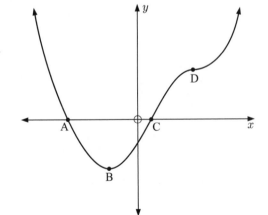

EXERCISE 13F

1 In the diagram alongside, each labelled point corresponds to a zero of $f(x)$, $f'(x)$, or $f''(x)$.

a Complete the table by indicating whether each value is zero, positive, or negative:

Point	$f(x)$	$f'(x)$	$f''(x)$
A			
B			
C			
D			

b Describe the turning point of $y = f(x)$.

c Describe the inflection points of $y = f(x)$.

2 Find and classify all points of inflection of:

a $f(x) = x^2 + 3$

b $f(x) = 2 - x^3$

c $f(x) = x^3 - 6x^2 + 9x + 1$

d $f(x) = -3x^4 - 8x^3 + 2$

e $f(x) = 3 - \dfrac{1}{\sqrt{x}}$

f $f(x) = x^3 + 6x^2 + 12x + 5$

g $f(x) = x^2 + 8\sqrt{x}$

h $f(x) = x^4 - 6x^2 + 10$

3 For each of the following functions:

  i Find and classify all turning points.

  ii Find and classify all points of inflection.

  iii Find intervals where the function is increasing or decreasing.

  iv Find intervals where the function is concave up or down.

  v Sketch the function showing the features you have found.

a $f(x) = x^2 - 5x + 4$ **b** $f(x) = x^3 + 4x^2$

c $f(x) = \sqrt{x}$ **d** $f(x) = x^3 - 3x^2 - 24x + 1$

e $f(x) = 3x^4 + 4x^3 - 2$ **f** $f(x) = (x - 1)^4$

g $f(x) = x^4 - 4x^2 + 3$ **h** $f(x) = 3 - \dfrac{4}{\sqrt{x}}$

Example 16   ◀)) Self Tutor

Consider the function $y = 2 - e^{-x}$.

  a Find the x-intercept.   **b** Find the y-intercept.

  c Show algebraically that the function is increasing for all x.

  d Show algebraically that the function is concave down for all x.

  e Explain why $y = 2$ is a horizontal asymptote.

  f Sketch $y = 2 - e^{-x}$, showing the features you have found.

---

a When $y = 0$, $e^{-x} = 2$ **b** When $x = 0$, $y = 2 - e^0 = 1$

$\qquad\qquad\quad \therefore \ -x = \ln 2$ $\therefore$ the y-intercept is 1.

$\qquad\qquad\quad \therefore \ \ x = -\ln 2$

$\therefore$ the x-intercept is $-\ln 2 \approx -0.693$

c $\dfrac{dy}{dx} = 0 - e^{-x}(-1) = e^{-x} = \dfrac{1}{e^x}$ **d** $\dfrac{d^2y}{dx^2} = e^{-x}(-1)$

$\quad$ Now $e^x > 0$ for all x, $= -\dfrac{1}{e^x}$ which is < 0 for all x.

$\quad$ so $\dfrac{dy}{dx} > 0$ for all x. $\therefore$ the function is concave down for all x.

$\quad \therefore$ the function is increasing for all x.

e As $x \to \infty$, $e^{-x} \to 0$ **f**

$\quad \therefore \ y \to 2$

Hence the horizontal asymptote is $y = 2$.

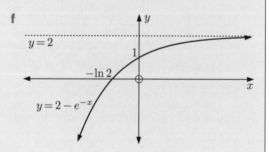

---

4 Consider the function $f(x) = e^{2x} - 3$.

  a Find the x and y-intercepts.

  b Show algebraically that the function is increasing for all x.

  c Find $f''(x)$, and hence explain why $f(x)$ is concave up for all x.

    d Explain why $y = -3$ is a horizontal asymptote.

    e Sketch $y = e^{2x} - 3$, showing the features you have found.

5 Suppose $f(x) = e^x - 3$ and $g(x) = 3 - 5e^{-x}$.

    a Find the x and y-intercepts of both functions.

    b Discuss $f(x)$ and $g(x)$ as $x \to \infty$ and as $x \to -\infty$.

    c Draw the sign diagrams of $f'(x)$, $f''(x)$, $g'(x)$, and $g''(x)$ and give a geometrical interpretation of each.

    d Find algebraically the point(s) of intersection of the functions.

    e Sketch the graphs of both functions on the same set of axes. Show all important features on your graph.

6 Consider the function $y = e^x - 3e^{-x}$.

    a Determine the x and y-intercepts.   **b** Prove that the function is increasing for all x.

    c Show that $\dfrac{d^2y}{dx^2} = y$. What can be deduced about the concavity of the function above and below the x-axis?

    d Use technology to help graph $y = e^x - 3e^{-x}$. Show the features you have found.

7 A function commonly used in statistics is the *standard normal curve* $f(x) = \dfrac{1}{\sqrt{2\pi}} e^{-\frac{1}{2}x^2}$.

    a Find the turning points of the function, and find the intervals where the function is increasing and decreasing.

    b Find all points of inflection.   **c** Discuss $f(x)$ as $x \to \infty$ and as $x \to -\infty$.

    d Sketch the graph of $y = f(x)$, showing all important features.

8 Consider the function $f(x) = \cos x$.

    a Show that $f''(x) = -f(x)$. What does this tell us about the location of the inflection points?

    b Find and classify the inflection points of $f(x)$ on $0 \leqslant x \leqslant 2\pi$.

    c Find the intervals on $0 \leqslant x \leqslant 2\pi$ where $f(x)$ is:

        i increasing   **ii** decreasing   **iii** concave up   **iv** concave down.

    d Sketch the graph of $y = f(x)$ on $0 \leqslant x \leqslant 2\pi$, showing all important features.

9 Consider the *surge function* $f(t) = Ate^{-bt}$, $t \geqslant 0$, where A and b are positive constants.

    a Prove that the function has:

        i a local maximum at $t = \dfrac{1}{b}$ **ii** a point of inflection at $t = \dfrac{2}{b}$.

    b Sketch the function, showing the features you have found.

10 Consider the *logistic function* $f(t) = \dfrac{C}{1 + Ae^{-bt}}$, $t \geqslant 0$, where A, b, and C are positive constants.

    a Find the y-intercept.

    b Prove that:

        i $y = C$ is its horizontal asymptote

        ii if $A > 1$, there is a point of inflection with y-coordinate $\dfrac{C}{2}$.

    c Sketch the function, showing the features you have found.

G   UNDERSTANDING FUNCTIONS
AND THEIR DERIVATIVES

In this Chapter we have seen that, given a function $f(x)$:

- The sign of $f'(x)$ tells us intervals where $f(x)$ is increasing or decreasing.
- The zeros of $f'(x)$ indicate stationary points.
- The sign of $f''(x)$ tells us the *shape* of $f(x)$.
- The zeros of $f''(x)$ indicate points of inflection provided $f''(x)$ changes sign at that point.

We can use these properties to analyse how the graphs of $y = f(x)$, $y = f'(x)$, and $y = f''(x)$ are related.

Example 17	◄» Self Tutor

Using the graph of $y = f(x)$ alongside, sketch the graphs of $y = f'(x)$ and $y = f''(x)$.

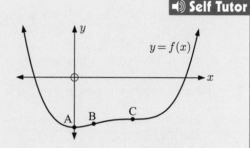

The local minimum A corresponds to $f'(x) = 0$ and $f''(x) \neq 0$.

The non-stationary point of inflection B corresponds to $f'(x) \neq 0$ and $f''(x) = 0$.

The stationary point of inflection C corresponds to $f'(x) = 0$ and $f''(x) = 0$.

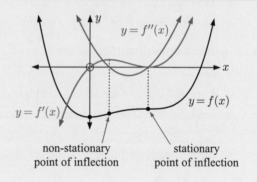

non-stationary point of inflection   stationary point of inflection

EXERCISE 13G

1 Using the graphs of $y = f(x)$ below, sketch the graphs of $y = f'(x)$ and $y = f''(x)$. Show clearly the axes intercepts and turning points.

a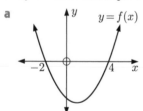
b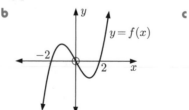
c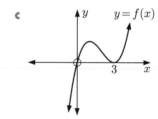

Example 18   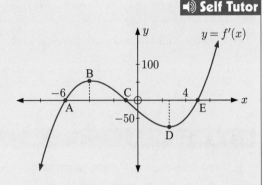 ◀)) **Self Tutor**

The graph alongside shows a gradient function $y = f'(x)$.

Sketch a graph which could be $y = f(x)$, showing clearly the x-values corresponding to all stationary points and points of inflection.

The stationary points of $f(x)$ are when $f'(x) = 0$. These correspond to A, C, and E.

The sign diagram of $f'(x)$ is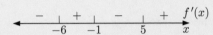

∴   A and E correspond to local minima, and C corresponds to a local maximum.

$f'(x)$ is a maximum when $x = -4$ and a minimum when $x \approx 2\frac{1}{2}$.

At these points $f''(x) = 0$ but $f'(x) \neq 0$, so they correspond to non-stationary points of inflection.

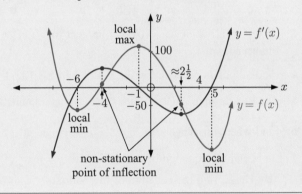

2 For each graph of $y = f'(x)$ below, sketch a graph which could be $y = f(x)$. Show clearly the location of any stationary points and points of inflection.

a
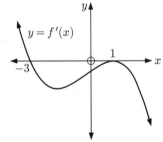

b
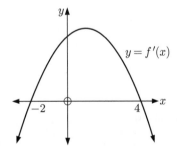

3 For the function $g(x)$, the sign diagrams for $g'(x)$ and $g''(x)$ are shown alongside.

The points A(0, 2), B(2, 0), and C(4, -2) all lie on $y = g(x)$.

Sketch $y = g(x)$, labelling the stationary points.

ACTIVITY

Click on the icon to run a card game on curve properties.

CARD GAME

REVIEW SET 13A

1 Find the equation of the tangent to:

    a $y = -2x^2$ at the point where $x = -1$ **b** $y = x^3 - 5x + 2$ at $(2, 0)$

    c $y = \dfrac{1 - 2x}{x^2}$ at $(1, -1)$ **d** $f(x) = e^{3x-1}$ at the point where $x = 0$

    e $f(x) = \ln(x^2)$ at the point where $x = e$.

2 Find the equation of the normal to:

    a $y = \sqrt{3x + 4}$ at $(4, 4)$ **b** $y = 3e^{2x}$ at the point where $x = 1$.

3 At the point where $x = 0$, the tangent to $f(x) = e^{4x} + px + q$ has equation $y = 5x - 7$. Find p and q.

4 Find all points on the curve $y = 4x^3 + 6x^2 - 13x + 1$ where the gradient of the tangent is 11.

5 The line through A$(2, 4)$ and B$(0, 8)$ is a tangent to $y = \dfrac{a}{(x + 2)^2}$. Find a.

6 Find where the tangent to $y = 2x^3 + 4x - 1$ at $(1, 5)$ meets the curve again.

7   **a** Find the equation of the normal to $y = e^{2x}$ at the point where $x = a$.

    b Hence find the equation of the normal to $y = e^{2x}$ which passes through the origin.

8 Find the coordinates of P and Q if (PQ) is the tangent to $y = \dfrac{5}{\sqrt{x}}$ at $(1, 5)$.

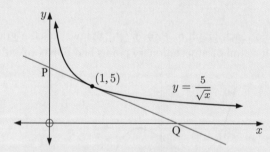

9 The tangent to $y = x^2\sqrt{1 - x}$ at $x = -3$ cuts the axes at points A and B. Determine the area of triangle OAB.

10 Find intervals where $f(x) = -x^3 - 6x^2 + 36x - 17$ is:

    a increasing   **b** decreasing.

11 Consider the function $f(x) = 2x^3 - 3x^2 - 36x + 7$.

    a Find and classify all stationary points.

    b Find intervals where the function is increasing and decreasing.

    c Describe the behaviour of the function as $x \to \infty$ and as $x \to -\infty$.

    d Sketch the graph of $y = f(x)$ showing the features you have found.

12 Consider the function $f(x) = \dfrac{3x-2}{x+3}$.

    a State the domain of $f(x)$.

    b Find the axes intercepts.

    c Find $f'(x)$ and draw its sign diagram.

    d Does $f(x)$ have any stationary points?

13 Find the greatest and least values of $x + \dfrac{32}{x^2}$ for $2 \leqslant x \leqslant 10$.

14 Consider $f(x) = xe^{1-2x}$.

    a Show that $f'(x) = e^{1-2x}(1-2x)$.

    b Find values of x for which:

       i $f(x) > 0$ **ii** $f'(x) > 0$

    c Find the stationary point of $y = f(x)$, and determine its nature.

15 Find intervals where $f(x)$ is increasing or decreasing:

    a $f(x) = x^3 - 6x$ **b** $f(x) = e^x(x-2)$ **c** $f(x) = 2x - \sin x$

16 Find and classify the stationary points of:

    a $f(x) = -x^3 + 2x^2 - x + 3$ **b** $f(x) = \dfrac{x^2}{x+3}$

17 For each of the following, determine the position and nature of the stationary points on the interval $-\pi \leqslant x \leqslant \pi$, then show them on a graph of the function.

    a $y = \sin \frac{x}{2}$ **b** $y = \cos^2 x$ **c** $y = \cos 2x - 2\sin x$

18 The graph of $f(x) = 2x^3 - 3x^2 + x - 12$ is shown alongside.

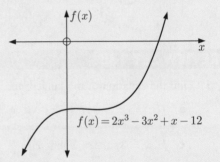

    a Find $f'(x)$ and $f''(x)$.

    b Draw the sign diagram of $f''(x)$.

    c State the interval on which the function is concave down.

    d Find the point at which the shape of $f(x)$ changes.

$f(x) = 2x^3 - 3x^2 + x - 12$

19 Find intervals where the curve is concave up or concave down:

    a $y = x^3 - 4x^2 + 11$ **b** $y = -\dfrac{x+1}{x^2}$ **c** $y = \dfrac{x+2}{x(x+4)}$

20 Consider the function $f(x) = x + \ln x$.

    a Find the values of x for which $f(x)$ is defined.

    b Draw the sign diagrams of $f'(x)$ and $f''(x)$, and give a geometrical interpretation of each.

    c Sketch the graph of $y = f(x)$.

21 Consider the function $f(x) = e^{x\sqrt{3}}\sin x$.

    a Find $f'(x)$.   **b** Find x on $0 \leqslant x \leqslant 2\pi$ such that $f'(x) = 0$.

    c Draw the sign diagram for $f'(x)$ on $0 \leqslant x \leqslant 2\pi$.

    d Determine the intervals on $0 \leqslant x \leqslant 2\pi$ for which $f(x)$ is:

       i increasing   **ii** decreasing.

22 Consider the function $f(x) = \ln(x^2 + 5)$.

    a Find and classify any turning points.   **b** Find and classify any points of inflection.

    c Find intervals where the function is increasing or decreasing.

    d Find intervals where the function is concave up or down.

    e Sketch the function, showing the features you have found.

23 Consider the function $f(x) = e^{\sin^2 x}$, $0 \leqslant x \leqslant \pi$.

    a Find the exact value(s) of x at which $f(x)$ has a maximum turning point.

    b Find any points of inflection in the given domain.

24 The graph of $y = f(x)$ is given.
On the same set of axes, sketch the graph of
$y = f'(x)$.

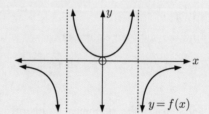

25

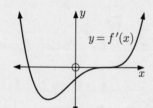

The graph of $y = f'(x)$ is drawn.
On the same set of axes, clearly draw a possible graph
of $y = f(x)$. Show all turning points and points of
inflection.

REVIEW SET 13B

1 Find the equation of the tangent to:

    a $f(x) = x^4 - 2x^2 + 7x - 3$ at $(2, 19)$ **b** $f(x) = \dfrac{1}{\sqrt{x+7}}$ at $(9, \frac{1}{4})$

    c $f(x) = 3\sin 2x$ when $x = \frac{\pi}{6}$ **d** $f(x) = \dfrac{e^x}{2-x}$ when $x = 0$.

2 Find the equation of the normal to:

    a $y = \dfrac{1}{x^2} - \dfrac{2}{x}$ at the point where $x = 1$ **b** $y = x\sin x$ at the origin.

3 The curve $y = 2x^3 + ax + b$ has a tangent with gradient 10 at the point $(-2, 33)$. Find the
values of a and b.

4 Show that $y = 2 - \dfrac{7}{1+2x}$ has no horizontal tangents.

5 $y = f(x)$ is the parabola shown.

    a Find $f(3)$ and $f'(3)$.

    b Hence find $f(x)$ in the form
       $f(x) = ax^2 + bx + c$.

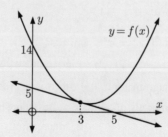

6 The tangent to $y = x^3 + ax^2 - 4x + 3$ at $x = 1$ is parallel to the line $y = 3x$.

    a Find a.

    b Find the equation of the tangent at $x = 1$.

    c Where does the tangent meet the curve again?

7 Find the point where the normal to $y = x^2 - 4x + 2$ at $x = 3$, meets the curve again.

8 Find the equation of the tangent to:

    a $y = \dfrac{1}{\sin x}$ at the point where $x = \frac{\pi}{3}$ **b** $y = \cos \frac{x}{2}$ at the point where $x = \frac{\pi}{2}$.

9 Show that the curves with equations $y = \sqrt{3x+1}$ and $y = \sqrt{5x - x^2}$ have a common tangent at their point of intersection. Find the equation of this common tangent.

10 The tangent to $y = \dfrac{ax + b}{\sqrt{x}}$ at $x = 1$ has equation $2x - y = 1$. Find a and b.

11 Find intervals where $f(x) = x^4 - 4x^3 - 8x^2 + 5$ is:

    a increasing   **b** decreasing.

12 $f(x) = x^3 - 3x^2 + ax + 50$ has a stationary point at $x = 3$.

    a Find a.

    b Find the position and nature of all stationary points.

13 Consider the function $f(x) = x^3 - 4x^2 + 4x$.

    a Find all axes intercepts.

    b Find and classify all stationary points.

    c Find intervals where the function is increasing and decreasing.

    d Describe the behaviour of the function as $x \to \infty$ and as $x \to -\infty$.

    e Sketch the graph of $y = f(x)$ showing the features you have found.

14 Consider the function $f(x) = e^x - x$.

    a Find and classify any stationary points of $y = f(x)$.

    b Discuss what happens to $f(x)$ as $x \to \infty$.

    c Find $f''(x)$ and draw its sign diagram. Give a geometrical interpretation for the sign of $f''(x)$.

    d Sketch the graph of $y = f(x)$.

    e Deduce that $e^x \geqslant x + 1$ for all x.

15 Suppose $f(x) = \dfrac{x + 1}{x^2 - 2x - 8}$.

    a Show that $f'(x) = -\dfrac{x^2 + 2x + 6}{(x^2 - 2x - 8)^2}$ and draw its sign diagram.

    b Hence show that $f(x)$ is never increasing.

16 Find and describe the stationary point of $y = \dfrac{x + a}{e^x}$, where a is a constant.

17 $f(x) = \dfrac{\ln(ax)}{bx}$ has a stationary point at $\left(\dfrac{e}{2}, \dfrac{2}{3e} \right)$. Find a and b.

18   Determine the interval(s) on which the function $f(x) = -\frac{1}{2}x^4 + x^3 + 6x^2 - 3x + 2$ is:

    a increasing   **b** decreasing   **c** concave upwards   **d** concave downwards.

19   Find and classify the inflection points of:

    a $y = x^4 - 3x^3 + 9$ **b** $y = -x^4 + x^3 + 9x^2 + 1$

20   Consider $f(x) = \sqrt{\cos x}$ for $0 \leqslant x \leqslant 2\pi$.

    a For what values of x in this interval is $f(x)$ defined?

    b Find $f'(x)$ and hence find intervals where $f(x)$ is increasing or decreasing.

    c Sketch the graph of $y = f(x)$ on $0 \leqslant x \leqslant 2\pi$.

21   Consider the function $f(x) = x^4 - 4x^3 + 7$.

    a Find $f'(x)$ and $f''(x)$, and draw their sign diagrams.

    b Find and classify any turning points.

    c Find and classify any points of inflection.

    d Find intervals where the function is:

        i increasing   **ii** decreasing   **iii** concave up   **iv** concave down.

    e Sketch the function, showing all important features.

22   For the function $f(x) = \cos^2 x,\ 0 \leqslant x \leqslant 2\pi$:

    a Find and classify all turning points.

    b Find and classify all points of inflection.

    c Sketch the function, showing the features you have found.

23   Consider the function $f(x) = \dfrac{e^x}{x - 1}$.

    a Find the y-intercept of the function.

    b For what values of x is $f(x)$ defined?

    c Find the signs of $f'(x)$ and $f''(x)$ and comment on the geometrical significance of each.

    d Sketch the graph of $y = f(x)$.

    e Find the equation of the tangent at the point where $x = 2$.

24   Given the graph of $y = f'(x)$ drawn alongside, sketch a possible curve for $y = f(x)$. Show clearly any turning points and points of inflection.

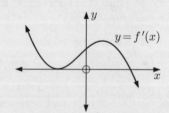

25   For the function $f(x)$, $f'(x) > 0$ and $f''(x) < 0$ for all $x \in \mathbb{R}$, $f(2) = 1$, and $f'(2) = 2$.

    a Find the equation of the tangent to $f(x)$ where $x = 2$.

    b On the same set of axes, sketch $y = f(x)$ and the tangent to the curve where $x = 2$.

    c Explain why $f(x)$ has exactly one zero.

    d Estimate an interval in which the zero of $f(x)$ lies.

Chapter 14

Applications of differentiation

Contents: A   Rates of change
                B   Optimisation

OPENING PROBLEM

On the Indonesian coast, the depth of water t hours after midnight is given by $D = 9.3 + 6.8 \cos(0.507t)$ metres.

Things to think about:

a What is the derivative function $\dfrac{dD}{dt}$ and what does it tell us?

b What is the depth of water at 8 am?

c Is the tide rising or falling at 8 am? Explain your answer.

d At what time(s) is the tide highest on this day? What is the maximum depth of water?

We have already seen that if $y = f(x)$ then $f'(x)$ or $\dfrac{dy}{dx}$ gives the gradient of the tangent to $y = f(x)$ for any value of x.

In this Chapter we consider some real-world applications of differential calculus, using derivatives to tell us how one variable changes relative to another.

A   RATES OF CHANGE

There are countless examples in the real world where quantities vary with time, or with respect to some other variable.

For example:

- temperature varies continuously
- the height of a tree varies as it grows
- the prices of stocks and shares vary with each day's trading.

$$\frac{dy}{dx} \text{ gives the } \textbf{rate of change in } y \textbf{ with respect to } x.$$

We can therefore use the derivative of a function to tell us the **rate** at which something is happening.

For example:

- $\dfrac{dH}{dt}$ or $H'(t)$ could be the instantaneous rate of ascent of a person in a Ferris wheel.

  It might have units metres per second or $\mathrm{m\,s^{-1}}$.

- $\dfrac{dC}{dt}$ or $C'(t)$ could be a person's instantaneous rate of change in lung capacity.

  It might have units litres per second or $\mathrm{L\,s^{-1}}$.

Example 1 　　　　　　　　　　　　　　　　　　　　　　　◀) **Self Tutor**

According to a psychologist, the ability of a child to understand spatial concepts is given by $A = \frac{1}{3}\sqrt{t}$ where t is the age in years, $5 \leqslant t \leqslant 18$.

   a Find the rate of improvement in ability to understand spatial concepts when a child is:

     i 9 years old　　　　　　　　　　　**ii** 16 years old.

   b Show that $\dfrac{dA}{dt} > 0$ for $5 \leqslant t \leqslant 18$.　Comment on the significance of this result.

   c Show that $\dfrac{d^2A}{dt^2} < 0$ for $5 \leqslant t \leqslant 18$.　Comment on the significance of this result.

---

  a　　$A = \frac{1}{3}\sqrt{t} = \frac{1}{3}t^{\frac{1}{2}}$

    $\therefore\ \dfrac{dA}{dt} = \frac{1}{6}t^{-\frac{1}{2}} = \dfrac{1}{6\sqrt{t}}$

    i When $t = 9$, $\dfrac{dA}{dt} = \frac{1}{18}$　　　　　**ii** When $t = 16$, $\dfrac{dA}{dt} = \frac{1}{24}$

      $\therefore$ the rate of improvement is $\frac{1}{18}$ units　　　 $\therefore$ the rate of improvement is $\frac{1}{24}$ units

      per year for a 9 year old child.　　　　per year for a 16 year old child.

  b Since $\sqrt{t}$ is never negative, $\dfrac{1}{6\sqrt{t}}$ is never negative

    $\therefore\ \dfrac{dA}{dt} > 0$ for all $5 \leqslant t \leqslant 18$.

  This means that the ability to understand spatial concepts increases with age.

  c　　$\dfrac{dA}{dt} = \frac{1}{6}t^{-\frac{1}{2}}$

    $\therefore\ \dfrac{d^2A}{dt^2} = -\frac{1}{12}t^{-\frac{3}{2}} = -\dfrac{1}{12t\sqrt{t}}$

    $\therefore\ \dfrac{d^2A}{dt^2} < 0$　for all $5 \leqslant t \leqslant 18$.

  This means that while the ability to understand spatial concepts increases with age, the rate of increase slows down with age.

You are encouraged to use technology to graph each function you need to consider. This is often useful in interpreting results.

GRAPHING PACKAGE

EXERCISE 14A

1 The estimated future profits of a small business are given by $P(t) = 2t^2 - 12t + 118$ thousand dollars, where t is the time in years from now.

   a What is the current annual profit?

   b Find $\dfrac{dP}{dt}$ and state its units.

   c Find $\dfrac{dP}{dt}$ when $t = 8$. Explain what this value means.

2 In a hot, dry summer, water is evaporating from a desert oasis. The volume of water remaining after t days is $V = 2(50 - t)^2$ m^3. Find:

   a the average rate at which the water evaporates in the first 5 days

   b the instantaneous rate at which the water is evaporating at $t = 5$ days.

3 The quantity of a chemical in human skin which is responsible for its "elasticity" is given by $Q(t) = 100 - 10\sqrt{t}$ where t is the age of a person in years.

   a Find $Q(t)$ when:

       i $t = 0$ **ii** $t = 25$ **iii** $t = 100$ years.

   b At what rate is the quantity of the chemical changing when the person is aged:

       i 25 years   **ii** 50 years?

   c Show that the quantity of the chemical is decreasing for all $t > 0$.

4 The height of *pinus sylvestris* is given by

$H = 35 - \dfrac{172.5}{t + 5}$ metres, where t is the number of years after

the tree was planted from an established seedling.

   a How high was the tree when it was planted?

   b Find the height of the tree after:

       i 4 years   **ii** 8 years   **iii** 12 years.

   c Find the rate at which the tree was growing after 0, 5, and 10 years.

   d Show that $\dfrac{dH}{dt} > 0$ for all $t \geqslant 0$. Explain the significance of this result.

Example 2   ◀») **Self Tutor**

The cost in dollars of producing x items in a factory each day is given by $C(x) = 9500 + 12x + 8x^{0.8}$.

   a Find $C'(x)$, which is called the marginal cost function.

   b Find the marginal cost when 150 items are produced. Interpret this result.

   c Find $C(151) - C(150)$. Compare this with the answer in **b**.

---

   a The marginal cost function is

       $C'(x) = 12 + 6.4x^{-0.2}$ dollars per item.

   b $C'(150) \approx \$14.35$

   This is the rate at which the costs are increasing with respect to the production level x when 150 items are made per day.

   It gives an estimate of the cost of making the 151st item each day.

   c $C(151) - C(150) \approx \$11\,754.87 - \$11\,740.52$

                                 $\approx \$14.35$

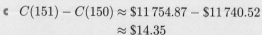

This is the actual cost of making the 151st item each day, so the answer in **b** gives a very good estimate.

5 Seablue make denim jeans. The cost model for making x pairs per day is
$$C(x) = 7800 + 6x + 12x^{0.7} \quad \text{dollars.}$$

   a Find the marginal cost function $C'(x)$.   **b** Find $C'(220)$. What does it estimate?

   c Find $C(221) - C(220)$. Discuss your answer.

6 The total cost of running a train from Paris to Marseille is
given by $C(v) = \frac{1}{5}v^2 + \dfrac{200\,000}{v}$ euros where v is the
average speed of the train in km h^{-1}.

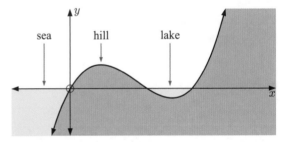

   a Find the total cost of the journey if the average speed is:

      i 50 km h^{-1} **ii** 100 km h^{-1}.

   b Find the rate of change in the cost of running the train
for the average speed:

      i 30 km h^{-1} **ii** 90 km h^{-1}.

   c At what speed will the cost be a minimum?

7 A tank contains $50\,000$ litres of water. The tap is left fully on and all the water drains from
the tank in 80 minutes. The volume of water remaining in the tank after t minutes is given by
$$V = 50\,000\left(1 - \frac{t}{80}\right)^2 \quad \text{litres} \quad \text{where} \ \ 0 \leqslant t \leqslant 80.$$

   a Find $\dfrac{dV}{dt}$, and draw the graph of $\dfrac{dV}{dt}$ against t.

   b At what time was the outflow fastest?

   c Show that $\dfrac{d^2V}{dt^2}$ is always constant and positive. Interpret this result.

8 Alongside is a land and sea profile where
the x-axis is sea level.
The function $y = \frac{1}{10}x(x-2)(x-3)$ km
gives the height of the land or sea bed
relative to sea level at distance x km from
the shore line.

   a Find where the lake is located relative to the shore line of the sea.

   b Find $\dfrac{dy}{dx}$ and interpret its value when $x = \frac{1}{2}$ km and when $x = 1\frac{1}{2}$ km.

   c Find the deepest point of the lake, and the depth at this point.

9 A radioactive substance decays according to the formula $W = 20e^{-kt}$ grams where t is the time
in hours.

   a Find k given that the weight is 10 grams after 50 hours.

   b Find the weight of radioactive substance present:

      i initially   **ii** after 24 hours   **iii** after 1 week.

   c How long will it take for the weight to reach 1 gram?

   d Find the rate of radioactive decay after:

      i 100 hours   **ii** 1000 hours.

   e Show that $\dfrac{dW}{dt} = bW$ for some constant b.

10 The temperature of a liquid after being placed in a refrigerator is given by $T = 5 + 95e^{-kt}$ °C where k is a positive constant and t is the time in minutes.

   a Find k if the temperature of the liquid is 20°C after 15 minutes.

   b What was the temperature of the liquid when it was first placed in the refrigerator?

   c Show that $\dfrac{dT}{dt} = c(T - 5)$ for some constant c.

   d At what rate is the temperature changing:

      i initially   **ii** after 10 minutes   **iii** after 20 minutes?

11 The height of a shrub t years after it was planted is given by $H(t) = 20\ln(3t+2) + 30$ cm, $t \geqslant 0$.

   a How high was the shrub when it was planted?

   b How long will it take for the shrub to reach a height of 1 m?

   c At what rate is the shrub's height changing:

      i 3 years after being planted   **ii** 10 years after being planted?

12 In the conversion of sugar solution to alcohol, the amount of alcohol produced t hours after the reaction commenced is given by $A = s(1 - e^{-kt})$ litres, where s is the original sugar concentration (%), $t \geqslant 0$.

   a Find A when $t = 0$.

   b Suppose $s = 10$, and $A = 5$ after 3 hours.

      i Find k.   **ii** Find the speed of the reaction after 5 hours.

Example 3   ◀)) **Self Tutor**

Cathy is using a compass to draw a circle. The arm with the needle is 8 cm long, and the arm with the pencil is 9 cm in total. The angle between the arms is θ.

   a Write the radius of the circle to be drawn in terms of θ.

   b Hence find the rate of change in r with respect to θ when $\theta = 60°$.

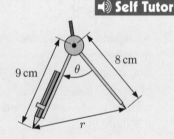

a Using the cosine rule, $r^2 = 9^2 + 8^2 - 2 \times 9 \times 8 \times \cos\theta$

$$\therefore \quad r = \sqrt{145 - 144\cos\theta} \qquad \{\text{since } r > 0\}$$

b $r = (145 - 144\cos\theta)^{\frac{1}{2}}$

$$\therefore \quad \frac{dr}{d\theta} = \tfrac{1}{2}(145 - 144\cos\theta)^{-\frac{1}{2}}(144\sin\theta)$$

$$= \frac{72\sin\theta}{\sqrt{145 - 144\cos\theta}}$$

> For calculus, θ must be measured in radians!

When $\theta = \frac{\pi}{3}$, $\dfrac{dr}{d\theta} = \dfrac{72\left(\frac{\sqrt{3}}{2}\right)}{\sqrt{145 - 144\left(\frac{1}{2}\right)}}$

$$\approx 7.30 \text{ cm per radian}$$

$$\approx 0.127 \text{ cm per degree}$$

13 Find exactly the rate of change in the area of triangle PQR as θ changes, at the time when $\theta = 45°$.

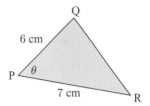

14

A set of retractable stairs is used to gain access to an attic. The frame uses a pantograph mechanism which is a set of rhombuses with variable angles to control the retraction. Each rhombus has side length 20 cm, and the angle where the arms meet is θ, as shown.

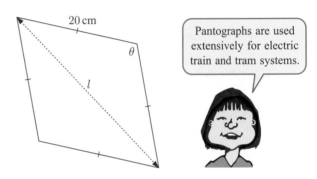

Pantographs are used extensively for electric train and tram systems.

a Find a formula for the length l between the pivots, in terms of θ.

b Hence find the rate of change in l at the time when $\theta = 120°$.

15 The voltage in a circuit is given by $V(t) = 340\sin(100\pi t)$ volts where t is the time in seconds.

a Find the voltage in the circuit:

   i initially   **ii** after 0.125 seconds.

b At what rate is the voltage changing:

   i when $t = 0.01$ **ii** when $V(t)$ is a maximum?

16 The number of bees in a hive after t months is modelled by $B(t) = \dfrac{3000}{1 + 0.5e^{-1.73t}}$.

a Find the initial bee population.

b Find the percentage increase in the population after 1 month.

c Is there a limit to the population size? If so, what is it?

d Find $B'(t)$, and use it to explain why the population is increasing over time.

e Find the rate at which the population is increasing after 6 months.

f Sketch the graph of $B(t)$.

B   OPTIMISATION

Optimisation is the process of finding the **maximum** or **minimum** value of a function. The solution is often referred to as the **optimal solution**.

We can find optimal solutions in several ways:

- using technology to graph the function and search for the maximum or minimum value
- using analytical methods such as the formula $x = -\dfrac{b}{2a}$ for the vertex of a parabola
- using differential calculus to locate the turning points of a function.

These last two methods are useful especially when exact solutions are required.

You should always be aware that:

> The maximum or minimum value does not always occur when the first derivative is zero.
>
> It is essential to also examine the values of the function at the end point(s) of the interval under consideration for global maxima and minima.

For example:

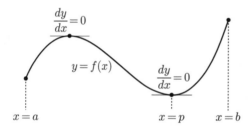

The maximum value of y occurs at the end point $x = b$.

The minimum value of y occurs at the local minimum $x = p$.

TESTING FOR LOCAL MAXIMA AND MINIMA

If we find a value $x = a$ such that $f'(a) = 0$, there are several tests we can use to see whether we have a local maximum or a local minimum at this point.

SIGN DIAGRAM TEST

If, near to $x = a$, the sign diagram is:

SECOND DERIVATIVE TEST

- If $f''(a) < 0$ we have   ⌢   shape, which indicates a **local maximum**.

- If $f''(a) > 0$ we have   ⌣   shape, which indicates a **local minimum**.

OPTIMISATION PROBLEM SOLVING METHOD

Step 1:   Draw a large, clear diagram of the situation.

Step 2:   Construct a **formula** with the variable to be optimised as the subject. It should be written in terms of one convenient variable, for example x. You should write down what domain restrictions there are on x.

Step 3:   Find the **first derivative** and find the value(s) of x which make the first derivative **zero**.

Step 4:   For each stationary point, use the **sign diagram test** or **second derivative test** to determine whether you have a local maximum or local minimum.

Step 5:   Identify the optimal solution, also considering end points where appropriate.

Step 6:   Write your answer in a sentence, making sure you specifically answer the question.

Example 4	◀) **Self Tutor**

A rectangular cake dish is made by cutting out squares from the corners of a 25 cm by 40 cm rectangle of tin-plate, and then folding the metal to form the container.

What size squares must be cut out to produce the cake dish of maximum volume?

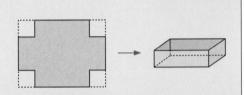

Step 1:   Let x cm be the side lengths of the squares that are cut out.

Step 2:   Volume = length × width × depth
$$= (40 - 2x)(25 - 2x)x$$
$$= (1000 - 80x - 50x + 4x^2)x$$
$$= 1000x - 130x^2 + 4x^3 \text{ cm}^3$$

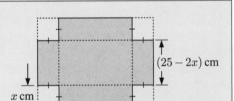

Since the side lengths must be positive,
$x > 0$ and $25 - 2x > 0$.
∴ $0 < x < 12.5$

Step 3: $\dfrac{dV}{dx} = 12x^2 - 260x + 1000$
$$= 4(3x^2 - 65x + 250)$$
$$= 4(3x - 50)(x - 5)$$

∴ $\dfrac{dV}{dx} = 0$ when $x = \frac{50}{3} = 16\frac{2}{3}$ or $x = 5$

∴ $x = 5$ as $0 < x < 12.5$

DEMO

Step 4: $\dfrac{dV}{dx}$ has sign diagram:

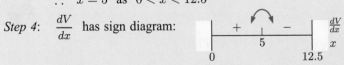

Step 5:   There is a local maximum when $x = 5$. This is the global maximum for the given domain.

Step 6:   The maximum volume is obtained when $x = 5$, which is when 5 cm squares are cut from the corners.

Example 5   ◄ᴺ) **Self Tutor**

A 4 litre container must have a square base, vertical sides, and an open top. Find the most economical shape which minimises the surface area of material needed.

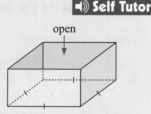
open

Step 1:

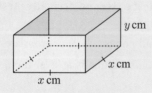
y cm
x cm
x cm

Let the base lengths be x cm and the depth be y cm.

The volume V = length × width × depth

$\therefore\ V = x^2 y$

$\therefore\ 4000 = x^2 y$ .... (1) {1 litre ≡ 1000 cm³}

Step 2: The total surface area

A = area of base + 4(area of one side)

$= x^2 + 4xy$

$= x^2 + 4x\left(\dfrac{4000}{x^2}\right)$ {using (1)}

$\therefore\ A(x) = x^2 + 16\,000x^{-1}$ where $x > 0$

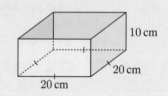
NORMAL FLOAT AUTO REAL RADIAN MP

Step 3: $\therefore\ A'(x) = 2x - 16\,000x^{-2}$

$\therefore\ A'(x) = 0$ when $2x = \dfrac{16\,000}{x^2}$

$\therefore\ 2x^3 = 16\,000$

$\therefore\ x = \sqrt[3]{8000} = 20$

Step 4: $A''(x) = 2 + 32\,000x^{-3}$

$\therefore\ A''(20) = 2 + \dfrac{32\,000}{20^3} = 6$

Since $A''(20) > 0$, there is a local minimum at $x = 20$.

Step 5: The minimum material is used to make the container

when $x = 20$ and $y = \dfrac{4000}{20^2} = 10$.

10 cm
20 cm
20 cm

Step 6: The most economical shape has a square base 20 cm × 20 cm, and height 10 cm.

Use **calculus techniques** to answer the following problems.

GRAPHING PACKAGE

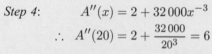

In cases where finding the zeros of the derivatives is difficult you may use the **graphing package** to help you.

EXERCISE 14B

1 When a manufacturer makes x items per day, the profit function is
   $P(x) = -0.022x^2 + 11x - 720$ pounds. Find the production level that will maximise profits.

2 The total cost of producing x blankets per day is $\frac{1}{4}x^2 + 8x + 20$ pounds, and for this production level each blanket may be sold for $\left(23 - \frac{1}{2}x\right)$ pounds.
   How many blankets should be produced per day to maximise the total profit?

3 60 metres of fencing is used to build a rectangular enclosure along an existing fence. Suppose the sides adjacent to the existing fence are x m long.

    a Show that the area A of the enclosure is given by $A(x) = x(60 - 2x)$ m^2.

    b Find the dimensions which maximise the area of the enclosure.

4 A duck farmer wishes to build a rectangular enclosure of area 100 m^2. The farmer must purchase wire netting for three of the sides, as the fourth side is an existing fence. Naturally, the farmer wishes to minimise the length (and therefore cost) of fencing required to complete the job.

    a If the sides adjacent to the existing fence have length x m, show that the required length of wire netting to be purchased is $L = 2x + \dfrac{100}{x}$.

    b Find the minimum value of L and the corresponding value of x when this occurs.

    c Sketch the optimal situation, showing all dimensions.

5 Radioactive waste is to be disposed of in fully enclosed lead boxes of inner volume 200 cm^3. The base of a box has dimensions in the ratio $2 : 1$.

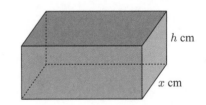

    a Show that $x^2 h = 100$.

    b Show that the inner surface area of the box is given by
$$A(x) = 4x^2 + \frac{600}{x} \ \text{cm}^2.$$

    c Find the minimum inner surface area of the box and the corresponding value of x.

    d Sketch the optimal box shape, showing all dimensions.

6 Brenda is designing a cylindrical tin can for a canned fruit company. The cans must have capacity 1 litre, and they must use as little metal as possible.

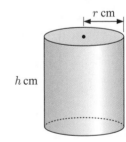

    a Explain why the height h is given by $h = \dfrac{1000}{\pi r^2}$ cm.

    b Show that the total surface area A is given by
$$A = 2\pi r^2 + \frac{2000}{r} \ \text{cm}^2.$$

    c Find the dimensions of the can which make A as small as possible.

7 Sam has sheets of metal which are 36 cm by 36 cm square. He wants to cut out identical squares which are x cm by x cm from the corners of each sheet. He will then bend the sheets along the dashed lines to form an open container.

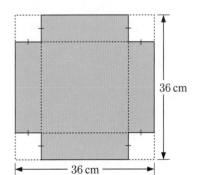

    a Show that the volume of the container is given by $V(x) = x(36 - 2x)^2$ cm^3.

    b What sized squares should be cut out to produce the container of greatest capacity?

8 An athletics track has two "straights" of length l m, and two semi-circular ends of radius x m. The perimeter of the track is 400 m.

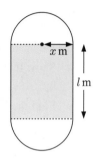

   a Show that $l = 200 - \pi x$ and write down the possible values that x may have.

   b What values of l and x maximise the shaded rectangle inside the track? What is this maximum area?

9 A 60 cm length of wire is bent into a rectangle with length x cm and width y cm.

   a Write an expression for y in terms of x.

   b Write an expression for the area $A(x)$ of the rectangle enclosed by the wire.

   c Find $A'(x)$.

   d Hence determine the value of x which maximises the area. What are the dimensions of the rectangle in this case?

Example 6   🔊 **Self Tutor**

Infinitely many rectangles can be inscribed in a semi-circle of diameter 20 cm.

Find the shape of the largest rectangle which can be inscribed.

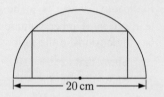

Step 1: Let $OB = x$ cm, $0 < x < 10$

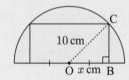

     In $\triangle OBC$, $\quad BC^2 + x^2 = 10^2 \qquad$ {Pythagoras}

     $\therefore \quad BC = \sqrt{100 - x^2} \quad$ {as $BC > 0$}

Step 2: The rectangle has area $\quad A = $ length $\times$ width

     $\therefore \quad A = 2x\sqrt{100 - x^2}$

     $\therefore \quad A^2 = 4x^2(100 - x^2)$

     $\qquad\quad = 400x^2 - 4x^4$

> Since $A > 0$, we can maximise A by maximising A^2. This makes the calculations easier!

Step 3: $\dfrac{d}{dx}(A^2) = 800x - 16x^3$

     $\qquad\quad\;\; = 16x(50 - x^2)$

     So, $\dfrac{d}{dx}(A^2) = 0$ when $x = 0$ or $\pm\sqrt{50}$.

Step 4: $\dfrac{d}{dx}(A^2)$ has sign diagram:

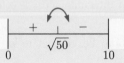

Step 5:   The area is maximised when $x = \sqrt{50}$ and $\text{BC} = \sqrt{100 - 50}$
$$= \sqrt{50} \text{ cm}$$

Step 6:   The largest rectangle which can be inscribed is
$2\sqrt{50}$ cm long and $\sqrt{50}$ cm wide.

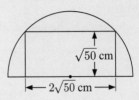

10   Infinitely many rectangles can be inscribed in a circle of diameter
10 cm. In the diagram alongside, suppose $\text{ON} = x$ cm.

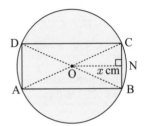

  a   Find the area of ABCD in terms of x only.

  b   Find the dimensions of ABCD which maximises its area.

11   A manufacturer of electric kettles performs a cost control study. They discover that to produce
x kettles per day, the cost per kettle is given by $C(x) = 4 \ln x + \left(\dfrac{30 - x}{10} \right)^2$ pounds   with a
minimum production capacity of 10 kettles per day.

How many kettles should be manufactured to keep the cost per kettle to a minimum?

12   Infinitely many rectangles which sit on the x-axis
can be inscribed under the curve $y = e^{-x^2}$.

Determine the coordinates of C such that
rectangle ABCD has maximum area.

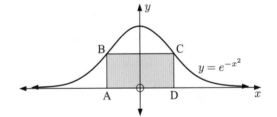

13

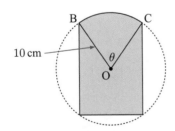

A circular piece of tin-plate with radius 10 cm has 3 segments
removed as illustrated. The angle θ is measured in radians.

  a   Show that the remaining area is given by
$A = 50(\theta + 3 \sin \theta)$ cm^2.

  b   Find θ such that the area A is a maximum, and find the
area A in this case.

14   A symmetrical gutter is made from a sheet of metal 30 cm
wide by bending it twice as shown.

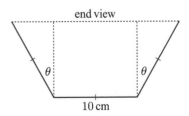

  a   Deduce that the cross-sectional area of the gutter is given
by $A = 100 \cos \theta (1 + \sin \theta)$ cm^2.

  b   Show that $\dfrac{dA}{d\theta} = 0$ when $\sin \theta = \frac{1}{2}$ or -1.

  c   For what value of θ does the gutter have maximum
carrying capacity? Find the cross-sectional area for this
value of θ.

15 When a new anaesthetic is administered, the effect is modelled by $E(t) = 750te^{-1.5t}$ units, where $t \geqslant 0$ is the time in hours after the injection.

   a Find $E'(t)$.

   b At what time is the anaesthetic most effective?

16

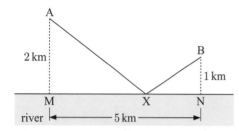

A pumphouse is to be placed at some point X along a river.

Two pipelines will then connect the pumphouse to homesteads A and B.

How far should point X be from M so that the total length of pipeline is minimised?

17 A small population of wasps is observed. After t weeks the population is modelled by

$$P(t) = \frac{50\,000}{1 + 1000e^{-0.5t}} \text{ wasps, where } 0 \leqslant t \leqslant 25.$$

Find when the wasp population is growing fastest.

Hint: You need to maximise $P'(t)$.

18 At 1:00 pm ship A leaves port P. It sails in the direction 30° east of north at 12 km h^{-1}. At the same time, ship B is 100 km due east of P, and is sailing at 8 km h^{-1} towards P.

   a Show that the distance between the two ships is given by $D(t) = \sqrt{304t^2 - 2800t + 10\,000}$ km, where t is the number of hours after 1:00 pm.

   b Find the minimum value of D^2 for all $t \geqslant 0$.

   c At what time, to the nearest minute, are the ships closest?

19 Hieu can row a boat at 3 km h^{-1}, and can walk at 6 km h^{-1}. He is currently at point P on the shore of a lake 2 km in radius. He will row to point Q, then walk around the shore to point R which is opposite P.

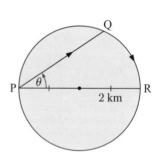

   a Show that $PQ = 4\cos\theta$ km.

   b Show that the time taken for Hieu's journey is given by $T = \frac{4}{3}\cos\theta + \frac{2\theta}{3}$ hours where $0 \leqslant \theta \leqslant \frac{\pi}{2}$.

   c Find θ such that $\frac{dT}{d\theta} = 0$ on $0 \leqslant \theta \leqslant \frac{\pi}{2}$.

   d Draw a sign diagram for $\frac{dT}{d\theta}$.

   e What route should Hieu take to travel from P to R in:

      i the longest time   **ii** the shortest time?

20 B is a boat 5 km out at sea from A. [AC] is a straight sandy beach, 6 km long. Peter can row the boat at 8 $km\,h^{-1}$ and run along the beach at 17 $km\,h^{-1}$. Suppose Peter rows directly from B to point X on [AC] such that AX = x km.

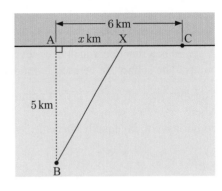

   a Explain why $0 \leqslant x \leqslant 6$.

   b Show that the *total time* Peter takes to row to X and then run along the beach to C, is given by

$$T = \frac{\sqrt{x^2 + 25}}{8} + \frac{6 - x}{17} \text{ hours, } 0 \leqslant x \leqslant 6.$$

   c Find x such that $\dfrac{dT}{dx} = 0$. Explain the significance of this value.

21 A mosquito flying with position M(x, y, z) is repelled by scent emitted from the origin O. At time t seconds, the coordinates of the mosquito are given by $x(t) = 3 - t^2$, $y(t) = 2 + \sqrt{t}$, and $z(t) = 2 - \sqrt{t}$, where all distance units are metres.

   a Show that if the mosquito is D m from the origin at time t, then $D^2 = t^4 - 6t^2 + 2t + 17$.

   b *Hence* find the closest the mosquito came to the source of the repellent.

THEORY OF KNOWLEDGE

Snell's law states the relationship between the angles of incidence and refraction when a ray of light passes from one medium to another with different optical density. It was first discovered in 984 AD by the Persian scientist **Ibn Sahl**, who was studying the shape of lenses. However, it is named after **Willebrord Snellius**, who rediscovered it during the Renaissance. The law was published by **René Descartes** in his *Discourse on the Method* published in 1637.

Willebrord Snellius

In the figure alongside, a ray passes from A to B via point R. We suppose the refractive indices of the two media are n and m, the angle of incidence is α, and the angle of refraction is β.

Snell's law states that: $n \sin \alpha = m \sin \beta$.

The law follows from Fermat's *principle of least time*, which says that a ray of light travelling between two points will take the path of least time.

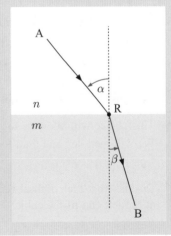

   1 Is optimisation a mathematical principle?

   2 Is mathematics an intrinsic or natural part of other subjects?

ACTIVITY   CUBIC SPLINES

A *spline* is a function which uses several polynomials to draw a smooth curve through a set of data points. The spline can be used in modelling to interpolate values between the data.

Consider a set of $(n + 1)$ data points (x_i, y_i) where $x_0 < x_1 < x_2 < \ldots < x_n$. The points do not have to be equally spaced.

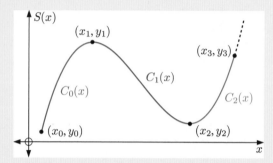

The **cubic spline** $S(x)$ is a piecewise function of the form

$$S(x) = \begin{cases} C_0(x), & x_0 \leqslant x \leqslant x_1 \\ \quad \vdots \\ C_i(x), & x_i < x \leqslant x_{i+1} \\ \quad \vdots \\ C_{n-1}(x), & x_{n-1} < x \leqslant x_n \end{cases}$$

$C_i(x)$ is the curve between data points (x_i, y_i) and (x_{i+1}, y_{i+1}).

where $C_i(x) = a_i(x - x_i)^3 + b_i(x - x_i)^2 + c_i(x - x_i) + d_i$ for $i = 0, \ldots, n - 1$.

What to do:

1 Discuss with your class what requirements we need to make sure that the cubic spline is smooth and continuous when it transitions from one cubic to the next.

2 a Show that in the ith cubic:

   i $C_i'(x) = 3a_i(x - x_i)^2 + 2b_i(x - x_i) + c_i$

   ii $C_i''(x) = 6a_i(x - x_i) + 2b_i$

  b Hence find $C_i(x_i)$, $C_i'(x_i)$, and $C_i''(x_i)$.

3 The four pieces of information we will use for each cubic are:

  • the *data point* at the left end
  • the *gradient* at the left end
  • the *curvature* at the left end
  • the *data point* at the right end.

This choice will allow us to calculate one cubic at a time. We will first determine $C_0(x)$. We will then demand that, for $i = 1, \ldots, n - 1$:

  • $C_i(x_i) = C_{i-1}(x_i)$ • $C_i'(x_i) = C_{i-1}'(x_i)$ • $C_i''(x_i) = C_{i-1}''(x_i)$

Discuss what each of these requirements means, and how they give us the 3 pieces of information at the left end of the cubic.

4 There are five data points on the graph alongside.

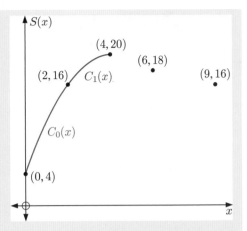

  a Consider the first cubic, $C_0(x)$.

   We need to choose sensible values for $C_0''(x_0)$ and $C_0'(x_0)$, so we consider the quadratic through the first three data points.

   i Verify that the first three data points lie on the quadratic $Q(x) = -x^2 + 8x + 4$.

   ii By letting $C_0''(x_0) = Q''(x_0)$, show that $b_0 = -1$.

   iii By letting $C_0'(x_0) = Q'(x_0)$, show that $c_0 = 8$.

   iv By letting $C_0(x_0) = y_0$, find d_0.

   v By letting $C_0(x_1) = y_1$, find a_0.

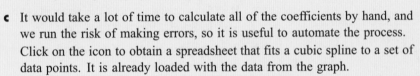

If the first three points were collinear, we would instead set $C_0''(x_0) = 0$ and $C_0'(x_0) = $ gradient of the line through the points.

  b Having fully determined $C_0(x)$, we now consider $C_1(x)$.

   i By letting $C_1''(x_1) = C_0''(x_1)$, find b_1.

   ii By letting $C_1'(x_1) = C_0'(x_1)$, find c_1.

   iii By letting $C_1(x_1) = C_0(x_1) = y_1$, find d_1.

   iv By letting $C_1(x_2) = y_2$, find a_1.

  c It would take a lot of time to calculate all of the coefficients by hand, and we run the risk of making errors, so it is useful to automate the process. Click on the icon to obtain a spreadsheet that fits a cubic spline to a set of data points. It is already loaded with the data from the graph.

   SPREADSHEET

   i Use the spreadsheet to find $C_2(x)$ and $C_3(x)$.

   ii Discuss with your class how the formulae have been implemented in the spreadsheet.

   iii Plot the complete cubic spline $y = S(x)$. Do you think the cubic spline is a good representation of the data?

5 We will now look at how splines can help approximate the known function $y = e^x$.

  a Enter the following data points into the spreadsheet:

   $(0, 1)$, $(2, 7.39)$, $(4, 54.6)$, $(6, 403.4)$, $(8, 2981)$, $(10, 22\,026)$.

   Hence complete the table alongside.

x	1	3.5	4.25	5.25	7.5	9
e^x						
$S(x)$						

  b Comment on the difference between $S(x)$ and e^x. How well does $S(x)$ approximate the function?

  c How could you improve the approximation? Test your hypothesis by using the spreadsheet.

6 Experiment with cubic splines with data of your choice.

  a Discuss what they are good at and what they are poor at.

  b Is it always helpful to increase the number of data values?

REVIEW SET 14A

1 The height of a tree t years after it was planted is given by $H(t) = 60 + 40\ln(2t + 1)$ cm, $t \geqslant 0$.

   a How tall was the tree when it was planted?

   b How long will it take for the tree to reach:

      i 150 cm   **ii** 300 cm?

   c At what rate is the tree's height increasing after:

      i 2 years   **ii** 20 years?

2 The value of a car t years after its purchase is given by $V = 20\,000e^{-0.4t}$ pounds. Calculate:

   a the purchase price of the car

   b the rate at which the value of the car is decreasing 10 years after it was purchased.

3 The cost per hour of running a freight train is given by $C(v) = \dfrac{v^2}{20} + \dfrac{50\,000}{v}$ dollars where v is the average speed of the train in km h^{-1}.

   a Find the cost of running the train for 5 hours at 64 km h^{-1}.

   b Find the rate of change in the hourly cost of running the train at speeds of:

      i 75 km h^{-1} **ii** 90 km h^{-1}.

   c At what speed will the cost per hour be a minimum?

4

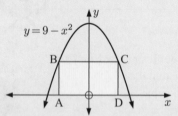

Rectangle ABCD is inscribed within the parabola $y = 9 - x^2$ and the x-axis, as shown.

   a If $OD = x$, show that the rectangle ABCD has area function $A(x) = 18x - 2x^3$.

   b Find the coordinates of C when rectangle ABCD has maximum area.

5 A 200 m fence is placed around a lawn which has the shape of a rectangle with a semi-circle on one of its sides.

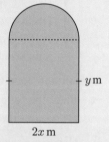

   a Using the dimensions shown on the figure, show that $y = 100 - x - \frac{\pi}{2}x$.

   b Find the area of the lawn A in terms of x only.

   c Find the dimensions of the lawn of maximum area.

6 A manufacturer of open steel boxes has to make one with a square base and a capacity of 1 kL. The steel costs £2 per square metre.

   a If the base measures x m by x m and the height is y m, find y in terms of x.

   b Hence show that the total cost of the steel is $C(x) = 2x^2 + \dfrac{8}{x}$ pounds.

   c Find the dimensions of the steel box which would cost the least to make.

7 Answer the **Opening Problem** on page 346.

REVIEW SET 14B

1 The cost in euros of producing x items in a factory each day is given by
$C(x) = 850 + 3.3x^{0.85} + 2.8x^{0.5}$.

   a Find the marginal cost function $C'(x)$.

   b Find $C'(1000)$ and explain what this result estimates.

   c Find $C(1001) - C(1000)$. Discuss your answer.

2 The size of a population at time t years is given by $P(t) = 60\,000\left(1 + 2e^{-\frac{t}{4}}\right)^{-1}$, $t \geqslant 0$.

   a Find the initial population.

   b Find $P'(t)$.

   c Show that $P'(t) > 0$ for all $t \geqslant 0$. Explain what this means.

   d Find $P''(t)$.

   e Find the maximum growth rate of the population, and the exact time when this occurs.

   f Discuss $P(t)$ as $t \to \infty$.

   g Sketch the population function, showing the information you have found.

3 Mark has set his compass so that both arms have length 11 cm. The angle between the arms is θ.

   a Write the area A of the circle Mark will draw in terms of θ.

   b Hence find the rate of change in A with respect to θ when $\theta = \frac{\pi}{4}$.

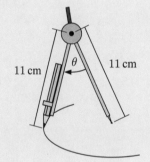

4 A rectangular gutter is formed by bending a 24 cm wide sheet of metal as shown.

Where must the bends be made in order to maximise the capacity of the gutter?

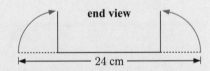

5

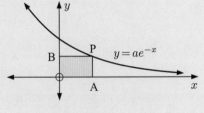

The graph of $y = ae^{-x}$ for $a > 0$ is shown. P is a moving point on the graph, and A and B lie on the axes as shown so that OAPB is a rectangle. Find the x-coordinate of P, in terms of a, such that the rectangle OAPB has minimum perimeter.

6

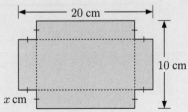

A rectangular sheet of tin-plate is 20 cm by 10 cm. Four squares, each with sides x cm, are cut from its corners. The remainder is bent into the shape of an open rectangular container. Find the value of x which will maximise the capacity of the container.

7 A light bulb hangs from the ceiling at height h metres above the floor, directly above point N. At any point A on the floor which is x metres from the light bulb, the illumination I is given by

$$I = \frac{\sqrt{8}\cos\theta}{x^2} \quad \text{units.}$$

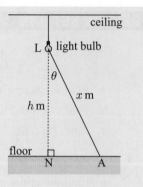

a If NA $= 1$ metre, show that at A, $I = \sqrt{8}\cos\theta\sin^2\theta$.

b The light bulb may be lifted or lowered to change the intensity at A. Assuming NA $= 1$ metre, find the height the bulb should be above the floor to provide the greatest illumination at A.

Chapter **15**

Introduction to integration

Contents:

OPENING PROBLEM

Another of **Archimedes'** achievements was devising a method for calculating the area under a curve.

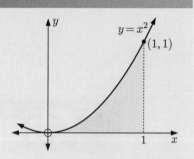

In an article containing 24 propositions, he provided essential theory for what, over 1800 years later, would be developed into **integral calculus**.

In the process, Archimedes found the exact area A between the curve $y = x^2$ and the x-axis, on the interval $0 \leqslant x \leqslant 1$.

Things to think about:

a Can you use the:

    i blue rectangle to explain why $A > \frac{1}{8}$ **ii** red rectangles to explain why $A < \frac{5}{8}$?

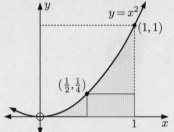 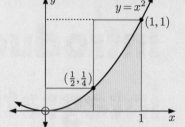

b How can we obtain a better estimate for A?

c What function has x^2 as its derivative?

In this Chapter we consider **integral calculus**. This involves **antidifferentiation**, which is the reverse process of differentiation.

A   APPROXIMATING THE AREA UNDER A CURVE

Consider the function $f(x) = x^2$ in the **Opening Problem**.

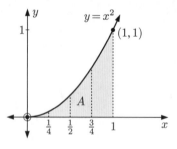

We wish to estimate the area A enclosed by $y = f(x)$, the x-axis, and the vertical line $x = 1$.

Suppose we divide the interval $0 \leqslant x \leqslant 1$ into 4 strips of width $\frac{1}{4}$ unit as shown. We obtain 4 subintervals of equal width.

The diagram alongside shows **lower rectangles**, which are rectangles with height equal to the *lower* value of the function at the endpoints of the subinterval.

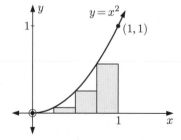

The total area of the lower rectangles is

$$A_L = \frac{1}{4} \times f(0) + \frac{1}{4} \times f(\tfrac{1}{4}) + \frac{1}{4} \times f(\tfrac{1}{2}) + \frac{1}{4} \times f(\tfrac{3}{4})$$
$$= \frac{1}{4}(0)^2 + \frac{1}{4}(\tfrac{1}{4})^2 + \frac{1}{4}(\tfrac{1}{2})^2 + \frac{1}{4}(\tfrac{3}{4})^2$$
$$= 0.218\,75$$

The next diagram shows **upper rectangles**, which are rectangles with height equal to the *upper* value of the function at the endpoints of the subinterval.

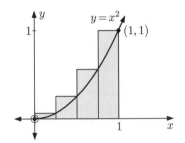

The total area of the upper rectangles is

$$A_U = \tfrac{1}{4} \times f(\tfrac{1}{4}) + \tfrac{1}{4} \times f(\tfrac{1}{2}) + \tfrac{1}{4} \times f(\tfrac{3}{4}) + \tfrac{1}{4} \times f(1)$$
$$= \tfrac{1}{4}(\tfrac{1}{4})^2 + \tfrac{1}{4}(\tfrac{1}{2})^2 + \tfrac{1}{4}(\tfrac{3}{4})^2 + \tfrac{1}{4}(1)^2$$
$$= 0.468\,75$$

Clearly, for increasing functions such as $f(x) = x^2$, $A_L < A < A_U$, so the area A lies between $0.218\,75$ units^2 and $0.468\,75$ units^2.

If the interval $0 \leqslant x \leqslant 1$ was divided into 8 subintervals instead, each of width $\tfrac{1}{8}$, then

$$A_L = \tfrac{1}{8}\left[f(0) + f(\tfrac{1}{8}) + f(\tfrac{1}{4}) + f(\tfrac{3}{8}) + f(\tfrac{1}{2}) + f(\tfrac{5}{8}) + f(\tfrac{3}{4}) + f(\tfrac{7}{8})\right]$$
$$= \tfrac{1}{8}\left[0 + \tfrac{1}{64} + \tfrac{1}{16} + \tfrac{9}{64} + \tfrac{1}{4} + \tfrac{25}{64} + \tfrac{9}{16} + \tfrac{49}{64}\right]$$
$$\approx 0.273\,44$$

$$A_U = \tfrac{1}{8}\left[f(\tfrac{1}{8}) + f(\tfrac{1}{4}) + f(\tfrac{3}{8}) + f(\tfrac{1}{2}) + f(\tfrac{5}{8}) + f(\tfrac{3}{4}) + f(\tfrac{7}{8}) + f(1)\right]$$
$$= \tfrac{1}{8}\left[\tfrac{1}{64} + \tfrac{1}{16} + \tfrac{9}{64} + \tfrac{1}{4} + \tfrac{25}{64} + \tfrac{9}{16} + \tfrac{49}{64} + 1\right]$$
$$\approx 0.398\,44$$

From this refinement we conclude that the area A lies between $0.273\,44$ units^2 and $0.398\,44$ units^2.

As we create more subintervals, the estimates A_L and A_U will become more and more accurate. In fact, as the subinterval width is reduced further and further, both A_L and A_U will **converge** to A.

Now suppose there are n subintervals between $x = 0$ and $x = 1$, each of width $\dfrac{1}{n}$.

You can use the **area finder** software or your **graphics calculator** to help calculate A_L and A_U for large values of n.

AREA FINDER

GRAPHICS
CALCULATOR
INSTRUCTIONS

n	A_L	A_U	Average
4	0.218 75	0.468 75	0.343 75
8	0.273 44	0.398 44	0.335 50
16	0.302 73	0.365 23	0.333 98
50	0.323 40	0.343 40	0.333 40
200	0.330 84	0.335 84	0.333 38
1000	0.332 83	0.333 83	0.333 33
10 000	0.333 28	0.333 38	0.333 33

The table alongside summarises the results you should obtain for $n = 4$, 8, 16, 50, 200, 1000, and 10 000.

From the table, it appears that both A_L and A_U are *converging* to $\tfrac{1}{3}$ as n increases.

EXERCISE 15A

1 Consider the area between $y = x$ and the x-axis from $x = 0$ to $x = 1$.

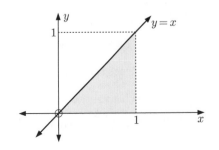

  a Divide the interval into 5 subintervals of equal width, then estimate the area using:

   i lower rectangles   **ii** upper rectangles.

  b Calculate the actual area and compare it with your answers in **a**.

2 Consider the area between $y = \dfrac{1}{x}$ and the x-axis from $x = 2$ to $x = 4$. Divide the interval into 6 subintervals of equal width, then estimate the area using:

    a lower rectangles   **b** upper rectangles.

3 Use rectangles to find lower and upper sums for the area between the graph of $y = x^2$ **AREA FINDER** and the x-axis for $1 \leqslant x \leqslant 2$. Use $n = 10$, 25, 50, 100, and 500. Give your answers to 4 decimal places.

As n gets larger, both A_L and A_U converge to the same rational number. What is it?

4   **a** Use lower and upper rectangle sums to estimate the area between each of the following functions and the x-axis for $0 \leqslant x \leqslant 1$. Use $n = 5$, 10, 50, 100, 500, 1000, and 10000. Give your answer to 5 decimal places in each case.

      i $y = x^3$ **ii** $y = x$ **iii** $y = x^{\frac{1}{2}}$ **iv** $y = x^{\frac{1}{3}}$

  b For each case in **a**, write down the value to which A_L and A_U converge.

  c Using your answer to **b**, predict the area between the graph of $y = x^a$ and the x-axis for $0 \leqslant x \leqslant 1$ and any number $a > 0$.

5 Consider the quarter circle with centre $(0,\ 0)$ and radius 2 units illustrated.

Its area is $\frac{1}{4}$(full circle with radius 2 units) $= \frac{1}{4} \times \pi \times 2^2$

$$= \pi \text{ units}^2$$

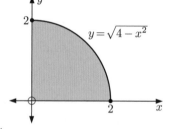

$y = \sqrt{4 - x^2}$

  a Estimate the area using lower and upper rectangles for $n = 10$, 50, 100, 200, 1000, and 10000. Hence find rational bounds for π.

  b Archimedes found the famous approximation $3\frac{10}{71} < \pi < 3\frac{1}{7}$.

    For what value of n is your estimate for π better than that of Archimedes?

INVESTIGATION 1   THE AREA UNDER $f(x) = x^2$

For the curve $f(x) = x^2$, we already have the tools necessary to calculate the area A between $y = f(x)$ and the x-axis on the interval $0 \leqslant x \leqslant 1$ exactly.

Suppose we divide the interval $0 \leqslant x \leqslant 1$ into n subintervals, each of width $\dfrac{1}{n}$.

What to do:

1   **a** Explain why the total area of lower rectangles can be written as $A_L = \dfrac{1}{n} \displaystyle\sum_{i=1}^{n} f\left(\dfrac{i-1}{n}\right)$.

  b Use the sum of series formulae $\displaystyle\sum_{i=1}^{n} i = \dfrac{n(n+1)}{2}$ and $\displaystyle\sum_{i=1}^{n} i^2 = \dfrac{n(n+1)(2n+1)}{6}$ to show that $A_L = \frac{1}{3} - \dfrac{1}{2n} + \dfrac{1}{6n^2}$.

  c What value does A_L approach as $n \to \infty$?

2   **a** Explain why the total area of upper rectangles can be written as $A_U = \dfrac{1}{n} \displaystyle\sum_{i=1}^{n} f\left(\dfrac{i}{n}\right)$.

  b Hence show that $A_U = \frac{1}{3} + \dfrac{1}{2n} + \dfrac{1}{6n^2}$.

  c What value does A_U approach as $n \to \infty$?

3 Use the results from **1** and **2** to explain why $A = \frac{1}{3}$ units^2.

B   THE RIEMANN INTEGRAL

We have seen that for the special case of a quadratic, we can use series formulae to evaluate the area under the curve exactly.

However, for most functions we do not have such formulae. We therefore need a more general method for finding the area under a curve.

HISTORICAL NOTE

Italian Mathematician **Bonaventura Cavalieri** (1598 - 1647) became Professor of Mathematics at Bologna in 1629. He published tables for many trigonometric and logarithmic functions. However, his best known contribution to mathematics was the invention of **indivisibles**.

In his Method of Indivisibles, Cavalieri considered that a moving point could be used to sketch a curve. The curve could therefore be considered as the set of an infinite number of points, each with no length.

In a similar way, the "indivisibles" that made up a surface were an infinite number of lines. Almost every introduction to integral calculus starts with the division of an area into a number of rectangular strips with finite width.

Bonaventura Cavalieri

Cavalieri's important step was to make the strips narrower and narrower until they were infinitely thin lines. This reduces the "jagged" steps of the strips until they exactly define the curved boundary of the area.

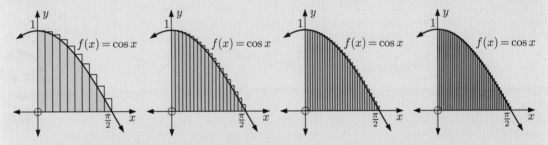

It was not until Englishman **Sir John Wallis** (1616 - 1703) formally introduced the idea of a **limit** in 1656 that Cavalieri's Method of Indivisibles progressed into the foundation for Integral Calculus.

Consider the lower and upper rectangle sums for a function which is positive and increasing on the interval $a \leqslant x \leqslant b$.

We divide the interval into n subintervals, each of width $w = \dfrac{b-a}{n}$.

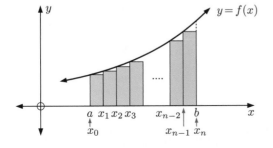
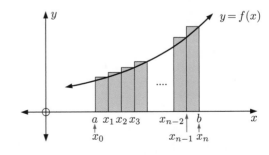

Since the function is increasing:

$$A_L = w\,f(x_0) + w\,f(x_1) + ... + w\,f(x_{n-2}) + w\,f(x_{n-1}) = w \sum_{i=0}^{n-1} f(x_i)$$

$$A_U = w\,f(x_1) + w\,f(x_2) + ... + w\,f(x_{n-1}) + w\,f(x_n) \quad = w \sum_{i=1}^{n} f(x_i)$$

$$\therefore \quad A_U - A_L = w\,(f(x_n) - f(x_0))$$

$$= \frac{1}{n}(b-a)\,(f(b) - f(a))$$

Following Cavalieri's suggestion, we allow there to be infinitely many subintervals, so $n \to \infty$.

In this case $\quad \displaystyle\lim_{n\to\infty} (A_U - A_L) = 0 \qquad$ {since $\displaystyle\lim_{n\to\infty} \frac{1}{n} = 0$}

$$\therefore \quad \lim_{n\to\infty} A_L = \lim_{n\to\infty} A_U \quad \text{\{provided both limits exist\}}$$

$\therefore \quad$ since $A_L < A < A_U$ for all values of n, it follows that

$$\lim_{n\to\infty} A_L = A = \lim_{n\to\infty} A_U$$

$\displaystyle\lim_{n\to\infty}$ means we have infinitely many subintervals.

We can obtain a result like this for every increasing and decreasing interval of a positive function provided the function is *continuous*. This means that the function must have a defined value $f(k)$ for all $a \leqslant k \leqslant b$, and that $\displaystyle\lim_{x\to k} f(x) = f(k)$ for all $a \leqslant k \leqslant b$.

If $f(x) \geqslant 0$ for all $a \leqslant x \leqslant b$, then

$\displaystyle\int_a^b f(x)\,dx$ is defined as the shaded area A.

This is known as the **Riemann integral**.

We would say "the integral of $f(x)$ from a to b with respect to x".

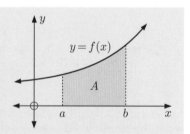

The symbol $\displaystyle\int$ is called an **integral sign**.

HISTORICAL NOTE

The word **integration** means "*to put together into a whole*". An **integral** is the "whole" produced from integration, since the areas of the thin rectangular strips are put together into one whole area.

The theory of integration was developed independently by **Sir Isaac Newton** and **Gottfried Wilhelm Leibniz**.

It was rigorously formalised using limits by the German mathematician **Bernhard Riemann** (1826 - 1866), whose name is given to the integral which calculates the area under a curve.

Bernhard Riemann

Example 1 ◀) **Self Tutor**

a Sketch the graph of $y = x^4$ for $0 \leqslant x \leqslant 1$. Shade the area described by $\displaystyle\int_0^1 x^4 \, dx$.

b Use technology to calculate the lower and upper rectangle sums for n equal subintervals where $n = 5, 10, 50, 100,$ and 500.

c Hence evaluate $\displaystyle\int_0^1 x^4 \, dx$ to 2 significant figures.

a

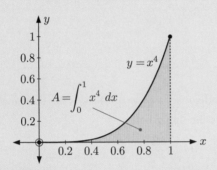

b

n	A_L	A_U
5	0.1133	0.3133
10	0.1533	0.2533
50	0.1901	0.2101
100	0.1950	0.2050
500	0.1990	0.2010

c When $n = 500$, $A_L \approx A_U \approx 0.20$, to 2 significant figures.

∴ since $A_L < \displaystyle\int_0^1 x^4 \, dx < A_U$, $\displaystyle\int_0^1 x^4 \, dx \approx 0.20$

EXERCISE 15B

1 **a** Sketch the graph of $y = \sqrt{x}$ for $0 \leqslant x \leqslant 1$. Shade the area described by $\displaystyle\int_0^1 \sqrt{x} \, dx$.

b Find the lower and upper rectangle sums for $n = 5, 10, 50, 100,$ and 500.

AREA FINDER

c Hence evaluate $\displaystyle\int_0^1 \sqrt{x} \, dx$ to 2 significant figures.

2 Consider the region enclosed by $y = \sqrt{1 + x^3}$ and the x-axis for $0 \leqslant x \leqslant 2$.

GRAPHING PACKAGE

a Write expressions for the lower and upper rectangle sums using n subintervals where $n \in \mathbb{Z}^+$.

b Find the lower and upper rectangle sums for $n = 50, 100,$ and 500.

c Hence estimate $\displaystyle\int_0^2 \sqrt{1 + x^3} \, dx$.

3 The integral $\displaystyle\int_{-3}^3 e^{-\frac{x^2}{2}} \, dx$ is of considerable interest to statisticians.

a Use the graphing package to help sketch $y = e^{-\frac{x^2}{2}}$ for $-3 \leqslant x \leqslant 3$.

b Calculate the lower and upper rectangle sums for the interval $0 \leqslant x \leqslant 3$ using $n = 2250$.

c Use the symmetry of $y = e^{-\frac{x^2}{2}}$ to find lower and upper rectangle sums for $-3 \leqslant x \leqslant 0$ for $n = 2250$.

d Hence estimate $\displaystyle\int_{-3}^3 e^{-\frac{x^2}{2}} \, dx$. Compare your answer with $\sqrt{2\pi}$.

Example 2   ◄)) **Self Tutor**

Use graphical evidence and known area facts to find:

a $\displaystyle\int_0^2 (2x+1)\, dx$ **b** $\displaystyle\int_0^1 \sqrt{1-x^2}\, dx$

a
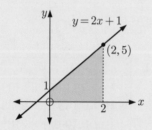

$\displaystyle\int_0^2 (2x+1)\, dx = $ shaded area

$$= \left(\frac{1+5}{2}\right) \times 2$$
$$= 6$$

b If $y = \sqrt{1-x^2}$ then $y^2 = 1-x^2$ and so $x^2 + y^2 = 1$. This is the equation of the unit circle, and $y = \sqrt{1-x^2}$ is the upper half.

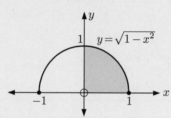

$\displaystyle\int_0^1 \sqrt{1-x^2}\, dx = $ shaded area

$$= \tfrac{1}{4} \times \pi \times 1^2$$
$$= \tfrac{\pi}{4}$$

4 Use graphical evidence and known area facts to find:

a $\displaystyle\int_1^3 (1+4x)\, dx$ **b** $\displaystyle\int_{-1}^2 (2-x)\, dx$ **c** $\displaystyle\int_{-2}^2 \sqrt{4-x^2}\, dx$

5 a Use the diagram alongside to show that for any positive function $f(x)$:

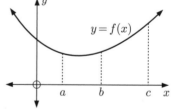

  i $\displaystyle\int_a^a f(x)\, dx = 0$

  ii $\displaystyle\int_a^b f(x)\, dx + \int_b^c f(x)\, dx = \int_a^c f(x)\, dx$

b For a positive function $f(x)$, $\displaystyle\int_2^5 f(x) = 10$, and $\displaystyle\int_5^9 f(x) = 12$. Find:

  i $\displaystyle\int_5^5 f(x)\, dx$ **ii** $\displaystyle\int_2^9 f(x)\, dx$

C   ANTIDIFFERENTIATION

In many problems in calculus, we know the rate of change of one variable with respect to another, but we do not have a formula which directly relates the variables. In other words, we know $\dfrac{dy}{dx}$, but we need to know y in terms of x.

The process of finding y from $\dfrac{dy}{dx}$, or $f(x)$ from $f'(x)$, is the reverse process of differentiation. We call it **antidifferentiation**.

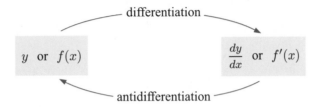

Consider $\dfrac{dy}{dx} = x^2$.

From our work on differentiation, we know that when we differentiate power functions the index reduces by 1. We hence know that y must involve x^3.

Now if $y = x^3$ then $\dfrac{dy}{dx} = 3x^2$, so if we start with $y = \frac{1}{3}x^3$ then $\dfrac{dy}{dx} = x^2$.

This is the correct result. However, for *all* of the cases $y = \frac{1}{3}x^3 + 2$, $y = \frac{1}{3}x^3 + 100$, and $y = \frac{1}{3}x^3 - 7$, we find that $\dfrac{dy}{dx} = x^2$.

In fact, there are infinitely many functions of the form $y = \frac{1}{3}x^3 + c$ where c is an arbitrary constant, which will give $\dfrac{dy}{dx} = x^2$. Ignoring the arbitrary constant, we say that $\frac{1}{3}x^3$ is the **antiderivative** of x^2. It is the simplest function which, when differentiated, gives x^2.

> If $F(x)$ is a function where $F'(x) = f(x)$ we say that:
> - the **derivative** of $F(x)$ is $f(x)$ and
> - the **antiderivative** of $f(x)$ is $F(x)$.

Example 3   ◀◎ Self Tutor

Find the antiderivative of:

a x^3 **b** e^{2x} **c** $\dfrac{1}{\sqrt{x}}$

a $\dfrac{d}{dx}(x^4) = 4x^3$

$\therefore \dfrac{d}{dx}(\frac{1}{4}x^4) = x^3$

$\therefore$ the antiderivative of x^3 is $\frac{1}{4}x^4$.

b $\dfrac{d}{dx}(e^{2x}) = e^{2x} \times 2 = 2e^{2x}$

$\therefore \dfrac{d}{dx}(\frac{1}{2}e^{2x}) = \frac{1}{2} \times 2e^{2x} = e^{2x}$

$\therefore$ the antiderivative of e^{2x} is $\frac{1}{2}e^{2x}$.

c $\dfrac{1}{\sqrt{x}} = x^{-\frac{1}{2}}$

Now $\dfrac{d}{dx}(x^{\frac{1}{2}}) = \frac{1}{2}x^{-\frac{1}{2}}$

$\therefore \dfrac{d}{dx}(2x^{\frac{1}{2}}) = 2(\frac{1}{2})x^{-\frac{1}{2}} = x^{-\frac{1}{2}}$

$\therefore$ the antiderivative of $\dfrac{1}{\sqrt{x}}$ is $2\sqrt{x}$.

EXERCISE 15C

1 **a** Find the antiderivative of:

   i x **ii** x^2 **iii** x^5 **iv** x^{-2}

   v x^{-4} **vi** $x^{\frac{1}{3}}$ **vii** $x^{-\frac{1}{3}}$ **viii** $x^{\frac{2}{3}}$

   b Predict a general rule for the antiderivative of x^n, for $n \neq -1$.

2 **a** Find the antiderivative of:

   i e^{3x} **ii** e^{5x} **iii** $e^{\frac{1}{2}x}$ **iv** $e^{0.01x}$ **v** $e^{\pi x}$ **vi** $e^{\frac{x}{3}}$

   b Predict a general rule for the antiderivative of e^{kx} where $k \neq 0$ is a constant.

3 Find the antiderivative of:

   a $6x^2 + 4x$ by first differentiating $x^3 + x^2$ **b** $\sqrt{x}$ by first differentiating $x\sqrt{x}$

   c $\dfrac{1}{x\sqrt{x}}$ by first differentiating $\dfrac{1}{\sqrt{x}}$.

D   THE FUNDAMENTAL THEOREM OF CALCULUS

We can now use the Riemann integral to explain the link between differential calculus and the definite integral or limit of an area sum we saw in **Section B**. This link is called the **Fundamental Theorem of Calculus**.

INVESTIGATION 2   THE AREA FUNCTION

Consider the constant function $f(t) = 5$.

We wish to find an **area function** which will give the area under the function between $t = a$ and some other value of t which we will call x.

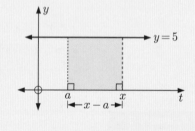

The area function is $A(x) = \displaystyle\int_a^x 5 \, dt$

$\qquad\qquad\qquad = $ shaded area

$\qquad\qquad\qquad = (x - a)5$

$\qquad\qquad\qquad = \boxed{5x} - 5a$

Since $f(t) = 5$ has the antiderivative $F(t) = 5t$, we can write $A(x)$ in the form $F(x) - F(a)$.

What to do:

1 What is the derivative $F'(t)$ of the function $F(t) = 5t$? How is this related to $f(t)$?

2 Consider the simplest linear function $f(t) = t$. The corresponding area function is

$$A(x) = \int_a^x t \, dt$$

$$= \text{shaded area}$$

$$= \left(\frac{x + a}{2}\right)(x - a)$$

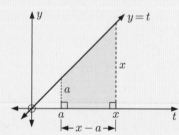

   a Write $A(x)$ in the form $F(x) - F(a)$.

   b What is the derivative $F'(t)$? How is this related to $f(t)$?

3 Consider $f(t) = 2t + 3$. The corresponding area function is

$$A(x) = \int_a^x (2t + 3)\, dt$$

$$= \text{shaded area}$$

$$= \left(\frac{2x + 3 + 2a + 3}{2}\right)(x - a)$$

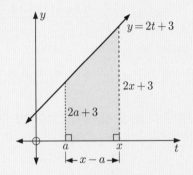

a Write $A(x)$ in the form $F(x) - F(a)$.

b What is the derivative $F'(t)$?
How is this related to $f(t)$?

4 Repeat the procedure in **2** and **3** to find area functions for:

a $f(t) = \frac{1}{2}t + 3$ **b** $f(t) = 5 - 2t$

Do your results fit with your earlier observations?

5 If $f(t) = 3t^2 + 4t + 5$, predict what $F(t)$ will be without performing the algebraic procedure.

From the **Investigation** you should have found that, for $f(t) \geqslant 0$,

$$\int_a^x f(t)\, dt = F(x) - F(a) \quad \text{where} \quad F'(t) = f(t). \quad F(t) \text{ is the } \textbf{antiderivative} \text{ of } f(t).$$

The following argument shows why this is true for all functions $f(t) \geqslant 0$.

Consider a function $y = f(t)$ which has antiderivative $F(t)$ and an area function $A(x) = \int_a^x f(t)\, dt$ which is the area from $t = a$ to $t = x$.

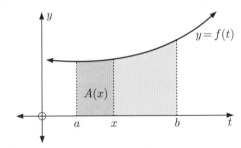

$A(x)$ is an increasing function since $f(x) \geqslant 0$, and $A(a) = 0$ .... (1)

Consider the narrow strip between $t = x$ and $t = x+h$. The area of this strip is $A(x + h) - A(x)$, but we also know it must lie between a lower and upper rectangle on the interval $x \leqslant t \leqslant x + h$ of width h.

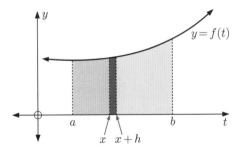

$$\text{area of lower rectangle} \leqslant A(x + h) - A(x) \leqslant \text{area of upper rectangle}$$

If $f(t)$ is increasing on this interval then

$$hf(x) \leqslant A(x + h) - A(x) \leqslant hf(x + h)$$

$$\therefore \ f(x) \leqslant \frac{A(x + h) - A(x)}{h} \leqslant f(x + h)$$

INTRODUCTION TO INTEGRATION   (Chapter 15)

Equivalently, if $f(t)$ is decreasing on this interval then

$$f(x+h) \leqslant \frac{A(x+h) - A(x)}{h} \leqslant f(x)$$

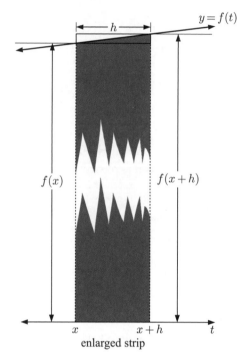

Taking the limit as $h \to 0$ gives

$$f(x) \leqslant A'(x) \leqslant f(x)$$
$$\therefore \quad A'(x) = f(x)$$

So, the area function $A(x)$ must only differ from the antiderivative of $f(x)$ by a constant.

$$\therefore \quad A(x) = F(x) + c$$

Letting $x = a$, $\quad A(a) = F(a) + c$

But from (1), $\quad A(a) = 0$ $\quad \therefore \quad c = -F(a)$

$$\therefore \quad A(x) = F(x) - F(a)$$

and so $\quad \displaystyle\int_a^x f(t)\, dt = F(x) - F(a)$

Letting $x = b$, $\quad \displaystyle\int_a^b f(t)\, dt = F(b) - F(a)$

enlarged strip

This result is in fact true for *all* continuous functions $f(t)$, even if they are negative.

However, in situations where a function is negative, the area between the curve and the x-axis is counted as negative. We therefore refer to $A(x)$ as a **signed area function**.

THE FUNDAMENTAL THEOREM OF CALCULUS

For a continuous function $f(x)$ with antiderivative $F(x)$, $\quad \displaystyle\int_a^b \boldsymbol{f(x)\, dx = F(b) - F(a)}$.

In general, $\displaystyle\int_a^b f(x)\, dx$ is called a **definite integral**.

PROPERTIES OF DEFINITE INTEGRALS

The following properties of definite integrals can all be deduced from the Fundamental Theorem of Calculus:

- $\displaystyle\int_a^a f(x)\, dx = 0$

- $\displaystyle\int_a^b k\, dx = k(b - a) \quad \{k \text{ is a constant}\}$

- $\displaystyle\int_b^a f(x)\, dx = -\int_a^b f(x)\, dx$

- $\displaystyle\int_a^b k\, f(x)\, dx = k \int_a^b f(x)\, dx$

- $\displaystyle\int_a^b f(x)\, dx + \int_b^c f(x)\, dx = \int_a^c f(x)\, dx$

- $\displaystyle\int_a^b [f(x) \pm g(x)]\, dx = \int_a^b f(x)\, dx \pm \int_a^b g(x)\, dx$

Example proof:

$$\int_a^b f(x)\,dx + \int_b^c f(x)\,dx = F(b) - F(a) + F(c) - F(b)$$
$$= F(c) - F(a)$$
$$= \int_a^c f(x)\,dx$$

In particular, for the case where $a \leqslant b \leqslant c$ and $f(x) \geqslant 0$ for $a \leqslant x \leqslant c$, we observe that

$$\int_a^b f(x)\,dx + \int_b^c f(x)\,dx = A_1 + A_2$$
$$= \int_a^c f(x)\,dx$$

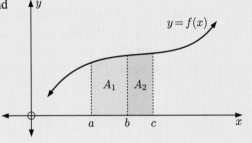

The Fundamental Theorem of Calculus allows us to calculate areas under curves that we could previously only estimate.

Example 4	◀) **Self Tutor**

Use the Fundamental Theorem of Calculus to find the area between:

a the x-axis and $y = x^2$ from $x = 0$ to $x = 1$

b the x-axis and $y = \sqrt{x}$ from $x = 1$ to $x = 9$.

a

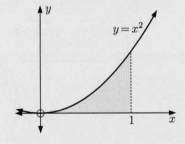

$f(x) = x^2$ has antiderivative $F(x) = \dfrac{x^3}{3}$

∴ shaded area $= \displaystyle\int_0^1 x^2\,dx$

$= F(1) - F(0)$

$= \tfrac{1}{3} - 0$

$= \tfrac{1}{3}$ units^2

b

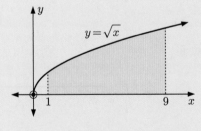

$f(x) = \sqrt{x} = x^{\frac{1}{2}}$ has antiderivative

$F(x) = \dfrac{x^{\frac{3}{2}}}{\frac{3}{2}} = \tfrac{2}{3}x\sqrt{x}$

∴ shaded area $= \displaystyle\int_1^9 x^{\frac{1}{2}}\,dx$

$= F(9) - F(1)$

$= \tfrac{2}{3} \times 27 - \tfrac{2}{3} \times 1$

$= 17\tfrac{1}{3}$ units^2

Instructions for evaluating definite integrals on your calculator can be found by clicking on the icon.

GRAPHICS
CALCULATOR
INSTRUCTIONS

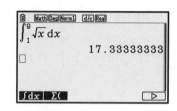

EXERCISE 15D

1   **a**   Differentiate x^2, and hence find the antiderivative of $2x$.

 b   Use the Fundamental Theorem of Calculus to find the area between the x-axis and $f(x) = 2x$ from $x = 1$ to $x = 3$.

 c   Use graphical methods to check your answer.

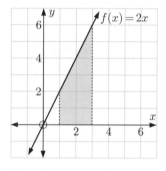

2   **a**   Find the antiderivative of $\sqrt{x}$.

 b   Use the Fundamental Theorem of Calculus to find the area between the x-axis and $y = \sqrt{x}$ from $x = 0$ to $x = 1$.

 c   Compare your answer to **Exercise 15B** question **1**.

3   **a**   Use the Fundamental Theorem of Calculus to find the area between the x-axis and $y = x^3$ from:

   i $x = 0$ to $x = 2$ **ii** $x = 2$ to $x = 3$ **iii** $x = 0$ to $x = 3$.

 b   Comment on your answers in **a**.

4   Use the Fundamental Theorem of Calculus to find the area between the x-axis and:

 a $y = x^3$ from $x = 1$ to $x = 2$

 b $y = x^2$ from $x = 1$ to $x = 3$

 c $y = \sqrt{x}$ from $x = 1$ to $x = 2$

 d $y = \dfrac{1}{\sqrt{x}}$ from $x = 1$ to $x = 4$.

Check your answers using technology.

5   Use the Fundamental Theorem of Calculus to show that:

 a $\displaystyle\int_{a}^{a} f(x)\, dx = 0$ and explain the result graphically

 b $\displaystyle\int_{a}^{b} k\, dx = k(b - a)$ where k is a constant   **c** $\displaystyle\int_{b}^{a} f(x)\, dx = -\int_{a}^{b} f(x)\, dx$

 d $\displaystyle\int_{a}^{b} k\, f(x)\, dx = k\int_{a}^{b} f(x)\, dx$ where k is a constant

 e $\displaystyle\int_{a}^{b} [f(x) + g(x)]\, dx = \int_{a}^{b} f(x)\, dx + \int_{a}^{b} g(x)\, dx$

6 Use technology to find the area between the x-axis and $y = \sqrt{9 - x^2}$ from $x = 0$ to $x = 3$.

Check your answer by direct calculation of the area.

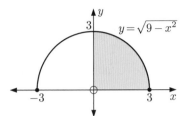

7

a Use the Fundamental Theorem of Calculus to show that

$$\int_a^b (-f(x))\, dx = -\int_a^b f(x)\, dx$$

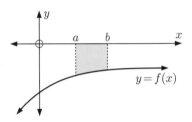

b Hence show that if $f(x) \leqslant 0$ for all x on $a \leqslant x \leqslant b$

then the shaded area $= -\displaystyle\int_a^b f(x)\, dx$ units^2.

c Calculate the following integrals, and give graphical interpretations of your answers:

i $\displaystyle\int_0^1 (-x^2)\, dx$ **ii** $\displaystyle\int_0^1 (x^2 - x)\, dx$ **iii** $\displaystyle\int_{-2}^0 3x\, dx$

d Use graphical evidence and known area facts to find $\displaystyle\int_0^2 \left(-\sqrt{4 - x^2}\right) dx$.

REVIEW SET 15A

1

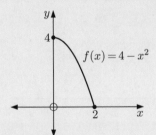

a Use *four* lower and upper rectangles to find rational numbers A and B such that:

$$A < \int_0^2 (4 - x^2)\, dx < B.$$

b Hence estimate $\displaystyle\int_0^2 (4 - x^2)\, dx$.

2

a Sketch the region between $y = \sin x$ and the x-axis for $0 \leqslant x \leqslant \frac{\pi}{2}$.

b Divide the interval into 3 equal parts and display the 3 upper and 3 lower rectangles. Hence find boundaries for the value of $\displaystyle\int_0^{\frac{\pi}{2}} \sin x\, dx$.

3 Find the antiderivative of:

a x^4 **b** $\dfrac{1}{2x^2}$ **c** $e^{-\frac{1}{2}x}$ **d** $\cos x$

4 The graph of $y = f(x)$ is illustrated.

Evaluate the following using area interpretation:

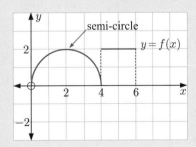

a $\displaystyle\int_0^4 f(x)\, dx$ **b** $\displaystyle\int_4^6 f(x)\, dx$

5   **a**   Use the Fundamental Theorem of Calculus to find the area between the x-axis and $y = x^2$ from:

     i $x = 0$ to $x = 1$ **ii** $x = 1$ to $x = 2$ **iii** $x = 0$ to $x = 2$.

   b   Comment on your answers in **a**.

REVIEW SET 15B

1   **a**   Sketch the region between the curve $y = \dfrac{4}{1+x^2}$ and the x-axis for $0 \leqslant x \leqslant 1$.

     Divide the interval into 5 equal parts and display the 5 upper and lower rectangles.

   b   Use the area finder software to find the lower and upper rectangle sums for   **AREA FINDER**
     $n = 5, 50, 100,$ and 500.

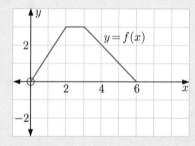

   c   Give your best estimate for $\displaystyle\int_0^1 \dfrac{4}{1+x^2}\,dx$ and compare this answer with π.

2   Use graphical evidence and known area facts to find:

   a $\displaystyle\int_2^4 (2x - 1)\,dx$ **b** $\displaystyle\int_{-1}^1 \sqrt{1 - x^2}\,dx$

3   Find the antiderivative of:

   a $3x^2 - 2$ by first differentiating $x^3 - 2x$

   b $\sqrt[3]{x}$ by first differentiating $x^{\frac{4}{3}}$.

4   The graph of $y = f(x)$ is illustrated.
Evaluate the following using area interpretation:

   a $\displaystyle\int_0^2 f(x)\,dx$ **b** $\displaystyle\int_2^6 f(x)\,dx$

5   Use the Fundamental Theorem of Calculus to find the area between the x-axis and:

   a $y = 4x$ from $x = 0$ to $x = 3$ **b** $y = \sqrt{x}$ from $x = 0$ to $x = 9$.

Chapter 16

Techniques for integration

Contents:

OPENING PROBLEM

The Fundamental Theorem of Calculus developed by Newton and Leibniz identifies the link between differential calculus and a definite integral.

If we are to use the Fundamental Theorem of Calculus to calculate areas, we need to be able to identify an area function from its derivative.

Things to think about:

a Can you identify the function which has derivative:

    i $3x^2$ **ii** $x^3 - x + 1$ **iii** $\cos 2x$?

b What can the rules of differentiation teach us about the reverse process of integration?

In our previous study of the Fundamental Theorem of Calculus, we showed that the **antiderivative** of x^2 is $\frac{1}{3}x^3$, and that any function of the form $\frac{1}{3}x^3 + c$ where c is a constant, has derivative x^2.

We say that the **indefinite integral** or **integral** of x^2 is $\frac{1}{3}x^3 + c$, and write $\displaystyle\int x^2\, dx = \frac{1}{3}x^3 + c$.

We read this as "the integral of x^2 with respect to x is $\frac{1}{3}x^3 + c$, where c is a constant".

$$\text{If } F'(x) = f(x) \text{ then } \int f(x)\, dx = F(x) + c.$$

The constant c is called the **constant of integration**.

This process of finding an indefinite integral is called **indefinite integration**.

A   DISCOVERING INTEGRALS

Just as we did in antidifferentiation, we can sometimes discover integrals by differentiation.

The following rules will prove useful:

- Any constant within the integral may be written in front of the integral sign.

$$\int k\,f(x)\, dx = k \int f(x)\, dx, \quad k \text{ is a constant}$$

Proof: Consider differentiating $k F(x)$ where $F'(x) = f(x)$.

$$\frac{d}{dx}\left(k\,F(x)\right) = k\,F'(x) = k\,f(x)$$

$$\therefore \int k\,f(x)\, dx = k\,F(x) + c$$

$$= k \int f(x)\, dx$$

- The integral of a sum is the sum of the separate integrals. This rule enables us to integrate term by term.

$$\int [f(x) + g(x)]\, dx = \int f(x)\, dx + \int g(x)\, dx$$

Example 1   ◀) **Self Tutor**

Find the derivative of $x^4 + 2x^3$, and hence find $\int (2x^3 + 3x^2)\, dx$.

$$\frac{d}{dx}(x^4 + 2x^3) = 4x^3 + 6x^2$$

$$\therefore \int (4x^3 + 6x^2)\, dx = x^4 + 2x^3 + c$$

$$\therefore \int 2(2x^3 + 3x^2)\, dx = x^4 + 2x^3 + c$$

$$\therefore 2\int (2x^3 + 3x^2)\, dx = x^4 + 2x^3 + c$$

$$\therefore \int (2x^3 + 3x^2)\, dx = \tfrac{1}{2}x^4 + x^3 + c$$

c represents an arbitrary constant, so is simply any value $c \in \mathbb{R}$. Instead of writing $\frac{c}{2}$, we can therefore still write just c.

EXERCISE 16A

1 **a** Find the derivative of x^7, and hence find $\int x^6\, dx$

   b Find the derivative of $x^{\frac{3}{2}}$, and hence find $\int \sqrt{x}\, dx$.

   c Find the derivative of $x^{-\frac{1}{2}}$, and hence find $\int x^{-\frac{3}{2}}\, dx$.

   d Find the derivative of x^{n+1}, $n \neq -1$. Hence find $\int x^n\, dx$, $n \neq -1$.

We can check that an integral is correct by differentiating the answer. It should give us the **integrand**, the function we originally integrated.

2 **a** Find the derivative of e^{4x}, and hence find $\int e^{4x}\, dx$.

   b Find the derivative of $e^{-\frac{x}{2}}$, and hence find $\int e^{-\frac{x}{2}}\, dx$.

   c Find the derivative of e^{kx}, $k \neq 0$. Hence find $\int e^{kx}\, dx$, $k \neq 0$.

3 **a** Find the derivative of $\sin x$, and hence find $\int \cos x\, dx$.

   b Find the derivative of $\cos x$, and hence find $\int \sin x\, dx$.

4 Find the derivative of $x^3 + x^2$, and hence find $\int (3x^2 + 2x)\, dx$.

5 Find the derivative of $3x^4 - 2x^2$, and hence find $\int (3x^3 - x)\, dx$.

6 Suppose $F(x)$ and $G(x)$ have the derivative functions $f(x)$ and $g(x)$ respectively.

   a Find the derivative of $F(x) + G(x)$.

   b Show that $\int [f(x) + g(x)]\, dx = \int f(x)\, dx + \int g(x)\, dx$.

Example 2   ◀)) **Self Tutor**

Find the derivative of $\cos\left(2x + \frac{\pi}{3}\right)$, and hence find $\displaystyle\int \sin\left(2x + \frac{\pi}{3}\right) dx$.

$$\frac{d}{dx}\left(\cos\left(2x + \tfrac{\pi}{3}\right)\right) = -\sin\left(2x + \tfrac{\pi}{3}\right)(2)$$
$$= -2\sin\left(2x + \tfrac{\pi}{3}\right)$$
$$\therefore \quad \int \left(-2\sin\left(2x + \tfrac{\pi}{3}\right)\right) dx = \cos\left(2x + \tfrac{\pi}{3}\right) + c$$
$$\therefore \quad -2 \int \sin\left(2x + \tfrac{\pi}{3}\right) dx = \cos\left(2x + \tfrac{\pi}{3}\right) + c$$
$$\therefore \quad \int \sin\left(2x + \tfrac{\pi}{3}\right) dx = -\tfrac{1}{2}\cos\left(2x + \tfrac{\pi}{3}\right) + c$$

7 **a** Find the derivative of $\sin 3x$, and hence find $\displaystyle\int \cos 3x \, dx$.

   b Find the derivative of $\cos\left(\frac{\pi}{3} - x\right)$, and hence find $\displaystyle\int \sin\left(\frac{\pi}{3} - x\right) dx$.

   c Find the derivative of e^{3x+1}, and hence find $\displaystyle\int e^{3x+1} \, dx$.

   d Find the derivative of $\sqrt{5x - 1}$, and hence find $\displaystyle\int \frac{1}{\sqrt{5x - 1}} \, dx$.

   e Find the derivative of $(2x + 1)^4$, and hence find $\displaystyle\int (2x + 1)^3 \, dx$.

8 **a** Find the derivative of $\ln x$, $x > 0$.   **b** Find the derivative of $\ln(-x)$, $x < 0$.

   c Hence explain why $\displaystyle\int \frac{1}{x} \, dx = \ln|x| + c$, $x \neq 0$.

B   RULES FOR INTEGRATION

In **Chapter 12** we developed a set of rules to help us differentiate functions more efficiently. These rules or combinations of them can be used to differentiate all of the functions we consider in this course.

However, the task of finding **antiderivatives** is not so easy. Many functions simply do not have antiderivatives which can be expressed easily using standard functions.

HISTORICAL NOTE

Robert Henry Risch (1939 -) is an American mathematician. He studied at the University of California, Berkeley.

In his doctorate studies in 1968, Risch devised a method for deciding if a function has an elementary antiderivative, and if it does, finding it. The original summary of his method took over 100 pages. Later developments from this are now used in all computer algebra systems.

After completing his doctorate, he worked at the IBM Thomas Watson Research Centre.

We *can* construct some rules which will allow us to integrate most of the function types we consider in this course.

INTEGRATING BASIC FUNCTION TYPES

For k a constant, $\dfrac{d}{dx}(kx + c) = k$ $\qquad \therefore \quad \displaystyle\int k\, dx = kx + c$

If $n \neq -1$, $\dfrac{d}{dx}\left(\dfrac{x^{n+1}}{n+1} + c\right) = \dfrac{(n+1)x^n}{n+1} = x^n$ $\quad \therefore \quad \displaystyle\int x^n\, dx = \dfrac{x^{n+1}}{n+1} + c,\ n \neq -1$

$\dfrac{d}{dx}(e^x + c) = e^x$ $\qquad \therefore \quad \displaystyle\int e^x\, dx = e^x + c$

For $x > 0$, $\dfrac{d}{dx}(\ln x + c) = \dfrac{1}{x}$

For $x < 0$, $\dfrac{d}{dx}(\ln(-x) + c) = \dfrac{-1}{-x} = \dfrac{1}{x}$

$| x |$ is the absolute value of x, which was studied in **Chapter 3**.

$\therefore \quad \displaystyle\int \dfrac{1}{x}\, dx = \begin{cases} \ln x + c & \text{if } x > 0 \\ \ln(-x) + c & \text{if } x < 0 \end{cases}$

$\therefore \quad \displaystyle\int \dfrac{1}{x}\, dx = \ln | x | + c,\ x \neq 0$

$\dfrac{d}{dx}(\sin x + c) = \cos x$ $\qquad \therefore \quad \displaystyle\int \cos x\, dx = \sin x + c$

$\dfrac{d}{dx}(-\cos x + c) = \sin x$ $\qquad \therefore \quad \displaystyle\int \sin x\, dx = -\cos x + c$

Function	Integral
k, a constant	$kx + c$
$x^n,\ n \neq -1$	$\dfrac{x^{n+1}}{n+1} + c$
e^x	$e^x + c$
$\dfrac{1}{x}$	$\ln | x | + c,\ x \neq 0$
$\cos x$	$\sin x + c$
$\sin x$	$-\cos x + c$

c is an arbitrary constant called the **constant of integration** or **integrating constant**.

GENERAL RULES FOR INTEGRATION

These rules can be combined with the results we saw in the previous Section:

- Any constant within the integral may be written in front of the integral sign.

$$\int k\,f(x)\,dx = k \int f(x)\,dx, \quad k \text{ is a constant}$$

- The integral of a sum is the sum of the separate integrals. This rule enables us to integrate term by term.

$$\int [f(x) + g(x)]\,dx = \int f(x)\,dx + \int g(x)\,dx$$

Example 3   ◀) **Self Tutor**

Find:

a $\displaystyle\int (-2x^3 + 5x - 2)\,dx$ **b** $\displaystyle\int \left(5e^x + \frac{2}{\sqrt{x}}\right)\,dx$ **c** $\displaystyle\int (2\sin x - \cos x)\,dx$

---

a $\displaystyle\int (-2x^3 + 5x - 2)\,dx$ **b** $\displaystyle\int \left(5e^x + \frac{2}{\sqrt{x}}\right)\,dx$ **c** $\displaystyle\int (2\sin x - \cos x)\,dx$

$= \dfrac{-2x^4}{4} + \dfrac{5x^2}{2} - 2x + c$ $= \displaystyle\int (5e^x + 2x^{-\frac{1}{2}})\,dx$ $= 2(-\cos x) - \sin x + c$

$= -\frac{1}{2}x^4 + \frac{5}{2}x^2 - 2x + c$ $= -2\cos x - \sin x + c$

$\phantom{= -\frac{1}{2}x^4}$ $= 5e^x + \dfrac{2x^{\frac{1}{2}}}{\frac{1}{2}} + c$

$\phantom{= -\frac{1}{2}x^4}$ $= 5e^x + 4\sqrt{x} + c$

There are no power or quotient rules for integration, so we often have to perform the multiplication or division first and then integrate.

Example 4   ◀) **Self Tutor**

Find: **a** $\displaystyle\int \left(x - \frac{1}{x}\right)^3\,dx$ **b** $\displaystyle\int \frac{3\sqrt{x} + x^2}{x}\,dx$

---

a $\displaystyle\int \left(x - \frac{1}{x}\right)^3\,dx$ **b** $\displaystyle\int \frac{3\sqrt{x} + x^2}{x}\,dx$

$= \displaystyle\int \left(x^3 + 3x^2\left(-\frac{1}{x}\right) + 3x\left(-\frac{1}{x}\right)^2 + \left(-\frac{1}{x}\right)^3\right)\,dx$ $= \displaystyle\int (3x^{-\frac{1}{2}} + x)\,dx$

 {binomial theorem} $= \dfrac{3x^{\frac{1}{2}}}{\frac{1}{2}} + \dfrac{x^2}{2} + c$

$= \displaystyle\int (x^3 - 3x + 3x^{-1} - x^{-3})\,dx$ $= 6\sqrt{x} + \frac{1}{2}x^2 + c$

$= \dfrac{x^4}{4} - \dfrac{3x^2}{2} + 3\ln|x| - \dfrac{x^{-2}}{(-2)} + c$

$= \frac{1}{4}x^4 - \frac{3}{2}x^2 + 3\ln|x| + \dfrac{1}{2x^2} + c$

EXERCISE 16B

1 Find:

   a $\displaystyle\int (x^2 + 3x - 2)\, dx$ **b** $\displaystyle\int (2x^2 - 3x + 1)\, dx$

   c $\displaystyle\int (-x^3 + 4x^2 - 3)\, dx$ **d** $\displaystyle\int \left(\tfrac{1}{2}x + x^2 + x^3\right) dx$

Remember that you can check your integration by differentiating the resulting function.

   e $\displaystyle\int (x^4 - x^2 - x + 2)\, dx$ **f** $\displaystyle\int \left(4x^2 + \tfrac{1}{x}\right) dx$

   g $\displaystyle\int \left(2\sqrt{x} - \dfrac{3}{\sqrt{x}}\right) dx$ **h** $\displaystyle\int \left(\dfrac{1}{3x} - \dfrac{2}{x^2}\right) dx$

   i $\displaystyle\int (x\sqrt{x} - 9)\, dx$ **j** $\displaystyle\int \left(3x^{-\frac{3}{2}} + x^{\frac{1}{4}}\right) dx$

2 Find:

   a $\displaystyle\int (2e^x - 3x)\, dx$ **b** $\displaystyle\int \left(\dfrac{4}{x} + x^2 - e^x\right) dx$ **c** $\displaystyle\int \left(5e^x + \tfrac{1}{2}x^2\right) dx$

3 Integrate with respect to x:

   a $3\sin x - 2$ **b** $4x - 2\cos x$ **c** $\sin x - 2\cos x + e^x$

   d $x^2\sqrt{x} - 10\sin x$ **e** $\dfrac{x(x-1)}{3} + \cos x$ **f** $-\sin x + 2\sqrt{x}$

4 Find y if:

   a $\dfrac{dy}{dx} = 6$ **b** $\dfrac{dy}{dx} = 4x^2$ **c** $\dfrac{dy}{dx} = \dfrac{1}{x^2}$

   d $\dfrac{dy}{dx} = \dfrac{2}{\sqrt[3]{x}}$ **e** $\dfrac{dy}{dx} = 2x^3 - 4$ **f** $\dfrac{dy}{dx} = 4x^3 + 3x^2$

   g $\dfrac{dy}{dx} = 2 - \dfrac{1}{x}$ **h** $\dfrac{dy}{dx} = \sin x + 2\cos x$ **i** $\dfrac{dy}{dx} = 2e^x - 5 + x$

5 Find:

   a $\displaystyle\int \left(\tfrac{1}{2}x^3 - x^4 + x^{\frac{1}{3}}\right) dx$ **b** $\displaystyle\int \left(\dfrac{4}{x^2} + x^2 - \tfrac{1}{4}x^3\right) dx$ **c** $\displaystyle\int \left(5x^4 + \tfrac{1}{3}x^3 - \sqrt{x}\right) dx$

6 Find:

   a $\displaystyle\int (2x + 1)^2\, dx$ **b** $\displaystyle\int \left(x + \tfrac{1}{x}\right)^2 dx$ **c** $\displaystyle\int \dfrac{1 - 4x}{x\sqrt{x}}\, dx$

   d $\displaystyle\int \dfrac{2x - 1}{\sqrt{x}}\, dx$ **e** $\displaystyle\int \left(\sqrt{x} - \dfrac{1}{\sqrt{x}}\right)^2 dx$ **f** $\displaystyle\int \dfrac{1 - x^2}{x}\, dx$

   g $\displaystyle\int \left(\dfrac{2}{x} + 1\right)^2 dx$ **h** $\displaystyle\int (x + 1)^3\, dx$ **i** $\displaystyle\int (x - 1)^4\, dx$

   j $\displaystyle\int \dfrac{x^2 - 4}{x\sqrt{x}}\, dx$ **k** $\displaystyle\int \dfrac{x^2 - 4x + 10}{x}\, dx$ **l** $\displaystyle\int \dfrac{3x^3 - 2x^2 + 5}{x^2}\, dx$

7 Find $f(x)$ if:

   a $f'(x) = (1 - 2x)^2$ **b** $f'(x) = \sqrt{x} - \dfrac{2}{\sqrt{x}}$ **c** $f'(x) = \dfrac{x^2 - 5}{x^2}$

8 Find:

   a $\displaystyle\int \left(\sqrt{x} + \tfrac{1}{2}\cos x\right) dx$ **b** $\displaystyle\int (2e^x - 4\sin x)\, dx$ **c** $\displaystyle\int (3\cos x - \sin x)\, dx$

9 Find:

   a $\displaystyle\int \left(x^2 - \frac{1}{x}\right)^2 dx$ **b** $\displaystyle\int \frac{x^2 - 4x + 2}{\sqrt{x}}\, dx$ **c** $\displaystyle\int \sqrt{x}(3x - 1)^2\, dx$

DISCUSSION

In the rule $\displaystyle\int x^n\, dx = \frac{x^{n+1}}{n+1} + c, \ n \neq -1,$ why did we exclude the value $n = -1$?

C   PARTICULAR VALUES

We can find the constant of integration c if we are given a particular value of the function.

Example 5   ◀) Self Tutor

Find $f(x)$ given that:

   a $f'(x) = x^3 - 2x^2 + 3$ and $f(0) = 2$ **b** $f'(x) = 2\sin x - \sqrt{x}$ and $f(0) = 4$.

  a $f'(x) = x^3 - 2x^2 + 3$

    $\therefore \ f(x) = \displaystyle\int (x^3 - 2x^2 + 3)\, dx$

    $\therefore \ f(x) = \dfrac{x^4}{4} - \dfrac{2x^3}{3} + 3x + c$

    But $f(0) = 2$, so $c = 2$

    Thus $f(x) = \dfrac{x^4}{4} - \dfrac{2x^3}{3} + 3x + 2.$

  b $f'(x) = 2\sin x - \sqrt{x}$

    $\therefore \ f(x) = \displaystyle\int (2\sin x - x^{\frac{1}{2}})\, dx$

    $\therefore \ f(x) = 2(-\cos x) - \dfrac{x^{\frac{3}{2}}}{\frac{3}{2}} + c$

    $\therefore \ f(x) = -2\cos x - \tfrac{2}{3}x^{\frac{3}{2}} + c$

    But $f(0) = 4$, so $-2\cos 0 - 0 + c = 4$

                      $\therefore \ c = 6$

    Thus $f(x) = -2\cos x - \tfrac{2}{3}x^{\frac{3}{2}} + 6.$

EXERCISE 16C

1 Find $f(x)$ given that:

   a $f'(x) = 2x - 1$ and $f(0) = 3$ **b** $f'(x) = 3x^2 + 2x$ and $f(2) = 5$

   c $f'(x) = 2 + \dfrac{1}{\sqrt{x}}$ and $f(1) = 1$ **d** $f'(x) = x - \dfrac{2}{\sqrt{x}}$ and $f(1) = 2$

   e $f'(x) = \sqrt{x} - 2$ and $f(4) = 0$ **f** $f'(x) = \dfrac{1}{x}$ and $f(e) = 2$.

2 A curve has gradient function $\dfrac{dy}{dx} = x - 2x^2$ and passes through $(2, 4)$. Find the equation of the curve.

3 A curve has gradient function $\dfrac{dy}{dx} = 1 - e^x$ and passes through $(3, e^3)$. Find the equation of the curve.

4 Find $f(x)$ given that:

    a $f'(x) = x^2 - 4\cos x$ and $f(0) = 3$ **b** $f'(x) = 2\cos x - 3\sin x$ and $f\left(\frac{\pi}{4}\right) = \frac{1}{\sqrt{2}}$

    c $f'(x) = \sqrt{x} - 2\sin x$ and $f(0) = -2$ **d** $f'(x) = e^x + 3\cos x$ and $f(\pi) = 0$.

5 A curve has gradient function $f'(x) = ax + 1$ where a is a constant. Find $f(x)$ given that $f(0) = 3$ and $f(3) = -3$.

6 A curve has gradient function $f'(x) = ax^2 + bx$ where a, b are constants. Find $f(x)$ given that $f(-1) = -2$, $f(0) = 1$, and $f(1) = 4$.

Example 6   ◀)) **Self Tutor**

Find $f(x)$ given that $f''(x) = 12x^2 - 4$, $f'(0) = -1$, and $f(1) = 4$.

If $f''(x) = 12x^2 - 4$

$\therefore\ f'(x) = \displaystyle\int (12x^2 - 4)\,dx$

$\qquad = \dfrac{12x^3}{3} - 4x + c$

$\qquad = 4x^3 - 4x + c$

But $f'(0) = -1$, so $c = -1$

Thus $f'(x) = 4x^3 - 4x - 1$

$\therefore\ f(x) = \displaystyle\int (4x^3 - 4x - 1)\,dx$

$\qquad = \dfrac{4x^4}{4} - \dfrac{4x^2}{2} - x + d$

$\qquad = x^4 - 2x^2 - x + d$

But $f(1) = 4$, so $1 - 2 - 1 + d = 4$ and hence $d = 6$

Thus $f(x) = x^4 - 2x^2 - x + 6$

---

7 Find $f(x)$ given that:

    a $f''(x) = 2x + 1$, $f'(1) = 3$, and $f(2) = 7$

    b $f''(x) = 15\sqrt{x} + \dfrac{3}{\sqrt{x}}$, $f'(1) = 12$, and $f(0) = 5$

    c $f''(x) = \cos x$, $f'\left(\frac{\pi}{2}\right) = 0$, and $f(0) = 3$

    d $f''(x) = 2x$ and the points $(1, 0)$ and $(0, 5)$ lie on the curve $y = f(x)$.

8 Suppose $f''(x) = 3e^{-x}$, $f(1) = \dfrac{3}{e}$, and $f(3) = \dfrac{3}{e^3} - 2$. Find $f(x)$.

D   INTEGRATING $f(ax+b)$

In this Section we deal with integrals of functions which are composite with the linear function $ax + b$.

Notice that $\dfrac{d}{dx}(e^{ax+b}) = ae^{ax+b}$

$$\therefore \quad \int e^{ax+b}\, dx = \frac{1}{a}e^{ax+b} + c \quad \text{for } a \neq 0.$$

Likewise if $n \neq -1$, $\dfrac{d}{dx}((ax+b)^{n+1}) = (n+1)(ax+b)^n \times a$

$$= a(n+1)(ax+b)^n$$

$$\therefore \quad \int (ax+b)^n\, dx = \frac{1}{a}\frac{(ax+b)^{n+1}}{(n+1)} + c \quad \text{for } n \neq -1,\ a \neq 0.$$

We can perform the same process for trigonometric functions:

$$\frac{d}{dx}(\sin(ax+b)) = a\cos(ax+b)$$

So,

$$\int \cos(ax+b)\, dx = \frac{1}{a}\sin(ax+b) + c \quad \text{for } a \neq 0.$$

Likewise we can show that

$$\int \sin(ax+b)\, dx = -\frac{1}{a}\cos(ax+b) + c \quad \text{for } a \neq 0.$$

Finally, $\dfrac{d}{dx}\left(\dfrac{1}{a}\ln(ax+b)\right) = \dfrac{1}{a}\left(\dfrac{a}{ax+b}\right) = \dfrac{1}{ax+b} \quad \text{for } ax+b > 0,\ a \neq 0$

$$\therefore \quad \int \frac{1}{ax+b}\, dx = \frac{1}{a}\ln(ax+b) + c \quad \text{for } ax+b > 0,\ a \neq 0$$

We can similarly show that $\displaystyle\int \frac{1}{ax+b}\, dx = \frac{1}{a}\ln(-(ax+b)) + c \quad \text{for } ax+b < 0,\ a \neq 0$

$$\therefore \quad \int \frac{1}{ax+b}\, dx = \frac{1}{a}\ln|ax+b| + c \quad \text{for } a \neq 0.$$

For a, b constants with $a \neq 0$, we have:

Function	Integral
e^{ax+b}	$\dfrac{1}{a}e^{ax+b} + c$
$(ax+b)^n,\ n \neq -1$	$\dfrac{1}{a}\dfrac{(ax+b)^{n+1}}{n+1} + c$
$\cos(ax+b)$	$\dfrac{1}{a}\sin(ax+b) + c$
$\sin(ax+b)$	$-\dfrac{1}{a}\cos(ax+b) + c$
$\dfrac{1}{ax+b}$	$\dfrac{1}{a}\ln|ax+b| + c$

Example 7   ◀ **Self Tutor**

Find: **a** $\int (2x+3)^4 \, dx$ **b** $\int \frac{1}{\sqrt{1-3x}} \, dx$

a $\int (2x+3)^4 \, dx = \frac{1}{2} \times \frac{(2x+3)^5}{5} + c$ **b** $\int \frac{1}{\sqrt{1-3x}} \, dx = \int (1-3x)^{-\frac{1}{2}} \, dx$

$\qquad = \frac{1}{10}(2x+3)^5 + c$

$\qquad\qquad\qquad = \frac{1}{-3} \times \frac{(1-3x)^{\frac{1}{2}}}{\frac{1}{2}} + c$

$\qquad\qquad\qquad = -\frac{2}{3}\sqrt{1-3x} + c$

EXERCISE 16D

1 Find:

a $\int (2x+5)^3 \, dx$ **b** $\int \frac{1}{(3-2x)^2} \, dx$ **c** $\int \frac{4}{(2x-1)^4} \, dx$

d $\int (4x-3)^7 \, dx$ **e** $\int \sqrt{3x-4} \, dx$ **f** $\int \frac{10}{\sqrt{1-5x}} \, dx$

g $\int 3(1-x)^4 \, dx$ **h** $\int \frac{4}{\sqrt{3-4x}} \, dx$ **i** $\int \frac{5}{(3x-2)^3} \, dx$

2 Find $y = f(x)$ given $\frac{dy}{dx} = \sqrt{2x-7}$ and that $f(8) = 11$.

3 The function $f(x)$ has gradient function $f'(x) = \frac{4}{\sqrt{1-x}}$, and the curve $y = f(x)$ passes through the point $(-3, -11)$.

Find the point on the graph of $y = f(x)$ with x-coordinate -8.

4 Find:

a $\int 3(2x-1)^2 \, dx$ **b** $\int (4x-5)^2 \, dx$ **c** $\int (1-3x)^3 \, dx$

d $\int (2-5x)^2 \, dx$ **e** $\int 4\sqrt{5-x} \, dx$ **f** $\int (7x+1)^4 \, dx$

5 Find an expression for y given that $\frac{dy}{dx} = x - \frac{5}{(1-x)^2}$ and that the curve passes through $(2, 0)$.

Example 8   ◀ **Self Tutor**

Integrate with respect to x:

a $2e^{2x} - e^{-3x}$ **b** $2\sin 3x + \cos(4x+\pi)$

a $\int (2e^{2x} - e^{-3x}) \, dx$ **b** $\int (2\sin 3x + \cos(4x+\pi)) \, dx$

$= 2(\frac{1}{2})e^{2x} - (\frac{1}{-3})e^{-3x} + c$ $= 2 \times -\frac{1}{3}\cos 3x + \frac{1}{4}\sin(4x+\pi) + c$

$= e^{2x} + \frac{1}{3}e^{-3x} + c$ $= -\frac{2}{3}\cos 3x + \frac{1}{4}\sin(4x+\pi) + c$

6 Integrate with respect to x:

    a $\sin 3x$

    b $2\cos(-4x) + 1$

    c $3\cos \frac{x}{2}$

    d $3\sin 2x - e^{-x}$

    e $2\sin\left(2x + \frac{\pi}{6}\right)$

    f $-3\cos\left(\frac{\pi}{4} - x\right)$

    g $\cos 2x + \sin 2x$

    h $2\sin 3x + 5\cos 4x$

    i $\frac{1}{2}\cos 8x - 3\sin x$

7 Find:

    a $\displaystyle\int (2e^x + 5e^{2x})\, dx$

    b $\displaystyle\int (3e^{5x-2})\, dx$

    c $\displaystyle\int (e^{7-3x})\, dx$

    d $\displaystyle\int (e^x + e^{-x})^2\, dx$

    e $\displaystyle\int (e^{-x} + 2)^2\, dx$

    f $\displaystyle\int \frac{(e^{2x} - 5)^2}{e^x}\, dx$

8 Find an expression for y given that $\dfrac{dy}{dx} = (1 - e^x)^2$, and that the graph has y-intercept 4.

9 Suppose $f'(x) = p\sin\frac{x}{2}$ where p is a constant. $f(0) = 1$ and $f(2\pi) = 0$. Find p and hence $f(x)$.

10 Consider a function g such that $g''(x) = -\sin 2x$.

    Show that the gradients of the tangents to $y = g(x)$ when $x = \pi$ and $x = -\pi$ are equal.

11 Find $f(x)$ given $f'(x) = 2e^{-2x}$ and $f(0) = 3$.

12 A curve has gradient function $\sqrt{x} + \frac{1}{2}e^{-4x}$ and passes through $(1, 0)$. Find the equation of the function.

13 Show that $(\sin x + \cos x)^2 = 1 + \sin 2x$, and hence determine $\displaystyle\int (\sin x + \cos x)^2\, dx$.

14   **a**   Rearrange the double angle formulae $\cos 2x = 1 - 2\sin^2 x$ and $\cos 2x = 2\cos^2 x - 1$ to write expressions for $\sin^2 x$ and $\cos^2 x$.

    b   Hence find:

        i $\displaystyle\int \sin^2 x\, dx$

        ii $\displaystyle\int \cos^2 x\, dx$

Example 9   ◀)) **Self Tutor**

Integrate $(2 - \sin x)^2$ with respect to x.

$\displaystyle\int (2 - \sin x)^2\, dx$

$= \displaystyle\int (4 - 4\sin x + \sin^2 x)\, dx$

$= \displaystyle\int \left(4 - 4\sin x + \frac{1}{2} - \frac{1}{2}\cos 2x\right) dx$

$= \displaystyle\int \left(\frac{9}{2} - 4\sin x - \frac{1}{2}\cos 2x\right) dx$

$= \frac{9}{2}x + 4\cos x - \frac{1}{2} \times \frac{1}{2}\sin 2x + c$

$= \frac{9}{2}x + 4\cos x - \frac{1}{4}\sin 2x + c$

> The identities
> $\cos^2\theta = \frac{1}{2} + \frac{1}{2}\cos 2\theta$
> $\sin^2\theta = \frac{1}{2} - \frac{1}{2}\cos 2\theta$
> are extremely useful!

15 Integrate with respect to x:

    a $\cos^2 x + 2$ **b** $\sin^2 x + 4x$ **c** $1 + \cos^2 2x$ **d** $3 - \sin^2 3x$

    e $\frac{1}{2}\cos^2 4x$ **f** $(1 + \cos x)^2$ **g** $\sin x(2\sin x - 1)$ **h** $(1 - 3\sin x)^2$

Example 10   ◀)) **Self Tutor**

Find:

    a $\displaystyle\int \frac{1}{5x - 3}\, dx$ **b** $\displaystyle\int \frac{4}{1 - 2x}\, dx$

    a $\displaystyle\int \frac{1}{5x - 3}\, dx$ **b** $\displaystyle\int \frac{4}{1 - 2x}\, dx$

       $= \frac{1}{5}\ln|5x - 3| + c$ $= 4\left(\frac{1}{-2}\right)\ln|1 - 2x| + c$

                                      $= -2\ln|1 - 2x| + c$

---

16 Find:

    a $\displaystyle\int \frac{6}{x + 4}\, dx$ **b** $\displaystyle\int \frac{1}{2x - 1}\, dx$ **c** $\displaystyle\int \frac{3}{1 - x}\, dx$

    d $\displaystyle\int \frac{5}{1 - 3x}\, dx$ **e** $\displaystyle\int \left(1 - 2x + \frac{4}{x - 3}\right) dx$ **f** $\displaystyle\int \left(4 + \frac{1}{5x - 2}\right) dx$

    g $\displaystyle\int \left(e^{-x} - \frac{4}{2x + 1}\right) dx$ **h** $\displaystyle\int \left(\frac{1}{x + 2} + \frac{2}{x - 3}\right) dx$ **i** $\displaystyle\int \left(\frac{5}{x - 6} - \frac{2}{3x - 1}\right) dx$

17 To find $\displaystyle\int \frac{1}{4x}\, dx$, Tracy's answer was $\displaystyle\int \frac{1}{4x}\, dx = \frac{1}{4}\ln|4x| + c$.

    Nadine's answer was $\displaystyle\int \frac{1}{4x}\, dx = \frac{1}{4}\int \frac{1}{x}\, dx = \frac{1}{4}\ln|x| + c$.

    Which of them has found the correct answer? Prove your statement.

18 Show that $\dfrac{3x - 1}{x + 2}$ may be written in the form $3 - \dfrac{7}{x + 2}$. Hence find $\displaystyle\int \frac{3x - 1}{x + 2}\, dx$.

19 Find $f(x)$ given $f'(x) = 2x - \dfrac{2}{1 - x}$ and $f(-1) = 3$.

E   INTEGRATION BY SUBSTITUTION

Consider the integral $\displaystyle\int (x^2 + 3x)^4 (2x + 3)\, dx$.

The function we are integrating is the product of two expressions:

- The first expression is $(x^2 + 3x)^4$, which has the form $f(u(x))$ where $f(u) = u^4$ and $u(x) = x^2 + 3x$.

- The second expression is $2x + 3$, and we notice that this is $\dfrac{du}{dx}$.

So, we can write the integral in the form $\displaystyle\int f(u(x)) \frac{du}{dx}\, dx$ where $f(u) = u^4$ and $u(x) = x^2 + 3x$.

Integrals in this form can be found using a method called **integration by substitution**.

Integration by substitution is the reverse process of differentiating using the **chain rule**.

Suppose $F(u)$ is the antiderivative of $f(u)$, so $\dfrac{dF}{du} = f(u)$

$$\therefore \quad \int f(u)\, du = F(u) + c \quad \dots (1)$$

But $\quad \dfrac{dF}{dx} = \dfrac{dF}{du} \dfrac{du}{dx} \qquad \{\text{chain rule}\}$

$$= f(u) \dfrac{du}{dx}$$

$$\therefore \quad \int f(u) \dfrac{du}{dx}\, dx = F(u) + c \quad \dots (2)$$

Comparing (1) and (2), we conclude that: $\quad \boxed{\displaystyle \int f(u) \dfrac{du}{dx}\, dx = \int f(u)\, du}$

Using this method,

$$\int (x^2 + 3x)^4 (2x + 3)\, dx$$

$$= \int u^4 \dfrac{du}{dx}\, dx \qquad \left\{ u = x^2 + 3x, \ \dfrac{du}{dx} = 2x + 3 \right\}$$

$$= \int u^4 \, du \qquad \left\{ \text{replacing } \dfrac{du}{dx}\, dx \text{ by } du \right\}$$

$$= \dfrac{u^5}{5} + c$$

$$= \tfrac{1}{5}(x^2 + 3x)^5 + c$$

> We use u in our solution, but we give our answer in terms of x, since the original integral was with respect to x.

Example 11   ◄)) Self Tutor

Use substitution to find:

a $\displaystyle \int \sqrt{x^3 + 2x}\,(3x^2 + 2)\, dx$

b $\displaystyle \int x e^{1 - x^2}\, dx$

---

a $\displaystyle \int \sqrt{x^3 + 2x}\,(3x^2 + 2)\, dx$

$$= \int \sqrt{u}\, \dfrac{du}{dx}\, dx \qquad \left\{ u = x^3 + 2x, \right.$$

$$= \int u^{\frac{1}{2}}\, du \qquad \left. \dfrac{du}{dx} = 3x^2 + 2 \right\}$$

$$= \dfrac{u^{\frac{3}{2}}}{\frac{3}{2}} + c$$

$$= \tfrac{2}{3}(x^3 + 2x)^{\frac{3}{2}} + c$$

b $\displaystyle \int x e^{1 - x^2}\, dx$

$$= -\tfrac{1}{2} \int (-2x) e^{1 - x^2}\, dx$$

$$= -\tfrac{1}{2} \int e^u \dfrac{du}{dx}\, dx \qquad \left\{ u = 1 - x^2, \right.$$

$$= -\tfrac{1}{2} \int e^u\, du \qquad \left. \dfrac{du}{dx} = -2x \right\}$$

$$= -\tfrac{1}{2} e^u + c$$

$$= -\tfrac{1}{2} e^{1 - x^2} + c$$

Example 12   ◀ **Self Tutor**

Integrate with respect to x:

a $\cos^3 x \sin x$

b $\dfrac{\cos x}{\sin x}$

a $\displaystyle\int \cos^3 x \sin x \, dx$

$= \displaystyle\int (\cos x)^3 \sin x \, dx$

$= \displaystyle\int u^3 \left(-\dfrac{du}{dx}\right) dx \qquad \{u = \cos x,$

$\qquad\qquad\qquad\qquad\qquad \dfrac{du}{dx} = -\sin x\}$

$= -\displaystyle\int u^3 \, du$

$= -\dfrac{u^4}{4} + c$

$= -\tfrac{1}{4}\cos^4 x + c$

b $\displaystyle\int \dfrac{\cos x}{\sin x} \, dx$

$= \displaystyle\int \dfrac{1}{u}\dfrac{du}{dx} \, dx \qquad \{u = \sin x,$

$\qquad\qquad\qquad\qquad \dfrac{du}{dx} = \cos x\}$

$= \displaystyle\int \dfrac{1}{u} \, du$

$= \ln|u| + c$

$= \ln|\sin x| + c$

The substitutions we make need to be chosen carefully.

For example, in **Example 12** part **b**, if we let $u = \cos x$, then $\dfrac{du}{dx} = -\sin x$ and we obtain

$\displaystyle\int \dfrac{\cos x}{\sin x} \, dx = \int \dfrac{u}{-\frac{du}{dx}} \, dx$. This is not in the correct form to apply our theorem, so we have made the

wrong substitution and we need to try another option.

EXERCISE 16E

1 Differentiate $(x^2 - x)^3$, and hence find $\displaystyle\int (2x - 1)(x^2 - x)^2 \, dx$.

2 Differentiate $\sin(x^2)$, and hence find $\displaystyle\int x \cos(x^2) \, dx$.

3 Differentiate $\ln(5 - 3x + x^2)$, and hence find $\displaystyle\int \dfrac{4x - 6}{5 - 3x + x^2} \, dx$.

4 Use the substitution given to perform each integration:

    a $\displaystyle\int 3x^2(x^3 + 1)^4 \, dx$ using $u = x^3 + 1$

    b $\displaystyle\int x^2 e^{x^3 + 1} \, dx$ using $u = x^3 + 1$

    c $\displaystyle\int \sin^4 x \cos x \, dx$ using $u = \sin x$

    d $\displaystyle\int 2x \cos(x^2 - 3) \, dx$ using $u = x^2 - 3$

5 Integrate by substitution:

    a $4x^3(2 + x^4)^3$

    b $\dfrac{2x}{\sqrt{x^2 + 3}}$

    c $\dfrac{6x^2}{(2x^3 - 1)^4}$

    d $(x^3 + 2x + 1)^4(3x^2 + 2)$

    e $\dfrac{x}{(1 - x^2)^5}$

    f $\dfrac{x + 2}{(x^2 + 4x - 3)^2}$

6 Find:

    a $\displaystyle\int -2e^{1 - 2x} \, dx$

    b $\displaystyle\int 2x e^{x^2} \, dx$

    c $\displaystyle\int \dfrac{e^{\sqrt{x}}}{\sqrt{x}} \, dx$

7 Find:

a $\displaystyle\int \frac{2x}{x^2+1}\,dx$

b $\displaystyle\int \frac{x}{2-x^2}\,dx$

c $\displaystyle\int \frac{2x-3}{x^2-3x}\,dx$

8 Integrate with respect to x:

a $x^2(3-x^3)^2$

b $x\sqrt{1-x^2}$

c xe^{1-x^2}

d $\dfrac{(\ln x)^3}{x}$

e $(2x-1)e^{x-x^2}$

f $\dfrac{1-x^2}{x^3-3x}$

9 Integrate with respect to x:

a $\sin^7 x \cos x$

b $\cos^5 x \sin x$

c $\dfrac{\sin x}{\sqrt{\cos x}}$

d $\tan x$

e $\sqrt{\sin x}\cos x$

f $\dfrac{\cos x}{(2+\sin x)^2}$

g $\dfrac{\sin x}{1-\cos x}$

h $\dfrac{\cos 2x}{\sin 2x-3}$

i $x\sin(x^2)$

10 Find:

a $\displaystyle\int \cos^3 x\,dx$

b $\displaystyle\int \sin^3 2x \cos 2x\,dx$

REVIEW SET 16A

1 Find the derivative of x^4-x^2, and hence find $\displaystyle\int (2x^3-x)\,dx$.

2 Find the derivative of $\sin\left(\frac{\pi}{3}-2x\right)$, and hence find $\displaystyle\int \cos\left(\frac{\pi}{3}-2x\right)dx$.

3 Find:

a $\displaystyle\int \left(\sqrt{x}-\frac{2}{x^2}\right)dx$

b $\displaystyle\int \left(2x-\frac{3}{\sqrt[3]{x}}\right)dx$

c $\displaystyle\int \frac{6x+5}{\sqrt{x}}\,dx$

4 Integrate with respect to x:

a $\dfrac{4}{\sqrt{x}}$

b $\frac{1}{3}x^3+2x$

c $\dfrac{1-2x}{x^3}$

5 Find:

a $\displaystyle\int (-3x^4+6x^2)\,dx$

b $\displaystyle\int \frac{3x^3-x^2-1}{x^2}\,dx$

c $\displaystyle\int (2x-\sqrt{x})^2\,dx$

d $\displaystyle\int \left(4e^x-\frac{3}{x}\right)dx$

e $\displaystyle\int \sin(4x-5)\,dx$

f $\displaystyle\int e^{4-3x}\,dx$

6 Find y if:

a $\dfrac{dy}{dx}=3e^{-x}-2\sin\left(\frac{\pi}{2}-x\right)$

b $\dfrac{dy}{dx}=\cos 4x-\frac{1}{2}x^2$

7 Given that $f'(x)=3x^2-4x+1$ and $f(0)=2$, find $f(x)$.

8 The curve $y = f(x)$ shown alongside has gradient function $f'(x) = ax + 3$.
Find the equation of the curve.

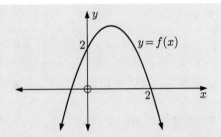

9 Given that $f'(x) = 3e^{2x}$ and $f(0) = 2$, find $f(x)$.

10 Find:

   a $\displaystyle\int \frac{x^2 - 7}{x}\,dx$ **b** $\displaystyle\int \left(e^{2x-3} - \frac{2}{3x-1}\right) dx$ **c** $\displaystyle\int \left((4 - 3x)^3 + \sin(-2x)\right) dx$

11 A curve has gradient function $f'(x) = a\cos 3x$ where a is a constant. $f(0) = -1$ and $f(\frac{\pi}{4}) = 1$. Find a and hence $f(x)$.

12 Find $\displaystyle\int (1 - \sin x)^2\,dx$ using the identity $\sin^2 x = \frac{1}{2} - \frac{1}{2}\cos 2x$.

13 Find the derivative of $\sqrt{x^2 - 4}$, and hence find $\displaystyle\int \frac{x}{\sqrt{x^2 - 4}}\,dx$.

14 Find $\displaystyle\int x\sin\left(x^2 + \frac{\pi}{3}\right) dx$ using $u = x^2 + \frac{\pi}{3}$.

15 Integrate by substitution:

   a $\displaystyle\int \frac{x + 2}{x^2 + 4x}\,dx$ **b** $\displaystyle\int 2xe^{x^2 - 1}\,dx$

   c $\displaystyle\int \sin^9 x \cos x\,dx$ **d** $\displaystyle\int \tan 2x\,dx$

REVIEW SET 16B

1 Find the derivative of $6e^{-2x}$, and hence find $\displaystyle\int e^{-2x}\,dx$.

2 Find the derivative of $\ln(2x + 1)$, and hence find $\displaystyle\int \frac{1}{2x+1}\,dx$.

3 Integrate with respect to x:

   a $\dfrac{x^2 - 2}{x^2}$ **b** $(3x - 4)^2$ **c** $4 - 2x^2$

4 Find:

   a $\displaystyle\int \left(x^{\frac{1}{3}} + 3\right) dx$ **b** $\displaystyle\int (3x^2 - 2)\,dx$ **c** $\displaystyle\int (3 + 2x)^2\,dx$

5 Given that $f'(x) = x^2 - 3x + 2$ and $f(1) = 3$, find $f(x)$.

6 Find y if:

   a $\dfrac{dy}{dx} = (x^2 - 1)^2$ **b** $\dfrac{dy}{dx} = 400 - 20x^{-\frac{1}{2}}$

7 Find:

a $\displaystyle\int (2x^3 - 5x + 7)\, dx$ **b** $\displaystyle\int \left(3x - \frac{1}{x}\right) dx$ **c** $\displaystyle\int (1 - x^2)^3\, dx$

d $\displaystyle\int (2e^{-x} + 3)\, dx$ **e** $\displaystyle\int 4\cos 2x\, dx$ **f** $\displaystyle\int (3 + e^{2x-1})^2\, dx$

8 Find $f(x)$ given $f'(x) = \dfrac{2}{x} - 1$ and $f(2) = e$.

9 A curve has gradient function $\dfrac{dy}{dx} = ax^2 + b\sqrt{x-1}$ where a, b are constants. Find the equation of the curve given that it contains the points $(1, 4)$, $(2, 4)$, and $(5, 1)$.

10 Find $f(x)$ given $f'(x) = \dfrac{3}{\sqrt{4 - 3x}}$ and $f(-4) = 0$.

11 Show that $(\sin x - \cos x)^2 = 1 - \sin 2x$, and hence determine $\displaystyle\int (\sin x - \cos x)^2\, dx$.

12 Find:

a $\displaystyle\int \frac{1}{3 - 2x}\, dx$ **b** $\displaystyle\int \frac{4}{5x + 1}\, dx$

13 By differentiating $(3x^2 + x)^3$, find $\displaystyle\int (3x^2 + x)^2 (6x + 1)\, dx$.

14 Integrate by substitution:

a $\displaystyle\int \frac{2x}{\sqrt{x^2 - 5}}\, dx$ **b** $\displaystyle\int \frac{\sin x}{\cos^4 x}\, dx$ **c** $\displaystyle\int 4x e^{-x^2}\, dx$ **d** $\displaystyle\int \sin^3 x\, dx$

15 Find $\displaystyle\int \frac{x}{x^2 - 9}\, dx$ using the substitution:

a $u = x^2 - 9$ **b** $x = 3\sin t$

Chapter 17

Definite integrals

OPENING PROBLEM

On August 8, the intensity of light entering a greenhouse is given by $I = 3\sin\frac{\pi t}{10}$ units per hour if the day is sunny, and $I = \sin\frac{\pi t}{10}$ units per hour if the day is overcast, where t is the number of hours after sunrise, $0 \leqslant t \leqslant 10$.

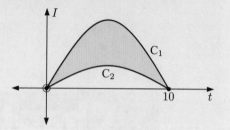

The graphs of these curves are shown alongside.

Things to think about:

a   Can you identify each curve?

b   Can you find the shaded area enclosed by C_1 and C_2 for $0 \leqslant t \leqslant 10$?

c   If the intensity of light is regarded as its rate of energy transfer, what does the area in b mean about the energy entering the greenhouse?

We have already seen how the Fundamental Theorem of Calculus gives meaning to a **definite integral** over a particular domain:

> For a continuous function $f(x)$ with antiderivative $F(x)$, $\displaystyle\int_a^b f(x)\,dx = F(b) - F(a)$.

In this Chapter we explore definite integrals and how they are used to calculate areas.

 ## DEFINITE INTEGRALS

The definite integral

$\displaystyle\int_a^b f(x)\,dx$ reads "the integral from $x = a$ to $x = b$ of $f(x)$ with respect to x"
or "the integral from a to b of $f(x)$ with respect to x".

When calculating definite integrals we can omit the constant of integration c as this will always cancel out in the subtraction process.

We write $F(b) - F(a)$ as $[F(x)]_a^b$, and so $\displaystyle\int_a^b f(x)\,dx = [F(x)]_a^b = F(b) - F(a)$.

For continuous functions, we can list the following properties of definite integrals:

- $\displaystyle\int_a^b f(x)\,dx = -\int_b^a f(x)\,dx$

- $\displaystyle\int_a^b k\,f(x)\,dx = k\int_a^b f(x)\,dx, \quad k$ is any constant

- $\displaystyle\int_a^b f(x)\,dx + \int_b^c f(x)\,dx = \int_a^c f(x)\,dx$

- $\displaystyle\int_a^b [f(x) + g(x)]\,dx = \int_a^b f(x)\,dx + \int_a^b g(x)\,dx$

Example 1 ◀) **Self Tutor**

Find:

a $\displaystyle\int_1^2 (x^3 - 4x + 5)\, dx$ **b** $\displaystyle\int_1^4 \left(2\sqrt{x} + \frac{3}{x}\right) dx$ **c** $\displaystyle\int_0^{\frac{\pi}{3}} \sin 2x\, dx$

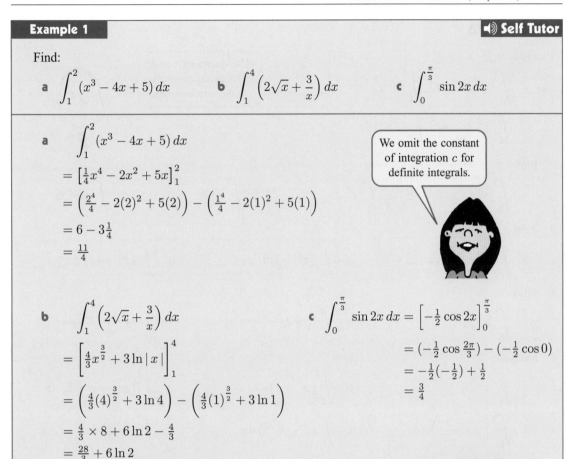

a $\displaystyle\int_1^2 (x^3 - 4x + 5)\, dx$

$= \left[\frac{1}{4}x^4 - 2x^2 + 5x\right]_1^2$

$= \left(\frac{2^4}{4} - 2(2)^2 + 5(2)\right) - \left(\frac{1^4}{4} - 2(1)^2 + 5(1)\right)$

$= 6 - 3\frac{1}{4}$

$= \frac{11}{4}$

> We omit the constant of integration c for definite integrals.

b $\displaystyle\int_1^4 \left(2\sqrt{x} + \frac{3}{x}\right) dx$

$= \left[\frac{4}{3}x^{\frac{3}{2}} + 3\ln|x|\right]_1^4$

$= \left(\frac{4}{3}(4)^{\frac{3}{2}} + 3\ln 4\right) - \left(\frac{4}{3}(1)^{\frac{3}{2}} + 3\ln 1\right)$

$= \frac{4}{3} \times 8 + 6\ln 2 - \frac{4}{3}$

$= \frac{28}{3} + 6\ln 2$

c $\displaystyle\int_0^{\frac{\pi}{3}} \sin 2x\, dx = \left[-\frac{1}{2}\cos 2x\right]_0^{\frac{\pi}{3}}$

$= \left(-\frac{1}{2}\cos\frac{2\pi}{3}\right) - \left(-\frac{1}{2}\cos 0\right)$

$= -\frac{1}{2}\left(-\frac{1}{2}\right) + \frac{1}{2}$

$= \frac{3}{4}$

Some definite integrals are difficult or even impossible to evaluate analytically. In these cases you are expected to use a graphics calculator to evaluate the integral.

GRAPHICS CALCULATOR INSTRUCTIONS

Example 2 ◀) **Self Tutor**

Evaluate $\displaystyle\int_2^5 xe^x\, dx$ correct to 4 significant figures.

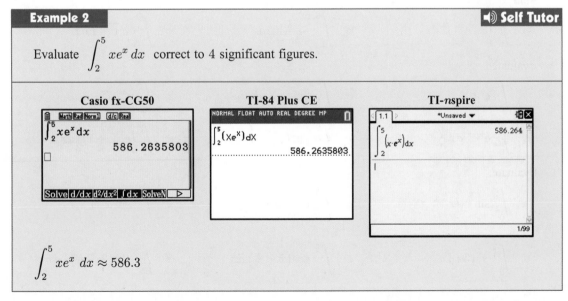

$\displaystyle\int_2^5 xe^x\, dx \approx 586.3$

EXERCISE 17A

1 Find:

a $\displaystyle\int_1^4 \sqrt{x}\,dx$ and $\displaystyle\int_1^4 (-\sqrt{x})\,dx$

b $\displaystyle\int_0^1 x^7\,dx$ and $\displaystyle\int_0^1 (-x^7)\,dx$

> Use questions **1** to **4** to check the properties of definite integrals.

2 Find:

a $\displaystyle\int_0^1 x^2\,dx$
b $\displaystyle\int_1^2 x^2\,dx$
c $\displaystyle\int_0^2 x^2\,dx$
d $\displaystyle\int_0^1 3x^2\,dx$

3 Find:

a $\displaystyle\int_0^2 (x^3 - 4x)\,dx$
b $\displaystyle\int_2^3 (x^3 - 4x)\,dx$
c $\displaystyle\int_0^3 (x^3 - 4x)\,dx$

4 Find:

a $\displaystyle\int_0^1 x^2\,dx$
b $\displaystyle\int_0^1 \sqrt{x}\,dx$
c $\displaystyle\int_0^1 (x^2 + \sqrt{x})\,dx$

5 Evaluate:

a $\displaystyle\int_0^1 x^3\,dx$
b $\displaystyle\int_0^2 (x^2 - x)\,dx$
c $\displaystyle\int_0^2 (3x^2 - x + 6)\,dx$

d $\displaystyle\int_1^4 \left(x - \frac{3}{\sqrt{x}}\right)dx$
e $\displaystyle\int_1^4 (x + 2\sqrt{x})\,dx$
f $\displaystyle\int_4^9 \frac{x-3}{\sqrt{x}}\,dx$

g $\displaystyle\int_1^3 \frac{1}{x^2}\,dx$
h $\displaystyle\int_1^2 (x+3)^2\,dx$
i $\displaystyle\int_1^4 \left(x^2 + \frac{1}{x}\right)dx$

6 Find m such that $\displaystyle\int_m^{2m} (2x - 1)\,dx = 4$.

7 Find:

a $\displaystyle\int_0^1 (3x + 1)^4\,dx$
b $\displaystyle\int_2^6 \frac{1}{\sqrt{2x - 3}}\,dx$
c $\displaystyle\int_{-3}^0 \sqrt{1 - x}\,dx$

8 Evaluate:

a $\displaystyle\int_0^1 e^x\,dx$
b $\displaystyle\int_0^3 (2e^x - 3)\,dx$
c $\displaystyle\int_0^2 e^{3x}\,dx$

d $\displaystyle\int_0^1 e^{1-x}\,dx$
e $\displaystyle\int_0^{\ln 4} e^x(e^x - 2)\,dx$
f $\displaystyle\int_1^2 (e^{-x} + 1)^2\,dx$

9 Evaluate:

a $\displaystyle\int_0^\pi \sin x\,dx$
b $\displaystyle\int_0^{\frac{\pi}{6}} \cos x\,dx$
c $\displaystyle\int_{\frac{\pi}{3}}^{\frac{\pi}{2}} \sin x\,dx$

d $\displaystyle\int_0^{\frac{\pi}{6}} \sin 3x\,dx$
e $\displaystyle\int_{\frac{\pi}{6}}^{\frac{\pi}{2}} \cos\left(x - \frac{\pi}{3}\right)dx$
f $\displaystyle\int_{\frac{\pi}{4}}^{\frac{\pi}{2}} \sin\left(2x - \frac{\pi}{4}\right)dx$

10 Use the identity $\cos^2 x = \frac{1}{2} + \frac{1}{2}\cos 2x$ to evaluate $\displaystyle\int_0^{\frac{\pi}{4}} \cos^2 x \, dx$.

11 Use the identity $\sin^2 x = \frac{1}{2} - \frac{1}{2}\cos 2x$ to evaluate $\displaystyle\int_0^{\frac{\pi}{2}} \sin^2 x \, dx$.

12 Evaluate: $\displaystyle\int_0^{\frac{\pi}{6}} (\sin 3x - \cos x) \, dx$

13 Write $\displaystyle\int_3^{12} \frac{1}{x} \, dx$ as a single logarithm.

14 Find:

  a $\displaystyle\int_{-6}^{-2} \frac{1}{x} \, dx$
  b $\displaystyle\int_{-1}^{5} \frac{1}{x+4} \, dx$
  c $\displaystyle\int_1^8 \frac{2}{3x+4} \, dx$
  d $\displaystyle\int_{-4}^0 \frac{4}{5-2x} \, dx$

15 Find m such that $\displaystyle\int_m^{-2} \frac{1}{4-x} \, dx = \ln\left(\frac{3}{2}\right)$.

16 Show that $\dfrac{4x+1}{x-1}$ may be written in the form $4 + \dfrac{5}{x-1}$.

  Hence show that $\displaystyle\int_3^5 \frac{4x+1}{x-1} \, dx = 8 + 5\ln 2$.

17 Evaluate using technology:

  a $\displaystyle\int_1^3 \ln x \, dx$
  b $\displaystyle\int_{-1}^1 e^{-x^2} \, dx$
  c $\displaystyle\int_{\frac{\pi}{4}}^{\frac{\pi}{6}} \sin(\sqrt{x}) \, dx$

18 Use the Fundamental Theorem of Calculus to prove that for continuous functions:

  a $\displaystyle\int_a^b f(x) \, dx = -\int_b^a f(x) \, dx$
  b $\displaystyle\int_a^b k \, f(x) \, dx = k \int_a^b f(x) \, dx, \quad k$ is any constant

  c $\displaystyle\int_a^b f(x) \, dx + \int_b^c f(x) \, dx = \int_a^c f(x) \, dx$

  d $\displaystyle\int_a^b [f(x) + g(x)] \, dx = \int_a^b f(x) \, dx + \int_a^b g(x) \, dx$

19 Write as a single integral:

  a $\displaystyle\int_2^4 f(x) \, dx + \int_4^7 f(x) \, dx$
  b $\displaystyle\int_4^5 f(x) \, dx - \int_6^5 f(x) \, dx$

  c $\displaystyle\int_1^3 g(x) \, dx + \int_3^8 g(x) \, dx + \int_8^9 g(x) \, dx$

20 **a** If $\displaystyle\int_1^3 f(x) \, dx = 2$ and $\displaystyle\int_1^6 f(x) \, dx = -3$, find $\displaystyle\int_3^6 f(x) \, dx$.

  b If $\displaystyle\int_0^2 f(x) \, dx = 5$, $\displaystyle\int_4^6 f(x) \, dx = -2$, and $\displaystyle\int_0^6 f(x) \, dx = 7$, find $\displaystyle\int_2^4 f(x) \, dx$.

21 Suppose $\displaystyle\int_{-1}^{1} f(x)\,dx = -4$. Determine the value of:

    a $\displaystyle\int_{1}^{-1} f(x)\,dx$
        b $\displaystyle\int_{-1}^{1} (2 + f(x))\,dx$
        c $\displaystyle\int_{-1}^{1} 2f(x)\,dx$

    d k such that $\displaystyle\int_{-1}^{1} kf(x)\,dx = 7$

22 If $g(2) = 4$ and $g(3) = 5$, calculate $\displaystyle\int_{2}^{3} (g'(x) - 1)\,dx$.

23   **a** Find $\displaystyle\int 2x(x^2 - 1)^3\,dx$ using an appropriate substitution.

    b *Hence* find $\displaystyle\int_{1}^{2} 2x(x^2 - 1)^3\,dx$.

24   **a** Find $\displaystyle\int xe^{-2x^2}\,dx$ using an appropriate substitution.

    b *Hence* find $\displaystyle\int_{1}^{2} xe^{-2x^2}\,dx$.

25   **a** Find $\displaystyle\int \frac{x}{2 - x^2}\,dx$ using an appropriate substitution.

    b *Hence* find $\displaystyle\int_{2}^{3} \frac{x}{2 - x^2}\,dx$.

26   **a** Find $\displaystyle\int \frac{x}{(x^2 + 2)^2}\,dx$ using an appropriate substitution.

    b *Hence* find $\displaystyle\int_{1}^{2} \frac{x}{(x^2 + 2)^2}\,dx$.

27   **a** Find $\displaystyle\int \sin^2 x \cos x\,dx$ using an appropriate substitution.

    b *Hence* find $\displaystyle\int_{0}^{\frac{\pi}{6}} \sin^2 x \cos x\,dx$.

B   THE AREA UNDER A CURVE

We have already established in **Chapter 15** that:

If $f(x)$ is positive and continuous on the interval $a \leqslant x \leqslant b$, then the area bounded by $y = f(x)$, the x-axis, and the vertical lines $x = a$ and $x = b$

is given by $\displaystyle A = \int_{a}^{b} f(x)\,dx$ or $\displaystyle\int_{a}^{b} y\,dx$.

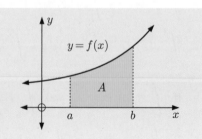

Example 3 ◀) **Self Tutor**

Find the area of the region enclosed by $y = 2x$, the x-axis, $x = 0$, and $x = 4$ using:

a a geometric argument **b** integration.

a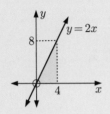

$$\text{Area} = \tfrac{1}{2} \times 4 \times 8$$
$$= 16 \text{ units}^2$$

b $\text{Area} = \displaystyle\int_0^4 2x\, dx$

$$= \left[x^2\right]_0^4$$
$$= 4^2 - 0^2$$
$$= 16 \text{ units}^2$$

Example 4 ◀) **Self Tutor**

Find the area of the region enclosed by $y = x^2 + 1$, the x-axis, $x = 1$, and $x = 2$.

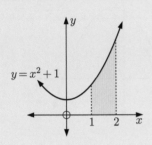

$$\text{Area} = \int_1^2 (x^2 + 1)\, dx$$
$$= \left[\frac{x^3}{3} + x\right]_1^2$$
$$= \left(\tfrac{8}{3} + 2\right) - \left(\tfrac{1}{3} + 1\right)$$
$$= 3\tfrac{1}{3} \text{ units}^2$$

It is helpful to sketch the region.

We can check this result using technology.

 GRAPHING PACKAGE

 GRAPHICS CALCULATOR INSTRUCTIONS

EXERCISE 17B

1 Find the shaded area using:
  a a geometric argument
  b integration.

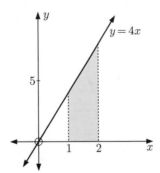

2 Find the area of each region described below using:

  i a geometric argument **ii** integration

  a the region enclosed by $y = 5$, the x-axis, $x = -6$, and $x = 0$
  b the region enclosed by $y = x$, the x-axis, $x = 4$, and $x = 5$
  c the region enclosed by $y = -3x$, the x-axis, $x = -3$, and $x = 0$.

3 Find the exact area of:

    a the blue shaded region

    b the yellow shaded region.

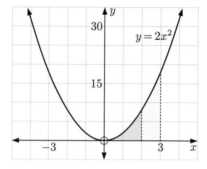

4 Find the area of the region bounded by:

    a $y = x^2$, the x-axis, and $x = 1$

    b $y = x^3$, the x-axis, $x = 1$, and $x = 4$

    c $y = \frac{1}{2}x^2 - 1$, the x-axis, $x = 2$, and $x = 3$.

5 The graph of $y = -x^2 + x + 6$ is shown alongside.

    a Find the coordinates of A and B.

    b Hence find the shaded area.

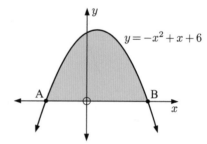

6 Find the area enclosed by each curve and the x-axis:

    a $y = -x^2 + 7x - 10$ **b** $y = -2x^2 + 2x + 4$ **c** $y = 3 - x^2$

Example 5   **◄))** Self Tutor

Find the area enclosed by one arch of the curve $y = \sin 2x$ and the x-axis.

The period of $y = \sin 2x$ is $\frac{2\pi}{2} = \pi$, so the first positive x-intercept is $\frac{\pi}{2}$.

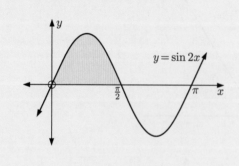

The required area $= \displaystyle\int_0^{\frac{\pi}{2}} \sin 2x \, dx$

$= \left[\frac{1}{2}(-\cos 2x) \right]_0^{\frac{\pi}{2}}$

$= -\frac{1}{2} \left[\cos 2x \right]_0^{\frac{\pi}{2}}$

$= -\frac{1}{2}(\cos \pi - \cos 0)$

$= 1 \text{ unit}^2$

---

7 Show that the area enclosed by $y = \sin x$ and the x-axis from $x = 0$ to $x = \pi$ is 2 units^2.

8 Find the area of the region bounded by $y = \cos x$, the x-axis, $x = 0$, and $x = \frac{\pi}{2}$.

9 Find the area enclosed by one arch of the curve $y = \cos 3x$ and the x-axis.

10

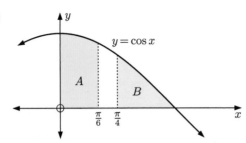

a Which of the shaded regions appears to be larger?

b Calculate the area of each region, and check your answer to **a**.

11 The graph alongside shows $y = \tan x$ for $-\frac{\pi}{2} < x < \frac{\pi}{2}$.

A is the point on the graph with y-coordinate 1.

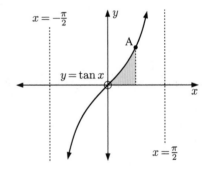

a Find the x-coordinate of A.

b Find $\int \tan x \, dx$.

c Hence find the shaded area.

12 Find the area of the region bounded by:

a $y = \dfrac{1}{x^2}$, the x-axis, $x = 1$, and $x = 2$

b $y = e^x$, the axes, and $x = 1$

c $y = 2 - \dfrac{1}{\sqrt{x}}$, the x-axis, and $x = 4$

d the axes and $y = \sqrt{9 - x}$

e $y = e^x + e^{-x}$, the x-axis, $x = -1$, and $x = 1$.

13 **a** Show that $\dfrac{d}{dx}\left(\dfrac{\sin x}{1 + \cos x}\right) = \dfrac{1}{1 + \cos x}$.

b Hence find the area of the region bounded by $y = \dfrac{1}{1 + \cos x}$, the x-axis, $x = 0$, and $x = 2$.

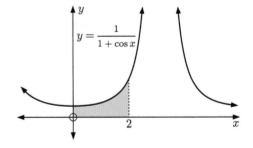

14 **a** Find b, correct to 4 decimal places.

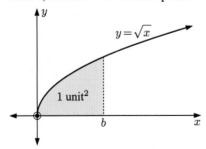

b Find the exact value of a.

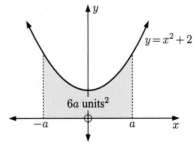

c Find k, correct to 4 decimal places.

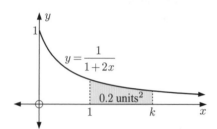

d Find k such that area A and area B are equal.

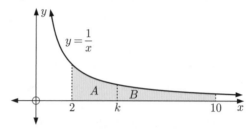

INVESTIGATION $\displaystyle\int_a^b f(x)\,dx$ AND AREAS

Can $\displaystyle\int_a^b f(x)\,dx$ always be interpreted as an area?

What to do:

1 **a** Find $\displaystyle\int_0^1 x^3\,dx$ and $\displaystyle\int_{-1}^1 x^3\,dx$.

b Using a graph, explain why the first integral in **a** gives an area, whereas the second integral does not.

c Find $\displaystyle\int_{-1}^0 x^3\,dx$ and explain why the answer is negative.

d Show that $\displaystyle\int_{-1}^0 x^3\,dx + \int_0^1 x^3\,dx = \int_{-1}^1 x^3\,dx$.

e Find $\displaystyle\int_0^{-1} x^3\,dx$ and interpret its meaning.

2 Suppose $f(x)$ is a function such that $f(x) \leqslant 0$ for all $a \leqslant x \leqslant b$. Write an expression for the area between the function and the x-axis for $a \leqslant x \leqslant b$.

3 Evaluate using area interpretation:

a $\displaystyle\int_0^3 f(x)\,dx$

b $\displaystyle\int_3^7 f(x)\,dx$

c $\displaystyle\int_2^4 f(x)\,dx$

d $\displaystyle\int_0^7 f(x)\,dx$

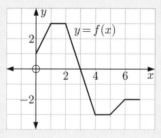

4 Evaluate using area interpretation:

a $\displaystyle\int_0^4 f(x)\,dx$

b $\displaystyle\int_4^6 f(x)\,dx$

c $\displaystyle\int_6^8 f(x)\,dx$

d $\displaystyle\int_0^8 f(x)\,dx$

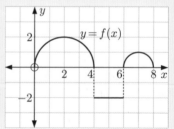

C | THE AREA ABOVE A CURVE

If $f(x)$ is negative and continuous on the interval $a \leqslant x \leqslant b$, then the area bounded by $y = f(x)$, the x-axis, and the vertical lines $x = a$ and $x = b$ is given by

$$A = -\int_a^b f(x)\,dx \quad \text{or} \quad -\int_a^b y\,dx.$$

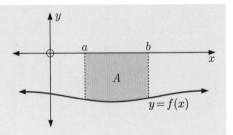

Proof:

The reflection of $y = f(x)$ in the x-axis is $y = -f(x)$.

By symmetry, $-f(x) \geqslant 0$ on the interval $a \leqslant x \leqslant b$, and the area bounded by $y = -f(x)$, the x-axis, $x = a$, and $x = b$ is also A.

$$\therefore \quad A = \int_a^b [-f(x)]\,dx$$

$$= -\int_a^b f(x)\,dx$$

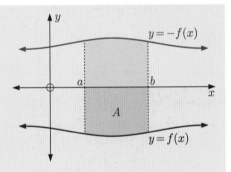

Example 6 | ◄♪ Self Tutor

Find the area bounded by the x-axis and $y = x^2 - 2x$.

The curve cuts the x-axis when $y = 0$

$\therefore \quad x^2 - 2x = 0$

$\therefore \quad x(x - 2) = 0$

$\qquad \therefore \quad x = 0$ or 2

$\therefore$ the x-intercepts are 0 and 2.

$$\text{Area} = -\int_0^2 (x^2 - 2x)\,dx$$

$$= -\left[\frac{x^3}{3} - x^2\right]_0^2$$

$$= -\left[\left(\tfrac{8}{3} - 4\right) - (0)\right] = \tfrac{4}{3}$$

$\therefore$ the area is $\frac{4}{3}$ units^2.

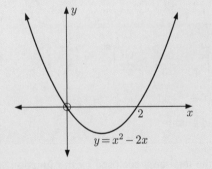

EXERCISE 17C

1 Find the shaded area:

a

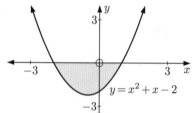

$y = x^2 + x - 2$

b

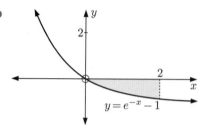

$y = e^{-x} - 1$

c

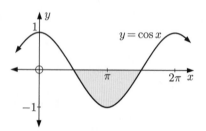

$y = \cos x$

d

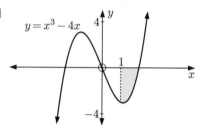

$y = x^3 - 4x$

Example 7   ◄)) **Self Tutor**

Find the total area of the regions contained by $y = f(x)$ and the x-axis for $f(x) = x^3 + 2x^2 - 3x$.

$f(x) = x^3 + 2x^2 - 3x$
$\quad = x(x^2 + 2x - 3)$
$\quad = x(x - 1)(x + 3)$

$\therefore \ y = f(x)$ cuts the x-axis at 0, 1, and -3.

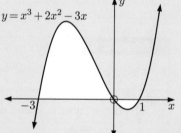

$y = x^3 + 2x^2 - 3x$

Total area

$= \displaystyle\int_{-3}^{0} (x^3 + 2x^2 - 3x)\,dx - \int_{0}^{1} (x^3 + 2x^2 - 3x)\,dx$

$= \left[\dfrac{x^4}{4} + \dfrac{2x^3}{3} - \dfrac{3x^2}{2}\right]_{-3}^{0} - \left[\dfrac{x^4}{4} + \dfrac{2x^3}{3} - \dfrac{3x^2}{2}\right]_{0}^{1}$

$= \left(0 - (-11\tfrac{1}{4})\right) - \left(-\tfrac{7}{12} - 0\right)$

$= 11\tfrac{5}{6}$ units^2

Graphing the function helps us see where it is above and below the x-axis.

---

2 Find the total area enclosed by the function $y = f(x)$ and the x-axis for:

a $f(x) = x^3 - 9x$ **b** $f(x) = -x(x - 2)(x - 4)$ **c** $f(x) = x^4 - 5x^2 + 4$.

3 a Explain why the total area shaded is *not* equal to

$\displaystyle\int_{1}^{7} f(x)\,dx.$

b Write an expression for the total shaded area in terms of integrals.

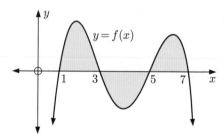

$y = f(x)$

4

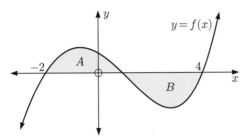

For the graph of $y = f(x)$ alongside,

$\displaystyle\int_{-2}^{4} f(x)\,dx = -6$. Which region is larger,

A or B? Explain your answer.

5 The area of the region bounded by $f(x) = -\dfrac{9}{x}$, the x-axis, $x = 3$, and $x = k$, is $9\ln 2$ units^2. Find the value of k.

6 **a** Sketch the graph of $y = 2\sin x + 1$ for $0 \leqslant x \leqslant 2\pi$.

    b Find the area between the x-axis and the part of $y = 2\sin x + 1$ that is below the x-axis on $0 \leqslant x \leqslant 2\pi$.

7

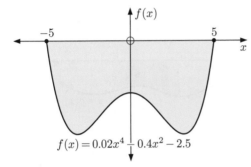

The cross-section of a roof gutter is defined by $f(x) = 0.02x^4 - 0.4x^2 - 2.5$, for $-5 \leqslant x \leqslant 5$ cm.

    a Find the cross-sectional area of the gutter.

    b The gutter is 20 m long. How much water can it hold in total?

8 **a** Find $\displaystyle\int x^2 \cos(x^3)\,dx$.

    b Show that the red shaded region is twice as large as the blue shaded region.

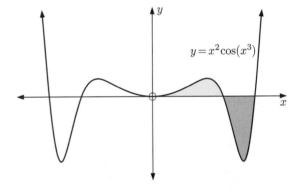

D   THE AREA BETWEEN TWO FUNCTIONS

Consider two functions $f(x)$ and $g(x)$ where $f(x) \geqslant g(x)$ for all $a \leqslant x \leqslant b$.

The area between the two functions on the interval $a \leqslant x \leqslant b$ is given by

$$A = \int_a^b [f(x) - g(x)]\,dx.$$

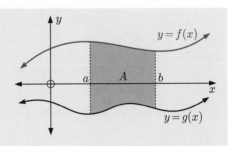

Proof:

If necessary, we translate each curve k units upwards until they are both above the x-axis on the interval $a \leqslant x \leqslant b$.

$\therefore \ A = (\text{area below } y = f(x) + k) - (\text{area below } y = g(x) + k)$

$$= \int_a^b [f(x) + k]\,dx - \int_a^b [g(x) + k]\,dx$$

$$= \int_a^b [f(x) - g(x)]\,dx$$

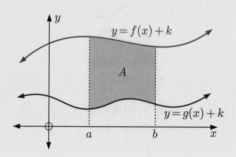

Notice that if $y = g(x)$ is negative on the interval $a \leqslant x \leqslant b$, we can let $f(x) = 0$ and hence derive the formula we saw in the last Section:

$$A = -\int_a^b g(x)\,dx$$

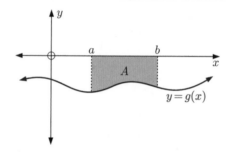

Example 8   ◀)) **Self Tutor**

Find the area of the region enclosed by $y = x + 2$ and $y = x^2 + x - 2$.

$y = x + 2$ meets $y = x^2 + x - 2$ where $x^2 + x - 2 = x + 2$

$$\therefore \ x^2 - 4 = 0$$
$$\therefore \ (x+2)(x-2) = 0$$
$$\therefore \ x = \pm 2$$

Since $x + 2 \geqslant x^2 + x - 2$ on the interval $-2 \leqslant x \leqslant 2$,

$$\text{area} = \int_{-2}^{2} [(x+2) - (x^2 + x - 2)]\,dx$$

$$= \int_{-2}^{2} (4 - x^2)\,dx$$

$$= \left[4x - \frac{x^3}{3} \right]_{-2}^{2}$$

$$= \left(8 - \tfrac{8}{3} \right) - \left(-8 + \tfrac{8}{3} \right)$$

$$= 10\tfrac{2}{3} \text{ units}^2$$

$\therefore$ the area is $10\tfrac{2}{3}$ units^2.

EXERCISE 17D

1 **a** Sketch the graphs of $y = x - 3$ and $y = x^2 - 3x$ on the same set of axes.

  b Find the coordinates of the points where the graphs meet.

  c Find the area of the region enclosed by the two graphs.

2 Find the area of the region enclosed by:

  a $y = x^2 - 2x$ and $y = 3$

  b $y = \sqrt{x}$ and $y = x^2$.

3 Find the area of the region bounded by $y = 2e^x$, $y = e^{2x}$, and $x = 0$.

4 On the same set of axes, sketch $y = 2x$ and $y = 4x^2$.
Find the area of the region enclosed by these functions.

5 The graphs of $y = \dfrac{5}{2x + 1}$ and $y = 3 - x$ are shown alongside.

  a Find the coordinates of A and B.

  b Find the exact value of the shaded area.

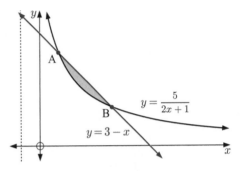

6 The shaded area is 2.4 units^2.
Find k, correct to 4 decimal places.

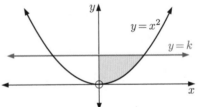

7 A region with $x \geqslant 0$ has boundaries defined by $y = \sin x$, $y = \cos x$, and the y-axis.
Sketch the region and find its area.

8 The illustrated curves are the graphs of $y = \sin x$ and $y = 4\sin x$.

  a Identify each curve.

  b Calculate the shaded area.

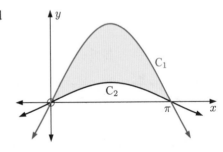

9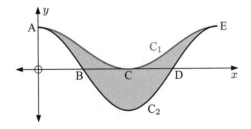

The illustrated curves are $y = \cos 2x$ and $y = \cos^2 x$.

  a Identify each curve.

  b Determine the coordinates of A, B, C, D, and E.

  c Show that the shaded area is $\frac{\pi}{2}$ units^2.

10 **a** On the same set of axes, graph $y = e^x - 1$ and $y = 2 - 2e^{-x}$. Show all axes intercepts and asymptotes.

    b Find the points of intersection of $y = e^x - 1$ and $y = 2 - 2e^{-x}$.

    c Find the area of the region enclosed by the two curves.

Example 9   ◀)) **Self Tutor**

Find the total area of the regions enclosed by $y = x^3 - 6x + 3$ and $y = x^2 + 3$.

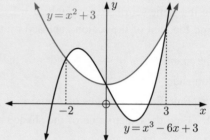

$y = x^3 - 6x + 3$ and $y = x^2 + 3$ meet where

$$x^3 - 6x + 3 = x^2 + 3$$
$$\therefore \ x^3 - x^2 - 6x = 0$$
$$\therefore \ x(x^2 - x - 6) = 0$$
$$\therefore \ x(x + 2)(x - 3) = 0$$
$$\therefore \ \ x = 0, \ -2, \ \text{or} \ 3$$

$$\text{Total area} = \int_{-2}^{0} ((x^3 - 6x + 3) - (x^2 + 3)) \, dx + \int_{0}^{3} ((x^2 + 3) - (x^3 - 6x + 3)) \, dx$$

$$= \int_{-2}^{0} (x^3 - x^2 - 6x) \, dx + \int_{0}^{3} (-x^3 + x^2 + 6x) \, dx$$

$$= \left[\frac{x^4}{4} - \frac{x^3}{3} - 3x^2 \right]_{-2}^{0} + \left[-\frac{x^4}{4} + \frac{x^3}{3} + 3x^2 \right]_{0}^{3}$$

$$= \left(0 - \frac{16}{4} + \frac{-8}{3} + 12 \right) + \left(-\frac{81}{4} + \frac{27}{3} + 27 - 0 \right)$$

$$= 21\tfrac{1}{12} \ \text{units}^2$$

11

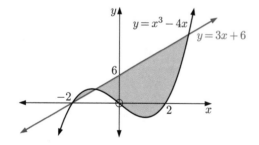

a Write the shaded area as the sum of two definite integrals.

b Find the total shaded area.

12 **a** Sketch the graphs of $y = x^3 - 5x$ and $y = 2x^2 - 6$ on the same set of axes.

    b Find the x-coordinates of their intersection points.

    c Hence find the area enclosed by $y = x^3 - 5x$ and $y = 2x^2 - 6$.

13 Find the area enclosed by:

    a $y = -x^3 + 3x^2 + 6x - 8$ and $y = 5x - 5$

    b $y = 2x^3 - 3x^2 + 18$ and $y = x^3 + 10x - 6$.

14 The illustrated curves are those of $y = \sin x$ and $y = \sin 2x$.

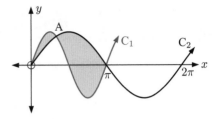

  a Identify each curve.

  b Find algebraically the coordinates of A.

  c Find the total area enclosed by C_1 and C_2 for $0 \leqslant x \leqslant \pi$.

ACTIVITY 1   **CALCULATING AREAS USING TECHNOLOGY**

We have seen many instances where we have had to add several areas together in order to find the total area between a function and the x-axis, or the total area between two functions.

For example:

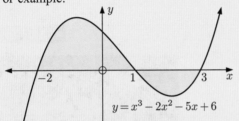

or

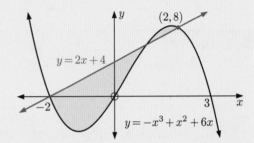

This has required us to find every point of intersection, and take care as to whether we are adding or subtracting a particular integral.

If we are using technology, we can save some work by using an absolute value function as seen in **Chapter 3**.

What to do:

1 **a** Copy the graph of $y = x^3 - 2x^2 - 5x + 6$, and on the same set of axes, plot $y = \left| x^3 - 2x^2 - 5x + 6 \right|$.

  b Explain why the total area enclosed between $y = x^3 - 2x^2 - 5x + 6$ and the x-axis is equal to $\displaystyle\int_{-2}^{3} \left| x^3 - 2x^2 - 5x + 6 \right| \, dx$.

  c Calculate this area using technology.

GRAPHICS
CALCULATOR
INSTRUCTIONS

2 Consider the total area enclosed between $y = -x^3 + x^2 + 6x$ and $y = 2x + 4$ on the interval $-2 \leqslant x \leqslant 2$.

  a Explain why the total area is equal to
  $$\int_{-2}^{2} \left| (-x^3 + x^2 + 6x) - (2x + 4) \right| \, dx = \int_{-2}^{2} \left| -x^3 + x^2 + 4x - 4 \right| \, dx$$

  b Calculate this area using technology.

3 Explain why the area between the functions $f(x)$ and $g(x)$ on the interval $a \leqslant x \leqslant b$ is
  $$A = \int_{a}^{b} \left| f(x) - g(x) \right| \, dx.$$

Use this formula to check your answers to some of the questions in the previous Exercise.

E   PROBLEM SOLVING BY INTEGRATION

When we studied differential calculus, we saw how to find the rate of change of a function by differentiation.

Since integration is the reverse process of differentiation, integration can be used to measure the change in a quantity from its rate of change.

When we introduced integration, we separated the area under a curve into rectangles. The area of each rectangle is the rate of change of the quantity times the subinterval width, which tells us the change in the quantity corresponding to that subinterval.

So, the area under a rate function for a particular interval tells us the overall change in the quantity over that interval.

Example 10   ◀)) **Self Tutor**

The rate of power consumption by the city of Bristol can be modelled by the function

$$E(t) = 0.3 \sin\left(\frac{(t-10)\pi}{12}\right) + 0.1 \cos\left(\frac{(t-6)\pi}{6}\right) + 0.775 \text{ GW}$$

where t is the number of hours after midnight each day, $0 \leqslant t \leqslant 24$.

Find the following quantities and explain what they represent:

a $\displaystyle\int_0^{12} E(t)\,dt$ **b** $\displaystyle\int_{12}^{24} E(t)\,dt$ **c** $\displaystyle\int_0^{24} E(t)\,dt$

lpgphotos/Shutterstock.com

$$E(t) = 0.3 \sin\left(\frac{(t-10)\pi}{12}\right) + 0.1 \cos\left(\frac{(t-6)\pi}{6}\right) + 0.775 \text{ GW}$$

$$\therefore \int E(t)\,dt = 0.3\left(-\cos\left(\frac{(t-10)\pi}{12}\right)\right)\left(\frac{12}{\pi}\right) + 0.1 \sin\left(\frac{(t-6)\pi}{6}\right)\left(\frac{6}{\pi}\right) + 0.775t + c$$

$$= -\frac{3.6}{\pi}\cos\left(\frac{(t-10)\pi}{12}\right) + \frac{0.6}{\pi}\sin\left(\frac{(t-6)\pi}{6}\right) + 0.775t + c$$

a $\displaystyle\int_0^{12} E(t)\,dt = \left(-\frac{3.6}{\pi}\cos\frac{\pi}{6} + \frac{0.6}{\pi}\cancel{\sin\pi} + 9.3\right) - \left(-\frac{3.6}{\pi}\cos\left(-\frac{5\pi}{6}\right) + \frac{0.6}{\pi}\cancel{\sin(-\pi)} + \cancel{0}\right)$

≈ 7.315 GWh

The morning power consumption of Bristol is about 7.32 GWh.

b $\displaystyle\int_{12}^{24} E(t)\,dt = \left(-\frac{3.6}{\pi}\cos\frac{7\pi}{6} + \frac{0.6}{\pi}\cancel{\sin 3\pi} + 18.6\right) - \left(-\frac{3.6}{\pi}\cos\frac{\pi}{6} + \frac{0.6}{\pi}\cancel{\sin\pi} + 9.3\right)$

≈ 11.285 GWh

The afternoon power consumption of Bristol is about 11.29 GWh.

c $\displaystyle\int_0^{24} E(t)\,dt = \int_0^{12} E(t)\,dt + \int_{12}^{24} E(t)\,dt \approx 18.6$ GWh

The total daily power consumption of Bristol is about 18.6 GWh.

EXERCISE 17E

1 The rate of traffic flow past a pedestrian crossing between 8 am and 8:30 am is given by

$$R(t) = \frac{t^3}{80} - \frac{t^2}{2} + 4t + 40 \text{ cars per minute,}$$

where t is the number of minutes after 8 am, $0 \leqslant t \leqslant 30$.

The graph of $R(t)$ against t is shown alongside.

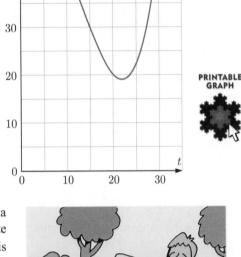

a Find the rate of traffic flow at 8:20 am.

b Use the graph to estimate the time at which the traffic flow was greatest.

c Copy the graph, and shade the region corresponding to $\displaystyle\int_{10}^{15} R(t)\, dt$. Explain what this region represents.

d How many cars passed the crossing between 8 am and 8:30 am?

2 Evan is happily paddling until his kayak strikes a sharp rock. Water begins to leak in at the rate $R_1(t) = 5 - 5e^{-0.2t}$ litres per minute, where t is the time in minutes. Evan tries to bail the water out of the kayak, removing the water at the rate $R_2(t) = 6 - 6e^{-0.1t}$ litres per minute.

a After 2 minutes, at what rate is water:

  i leaking into the kayak

  ii being bailed from the kayak?

b Is the amount of water in the kayak increasing or decreasing after 2 minutes? Explain your answer.

c Evaluate the following integrals, and interpret their meaning:

  i $\displaystyle\int_0^3 R_1(t)\, dt$
    ii $\displaystyle\int_2^5 R_2(t)\, dt$
    iii $\displaystyle\int_0^8 [R_1(t) - R_2(t)]\, dt$

d How much water is in the kayak after 10 minutes?

3 Answer the **Opening Problem** on page **400**.

4 The rate of power consumption of the United Kingdom can be modelled by the function

$$E(t) = 13\sin\left(\frac{(t+3)\pi}{3}\right) + 70\cos\left(\frac{(t-1)\pi}{6}\right) + 196 \text{ TWh per month}$$

where t is the number of months after January 1st, $0 \leqslant t \leqslant 12$.

a Use technology to help sketch the function.

b Find the following quantities and explain what they represent:

  i $\displaystyle\int_3^4 E(t)\, dt$
    ii $\displaystyle\int_5^8 E(t)\, dt$
    iii $\displaystyle\int_0^{12} E(t)\, dt$

ACTIVITY 2   BUFFON'S NEEDLE PROBLEM

The French naturalist and mathematician **Georges-Louis Leclerc, Comte de Buffon** (1707 - 1788) is best known for his challenges to previously held views of natural history. While ultimately incorrect, they gave spark to new and better models from those who followed.

For example, he proposed that the planets were formed from the collision of a comet with the Sun, and thus estimated the planets must be around 70 000 years old.

He also decided that given the correct conditions, life could be spontaneously created. However, he thought that even large animals could be instantly created.

In mathematics, Buffon was the first person to apply ideas in calculus to probability.

Buffon's needle problem is named after him:

> *Given a series of parallel planks w units apart, what is the probability that a needle of length l units, when tossed onto the planks, will lie on a line between two planks?*

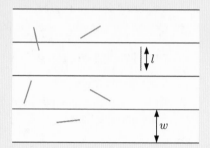

To solve this problem, we must separately consider the "short needle" case where $l \leqslant w$, and the "long needle" case where $l > w$.

CASE 1:   THE SHORT NEEDLE

Suppose a needle of length $l \leqslant w$ is tossed onto the planks.

Let θ be the angle between the needle and the plank lines (measured anticlockwise as shown), and D be the distance between the centre of the needle and the nearest plank line.

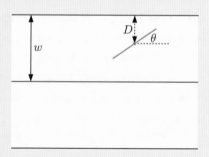

What to do:

1   Determine the range of possible values of: **a** θ **b** D

2   Is it reasonable to assume that θ and D will take values in their ranges with equal probability? Explain your answer.

3   Explain why the needle will lie on a line if $D \leqslant \dfrac{l}{2}\sin\theta$.

4   Use **1** to **3** to explain why the probability of the needle lying on a line is equal to the probability that a randomly chosen point from rectangle ABCD lies in the shaded area.

5   Find the shaded area, in terms of l.

6   Hence show that the probability that the needle lies on a line is $\dfrac{2l}{w\pi}$.

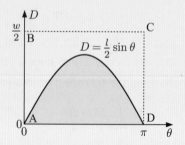

CASE 2:   THE LONG NEEDLE

Now suppose the needle has length $l > w$.

What to do:

1 Use the diagram alongside to explain why the reasoning for $l \leqslant w$ is not valid for $l > w$.

2 Show that $\theta^* = \sin^{-1}\left(\frac{w}{l}\right)$.

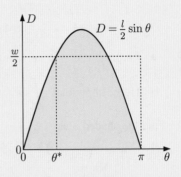

3 **a** Explain why the probability that a needle of length $l > w$ lies on a line is given by

$$\frac{(\pi - 2\theta^*)\frac{w}{2} + 2\int_0^{\theta^*} \left(\frac{l}{2}\sin\theta\right) d\theta}{\frac{w\pi}{2}}.$$

b Hence show that this probability is $1 - \dfrac{2}{\pi}\sin^{-1}\left(\dfrac{w}{l}\right) + \dfrac{2l}{w\pi}\left(1 - \dfrac{\sqrt{l^2 - w^2}}{l}\right)$.

4 Verify that the short needle and long needle formulae give the same probability for the boundary case $l = w$.

REVIEW SET 17A

1 Find the exact value of:

   a $\displaystyle\int_{-2}^0 (1 - 3x)\, dx$
   b $\displaystyle\int_0^{\frac{1}{2}} \left(x - \sqrt{x}\right) dx$
   c $\displaystyle\int_1^2 (x^2 + 1)^2\, dx$

2 Find b such that:

   a $\displaystyle\int_0^b (x - b)^2\, dx = 9$
   b $\displaystyle\int_0^b \left(x^2 + \tfrac{1}{2}x\right) dx = 3$

3 Find the exact value of:

   a $\displaystyle\int_{-5}^{-1} \sqrt{1 - 3x}\, dx$
   b $\displaystyle\int_0^{\frac{\pi}{2}} \cos\tfrac{x}{2}\, dx$
   c $\displaystyle\int_2^6 \frac{2}{x}\, dx$

4 If $\displaystyle\int_0^a e^{1-2x}\, dx = \frac{e}{4}$, find the exact value of a.

5 Use the identity $\sin^2 x = \tfrac{1}{2} - \tfrac{1}{2}\cos 2x$ to help evaluate $\displaystyle\int_0^{\frac{\pi}{6}} \sin^2\left(\tfrac{x}{2}\right) dx$.

6 Find $\dfrac{d}{dx}(e^{-2x}\sin x)$ and hence evaluate $\displaystyle\int_0^{\frac{\pi}{2}} \left[e^{-2x}(\cos x - 2\sin x)\right] dx$.

7 Evaluate correct to 6 significant figures:

   a $\displaystyle\int_3^4 \frac{x}{\sqrt{2x + 1}}\, dx$
   b $\displaystyle\int_0^1 x^2 e^{x+1}\, dx$

8 **a** Find $\displaystyle\int 2x(x^2+1)^3\,dx$ using the substitution $u = x^2 + 1$.

b *Hence* evaluate:

i $\displaystyle\int_0^1 2x(x^2+1)^3\,dx$ **ii** $\displaystyle\int_{-1}^2 -x(1+x^2)^3\,dx$

9 **a** Find $\displaystyle\int x^2 e^{1-x^3}\,dx$ using an appropriate substitution.

b Hence show that $\displaystyle\int_0^1 x^2 e^{1-x^3}\,dx = \dfrac{e-1}{3}$.

10 Find the shaded area:

a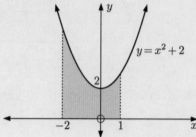

b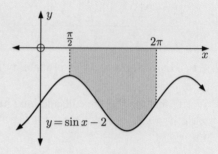

c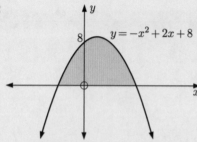

d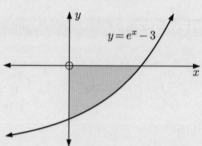

11 Find the area of the region bounded by:

a $y = x^2$, the x-axis, $x = 2$, and $x = 5$

b $y = \sqrt{5-x}$, the x-axis, $x = 1$, and $x = 2$

c $y = \sin\frac{x}{3}$, the x-axis, $x = \pi$, and $x = 2\pi$.

12 **a** Sketch the graphs of $y = x^2 + 4x + 1$ and $y = 3x + 3$ on the same set of axes.

b Find the points where the graphs meet.

c Hence find the area of the region enclosed by $y = x^2 + 4x + 1$ and $y = 3x + 3$.

13 Does $\displaystyle\int_{-1}^3 f(x)\,dx$ represent the area of the

shaded region? Explain your answer.

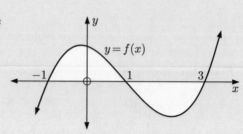

14   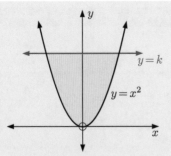   Determine k given that the enclosed region has area $5\frac{1}{3}$ units^2.

15   **a**   Find a given that the area of the region between $y = e^x$ and the x-axis from $x = 0$ to $x = a$ is 2 units^2.

  b   Hence determine b such that the area of the region from $x = a$ to $x = b$ is also 2 units^2.

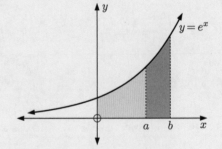

16   Find the area of the region enclosed by $y = x^3 + x^2 + 2x + 6$ and $y = 7x^2 - x - 4$.

17   **a**   Sketch the graphs of $y = \sin^2 x$ and $y = \sin x$ on the same set of axes for $0 \leqslant x \leqslant \pi$.

  b   Find the exact value of the area enclosed by these curves for $0 \leqslant x \leqslant \frac{\pi}{2}$.

18   Bettina is filling a watering can with water from a tap. The water enters at the rate $R_1(t) = 6.4$ litres per minute.

Bettina's watering can starts empty, and has capacity 16 litres. Unfortunately it has a hole in the bottom, so it leaks water at the rate $R_2(t) = 2.5 - 1.25e^{-0.2t}$ litres per minute, where t is the time in minutes.

  a   Evaluate the following integrals, and interpret their meaning:

  i $\displaystyle\int_0^{\frac{1}{2}} R_2(t)\, dt$ **ii** $\displaystyle\int_0^1 [R_1(t) - R_2(t)]\, dt$

  b   How long will it take for the watering can to be full? Give your answer to the nearest second.

19   **a**   Find $\displaystyle\int x \sin(x^2)\, dx$.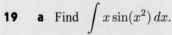

  b   Show that the shaded regions have equal area.

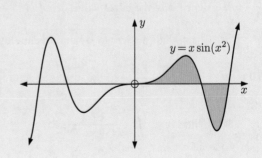

REVIEW SET 17B

1   Find the exact value of:

 a $\displaystyle\int_2^3 \frac{1}{\sqrt{3x}}\, dx$
 b $\displaystyle\int_1^4 (x - \tfrac{1}{2}x^2)\, dx$
 c $\displaystyle\int_0^1 (x^2 + \tfrac{1}{3})^2\, dx$

2   If $\displaystyle\int_0^a (x^2 - \tfrac{1}{2}x)\, dx = \tfrac{9}{16}$,   find the exact value of a.

3   Find the exact value of:

 a $\displaystyle\int_2^3 \frac{1}{\sqrt{3x - 4}}\, dx$
 b $\displaystyle\int_{2e}^{3e} \frac{4}{x + e}\, dx$
 c $\displaystyle\int_{\frac{\pi}{4}}^{\frac{\pi}{2}} (2\sin x + 1)\, dx$

4   Find the values of b such that $\displaystyle\int_0^b \cos x\, dx = \frac{1}{\sqrt{2}}$, $\ 0 < b < \pi$.

5   Use the identity $\cos^2 x = \tfrac{1}{2} + \tfrac{1}{2}\cos 2x$ to help evaluate $\displaystyle\int_0^{\frac{\pi}{3}} \cos^2\left(\tfrac{x}{2}\right) dx$.

6   Evaluate correct to 4 significant figures:

 a $\displaystyle\int_{-2}^0 4e^{-x^2}\, dx$
 b $\displaystyle\int_0^1 \frac{10x}{\sqrt{3x + 1}}\, dx$

7   If $\displaystyle\int_1^4 f(x)\, dx = 3$,   determine:

 a $\displaystyle\int_1^4 (f(x) + 1)\, dx$
 b $\displaystyle\int_1^2 f(x)\, dx - \int_4^2 f(x)\, dx$

 c k given that $\displaystyle\int_4^1 k\, f(x)\, dx = 5$.

8   **a**   Show that $(\sin\theta - \cos\theta)^2 = 1 - \sin 2\theta$.

 b   Hence find $\displaystyle\int_0^{\frac{\pi}{4}} (\sin\theta - \cos\theta)^2\, d\theta$.

9   **a**   Find $(e^x + 2)^3$ using the binomial expansion.

 b   Hence find the exact value of $\displaystyle\int_0^1 (e^x + 2)^3\, dx$.

 c   Check your answer to **b** using technology.

10   **a**   Find $\displaystyle\int \frac{\cos x}{(1 + \sin x)^3}\, dx$ using an appropriate substitution.

 b   *Hence* find $\displaystyle\int_0^{\frac{\pi}{6}} \frac{\cos x}{(1 + \sin x)^3}\, dx$.

11 Find the area of the region bounded by:

    a $y = x^3 + 1$, the x-axis, $x = 1$, and $x = 3$

    b $y = \dfrac{1}{x}$, the x-axis, $x = 3$, and $x = 9$

    c $y = e^{2x}$, the x-axis, $x = 0$, and $x = 2$

    d $y = -2 - 2\cos 3x$ and the x-axis from $x = -\frac{\pi}{3}$ to $x = \frac{\pi}{3}$.

12 Find the shaded area.

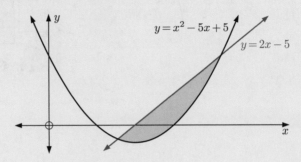

13 Determine the area enclosed by the axes and $y = 4e^x - 1$.

14   **a** Sketch the graphs of $y = x^4 - 12$ and $y = -x^2$ on the same set of axes.

    b Find the points where the graphs meet.

    c Find the exact area of the region enclosed by $y = x^4 - 12$ and $y = -x^2$.

15 OABC is a rectangle and the two shaded regions are equal in area. Find k.

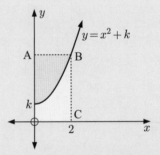

16

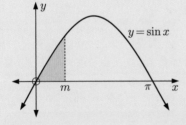

The shaded region has area $\frac{1}{2}$ unit^2.
Find the value of m.

17 Determine the total area enclosed by $y = x^3$ and $y = 7x^2 - 10x$.

18

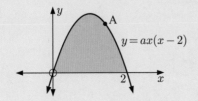

    a Find a given that the shaded area is 4 units^2.

    b Find the x-coordinate of A given [OA] divides the shaded region into equal areas.

19 Over the course of a day, the rate of solar energy being transferred into Callum's solar panels is given by

$$E(t) = 2\sin\left(\tfrac{t-5}{5}\right) + \tfrac{1}{2}\sin\left(\tfrac{t-5}{4}\right) \text{ kW}$$

where t is the time in hours after midnight, $5 \leqslant t \leqslant 20$. Find the following quantities and explain what they represent:

a $\displaystyle\int_5^{12} E(t)\, dt$

b $\displaystyle\int_{12}^{20} E(t)\, dt$

c $\displaystyle\int_5^{20} E(t)\, dt$

Chapter 18

Kinematics

Contents:

OPENING PROBLEM

Michael rides up a hill and down the other side to his friend's house. The dots on the graph show Michael's position at various times t.

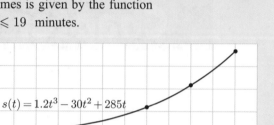

The distance Michael has travelled at various times is given by the function
$s(t) = 1.2t^3 - 30t^2 + 285t$ metres for $0 \leqslant t \leqslant 19$ minutes.

Things to think about:

a At what point do you think the hill was steepest? How far had Michael travelled to this point?

b How can we find Michael's *average* speed between $t = 5$ and $t = 15$ minutes?

c How can we find Michael's speed at a particular instant? Can we write a *function* which will tell us Michael's speed at any time t?

Kinematics is the study of motion.

In previous years you should have studied **travel graphs** which plot distance travelled against time taken.

In this Chapter we consider kinematics more formally, taking into account *direction* as well as distance and speed. This will lead us to functions for **displacement**, **velocity**, and **acceleration**, and how they are linked by calculus.

THE LANGUAGE OF MOTION

Consider an object P which is in motion along a straight line.

- The **distance** it travels accumulates over time, irrespective of its direction of travel.
- The **speed** S of P is how fast it is travelling.
- The **displacement** s of P is its position relative to a fixed origin O.
- The **velocity** v of P is its rate of change of displacement.
- The **acceleration** a of P is its rate of change of velocity.

DISCUSSION

1 What is the difference between:

   a distance travelled and displacement   **b** speed and velocity?

2 Each of the following expressions refers to a zero of one of the variables time t, displacement s, velocity v, or acceleration a. Discuss which variable each expression refers to and what it means.

QUICK
REFERENCE
SUMMARY

   a initial conditions   **b** at the origin

   c stationary   **d** reverses direction

   e maximum or minimum displacement   **f** constant velocity

   g maximum or minimum velocity

3 Does a zero displacement correspond to:

   a zero distance travelled   **b** zero speed?

4 How should we interpret the sign of:

   a displacement   **b** velocity   **c** acceleration?

A   DISPLACEMENT

For an object P which is in motion along a straight line:

- The **displacement** s of P is its position relative to a fixed origin O.

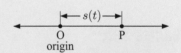

- The **displacement function** $s(t)$ gives the displacement of the object at any time $t \geqslant 0$.

   ▸ When $s(t) > 0$, P is to the right of the origin.

   ▸ When $s(t) < 0$, P is to the left of the origin.

Example 1   ◀⋙ Self Tutor

A lighthouse is situated on the top of a cliff. A stone is thrown from the top of the lighthouse. The stone falls past the base of the lighthouse, and lands after 6 seconds in the water below.

The displacement of the stone above ground level
$s(t) = -5t^2 + 20t + 25$ m for $0 \leqslant t \leqslant 6$ s.

   a Find the initial displacement of the stone.

   b Use quadratic theory to graph $s(t)$.

   c At what time and place does the stone change direction?

   d For what time interval is the stone above ground level?

   a $s(0) = 25$

      $\therefore$ the initial displacement of the stone is 25 m.

b $s(t) = -5t^2 + 20t + 25$
$\quad = -5(t^2 - 4t - 5)$
$\quad = -5(t - 5)(t + 1)$

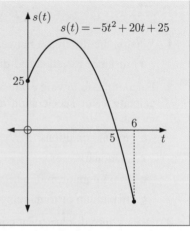

$s(t) = -5t^2 + 20t + 25$

c The stone changes direction at the turning point of $s(t)$.

This occurs when $t = \dfrac{-20}{2(-5)} = 2$ s.

$s(2) = -5(2)^2 + 20(2) + 25 = 45$ m

The stone changes direction after 2 seconds, when it is 45 m above ground level.

d The stone is above ground level whenever $s(t) > 0$.
This occurs for $0 \leqslant t < 5$ s.

A **motion diagram** is used to plot the position of an object on a single number line. It can be helpful in reminding us that we are looking at motion in one dimension only.

For the object in **Example 1**, the motion diagram is:

Click on the icon to explore motion diagrams for other displacement functions.

MOTION
DIAGRAMS

EXERCISE 18A

1 An object travels with displacement function $s(t) = 5 - t$ cm for $0 \leqslant t \leqslant 10$ s.

  a Find the initial displacement of the object.

  b Find the displacement of the object at time:

    i $t = 3$ s   **ii** $t = 10$ s.

  c At what time does the object reach the origin?

  d Does the object ever change direction? Explain your answer.

  e Draw a motion diagram showing the information you have found.

2 An object travels with displacement function $s(t) = 10t^2 - 7t + 1$ m for $0 \leqslant t \leqslant 1$ s.

  a Find the initial displacement of the object.

  b Use quadratic theory to graph $s(t)$.

  c At what time and place does the object change direction?

  d For what time interval is the object to the right of the origin?

  e Draw a motion diagram showing the information you have found.

3 A mass on a spring oscillates with displacement $s(t) = 8\sin 8\pi t + 6$ cm where $0 \leqslant t \leqslant 0.25$ s.

  a At what times is the displacement 6 cm?

  b Plot the graph of $s(t)$ for $0 \leqslant t \leqslant 0.25$ s.

  c Find where and when the mass changes direction.

  d Draw a motion diagram showing the information you have found.

B VELOCITY

The **velocity** of an object is its rate of change of displacement.

AVERAGE VELOCITY

In many real-world scenarios, we only know certain data points for where an object was at a particular time. In these cases, we can only calculate the *average* velocity between data points.

"Rate of change" tells us immediately to think about a gradient.

The **average velocity** of an object moving in the time interval from $t = t_1$ to $t = t_2$ is given by

$$\text{average velocity} = \frac{\textbf{change in displacement}}{\textbf{change in time}}$$

$$= \frac{s(t_2) - s(t_1)}{t_2 - t_1}$$

On a graph of $s(t)$ against t, the average velocity is the gradient of the chord through the points $P_1(t_1, s(t_1))$ and $P_2(t_2, s(t_2))$.

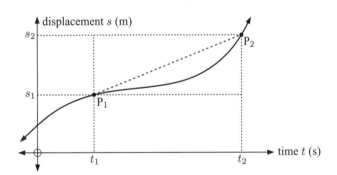

INSTANTANEOUS VELOCITY

If we know the complete function $s(t)$, we can find the instantaneous velocity of the object at any time.

The **instantaneous velocity** or **velocity function** of the object at time t is $v(t) = s'(t)$.
It is the gradient of the tangent to the function $s(t)$ at any given time.

Notice that:

- When $v(t) > 0$, the object is moving to the right.
- When $v(t) < 0$, the object is moving to the left.
- When $v(t) = 0$, the object is instantaneously at rest. A change in the sign of $v(t)$ at this time indicates that the object has changed direction.

When we take a derivative with respect to t, we calculate a rate per unit of time. So, for a displacement in metres and time in seconds, the units of velocity are $m\,s^{-1}$.

Example 2   ◄⁾ **Self Tutor**

A particle moves in a straight line with displacement from O given by $s(t) = 3t - t^2$ metres at time t seconds. Find:

- **a** the average velocity for the time interval from $t = 2$ to $t = 5$ seconds
- **b** the instantaneous velocity at $t = 2$ seconds.

a average velocity $= \dfrac{s(5) - s(2)}{5 - 2}$

$= \dfrac{(15 - 25) - (6 - 4)}{3}$

$= \dfrac{-10 - 2}{3}$

$= -4 \text{ m s}^{-1}$

b $\quad s(t) = 3t - t^2$

$\therefore \ v(t) = s'(t) = 3 - 2t$

$\therefore \ v(2) = 3 - 2(2)$

$\qquad \quad = -1 \text{ m s}^{-1}$

The particle is travelling at 1 m s^{-1} to the left.

EXERCISE 18B.1

1 Consider the displacement-time graph alongside.

- **a** Find the displacement of the object when:
    - **i** $t = 2$ seconds   **ii** $t = 8$ seconds.
- **b** Find the average velocity of the object from $t = 2$ to $t = 3$ seconds.
- **c** Find the instantaneous velocity of the object when $t = 5$ seconds.

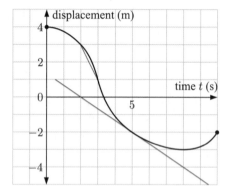

2 A particle moves in a straight line with displacement from O given by $s(t) = t^2 - 6t + 1$ metres at time t seconds, $t \geqslant 0$.

- **a** Find the average velocity from $t = 1$ to $t = 3$ seconds.
- **b** Find $v(t)$.
- **c** Hence find the instantaneous velocity at:
    - **i** $t = 1$ second   **ii** $t = 5$ seconds.

3 Consider the displacement-time graph alongside.

- **a** Describe the initial position of the object.
- **b** At what time is the object at the origin?
- **c** In which direction is the object moving when $t = 5$ seconds?
- **d** At what times does the object change direction?
- **e** Draw a sign diagram for:
    - **i** the displacement function $s(t)$
    - **ii** the velocity function $v(t)$.
- **f** Find the instantaneous velocity of the object when $t = 7$ seconds.

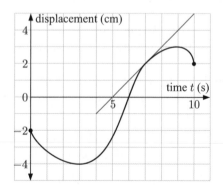

4 An object moves in a straight line with displacement function $s(t) = 2\sqrt{t} + 3$ cm, where t is in seconds, $t \geqslant 0$.

    a Find the average velocity from $t = 1$ to $t = 4$ seconds.

    b Find the initial position of the object.

    c Find $v(t)$.

    d Hence find the instantaneous velocity at:

        i $t = 4$ seconds   **ii** $t = 16$ seconds.

5 An object moves in a straight line with position given by $s(t) = t^3 - 11t^2 + 24t$ m from O, where t is in seconds, $t \geqslant 0$.

    a Find the velocity function $v(t)$.

    b Describe the initial conditions of the object.

    c Draw a sign diagram for $s(t)$ and $v(t)$.

    d At what times is the object at O?

    e At which times does the object reverse direction? Find the position of the object at each of these times.

    f Describe in words the motion of the object.

    g Draw a motion diagram for the object.

6 A shell is accidentally fired vertically from a mortar at ground level. Its height above the ground after t seconds is given by $s(t) = bt - 4.9t^2$ metres where b is constant.

    a Show that the initial velocity of the shell is b m s^{-1} upwards.

    b The shell reaches its maximum height after 7.1 seconds.

        i Find the initial velocity of the shell.

        ii Find the maximum height reached by the shell.

FINDING DISPLACEMENT FROM VELOCITY

Since the velocity function is the derivative of the displacement function, we can use integration to reverse the process.

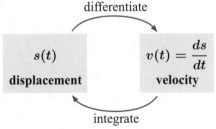

To find the constant of integration, we would need to know the displacement at a particular time. Most commonly, this would be the initial displacement $s(0)$.

CHANGE IN DISPLACEMENT

We can determine the change in displacement in a time interval $t_1 \leqslant t \leqslant t_2$ using the integral:

$$\text{Change in displacement} = s(t_2) - s(t_1) = \int_{t_1}^{t_2} v(t)\, dt$$

DISTANCE TRAVELLED

For a velocity-time function $v(t)$ where $v(t) \geqslant 0$ on the interval $t_1 \leqslant t \leqslant t_2$, the distance travelled will simply be the change in displacement $\displaystyle\int_{t_1}^{t_2} v(t)\, dt$.

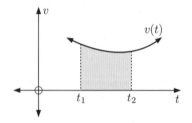

If $v(t) \geqslant 0$, the distance travelled is the area under the velocity curve.

If we have a change of direction within the time interval then the velocity will change sign. To find the total distance travelled, we therefore need to add the components of area above and below the t-axis. Alternatively, we can integrate the absolute value of the velocity, which is the object's **speed**.

$$\text{Distance travelled} = \int_{t_1}^{t_2} |\,v(t)\,|\, dt$$

Example 3   ◀)) **Self Tutor**

The velocity-time graph for a train journey is illustrated in the graph alongside. Find the total distance travelled by the train.

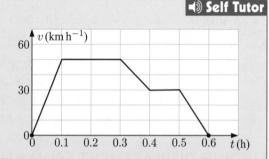

Total distance travelled

= total area under the graph

= area A + area B + area C + area D + area E

= $\frac{1}{2}(0.1)50 + (0.2)50 + \left(\frac{50+30}{2}\right)(0.1) + (0.1)30 + \frac{1}{2}(0.1)30$

= $2.5 + 10 + 4 + 3 + 1.5$

= 21 km

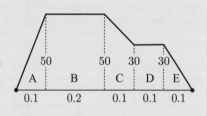

Example 4   ◀)) **Self Tutor**

A particle P moves in a straight line with velocity function $v(t) = t^2 - 3t + 2$ m s^{-1}.

a Find the times when P reverses direction.

b Hence find the distance P travels in the first 4 seconds of motion.

Check your answer by evaluating $\displaystyle\int_0^4 |\,v(t)\,|\, dt$.

c Find the change in displacement of P in the first 4 seconds.

a $v(t) = s'(t) = t^2 - 3t + 2$

$\qquad\qquad = (t-1)(t-2)$

$\therefore$ the sign diagram of v is:

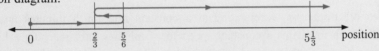

Since the signs change, P reverses direction at $t = 1$ and $t = 2$ seconds.

b Now $s(t) = \displaystyle\int (t^2 - 3t + 2)\, dt$

$\qquad\qquad = \dfrac{t^3}{3} - \dfrac{3t^2}{2} + 2t + c$

We choose the initial displacement to be zero, so $s(0) = c = 0$.

$\therefore \quad s(1) = \frac{1}{3} - \frac{3}{2} + 2 + c = \frac{5}{6}$

$\qquad s(2) = \frac{8}{3} - 6 + 4 + c = \frac{2}{3}$

$\qquad s(4) = \frac{64}{3} - 24 + 8 + c = 5\frac{1}{3}$

> We are not told the displacement of the particle at any given time, so we can *choose* the origin to be its initial position.

Motion diagram:

$\therefore \quad$ total distance travelled $= \frac{5}{6} + (\frac{5}{6} - \frac{2}{3}) + (5\frac{1}{3} - \frac{2}{3}) = 5\frac{2}{3}$ m

Casio fx-CG50	TI-84 Plus CE	HP Prime

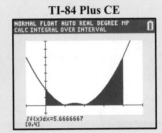
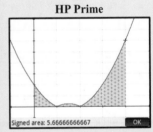

c Change in displacement = final position $-$ original position

$\qquad\qquad = s(4) - s(0)$

$\qquad\qquad = 5\frac{1}{3}$ m

So, the displacement is $5\frac{1}{3}$ m to the right.

EXERCISE 18B.2

1 A runner has the velocity-time graph shown. Find the total distance travelled by the runner.

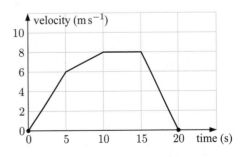

2

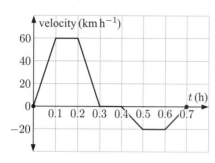

A car travels along a straight road with the velocity-time graph illustrated.

a What is the significance of the graph:

    i above the t-axis

    ii below the t-axis?

b Find the total *distance* travelled by the car.

c Find the final *displacement* of the car from its starting point.

3 After leaving a station, a train accelerates at a constant rate for 40 seconds until its speed reaches 15 m s^{-1}. The train then travels at this speed for 160 seconds. On its approach to the next station, the train slows down at a constant rate for 80 seconds until it is at rest.

    a Draw a graph to show the train's motion.

    b How far did the train travel between the stations?

4 A cyclist rides off from rest, accelerating at a constant rate for 3 minutes until she reaches 40 km h^{-1}. She then maintains a constant speed for 4 minutes until reaching a hill. She slows down at a constant rate over one minute to 20 km h^{-1}, then continues at this speed for 5 minutes. At the top of the hill she reduces her speed uniformly, and she is stationary 2 minutes later.

    a Draw a graph to show the cyclist's motion.

    b How far has the cyclist travelled?

5 A particle has velocity function $v(t) = 1 - 2t \text{ cm s}^{-1}$ as it moves in a straight line.

    a Find the time when the particle reverses direction.

    b Hence find the total distance travelled in the first second of motion.

        Check your answer by evaluating $\displaystyle\int_0^1 |v(t)| \, dt$.

    c Find the change in displacement of the particle in the first second.

6 Particle P is initially at the origin O. It moves with the velocity function $v(t) = t^2 - t - 2 \text{ cm s}^{-1}$.

    a Write a formula for the displacement function $s(t)$.

    b Find the total distance travelled in the first 3 seconds of motion.

    c Find the particle's displacement from its starting position after three seconds.

7 A ball is thrown from 1 m above ground level. Its velocity is $v(t) = 29.4 - 9.8t \text{ m s}^{-1}$.

    a Find the displacement function $s(t)$.

    b Find the maximum height reached by the ball.

8 The velocity of a moving object is given by $v(t) = 32 + 4t$ m s^{-1}.

   a If $s = 16$ m when $t = 0$ seconds, find the displacement function.

   b Explain why the change in displacement of the object and its total distance travelled in the interval $0 \leqslant t \leqslant \tau$, can both be represented by the definite integral $\displaystyle\int_0^\tau (32 + 4t)\, dt$.

   c Find the distance travelled by the object in the first 4 seconds.

9 An object has velocity function $v(t) = \cos 2t$ m s^{-1}.

   a Show that the particle oscillates between two points, and find the distance between them.

   b If $s(\frac{\pi}{4}) = 1$ m, determine $s(\frac{\pi}{3})$ exactly.

10 When a pendulum is released, its velocity along the arc of motion after t seconds is given by $v(t) = 20 + 5\sin 4t$ cm s^{-1}.

   a Sketch the graph of $v(t)$ against t for $0 \leqslant t \leqslant 6$.

   b Find the pendulum's velocity after 4.5 seconds.

   c Find the total distance travelled by the tip of the pendulum in the first 2 seconds.

11 The velocity of a moving object is given by $v(t) = -4 + \sqrt{t}$ m s^{-1}. Suppose the object is initially at the origin. Find:

   a the displacement function

   b the time when the object changes direction

   c the change in displacement after the first 30 seconds

   d the total distance travelled in the first 30 seconds.

12 A stunt motorcyclist rides towards a ramp. His velocity after t seconds is given by $v(t) = 10\sqrt{t}$ m s^{-1}.

   a Find the motorcyclist's velocity after:

     i 1 second   **ii** 2 seconds.

   b Write a function $s(t)$ for the displacement of the motorcyclist after t seconds.

   c Find $\displaystyle\int_0^2 v(t)\, dt$, and interpret your answer.

   d In order to perform his stunt, the motorcyclist needs to be travelling at 20 m s^{-1} or faster when he reaches the ramp.

     i How long will he take to reach a speed of 20 m s^{-1}?

     ii The motorcyclist started his approach 55 m from the ramp. Has he given himself enough distance to reach the required speed?

13 Use technology and the formula $\text{distance travelled} = \displaystyle\int_{t_1}^{t_2} |v(t)|\, dt$ to find the total distance travelled in the following scenarios:

   a a skydiver has velocity $v(t) = -54(1 - e^{-\frac{t}{6}})$ m s^{-1} for the first 15 seconds

   b a mass on a spring has velocity $v(t) = e^{-t}\cos 16t$ cm s^{-1} for 10 seconds.

C | ACCELERATION

The **acceleration** of an object is its rate of change of velocity.

If an object moves in a straight line with displacement function $s(t)$ and velocity function $v(t)$, then:

- The **average acceleration** for the time interval from $t = t_1$ to $t = t_2$ is given by

$$\text{average acceleration} = \frac{v(t_2) - v(t_1)}{t_2 - t_1}$$

- The **acceleration function** $a(t)$ of the object is given by $a(t) = v'(t) = s''(t)$.

The displacement, velocity, and acceleration functions are therefore connected as follows:

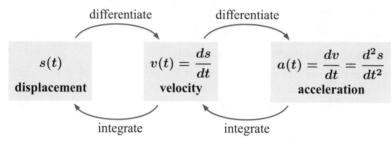

To obtain acceleration from velocity, we must calculate a rate per unit of time. So, for displacement in metres and time in seconds, the units of acceleration are $m\,s^{-2}$.

Example 5   ◄)) **Self Tutor**

A particle moves in a straight line with position relative to O given by $s(t) = t^3 - 6t^2 + 9t - 1$ cm, where t is the time in seconds, $t \geqslant 0$.

a Find expressions for the particle's velocity and acceleration, and draw sign diagrams for each of them.

> The *initial conditions* describe the particle's motion when $t = 0$.

b Find the initial conditions and hence describe the motion at this instant.

c Find the position of the particle when it changes direction.

d Draw a motion diagram for the particle.

e Find the total distance travelled in the first 3 seconds.

---

a $s(t) = t^3 - 6t^2 + 9t - 1$ cm

$\therefore\ v(t) = 3t^2 - 12t + 9 \qquad \{v(t) = s'(t)\}$

$ = 3(t^2 - 4t + 3)$

$ = 3(t - 1)(t - 3)$ cm s^{-1}

which has sign diagram:

and $a(t) = 6t - 12$ cm s^{-2} $\qquad \{a(t) = v'(t)\}$

which has sign diagram:

b When $t = 0$, $s(0) = -1$ cm
$$v(0) = 9 \text{ cm s}^{-1}$$
$$a(0) = -12 \text{ cm s}^{-2}$$

$\therefore$ the particle is 1 cm to the left of O, moving to the right with speed 9 cm s^{-1}, and has acceleration -12 cm s^{-2}.

c Since $v(t)$ changes sign when $t = 1$ and $t = 3$, a change of direction occurs at these instants.
$s(1) = 1 - 6 + 9 - 1 = 3$, and $s(3) = 27 - 54 + 27 - 1 = -1$.
So, the particle changes direction when it is 3 cm to the right of O, and when it is 1 cm to the left of O.

d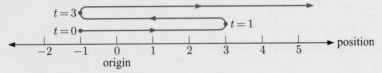

e The total distance travelled $= 4 + 4 = 8$ cm.

EXERCISE 18C

1 A particle moves with velocity function $v(t) = 10t - t^2$ cm s^{-1}, $t \geqslant 0$. Find:

  a the velocity of the particle when $t = 2$ seconds

  b the average acceleration of the particle from $t = 1$ to $t = 3$ seconds

  c the acceleration function $a(t)$

  d the instantaneous acceleration of the particle when $t = 3$ seconds.

2 An object moves in a straight line with displacement function $s(t) = t^3 - t^2 - 5$ metres at time t seconds, $t \geqslant 0$.

  a Find the object's displacement, velocity, and acceleration when $t = 2$ seconds.

  b Find the time at which the object has zero acceleration.

3 A stone is fired from a catapult so that its position above ground level after t seconds is given by $s(t) = 98t - 4.9t^2$ metres, $t \geqslant 0$.

  a Find the velocity and acceleration functions for the stone, and draw sign diagrams for each function.

  b Find the initial position and velocity of the stone.

  c Describe the stone's motion at times $t = 5$ and $t = 12$ seconds.

  d Find the maximum height reached by the stone.

  e Find the time taken for the stone to hit the ground.

4 A particle P moves in a straight line with displacement function $s(t) = 100t + 200e^{-\frac{t}{5}}$ cm, where t is the time in seconds, $t \geqslant 0$.

  a Find the velocity and acceleration functions.

  b Find the initial position, velocity, and acceleration of P.

  c Discuss the velocity of P as $t \to \infty$.

  d Discuss the acceleration of P as $t \to \infty$.

5 An object has displacement function $s(t) = t - \ln(2t + 1)$ cm, where t is in seconds, $t \geqslant 0$.

   a Show that the object is initially at the origin.

   b Find the velocity function.

   c Over what time interval is the object moving:

      i to the right   **ii** to the left?

   d Show that the object's acceleration is positive for all $t \geqslant 0$.

   e Find the acceleration of the object after 2 seconds.

   f Find the distance travelled by the object in the first 2 seconds.

6 The velocity of a particle travelling in a straight line is given by $v(t) = 50 - 10e^{-0.5t}$ m s^{-1}, where $t \geqslant 0$, t in seconds.

   a State the initial velocity of the particle.

   b Find the velocity of the particle after 3 seconds.

   c How long will it take for the particle's velocity to reach 45 m s^{-1}?

   d Discuss $v(t)$ as $t \to \infty$.

   e Show that the particle's acceleration is always positive.

   f Find the exact time at which the acceleration of the particle is 2 m s^{-2}.

   g Draw the graph of $v(t)$ against t.

   h Find the total distance travelled by the particle in the first 3 seconds of motion.

Example 6　　　　　　　　　　　　　　　　　　◀》 **Self Tutor**

A train is initially at rest at a station. It begins to accelerate according to the function $a(t) = \frac{1}{2}e^{-\frac{t}{100}}$ m s^{-2}.

   a Find the velocity function of the train, and sketch its graph.

   b How long will it take for the train to reach the speed 40 m s^{-1}?

   c How far will the train travel in this time?

a　　$a(t) = \frac{1}{2}e^{-\frac{t}{100}}$ m s^{-2}

$\therefore v(t) = \int \frac{1}{2}e^{-\frac{t}{100}}\, dt$

$= -50e^{-\frac{t}{100}} + c$ m s^{-1}

The train was initially stationary.

$\therefore -50e^{0} + c = 0$

$\therefore c = 50$

$\therefore v(t) = 50 - 50e^{-\frac{t}{100}}$ m s^{-1}

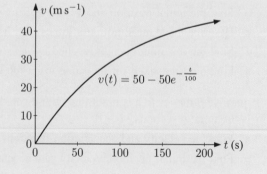

b If $v = 40$ then

$$50 - 50e^{-\frac{t}{100}} = 40$$

$$\therefore \ 50e^{-\frac{t}{100}} = 10$$

$$\therefore \ e^{-\frac{t}{100}} = \tfrac{1}{5}$$

$$\therefore \ -\frac{t}{100} = \ln\left(\tfrac{1}{5}\right) = -\ln 5$$

$$\therefore \ t = 100\ln 5 \approx 160.9 \text{ s}$$

c The train does not change direction.

$$\therefore \quad \text{distance travelled}$$

$$= \int_0^{100\ln 5} \left(50 - 50e^{-\frac{t}{100}}\right) dt$$

$$= \left[50t + 5000e^{-\frac{t}{100}}\right]_0^{100\ln 5}$$

$$= 50(100\ln 5) + 5000e^{-\frac{100\ln 5}{100}} - 5000e^0$$

$$= 5000\ln 5 + \frac{5000}{5} - 5000$$

$$= 5000\ln 5 - 4000$$

$$\approx 4047 \text{ m}$$

7 A train moves along a straight track with acceleration $a(t) = \frac{t}{10} - 3$ m s^{-2}. The initial velocity of the train is 45 m s^{-1}.

   a Determine the velocity function $v(t)$.

   b Evaluate $\int_0^{60} v(t)\,dt$ and explain what this value represents.

8 An object has initial velocity 20 m s^{-1} as it moves in a straight line with acceleration function $a(t) = 4e^{-\frac{t}{20}}$ m s^{-2}.

   a Show that as t increases, the object approaches a limiting velocity.

   b Find the total distance travelled in the first 10 seconds of motion.

9 A particle is initially stationary at the origin. It accelerates according to the function $a(t) = \frac{2}{(t+1)^3}$ m s^{-2}.

   a Find the velocity function $v(t)$ for the particle.

   b Find the displacement function $s(t)$ for the particle.

   c Describe the motion of the particle at the time $t = 2$ seconds.

D   SPEED

We have seen that velocities have size (magnitude) and sign (direction). In contrast, speed simply measures *how fast* something is travelling, regardless of the direction of travel. Speed is a *scalar* quantity which has size but no sign. Speed cannot be negative.

> The **speed** S of an object at any instant is the magnitude of the object's velocity.
> $$S = |v|$$

For example, an object with velocity -5 m s^{-1} is moving to the left with speed 5 m s^{-1}.

To determine when the speed of an object P with displacement $s(t)$ is increasing or decreasing, we use a **sign test**.

- If the signs of $v(t)$ and $a(t)$ are the same (both positive or both negative), then the speed of P is increasing.
- If the signs of $v(t)$ and $a(t)$ are opposite, then the speed of P is decreasing.

DISCUSSION

Discuss why the sign test for speed works by considering each case below:
- The object is travelling to the right $(v > 0)$ and the acceleration $a > 0$.
- The object is travelling to the right $(v > 0)$ and the acceleration $a < 0$.
- The object is travelling to the left $(v < 0)$ and the acceleration $a > 0$.
- The object is travelling to the left $(v < 0)$ and the acceleration $a < 0$.

Example 7   ◀) Self Tutor

A particle moves in a straight line with position relative to O given by $s(t) = t^3 - 3t + 1$ cm, where t is the time in seconds, $t \geqslant 0$.

a Find expressions for the particle's velocity and acceleration, and draw sign diagrams for each of them.

b Find the initial conditions and hence describe the motion of the particle at this instant.

c Describe the motion of the particle at $t = 2$ seconds.

d Find the position of the particle when it changes direction.

e Draw a motion diagram for the particle.

f For what time interval is the particle's speed increasing?

a $s(t) = t^3 - 3t + 1$ cm

$\therefore\ v(t) = 3t^2 - 3$ $\{v(t) = s'(t)\}$

$= 3(t^2 - 1)$

$= 3(t+1)(t-1)$ cm s^{-1}

which has sign diagram:

> Since $t \geqslant 0$, the stationary point at $t = -1$ is not required.

and $a(t) = 6t$ cm s^{-2} $\{a(t) = v'(t)\}$

which has sign diagram:

b When $t = 0$, $s(0) = 1$ cm

$v(0) = -3$ cm s^{-1}

$a(0) = 0$ cm s^{-2}

$\therefore$ the particle is 1 cm to the right of O, moving to the left at a speed of 3 cm s^{-1}.

c When $t = 2$, $s(2) = 8 - 6 + 1 = 3$ cm

$v(2) = 12 - 3 = 9$ cm s^{-1}

$a(2) = 12$ cm s^{-2}

$\therefore$ the particle is 3 cm to the right of O, moving to the right at a speed of 9 cm s^{-1}.

Since a and v have the same sign, the speed of the particle is increasing.

d Since $v(t)$ changes sign when $t = 1$, a change of direction occurs at this instant.

$s(1) = 1 - 3 + 1 = -1$, so the particle changes direction when it is 1 cm to the left of O.

e
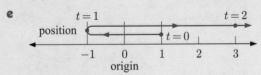

f Speed is increasing when $v(t)$ and $a(t)$ have the same sign. This is for $t \geqslant 1$.

EXERCISE 18D

1 An object moves in a straight line with position from O given by $s(t) = t^2 - 6t + 7$ m, where t is in seconds, $t \geqslant 0$.

  a Find expressions for the object's velocity and acceleration, and show sign diagrams for each of them.

  b Find the initial conditions and hence describe the motion at this instant.

  c Find the position of the object when it changes direction.

  d Draw a motion diagram for the object.

  e During which time interval is the object's speed decreasing?

2 When a ball is thrown, its height above the ground is given by $s(t) = 1.2 + 28.1t - 4.9t^2$ metres, where t is the time in seconds.

  a From what distance above the ground was the ball released?

  b Find $s'(t)$ and state what it represents.

  c Find the maximum height reached by the ball.

  d Find the ball's speed:

    i when released   **ii** at $t = 2$ s   **iii** at $t = 5$ s.

3 A particle moves in a straight line with displacement function $s(t) = 12t - 2t^3 - 1$ cm where t is in seconds, $t \geqslant 0$.

  a Find velocity and acceleration functions for the particle's motion.

  b Find the initial conditions, and interpret their meaning.

  c Find the times and positions when the particle reverses direction.

  d At what times is the particle's:

    i speed increasing   **ii** velocity increasing?

  e Draw a motion diagram for the particle.

4 A particle has displacement function $s(t) = 4 - \sqrt{t+1}$ m, where t is in seconds, $t \geqslant 0$.

  a Find the velocity and acceleration functions for the particle's motion, and draw sign diagrams for each of them.

  b Find the initial conditions and interpret their meaning.

  c Describe the motion of the particle after 3 seconds.

  d Describe what is happening to the speed of the particle.

5 A flotation device is thrown from a jetty into the water below.   It takes k seconds for the device to reach the water.   The height of the device above sea level is given by $s(t) = -4.9t^2 + 4.9t + 8$ m,   where t is in seconds, $0 \leqslant t \leqslant k$ seconds.

   a Find the value of k.

   b Draw sign diagrams for the device's velocity and acceleration functions.

   c Was the speed of the device increasing or decreasing after:

      i 0.2 seconds   **ii** 1 second?

6 A particle P moves along the x-axis with position given by $x(t) = 1 - 2\cos t$ cm, $t \geqslant 0$ seconds.

   a State the initial position, velocity, and acceleration of P.

   b Describe the motion of P when $t = \frac{\pi}{4}$ seconds.

   c Find the times when the particle reverses direction on $0 < t < 2\pi$, and find the position of the particle at these instants.

   d When is the particle's speed increasing on $0 \leqslant t \leqslant 2\pi$?

7 A dog paces back and forth along a fence, guarding its owner's property. The dog's horizontal displacement relative to its kennel is given by $s(t) = 8\sin\frac{t}{2}$ m, $t \geqslant 0$ seconds.

   a Is the dog to the left or the right of its kennel after: **i** 3 seconds   **ii** 7 seconds?

   b Find the velocity function $v(t)$.

   c Is the dog moving to the left or the right after: **i** 4 seconds   **ii** 10 seconds?

   d Find the acceleration function $a(t)$.

   e Is the dog's speed increasing or decreasing after 2 seconds?

   f Show that the dog's speed is maximised when it is moving past its kennel.

8 The velocity of an object after t seconds is given by $v(t) = 25te^{-2t}$ cm s^{-1}, $t \geqslant 0$.

   a Use technology to help sketch the velocity function.

   b Show that the object's acceleration at time t is given by $a(t) = 25(1 - 2t)e^{-2t}$ cm s^{-2}, $t \geqslant 0$.

   c When is the velocity of the object increasing?

   d When is the speed of the object decreasing?

9 A lion is chasing a zebra. The zebra notices the lion when the lion is 40 m away. From this time, the lion approaches with speed $v_1(t) = 15e^{-0.1t}$ m s^{-1}, and the zebra runs away with speed $v_2(t) = 20 - 20e^{-0.1t}$ m s^{-1}.

   a Find the speed of each animal after 1 second.

   b Show that the lion's speed decreases over time, whereas the zebra's speed increases over time.

   c Find $\displaystyle\int_0^3 v_1(t)\,dt$, and interpret your answer.

   d Find $\displaystyle\int_0^3 [v_1(t) - v_2(t)]\,dt$, and interpret your answer.

   e Explain why the lion will be closest to the zebra when $v_1(t) = v_2(t)$.

   f Find the time at which $v_1(t) = v_2(t)$.

   g Did the lion catch the zebra? If not, how close did the lion get to the zebra?

INVESTIGATION   PROJECTILE MOTION

A **projectile** is an object upon which the only force acting is gravity. If we ignore air resistance, balls and missiles travel through the air with **projectile motion**.

For example, the trebuchet at Warwick Castle in England is claimed to be the largest working siege machine in the world. It is constructed mainly of oak, with the long throwing arm made of ash, a more flexible wood. It is 8.7 m high, increasing to 18 m high with the arm fully extended. Using a counterweight of approximately 6 tonnes, it is capable of throwing an 18 kg projectile a horizontal distance of up to 242 m.

The theory of projectile motion was developed in Europe in the 14th century, driven by the desire to improve guns and cannons. At that time, scientists were still using Aristotle's theory of motion which suggested that forces gave rise to momentum. This would mean that as soon as you stopped pushing something (even an object on wheels) it would stop moving.

It was **Galileo Galilei** (1564 - 1642) who first suggested that in the absence of resistance, a projectile would move in a quadratic curve.

Within his research he conducted a series of experiments on the paths of projectiles, attempting to find a mathematical description of falling bodies.

Two of Galileo's experiments consisted of rolling a ball down a grooved ramp that was placed at a fixed height above the floor and inclined at a fixed angle to the horizontal. In one experiment the ball left the end of the ramp and descended to the floor. In the second, a horizontal shelf was placed at the end of the ramp, and the ball travelled along this shelf before descending to the floor.

Galileo

In both experiments Galileo found that once the ball left the ramp or shelf, its path was *parabolic* and could therefore be modelled by a quadratic function.

In this Investigation we suppose you are operating a cannon. Your task is to fire the cannonball as far as possible. At what angle to the ground should you fire the cannonball?

- If the angle is too high, the cannonball will go high into the air, but will not travel very far horizontally.

- If the angle is too low, the cannonball will reach its maximum height too soon, and will not travel very far.

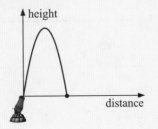

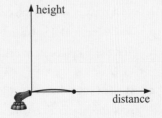

Suppose the cannonball is fired at an angle θ to the ground, with initial velocity v_0 m s^{-1}. The motion of the cannonball has both a **vertical component** and a **horizontal component**. We will consider these components separately.

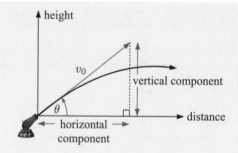

What to do:

1   **a** If the cannon is fired from ground level, what is the initial vertical height of the cannonball?

   b Use the diagram above to show that the initial vertical velocity of the cannonball is $v_0 \sin \theta$ m s^{-1}.

   c The path of the cannonball is affected by gravity, which acts downwards on the cannonball at a rate of 9.8 m s^{-2}.
   Explain why the vertical acceleration of the cannonball is given by $a(t) = -9.8$ m s^{-2}.

   d Show that the vertical displacement function $s(t) = -4.9t^2 + [v_0 \sin \theta]t$ satisfies the properties in **a**, **b**, and **c**.

   e Hence show that the cannonball takes $\dfrac{v_0 \sin \theta}{4.9}$ seconds to hit the ground.

2   **a** Show that the horizontal velocity of the cannonball is $v_0 \cos \theta$ m s^{-1}.

> The horizontal velocity is not affected by gravity, so it remains constant throughout the cannonball's flight.

   b Hence show that the horizontal distance travelled by the cannonball before it hits the ground is $\dfrac{v_0^2 \sin 2\theta}{9.8}$ metres.

   c Suppose a cannonball is fired with initial velocity 200 m s^{-1}. Find the horizontal distance travelled by the cannonball if it is fired at an angle of:
   i $20°$ **ii** $50°$ **iii** $80°$

   d Find the angle θ which maximises the range of the cannonball.

3   Click on the icon to run a cannon simulation.
   Change the initial velocity and angle of trajectory, and observe the effect these have on the path of the cannonball.
   Use the simulation to check that your answer to **2 d** is correct.

   SIMULATION

REVIEW SET 18A

1   An object travels with displacement function $s(t) = 12 - 2t$ m for $0 \leqslant t \leqslant 10$ s.
   a Find the initial displacement of the object.
   b Find the displacement of the object at time:
   i $t = 1$ s   **ii** $t = 3$ s.
   c At what time does the object reach the origin?
   d Does the object ever change direction? Explain your answer.
   e Draw a motion diagram showing the information you have found.

2 A particle moves in a straight line with displacement from O given by $s(t) = 2t^2 + t - 5$ cm at time t seconds, $t \geqslant 0$.

   a Find the average velocity from $t = 1$ to $t = 5$ seconds.

   b Find the instantaneous velocity at:

      i $t = 2$ seconds   **ii** $t = 4$ seconds.

   c Find the acceleration function $a(t)$.

3 A particle P moves in a straight line with position relative to the origin O given by $s(t) = 2t^3 - 9t^2 + 12t - 5$ cm, where t is the time in seconds, $t \geqslant 0$.

   a Find the velocity and acceleration functions, and draw a sign diagram for each.

   b Find the initial conditions.

   c Describe the motion of the particle at time $t = 2$ seconds.

   d Find the times and positions where the particle changes direction.

   e Draw a diagram to illustrate the motion of P.

   f Determine the time intervals when the particle's speed is increasing.

4 A particle moves in a straight line with velocity $v(t) = t^2 - 6t + 8$ m s^{-1}, $t \geqslant 0$ seconds.

   a Draw a sign diagram for $v(t)$.

   b Describe what happens to the particle in the first 5 seconds of motion.

   c After 5 seconds, how far is the particle from its original position?

   d Find the total distance travelled in the first 5 seconds of motion.

5 When a kayaker stops paddling, the velocity of the kayak in the following 6 seconds is given by $v(t) = 2.75 - t + 0.5t^{1.2}$ m s^{-1}, where t is the time in seconds.

   a Find the velocity of the kayak:

      i when the kayaker stops paddling

      ii after 3 seconds.

   b Show that the kayak's speed is decreasing during the 6 second period.

   c Find $\displaystyle\int_0^2 v(t)\, dt$ and interpret your answer.

6 A particle P moves in a straight line with position from O given by $s(t) = 15t - \dfrac{60}{(t+1)^2}$ cm, where t is the time in seconds, $t \geqslant 0$.

   a Find velocity and acceleration functions for P's motion.

   b Describe the motion of P at $t = 3$ seconds.

   c For what values of t is the particle's speed increasing?

7 A spotlight moves back and forth across a stage at a concert. Its position after t seconds is given by $x(t) = 3 + 2\sin \pi t$ m.

   a Find the initial position, velocity, and acceleration of the spotlight.

   b Find the times when the spotlight changes direction during $0 \leqslant t \leqslant 5$ seconds.

   c Find the total distance travelled by the spotlight in the first 5 seconds.

8 A particle has velocity function $v(t) = 2 \cos 4t$ ms^{-1}.

    a Show that the particle oscillates between two points, and find the distance between them.

    b Given that $s\left(\frac{\pi}{12}\right) = 6$ m, determine $s\left(\frac{\pi}{6}\right)$.

    c Find the total distance travelled by the particle in the first π seconds.

9 When an aeroplane lands, its velocity is 65 ms^{-1}. Its acceleration t seconds after landing is given by $a(t) = -2$ ms^{-2}.

    a Find the velocity $v(t)$ of the plane t seconds after landing.

    b Find the displacement $s(t)$ of the plane t seconds after landing.

    c   **i** How long will it take the plane to reduce its speed to 3 ms^{-1}?

        ii How far would the plane have travelled along the runway at this time?

10 A boat travelling in a straight line has its engine turned off at time $t = 0$. Its velocity at time t seconds thereafter is given by $v(t) = \dfrac{100}{(t+2)^2}$ ms^{-1}.

    a Find the initial velocity of the boat, and its velocity after 3 seconds.

    b Discuss $v(t)$ as $t \to \infty$.

    c Sketch the graph of $v(t)$ against t.

    d Find $\displaystyle\int_0^2 v(t)\, dt$, and interpret your answer.

    e From when the engine is turned off, how long will it take for the boat to travel 30 metres?

REVIEW SET 18B

1 An object moves in a straight line with displacement function $s(t) = t^2 + 4t + 1$ m, where t is in seconds, $t \geqslant 0$.

    a Find the initial position of the object.

    b Find the average velocity from $t = 1$ to $t = 3$ seconds.

    c Find $v(t)$.

    d Find the instantaneous velocity at $t = 1$ second.

2 A jogger has the velocity-time graph shown. Find the total distance travelled by the jogger.

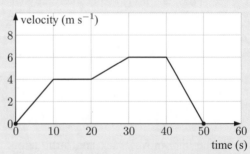

3 At time $t = 0$ a particle passes through the origin with velocity 27 cms^{-1}. Its acceleration t seconds later is $6t - 30$ cms^{-2}.

    a Write an expression for the particle's velocity.

    b Calculate the displacement from the origin after 6 seconds.

4 A particle moves along the x-axis with position relative to origin O given by
$x(t) = 3t - t\sqrt{t}$ cm, where t is the time in seconds, $t \geqslant 0$.

   a Find the velocity and acceleration functions, and draw a sign diagram for each.

   b Find the initial position and velocity of the particle and hence describe the motion at that instant.

   c Describe the motion of the particle at $t = 2$ seconds.

   d Find the time and position when the particle reverses direction.

   e Determine the time interval when the particle's speed is decreasing.

   f Draw a motion diagram for the particle.

   g Find the distance travelled by the particle in the first 6 seconds of motion.

5 The velocity of a human cannonball is given by
$v(t) = 4.8t^2 - 0.8t^3$ m s^{-1} for $0 \leqslant t \leqslant 6$ seconds.

   a Find the acceleration of the human cannonball after:

   i 1 second   **ii** 2 seconds

   iii 4 seconds   **iv** 5 seconds.

   b Find $\displaystyle\int_0^3 v(t)\, dt$ and interpret your answer.

   c How long does it take for the human cannonball to travel 30 m?

6 A particle P moves in a straight line with position given by $s(t) = 80e^{-\frac{t}{10}} - 40t$ m, $t \geqslant 0$ seconds.

   a Find the velocity and acceleration functions.

   b Find the initial position, velocity, and acceleration of P.

   c Sketch the graph of the velocity function.

   d Find the exact time when the velocity is -44 m s^{-1}.

7 A cork bobs up and down in a bucket of water. The distance from the centre of the cork to the bottom of the bucket is given by $s(t) = 30 + \cos \pi t$ cm, $t \geqslant 0$ seconds.

   a Find the cork's velocity at times $t = 0$, $\frac{1}{2}$, 1, $1\frac{1}{2}$, and 2 seconds.

   b Find the time intervals when the cork is falling.

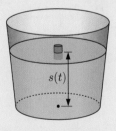

8 A skier is travelling down a hill. Her velocity after t seconds is given by
$$v(t) = \frac{\left(t^{1.1} + 3t\right)^{1.5}}{10} \text{ m s}^{-1}.$$

   a Find the velocity of the skier after 4 seconds.

   b Write an expression for the acceleration of the skier after t seconds.

   c Find the acceleration of the skier after 2 seconds.

   d Use technology to find the total distance travelled by the skier in the first 10 seconds.

9 A feather is falling with velocity function $v(t) = -\frac{1}{24}t^3 - \frac{1}{12}t$ m s^{-1}. The feather is initially 2 metres above the ground.

    a Find the displacement function $s(t)$.

    b Find the time taken for the feather to reach the ground.

10 Tyson and Maurice are competing in a 100 m sprint. Tyson runs with speed $v_1(t) = 10(1 - e^{-1.25t})$ m s^{-1}, and Maurice runs with speed $v_2(t) = 10.5(1 - e^{-t})$ m s^{-1}, for $t \geqslant 0$ seconds.

    a Who is travelling faster after 2 seconds?

    b Find $\displaystyle\int_0^5 v_1(t)\,dt$, and interpret your answer.

    c Find displacement functions $s_1(t)$ and $s_2(t)$ for each sprinter.

    d Who is winning the race after 3 seconds?

    e Show that Tyson completes the 100 m in approximately 10.8 seconds.

    f Who will win the race?

Chapter 19

Bivariate statistics

Contents:

OPENING PROBLEM

At a junior tournament, some young athletes each throw a discus. The *age* and *distance thrown* are recorded for each athlete.

Athlete	A	B	C	D	E	F	G	H	I	J	K	L
Age (years)	12	16	16	18	13	19	11	10	20	17	15	13
Distance thrown (m)	20	35	23	38	27	47	18	15	50	33	22	20

Things to think about:

a Do you think the distance an athlete can throw is related to the person's age?

b What happens to the distance thrown as the age of the athlete increases?

c How could you graph the data to more clearly see the relationship between the variables?

d How can we *measure* the relationship between the variables?

In the **Opening Problem**, each athlete has had *two* variables (*age* and *distance thrown*) recorded about them. This type of data is called **bivariate data**. We study it to understand the **relationship** between the two variables.

For example, we expect the *distance thrown* will *depend* on the athlete's *age*, so *age* is the **independent variable** and *disance thrown* is the **dependent variable**.

The **independent** and **dependent** variables are sometimes called the **explanatory** and **response** variables respectively.

In this Chapter we **describe** and **model** relationships between pairs of numerical variables.

A   ASSOCIATION BETWEEN NUMERICAL VARIABLES

We can observe the relationship between two numerical variables using a **scatter diagram**. We usually place the independent variable on the horizontal axis, and the dependent variable on the vertical axis.

In the **Opening Problem**, the independent variable *age* is placed on the horizontal axis, and the dependent variable *distance thrown* is placed on the vertical axis.

We then graph each data value as a point on the scatter diagram. For example, the red point represents athlete H, who is 10 years old and threw the discus 15 metres.

From the general shape formed by the dots, we can see that as the *age* increases, so does the *distance thrown*.

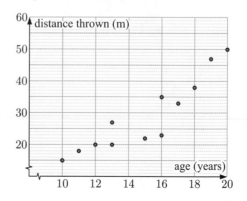

CORRELATION

Correlation refers to the relationship or association between two numerical variables.

There are several characteristics we consider when describing the correlation between two variables: direction, linearity, strength, outliers, and causation.

DIRECTION

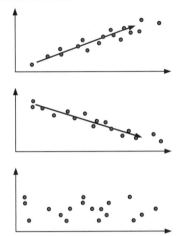

For a generally *upward* trend, we say that the correlation is **positive**. An increase in the independent variable generally results in an increase in the dependent variable.

For a generally *downward* trend, we say that the correlation is **negative**. An increase in the independent variable generally results in a decrease in the dependent variable.

For *randomly scattered* points, with no upward or downward trend, we say there is **no correlation**.

LINEARITY

When a trend exists, if the points approximately form a straight line, we say the trend is **linear**.

These points are roughly linear.

These points do not follow a linear trend.

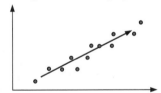
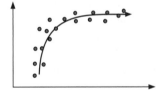

STRENGTH

To describe how closely the data follows a pattern or trend, we talk about the **strength** of correlation. It is usually described as either **strong**, **moderate**, or **weak**.

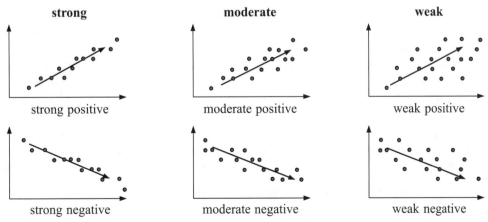

OUTLIERS

Outliers are isolated points which do not follow the trend formed by the main body of data.

If an outlier is the result of a recording or graphing error, it should be discarded. However, if the outlier is a genuine piece of data, it should be kept.

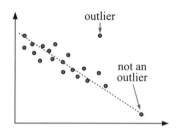

For the scatter diagram of the data in the **Opening Problem**, we can say that there is a strong positive correlation between *age* and *distance thrown*. The relationship appears to be linear, with no outliers.

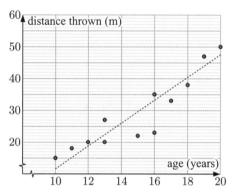

CAUSALITY

Correlation between two variables does not necessarily mean that one variable *causes* the other.

For example:

- The *arm length* and *running speed* of a sample of young children were measured, and a strong, positive correlation was found between the variables.

  This does *not* mean that short arms cause a reduction in running speed, or that a high running speed causes your arms to grow long.

  Rather, there is a strong, positive correlation between the variables because both *arm length* and *running speed* are closely related to a third variable, *age*. Up to a certain age, both *arm length* and *running speed* increase with *age*.

- The number of television sets sold in London and the number of stray dogs collected in Boston were recorded over several years. A strong, positive correlation was found between the variables.

  Obviously the number of television sets sold in London was not influencing the number of stray dogs collected in Boston. It is coincidental that the variables both increased over this period of time.

If a change in one variable *causes* a change in the other variable then we say that a **causal relationship** exists between them. In these cases, we can say that the independent variable *explains* the dependent variable. It may be more natural to use the terminology **explanatory variable** and **response variable**.

In cases where a causal relationship is not apparent, we cannot conclude that a causal relationship exists based on high correlation alone.

EXERCISE 19A

1 For each scatter diagram, describe the relationship between the variables. Consider the direction, linearity, and strength of the relationship, as well as the presence of any outliers.

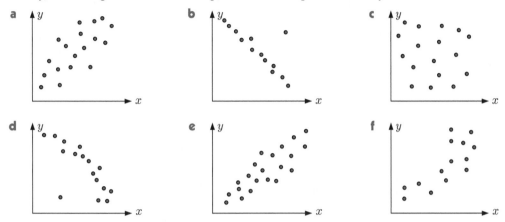

2 Tiffany is a hairdresser. The table below shows the number of hours she worked each day last week, and the number of customers she had.

Day	Mon	Tue	Wed	Thu	Fri	Sat	Sun
Hours worked	8	4	5	10	8	3	6
Number of customers	9	6	5	12	7	4	5

a Which is the explanatory variable, and which is the response variable?

b Draw a scatter diagram of the data.

c On which two days did Tiffany:

i work the same number of hours

ii have the same number of customers?

d Explain why you would expect a positive correlation between the variables.

You can use technology to help draw scatter diagrams.

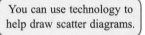

GRAPHICS CALCULATOR INSTRUCTIONS

3 The scores awarded by two judges at an ice skating competition are shown in the table.

Competitor	P	Q	R	S	T	U	V	W	X	Y
Judge A	5	6.5	8	9	4	2.5	7	5	6	3
Judge B	6	7	8.5	9	5	4	7.5	5	7	4.5

a Construct a scatter diagram for the data, with Judge A's scores on the horizontal axis and Judge B's scores on the vertical axis.

b Copy and complete the following comments about the scatter diagram:
There appears to be ......, ..., ... correlation between Judge A's scores and Judge B's scores. This means that as Judge A's scores increase, Judge B's scores ......

c Would it be reasonable to conclude that an increase in Judge A's scores *causes* an increase in Judge B's scores? Explain your answer.

4 Paul owns a company which installs industrial air conditioners. The table below shows the number of workers at the company's last 10 jobs, and the time it took to complete the job.

Job	A	B	C	D	E	F	G	H	I	J
Number of workers	5	3	8	2	5	6	1	4	2	7
Time (hours)	4	6	2.5	9	3	4	10	4	7.5	3

   a Which job: **i** took the longest   **ii** involved the most workers?

   b Draw a scatter diagram to display the data.

   c Describe the relationship between the variables *number of workers* and *time*.

5 Choose the scatter diagram which would best illustrate the relationship between the variables x and y.

   a $x =$ the number of apples bought by customers, $y =$ the total cost of apples bought

   b $x =$ the number of pushups a student can perform in one minute,
      $y =$ the time taken for the student to run 100 metres

   c $x =$ the height of a person, $y =$ the weight of the person

   d $x =$ the distance a student travels to school, $y =$ the height of the student's uncle

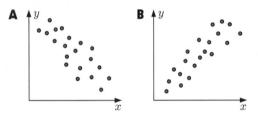
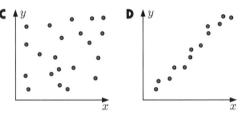

6 The scatter diagram shows the marks obtained by students in a test out of 50 marks, plotted against the number of hours each student studied for the test.

   a Describe the correlation between the variables.

   b How should the outlier be treated? Explain your answer.

   c Do you think there is a causal relationship between the variables? Explain your answer.

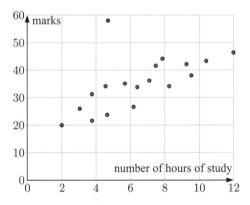

7 When the following pairs of variables were measured, a strong, positive correlation was found between each pair. Discuss whether a causal relationship exists between the variables. If not, suggest a third variable to which they may both be related.

   a The lengths of one's left and right feet.

   b The damage caused by a fire and the number of firefighters who attend it.

   c A company's expenditure on advertising, and the sales they make the following year.

   d The heights of parents and the heights of their adult children.

   e The numbers of hotels and numbers of service stations in rural towns.

B | PEARSON'S PRODUCT-MOMENT CORRELATION COEFFICIENT

In the previous Section, we classified the strength of the correlation between two variables as either strong, moderate, or weak. We observed the points on a scatter diagram, and judged how clearly the points formed a linear relationship.

Since this method is *subjective* and relies on the observer's opinion, it is important to get a more precise measure of the strength of linear correlation between the variables. We achieve this using **Pearson's product-moment correlation coefficient** r.

> For a set of n data given as ordered pairs $(x_1,\, y_1)$, $(x_2,\, y_2)$, $(x_3,\, y_3)$, ..., $(x_n,\, y_n)$,
>
> **Pearson's product-moment correlation coefficient** is $r = \dfrac{\sum (x_i - \overline{x})(y_i - \overline{y})}{\sqrt{\sum (x_i - \overline{x})^2 \sum (y_i - \overline{y})^2}}$
>
> where $\overline{x}$ and $\overline{y}$ are the means of the x and y data respectively, and $\sum$ means the sum over all the data values.

You are not required to learn this formula, but you should be able to calculate the value of r using technology.

**GRAPHICS
CALCULATOR
INSTRUCTIONS**

HISTORICAL NOTE

Karl Pearson (1857 - 1936) was an English statistician who developed the product-moment correlation coefficient together with his academic advisor **Sir Francis Galton**.

Pearson made many other contributions to statistics including the use of histograms in exploratory data analysis, parameter estimation, and hypothesis testing.

He is considered a key figure in the development of mathematical statistics.

PROPERTIES OF PEARSON'S PRODUCT-MOMENT CORRELATION COEFFICIENT

- The values of r range from -1 to $+1$.
- The **sign** of r indicates the **direction** of the correlation.
  - ▸ A positive value for r indicates the variables are **positively correlated**. An increase in one variable results in an increase in the other.
  - ▸ A negative value for r indicates the variables are **negatively correlated**. An increase in one variable results in a decrease in the other.
  - ▸ If $r = 0$ then there is **no correlation** between the variables.
- The **size** of r indicates the **strength** of the correlation.
  - ▸ A value of r close to $+1$ or -1 indicates strong correlation between the variables.
  - ▸ A value of r close to zero indicates weak correlation between the variables.

The following table is a guide for describing the strength of linear correlation using r.

Positive correlation			Negative correlation		
$r = 1$	perfect positive correlation		$r = -1$	perfect negative correlation	
$0.95 \leqslant r < 1$	very strong positive correlation		$-1 < r \leqslant -0.95$	very strong negative correlation	
$0.87 \leqslant r < 0.95$	strong positive correlation		$-0.95 < r \leqslant -0.87$	strong negative correlation	
$0.7 \leqslant r < 0.87$	moderate positive correlation		$-0.87 < r \leqslant -0.7$	moderate negative correlation	
$0.5 \leqslant r < 0.7$	weak positive correlation		$-0.7 < r \leqslant -0.5$	weak negative correlation	
$0 < r < 0.5$	very weak positive correlation		$-0.5 < r < 0$	very weak negative correlation	

Example 1   ◄⦆ Self Tutor

The Department of Road Safety wants to know if there is any association between *average speed* in the metropolitan area and the *age of drivers*. They commission a device to be fitted in the cars of drivers of different ages.

The results are shown in the scatter diagram. The r-value for this association is $+0.027$. Describe the association.

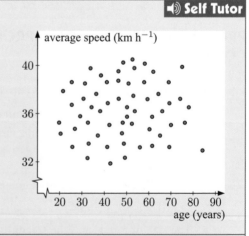

Since $0 < r < 0.5$, there is a very weak positive correlation between the two variables.
We observe this in the graph as the points are randomly scattered.

Example 2

◄) **Self Tutor**

The botanical gardens have been trying a new chemical to control the number of beetles infesting their plants. The results of one of their tests are shown in the table.

Sample	Quantity of chemical (g)	Number of surviving beetles
A	2	11
B	5	6
C	6	4
D	3	6
E	9	3

a Draw a scatter diagram for the data.

b Determine the correlation coefficient r.

c Describe the correlation between the *quantity of chemical* and the *number of surviving beetles*.

We first enter the data into separate lists:

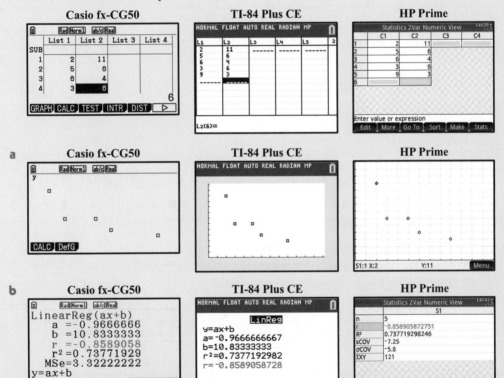

So, $r \approx -0.859$.

c There is a moderate negative correlation between the *quantity of chemical used* and the *number of surviving beetles*.

In general, the more chemical that is used, the fewer beetles that survive.

EXERCISE 19B

1 In a recent survey, the Department of International Commerce compared the *number of employees of a company* with its *export earnings*. A scatter diagram of their data is shown alongside. The corresponding value of r is 0.556.

Describe the association between the variables.

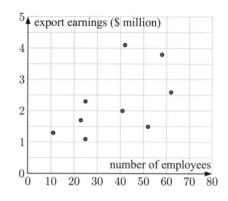

2 Match each scatter diagram with the correct value of r.

a
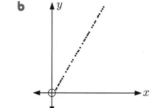

b

c
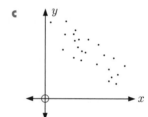

d
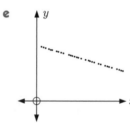

e

A $r = 1$ **B** $r = 0.6$ **C** $r = 0$ **D** $r = -0.7$ **E** $r = -1$

3 For each of the following data sets:

    i Draw a scatter diagram for the data.

    ii Calculate Pearson's product-moment correlation coefficient r.

    iii Describe the linear correlation between x and y.

a

x	1	2	3	4	5	6
y	3	2	5	5	9	6

b

x	3	8	5	14	19	10	16
y	17	12	15	6	1	10	4

c

x	3	6	11	7	5	6	8	10	4
y	2	8	8	4	7	9	11	1	5

4 A selection of students was asked how many phone calls and text messages they received the previous day. The results are shown alongside.

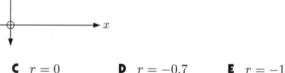

Student	A	B	C	D	E	F	G	H
Phone calls received	4	7	1	0	3	2	2	4
Text messages received	6	9	2	2	5	8	4	7

    a Draw a scatter diagram for the data.   **b** Calculate r.

    c Describe the linear correlation between *phone calls received* and *text messages received*.

    d Give a reason why this correlation may occur.

5 Consider the **Opening Problem** on page **450**.

   a Calculate r for the data.

   b Hence describe the association between the variables.

6 Jill does her washing every Saturday and hangs her clothes out to dry. She notices that the clothes dry faster some days than others. She investigates the relationship between the temperature and the time her clothes take to dry:

Temperature ($x\,°C$)	25	32	27	39	35	24	30	36	29	35
Drying time (y minutes)	100	70	95	25	38	105	70	35	75	40

   a Draw a scatter diagram for the data.

   b Calculate r.

   c Describe the correlation between *temperature* and *drying time*.

7 This table shows the number of supermarkets in 10 towns, and the number of car accidents that have occurred in these towns in the last month.

Number of supermarkets	5	8	12	7	6	2	15	10	7	3
Number of car accidents	10	13	27	19	10	6	40	30	22	37

   a Draw a scatter diagram for the data.

   b Calculate r.

   c Identify the outlier in the data.

   d It was found that the outlier was due to an error in the data collection process.

     i Recalculate r with the outlier removed.

     ii Describe the relationship between the variables.

     iii Discuss the effect of removing the outlier on the value of r.

   e Do you think there is a causal relationship between the variables? Explain your answer.

8 A health researcher notices that the incidence of Multiple Sclerosis (MS) is higher in some parts of the world than in others.

To investigate further, she records the *latitude* and *incidence of MS per 100 000 people* of 20 countries.

Latitude (degrees)	55	25	41	22	47	37	56	14	34	25
MS incidence per 100 000	165	95	75	20	180	140	230	15	45	65

Latitude (degrees)	27	65	10	24	4	56	46	8	50	40
MS incidence per 100 000	30	140	5	15	2	290	95	8	160	105

   a Draw a scatter diagram for the data.

   b Calculate the value of r.

   c Describe the relationship between the variables.

   d Is the incidence of MS higher near the equator, or near the poles?

> Higher latitudes occur near the poles. Lower latitudes occur near the equator.

ACTIVITY 1   COMPARING HEIGHT AND FOOT LENGTH

In this Activity, you will explore the relationship between the *height* and *foot length* of the students in your class.

You will need: ruler, tape measure

What to do:

1   Predict whether there will be positive correlation, no correlation, or negative correlation between the *height* and *foot length* of the students in your class.

2   Measure the height and foot length of each student in your class. Record your measurements in a table like the one below:

Student	Height (cm)	Foot length (cm)

3   Use technology to draw a scatter diagram for the data.

4   Calculate Pearson's product-moment correlation coefficient r for the data.

5   Describe the relationship between *height* and *foot length*. Was your prediction correct?

6   Do you think that a high value of r indicates a causal relationship in this case?

C   LINE OF BEST FIT BY EYE

If there is a sufficiently strong linear correlation between two variables, we can draw a line of best fit to illustrate their relationship. In general, it is only worth drawing a line of best fit if the correlation between the variables is strong. There is no fixed rule, but we suggest that a line of best fit is not appropriate if $|r| < 0.85$.

If we draw the line just by observing the points, we call it a **line of best fit by eye**. This line will vary from person to person.

We draw a line of best fit connecting variables x and y as follows:

Step 1:   Calculate the mean of the x values $\overline{x}$, and the mean of the y values $\overline{y}$.

Step 2:   Mark the **mean point** $(\overline{x}, \overline{y})$ on the scatter diagram.

Step 3:   Draw a line through the mean point which fits the trend of the data, and so that about the same number of data points are above the line as below it.

Consider again the data from the **Opening Problem**:

Athlete	A	B	C	D	E	F	G	H	I	J	K	L
Age (years)	12	16	16	18	13	19	11	10	20	17	15	13
Distance thrown (m)	20	35	23	38	27	47	18	15	50	33	22	20

We have seen that there is a strong positive linear correlation between *age* and *distance thrown*.

We can therefore model the data using a line of best fit.

The mean age is 15 years and the mean distance thrown is 29 m. We therefore draw our line of best fit through the mean point (15, 29).

We can use the line of best fit to estimate the value of y for any given value of x, and vice versa.

We draw the line through the mean point so it follows the trend of the data and there are about the same number of points above the line as below the line.

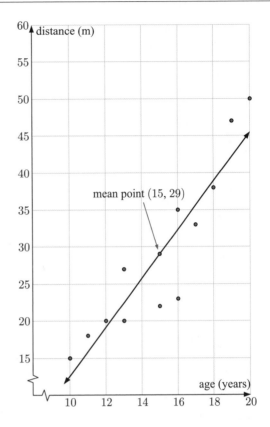

INTERPOLATION AND EXTRAPOLATION

Consider the data in the scatter diagram alongside. The data with the highest and lowest values are called the **poles**.

The line of best fit for the data is also drawn on the scatter diagram. We can use this line to predict the value of one variable for a given value of the other.

- If we predict a y value for an x value **in between** the poles, we say we are **interpolating** in between the poles.

- If we predict a y value for an x value **outside** the poles, we say we are **extrapolating** outside the poles.

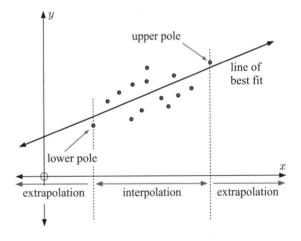

The accuracy of an interpolation depends on how well the linear model fits the data. This can be gauged by the correlation coefficient and by ensuring that the data is randomly scattered around the line of best fit.

The accuracy of an extrapolation depends not only on how well the model fits, but also on the assumption that the linear trend will continue past the poles. The validity of this assumption depends greatly on the situation we are looking at.

For example, consider the line of best fit for the data in the **Opening Problem**. It can be used to predict the distance a discus will be thrown by an athlete of a particular age.

The age 14 is within the range of ages in the original data, so it is reasonable to predict that a 14 year old will be able to throw the discus 26 m.

However, it is unlikely that the linear trend shown in the data will continue far beyond the poles. For example, according to the model, a 50 year old might throw the discus 144 m. This is almost twice the current world record of 76.8 m, so it would clearly be an unreasonable prediction.

Example 3   ◄)) **Self Tutor**

On a hot day, six cars were left in the sun in a car park. The length of time each car was left in the sun was recorded, as well as the temperature inside the car at the end of the period.

Car	A	B	C	D	E	F
Time (x minutes)	50	5	25	40	15	45
Temperature ($y\,°$C)	47	28	36	42	34	41

a Calculate $\overline{x}$ and $\overline{y}$.   **b** Draw a scatter diagram for the data.

c Locate the mean point $(\overline{x},\,\overline{y})$ on the scatter diagram, then draw a line of best fit through this point.

d Predict the temperature of a car which has been left in the sun for 35 minutes.

e Predict how long it would take for a car's temperature to reach 55°C.

f Comment on the reliability of your predictions in **d** and **e**.

a $\overline{x} = \dfrac{50 + 5 + 25 + 40 + 15 + 45}{6} = 30, \qquad \overline{y} = \dfrac{47 + 28 + 36 + 42 + 34 + 41}{6} = 38$

b, c

mean point $(30, 38)$

> **d** When $x = 35$, $y \approx 40$.
>
>   The temperature of a car left in the sun for 35 minutes will be approximately 40°C.
>
> **e** When $y = 55$, $x \approx 75$.
>
>   It would take approximately 75 minutes for a car's temperature to reach 55°C.
>
> **f** The prediction in **d** is reliable, as the data appears linear, and this is an interpolation.
>
>   The prediction in **e** may be unreliable, as it is an extrapolation and the linear trend displayed by the data may not continue beyond the 50 minute mark.

EXERCISE 19C

1 Consider the data set:

x	5	12	20	17	10	8	25	15
y	28	19	4	18	22	20	7	10

  a Draw a scatter diagram for the data.

  b Does the data appear to be positively or negatively correlated?

  c Calculate r for the data.

  d Describe the strength of the relationship between x and y.

  e Calculate the mean point $(\overline{x}, \overline{y})$.

  f Locate the mean point, then use it in drawing a line of best fit.

  g Estimate the value of y when $x = 22$.

2 Fifteen students were weighed and their pulse rates were measured:

Weight (x kg)	46	37	32	57	47	64	42	30	52	56	65	43	36	28	40
Pulse rate (y beats per min)	65	59	54	74	69	87	61	59	70	69	75	60	56	53	58

  a Draw a scatter diagram for the data.　　**b** Calculate r.

  c Describe the relationship between *weight* and *pulse rate*.

  d Calculate the mean point $(\overline{x}, \overline{y})$.

  e Locate the mean point on the scatter diagram, then use it in drawing a line of best fit.

  f Estimate the pulse rate of a 50 kg student. Comment on the reliability of your estimate.

3 The trunk widths and heights of the trees in a garden are given below:

Trunk width (x cm)	35	47	72	40	15	87	20	66	57	24	32
Height (y m)	11	18	24	12	3	30	22	21	17	5	10

  a Draw a scatter diagram for the data.

  b Which of the points is an outlier?

  c How would you describe the tree represented by the outlier?

  d Calculate the mean point $(\overline{x}, \overline{y})$.

  e Locate the mean point on the scatter diagram, then draw a line of best fit through the mean point.

  f Predict the height of a tree with trunk width 120 cm. Comment on the reliability of your prediction.

  g Predict the trunk width of a tree with height 10 m. Comment on the reliability of your prediction.

D   THE LEAST SQUARES REGRESSION LINE

The problem with drawing a line of best fit by eye is that the line drawn will vary from one person to another. For consistency, we use a method known as **linear regression** to find the equation of the line which best fits the data. The most common method is the method of "**least squares**".

In least squares linear regression, we minimise the sum of the squares of the *vertical* distances between each data point and the **regression line**.

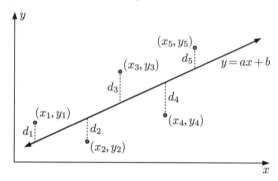

In other words, we need to find the straight line $y = ax + b$ where a and b are chosen to minimise $D = \sum_{i=1}^{n} d_i^2$.

The required values of a and b are $\quad a = \dfrac{\sum (x_i - \overline{x})(y_i - \overline{y})}{\sum (x_i - \overline{x})^2} \quad$ and $\quad b = \overline{y} - a\overline{x}$.

Click on the icon to see how these formulae are derived.

LEAST SQUARES
REGRESSION

In this course you will not be required to find the equation of the least squares regression line by hand.

Instead, you can use your **graphics calculator** or the **statistics package**.

STATISTICS
PACKAGE

GRAPHICS
CALCULATOR
INSTRUCTIONS

Example 4   ◄》 **Self Tutor**

The annual income and average weekly grocery bill for a selection of families is shown below:

Income (x thousand pounds)	55	36	25	47	60	64	42	50
Grocery bill (y pounds)	120	90	60	160	190	250	110	150

a Construct a scatter diagram to illustrate the data.

b Use technology to find the equation of the regression line.

c State and interpret the gradient of the regression line.

d Estimate the weekly grocery bill for a family with an annual income of £95 000.

e Estimate the annual income of a family whose weekly grocery bill is £100.

f Comment on whether the estimates in d and e are likely to be reliable.

a

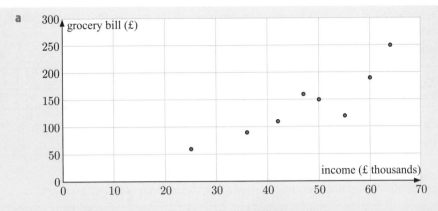

b

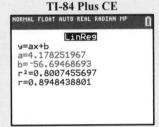

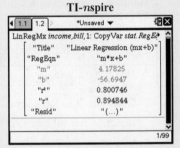

Using technology, the regression line is $y \approx 4.18x - 56.7$

c The gradient of the regression line ≈ 4.18. This means that for every additional £1000 of income, a family's weekly grocery bill will increase by an average of £4.18.

d When $x = 95$, $y \approx 4.18(95) - 56.7 \approx 340$

So, we expect a family with an income of £95 000 to have a weekly grocery bill of approximately £340.

e When $y = 100$, $\quad 100 \approx 4.18x - 56.7$

$$\therefore \quad 156.7 \approx 4.18x \qquad \{\text{adding 56.7 to both sides}\}$$

$$\therefore \quad x \approx 37.5 \qquad \{\text{dividing both sides by 4.18}\}$$

So, we expect a family with a weekly grocery bill of £100 to have an annual income of approximately £37 500.

f The estimate in **d** is an extrapolation, so the estimate may not be reliable.

The estimate in **e** is an interpolation and there is strong linear correlation between the variables. We therefore expect this estimate to be reliable.

EXERCISE 19D

1 Consider the data set below.

x	10	4	6	8	9	5	7	1	2	3
y	20	6	8	13	20	12	13	4	2	7

GRAPHICS
CALCULATOR
INSTRUCTIONS

a Draw a scatter diagram for the data.

b Use technology to find the equation of the regression line, and plot the line on your calculator.

c Use **b** to draw the regression line on your scatter diagram.

2 Steve wanted to see whether there was any relationship between the temperature when he leaves for work in the morning, and the time it takes for him to get to work.

He collected data over a 14 day period:

Temperature (x °C)	25	19	23	27	32	35	29	27	21	18	16	17	28	34
Time (y minutes)	35	42	49	31	37	33	31	47	42	36	45	33	48	39

   a Draw a scatter diagram for the data.   **b** Calculate r.

   c Describe the relationship between the variables.

   d Is it reasonable to fit a linear model to this data? Explain your answer.

3 The prices of petrol and the number of customers per hour for sixteen petrol stations are:

Petrol price (x cents per litre)	105.9	106.9	109.9	104.5	104.9	111.9	110.5	112.9
Number of customers (y)	45	42	25	48	43	15	19	10

Petrol price (x cents per litre)	107.5	108.0	104.9	102.9	110.9	106.9	105.5	109.5
Number of customers (y)	30	23	42	50	12	24	32	17

   a Calculate Pearson's product-moment correlation coefficient for the data.

   b Describe the relationship between the *petrol price* and the *number of customers*.

   c Use technology to find the equation of the regression line.

   d State and interpret the gradient of the regression line.

   e Estimate the number of customers per hour for a petrol station which sells petrol at 115.9 cents per litre.

   f Estimate the petrol price at a petrol station which has 40 customers per hour.

   g Comment on the reliability of your estimates in **e** and **f**.

4 To investigate whether speed cameras have an impact on road safety, data was collected from several cities. The number of speed cameras in operation was recorded for each city, as well as the number of accidents over a 7 day period.

Number of speed cameras (x)	7	15	20	3	16	17	28	17	24	25	20	5	16	25	15	19
Number of car accidents (y)	48	35	31	52	40	35	28	30	34	19	29	42	31	21	37	32

   a Construct a scatter diagram to display the data.

   b Calculate r for the data.

   c Describe the relationship between the *number of speed cameras* and the *number of car accidents*.

   d Find the equation of the regression line.

   e State and interpret the gradient and y-intercept of the regression line.

   f Estimate the number of car accidents in a city with 10 speed cameras.

5 The table following contains information about the *maximum speed* and *ceiling* (maximum altitude obtainable) for nineteen World War II fighter planes. The maximum speed is given in km h^{-1}, and the ceiling is given in km.

Maximum speed	Ceiling	Maximum speed	Ceiling	Maximum speed	Ceiling
460	8.84	680	10.66	670	12.49
420	10.06	720	11.27	570	10.66
530	10.97	710	12.64	440	10.51
530	9.906	660	11.12	670	11.58
490	9.448	780	12.80	700	11.73
530	10.36	730	11.88	520	10.36
680	11.73				

a Draw a scatter diagram for the data.   **b** Calculate r.

c Describe the association between *maximum speed* (x) and *ceiling* (y).

d Use technology to find the regression line, and draw the line on your scatter diagram.

e State and interpret the gradient of the regression line.

f Estimate the ceiling for a fighter plane with a maximum speed of 600 km h^{-1}.

g Estimate the maximum speed for a fighter plane with a ceiling of 11 km.

6 A group of children was asked the numbers of hours they spent exercising and watching television each week.

Exercise (x hours per week)	4	1	8	7	10	3	3	2
Television (y hours per week)	12	24	5	9	1	18	11	16

a Draw a scatter diagram for the data.   **b** Calculate r.

c Describe the correlation between *time exercising* and *time watching television*.

d Find the equation of the regression line, and draw the line on your scatter diagram.

e State and interpret the gradient and y-intercept of the regression line.

f   **i** One of the children in the group exercised for 7 hours each week. How much television does this child watch weekly?

   ii Use the regression line to predict the amount of television watched each week by a child who exercises for 7 hours each week.

   iii Compare your answers to **i** and **ii**.

7 The yield of pumpkins on a farm depends on the quantity of fertiliser used.

Fertiliser (x g per m^2)	4	13	20	26	30	35	50
Yield (y kg)	1.8	2.9	3.8	4.2	4.7	5.7	4.4

a Draw a scatter diagram for the data, and identify the outlier.

b What effect do you think the outlier has on:

   i the strength of correlation of the data   **ii** the gradient of the regression line?

c Calculate the correlation coefficient:

   i with the outlier included   **ii** without the outlier.

d Calculate the equation of the regression line:

   i with the outlier included   **ii** without the outlier.

e If you wish to estimate the yield when 15 g per m^2 of fertiliser is used, which regression line from **d** should be used? Explain your answer.

f Can you explain what may have caused the outlier? Do you think the outlier should be kept when analysing the data?

ACTIVITY 2   ANSCOMBE'S QUARTET

Anscombe's quartet is a collection of four bivariate data sets which have interesting statistical properties.

It was first described in 1973 by the English statistician **Francis Anscombe** (1918 - 2001). At the time, computers were becoming increasingly popular in statistics, as they allowed for more large scale and complex computations to be done within a reasonable amount of time. However, many common statistical packages primarily performed numerical calculations rather than produce graphs. Such output was often limited to those with advanced programming skills.

Francis Anscombe
Photo courtesy of
Yale University.

In his 1973 article, Anscombe stressed that:

> "*A computer should make* both *calculations* and *graphs. Both sorts of output should be studied; each will contribute to understanding.*"

The data values for Anscombe's quartet are given in the tables below:

Data set A:

x	10	8	13	9	11	14	6	4	12	7	5
y	8.04	6.95	7.58	8.81	8.33	9.96	7.24	4.26	10.84	4.82	5.68

Data set B:

x	10	8	13	9	11	14	6	4	12	7	5
y	9.14	8.14	8.74	8.77	9.26	8.1	6.13	3.1	9.13	7.26	4.74

Data set C:

x	10	8	13	9	11	14	6	4	12	7	5
y	7.46	6.77	12.74	7.11	7.81	8.84	6.08	5.39	8.15	6.42	5.73

Data set D:

x	8	8	8	8	8	8	8	19	8	8	8
y	6.58	5.76	7.71	8.84	8.47	7.04	5.25	12.5	5.56	7.91	6.89

Enter the data into your **graphics calculator** or click on the icon to access the data in the **statistics package**.

STATISTICS
PACKAGE

What to do:

1 For each data set, use technology to calculate:

    a the mean of each variable   **b** the population variance of each variable.

    Comment on your answers.

2 Find the regression line for each data set. What do you notice?

3 Construct a scatter diagram for each data set, and plot the corresponding regression line on the same set of axes.

4 How do your calculations in **1** and **2** compare to your graphs in **3**? Is a linear model necessarily appropriate for each data set?

5 Why is it important to consider both graphs *and* descriptive statistics when analysing data?

ACTIVITY 3   RESIDUAL PLOTS

In addition to the *correlation coefficient* and the *linearity* of a scatter diagram, we can use a **residual plot** to decide whether a linear model is appropriate. Click on the icon to explore these graphs.

RESIDUAL PLOTS

THEORY OF KNOWLEDGE

The use of extrapolation for predicting the future leads to debate on many global issues. Even when data shows a strong linear correlation, we need to consider whether it is reasonable for the trend to continue in the long term.

For example, the graph below is based on the article by Oeppen and Vaupel (2002)[1]. It shows female life expectancy from 1840 to the early 2000s, and the country with the highest female life expectancy at each point in time.

Notice that:

- The linear regression trend line is drawn in black, and extrapolated in grey.

- The horizontal black lines show asserted "ceilings" on life expectancy. The vertical line at the left end shows the year of publication.

- The dashed red lines denote projections of female life expectancy in Japan published by the United Nations (UN) in 1986, 1999, and 2001.

Record female life expectancy from 1840 to the present - Oeppen and Vaupel (2002)

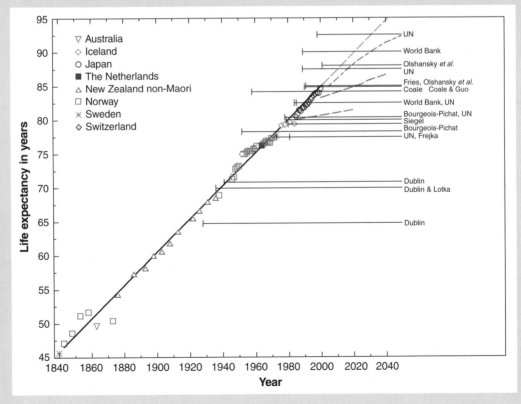

1   Discuss the relationship between the variables.

2   Use the regression line to predict female life expectancy in the year 2100. Do you think this is realistic?

3   Discuss the "ceilings" suggested by publishers over time. Is there evidence to suggest that human life expectancy will approach a limiting "ceiling"?

4   Discuss the accuracy of the UN projections for females in Japan from 1986 to 1999. Is there reason to expect the latest projection will be more reliable?

The graph below shows data from the NASA Goddard Institute for Space Studies[2]. The data for each point is for the first six months of the corresponding year.

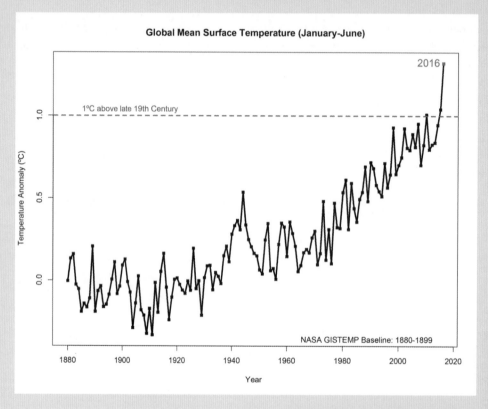

5   Discuss the relationship between the variables. Is it reasonable to use a linear model to describe the mean surface temperature of the Earth over time? Is it reasonable to even conclude that the mean surface temperature of the Earth is increasing?

6   How can we predict the mean surface temperature of the Earth in the future?

7   Is mathematical extrapolation valid evidence for dictating environmental policy?

References:

[1]   Oeppen and Vaupel, *Broken limits to life expectancy*, Science, **296**, 5570, 1029-1031, 2002.

[2]   www.nasa.gov/feature/goddard/2016/climate-trends-continue-to-break-records

E THE REGRESSION LINE OF x AGAINST y

In the previous Section, we saw how linear regression can be used to find a linear model for the response variable y in terms of the explanatory variable x.

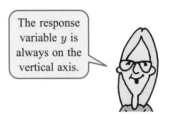

The response variable y is always on the vertical axis.

In these cases, we generally rely on the x-values being more precise than the y-values. This means that either there is less error involved with their measurement, or that there is naturally less variation associated with the x variable. The distance of each data point from the line is measured in the y-direction, so we are associating all of the "error" with the response variable y. However, in some cases the y-values may be more precisely measured.

For example:

- When a student studies for a test, their time spent studying x explains their test score y. However, the test score will be more precisely measured than the amount of time spent studying.

- At a breath testing station, police use a breathalyser to estimate the blood alcohol concentration (BAC) of drivers. If the result x is sufficiently high, the driver is required to take a blood test to establish their actual BAC. The blood test result y is a much more precise measurement.

In these scenarios, we consider the regression line of x **against** y. This means that we minimise the *horizontal* distances of points from the line, so all of the "error" is associated with the explanatory variable x.

We consider a line of the form $x = my + c$, and choose the constants m and c to minimise

$$H = \sum_{i=1}^{n} h_i^2.$$

It can be shown that $m = \dfrac{\sum (x_i - \overline{x})(y_i - \overline{y})}{\sum (y_i - \overline{y})^2}$ and $c = \overline{x} - m\overline{y}$.

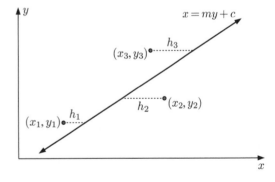

Rearranging the regression line $x = my + c$ into gradient-intercept form gives $y = \dfrac{1}{m}x - \dfrac{c}{m}$.

The gradient of the rearranged line is $\dfrac{1}{m} = \dfrac{\sum (y_i - \overline{y})^2}{\sum (x_i - \overline{x})(y_i - \overline{y})} \neq a$

and the y-intercept is
$$
\begin{aligned}
-\frac{c}{m} &= \frac{-(\overline{x} - m\overline{y})}{m} \\
&= \frac{m\overline{y} - \overline{x}}{m} \\
&= \overline{y} - \frac{1}{m}\overline{x} \\
&\neq b \qquad \left\{\text{since } \frac{1}{m} \neq a\right\}
\end{aligned}
$$

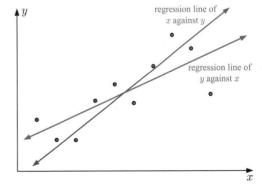

regression line of x against y

regression line of y against x

So, in general, the regression line of x against y is **not** the same as the regression line of y against x.

Example 5   ◆)) **Self Tutor**

The data below shows the quantity of feed eaten and the number of eggs laid in a fortnight for 12 Leghorn chickens:

Feed (x kg)	0.57	0.86	0.49	1.37	0.91	0.50
Number of eggs (y)	4	6	3	9	6	3

Feed (x kg)	0.97	1.06	1.00	0.68	1.34	0.94
Number of eggs (y)	6	7	7	4	9	6

a Explain why it would be appropriate to use the regression line of x against y in this case.

b Find the regression line of x against y.

c Use the regression line to estimate:

   i the quantity of feed required for a Leghorn chicken to lay a dozen eggs

   ii the number of eggs laid in a fortnight by a hen that ate 1.2 kg of feed.

---

a The number of eggs laid can be counted exactly, whereas the quantity of feed usually cannot be measured exactly.

Since the response variable y is more precisely measured than the explanatory variable x, it would be appropriate to use the regression line of x against y in this case.

b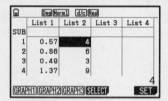

The regression line of x against y is $x \approx 0.142y + 0.0603$ kg.

c   **i** When $y = 12$, $x \approx 0.142(12) + 0.0603$
$$\approx 1.76$$

We expect a Leghorn chicken to need about 1.76 kg of feed to lay a dozen eggs.

   ii When $x = 1.2$, $1.2 \approx 0.142y + 0.0603$
$$\therefore \quad 1.1397 \approx 0.142y$$
$$\therefore \quad y \approx 8$$

We expect a Leghorn chicken eating 1.2 kg of feed to lay about 8 eggs.

EXERCISE 19E

1 The table below shows the amount of time a sample of families spend preparing homemade meals each week, and the amount of money they spend each week on fast food.

Time on homemade meals (x hours)	3.5	6.0	4.0	8.5	7.0	2.5	9.0	7.0	4.0	7.5
Money on fast food ($\$y$)	85	0	60	0	27	100	15	40	59	29

a Explain why it would be appropriate to use the regression line of x against y in this case.

b Find the regression line of x against y.

c Use the regression line to estimate:

    i the time spent preparing homemade meals each week by a family that spends \$45 on fast food each week

    ii the amount of money spent on fast food each week by a family that spends 5 hours each week preparing homemade meals.

2 The table below shows how far a group of students live from school, and how long it takes them to travel there each day.

Distance from school (x km)	7.2	4.5	13	1.3	9.9	12.2	19.6	6.1	23.1
Time to travel to school (y min)	17	13	29	2	25	27	41	15	53

a Draw a scatter diagram of the data.

b Which regression line should be used to model the relationship between the variables? Explain your answer.

c Use an appropriate regression line to estimate the travel time of a student who lives 15 km from school.

d Comment on the reliability of your estimate.

3 Eight students swim 200 m breaststroke. Their times y in seconds, and arm lengths x in cm, are shown in the table below:

Length of arm (x cm)	78	73	71	68	76	72	63	69
Breaststroke (y seconds)	123.1	123.7	127.3	132.0	120.8	125.0	140.9	129.0

a Draw a scatter diagram for the data.

b Find the equation of the regression line of:

    i y against x **ii** x against y.

c Plot both regression lines on your scatter diagram. What do you notice?

4 Consider the bivariate data set $\{(x_1, y_1), (x_2, y_2), ..., (x_n, y_n)\}$. The equation of the regression line of y against x is $y = ax + b$ and the equation of the regression line of x against y is $x = my + c$.

a Show that $ma = r^2$, where r is Pearson's product-moment correlation coefficient.

b Hence find the condition(s) under which the two regression lines will be the same.

DISCUSSION

Suppose the variables x and y are measured with equally poor precision.

1 Is it necessarily appropriate to choose one regression line over the other in this case?

2 How could we take the poor precision of *both* variables into account when formulating the linear regression model? Consider the "distance" that we minimise when we perform the linear regression.

3 In some situations, the variables depend equally on each other. In these cases we say that the variables are **co-dependent**, and the variables can be placed on either axis of the scatter diagram. Is it sensible to use a regression line to describe the relationship between co-dependent variables?

THEORY OF KNOWLEDGE

Since the 1970s and 1980s, wage discrimination between men and women has been a topic of debate. During that time, Conway and Roberts[1] published a study which used linear regression to show that on average, women with the same qualifications as men were paid less. This would seem to imply that given the same salary, women would be more qualified. However, when the regression was applied the other way, the opposite conclusion was observed.

1 Can you explain why this occurred?
2 Are these two questions necessarily equivalent?
   - "Given the same qualifications, do men and women earn the same wage?"
   - "Given the same wage, do men and women have the same qualifications?"
3 Is it necessary to consider both regression lines in order to conclude whether discrimination has occurred?
4 Should people be paid according to their qualifications, the job they do, or their capability in doing that job?

[1] Conway, Delores A. and Harry V. Roberts (1983). "Reverse Regression, Fairness, and Employment Discrimination". In: *Journal of Business & Economic Statistics* 1.1, pp. 75-85.

REVIEW SET 19A

1 For each scatter diagram, describe the relationship between the variables. Consider the direction, linearity, and strength of the relationship, as well as the presence of any outliers.

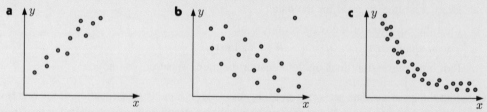

2 Kerry wants to investigate the relationship between the *water bill* and the *electricity bill* for the houses in her neighbourhood.
   a Do you think the correlation between the variables is likely to be positive or negative? Explain your answer.
   b Is there a causal relationship between the variables? Justify your answer.

3 Consider the data set alongside.
   a Draw a scatter diagram for the data.
   b Does the correlation between the variables appear to be positive or negative?
   c Calculate Pearson's product-moment correlation coefficient r.

x	2	5	7	10	12	15
y	18	10	13	7	7	5

4 The table below shows the ticket and beverage sales for each day of a 12 day music festival:

Ticket sales (\$$x$ × 1000)	25	22	15	19	12	17	24	20	18	23	29	26
Beverage sales (\$$y$ × 1000)	9	7	4	8	3	4	8	10	7	7	9	8

   a Draw a scatter diagram for the data.

b Calculate Pearson's product-moment correlation coefficient r.

c Describe the correlation between *ticket sales* and *beverage sales*.

5 A clothing store recorded the length of time customers were in the store and the amount they spent.

Time (min)	8	18	5	10	17	11	2	13	18	4	11	20	23	22	17
Money (€)	40	78	0	46	72	86	0	59	33	0	0	122	90	137	93

a Find the mean for each variable.

b Draw a scatter diagram for the data. Plot the mean point, and draw a line of best fit by eye.

c Describe the relationship between *time in the store* and the *money spent*.

6 The ages and heights of children at a playground are given below:

Age (x years)	3	9	7	4	4	12	8	6	5	10	13
Height (y cm)	94	132	123	102	109	150	127	110	115	145	157

a Draw a scatter diagram for the data.

b Use technology to find the regression line of y against x.

c State and interpret the gradient of the regression line.

d Use the regression line to predict the height of a 5 year old child.

e Based on the given data, at what age would you expect a child to reach 140 cm in height?

7 Tomatoes are sprayed with a pesticide-fertiliser mix. The table below shows the *yield of tomatoes* per bush for various *spray concentrations*.

Spray concentration (x mL per L)	3	5	6	8	9	11	15
Yield of tomatoes per bush (y)	67	90	103	120	124	150	82

a Draw a scatter diagram to display the data.

b Determine the value of r and interpret your answer.

c Is there an outlier present that is affecting the correlation?

d The outlier was found to be a recording error. Remove the outlier from the data set, and recalculate r. Is it reasonable to now fit a linear model?

e Determine the equation of the regression line of y against x.

f State and interpret the gradient and y-intercept of the regression line.

g Use your line to estimate:

    i the yield if the spray concentration is 7 mL per L

    ii the spray concentration if the yield is 200 tomatoes per bush.

h Comment on the reliability of your estimates in **g**.

8 Thomas rode his bicycle for an hour each day for eleven days. He recorded the number of kilometres he rode, along with his estimate of the temperature that day:

Temperature (T °C)	23	24	25	27	28	20	22	21	25	26	24
Distance (d km)	26.5	26.7	24.4	22.8	23.5	32.6	28.7	29.4	24.2	23.2	29.7

a Draw a scatter diagram for the data.

b Explain why it would be appropriate to use the regression line of T against d in this case.

c Find the equation of the regression line of T against d.

d How far would you expect Thomas to ride on a 30°C day?

REVIEW SET 19B

1 For each pair of variables, discuss whether the correlation between the variables is likely to be positive or negative, and whether a causal relationship exists between the variables:

a *price of tickets* and *number of tickets sold*

b *ice cream sales* and *number of shark attacks*.

2 A group of students is comparing their results for a Mathematics test and an Art project:

Student	A	B	C	D	E	F	G	H	I	J
Mathematics test	64	67	69	70	73	74	77	82	84	85
Art project	85	82	80	82	72	71	70	71	62	66

a Construct a scatter diagram for the data.

b Describe the relationship between the Mathematics and Art marks.

c Calculate the correlation coefficient r between the variables.

3 Safety authorities advise drivers to travel three seconds behind the car in front of them. This gives the driver a greater chance of avoiding a collision if the car in front has to brake quickly or is itself involved in an accident.

A test was carried out to find out how long it would take a driver to bring a car to rest from the time a red light was flashed. The following results were recorded for a particular driver in the same car under the same test conditions.

Speed (v km h^{-1})	10	20	30	40	50	60	70	80	90
Stopping time (t s)	1.23	1.54	1.88	2.20	2.52	2.83	3.15	3.45	3.83

a Find the mean point $(\overline{v}, \overline{t})$.

b Draw a scatter diagram of the data. Add the mean point and draw a line of best fit by eye.

c Hence estimate the stopping time for a speed of:

  i 55 km h^{-1} **ii** 110 km h^{-1}

d Which of your estimates in **c** is more likely to be reliable?

4 Consider the data set alongside.

x	2	3	6	8	13	16
y	12	17	32	41	50	61

    a Calculate the correlation coefficient r.

    b Find the regression line of y against x.

    c Estimate the value of y when $x = 10$.

5 A craft shop sells canvasses in a variety of sizes. The table below shows the area and price of each canvas type.

Area (x cm^2)	100	225	300	625	850	900
Price (£y)	6	12	13	24	30	35

    a Construct a scatter diagram for the data.

    b Calculate the correlation coefficient r.

    c Describe the correlation between *area* and *price*.

    d Find the regression line of y against x, then draw the line on the scatter diagram.

    e Estimate the price of a canvas with area 1200 cm^2. Discuss whether your estimate is likely to be reliable.

6 A drinks vendor varies the price of Supa-fizz on a daily basis. He records the number of sales of the drink as shown:

Price ($\$p$)	2.50	1.90	1.60	2.10	2.20	1.40	1.70	1.85
Sales (s)	389	450	448	386	381	458	597	431

    a Produce a scatter diagram for the data.

    b Are there any outliers? If so, should they be included in the analysis?

    c Calculate the equation of the regression line of s against p.

    d State and interpret the gradient of the regression line.

    e Do you think the regression line would give a reliable prediction of sales if Supa-fizz was priced at 50 cents? Explain your answer.

7 Eight identical flower beds contain petunias. The different beds were watered different numbers of times each week, and the number of flowers each bed produced was recorded in the table below:

Number of waterings (n)	0	1	2	3	4	5	6	7
Flowers produced (f)	18	52	86	123	158	191	228	250

    a Draw a scatter diagram for the data, and describe the correlation between the variables.

    b Find the equation of the regression line of f against n.

    c Is it likely that a causal relationship exists between these two variables? Explain your answer.

    d Plot the regression line on the scatter diagram.

    e Violet has two beds of petunias. She waters one of the beds 5 times a fortnight and the other 10 times a week.

       i How many flowers can she expect from each bed?

      ii Discuss which of your estimates is likely to be more reliable.

8 An archer shoots 10 arrows at a target from each of 12 different positions. The table below shows the distance of each position from the target, and how many shots were successful.

Distance from target (x m)	20	25	15	35	40	55	30	45	60	80	65	70
Hits (y)	9	8	8	8	7	6	9	7	4	2	3	3

a Draw a scatter diagram for the data.

b Explain why it would be appropriate to use the regression line of x against y in this case.

c Find the equation of the regression line of x against y.

d Predict the number of hits out of 10 shots fired at a distance of 100 m. Discuss the reliability of your estimate.

Chapter 20

Discrete random variables

Contents:

OPENING PROBLEM

In a sideshow game, players have a 50% chance of winning a prize worth $2, $5, $10, or $20. The probabilities of winning these prizes are given in the table below.

Prize value	$0	$2	$5	$10	$20
Probability	0.5	0.35	0.1	0.04	0.01

Things to think about:

a What is the sum of the probabilities in the table? Why must this be the answer?

b What is the most likely outcome from playing the game?

c What is the *average* result from playing the game?

d What is a *fair* price for playing the game?

Many variables in the world around us depend on chance events. Examples of such variables are:

- the number of players in your football team who will score a goal in the next match
- the time it will take you to travel to school tomorrow
- the sum of the numbers when three dice are rolled.

Because of the element of chance in these variables, we cannot predict the exact value they will take when next measured. However, we can often determine the *possible values* the variable can take, and we can assign to each possible value the **probability** of it occurring.

In this Chapter we will extend the ideas of probability we have studied to model the random variation or **distribution** of numerical variables.

 # A RANDOM VARIABLES

> A **random variable** uses numbers to describe the possible outcomes which could result from a random experiment.

A random variable is often represented by a capital letter such as X.

Random variables can be either **discrete** or **continuous**.

> A **discrete random variable** X has a set of distinct possible values.

For example, X could be:

- the number of wickets a bowler takes in an innings of cricket, so X could take the values 0, 1, 2, ..., 10
- the number of defective light bulbs in a purchase order of 50, so X could take the values 0, 1, 2, ..., 50.

To determine the value of a discrete random variable, we need to **count**.

> A **continuous random variable** X can take any value within some interval on the number line.

For example, X could be:

- the heights of men, which lie in the interval $50 \text{ cm} < X < 250 \text{ cm}$
- the volume of water in a tank, which could lie in the interval $0 \text{ m}^3 < X < 100 \text{ m}^3$.

To determine the value of a continuous random variable, we need to **measure**.

DISCRETE RANDOM VARIABLES

In this Chapter, we will focus on how discrete random variables and their distributions arise.

Example 1	◀)) Self Tutor

A supermarket has three checkouts A, B, and C. A government inspector checks the weighing scales for accuracy at each checkout. The random variable X is the number of accurate weighing scales at the supermarket.

a List the possible outcomes and the corresponding values of X.

b What value(s) of X correspond to there being:

    i one accurate scale   **ii** at least one accurate scale?

a Possible outcomes:

A	B	C	X
✗	✗	✗	0
✓	✗	✗	1
✗	✓	✗	1
✗	✗	✓	1
✗	✓	✓	2
✓	✗	✓	2
✓	✓	✗	2
✓	✓	✓	3

b   **i** $X = 1$

     ii $X = 1, 2,$ or 3

EXERCISE 20A

1 Classify each random variable as continuous or discrete:

    a the quantity of fat in a sausage   **b** the mark out of 50 for a geography test

    c the weight of a Year 12 student   **d** the volume of water in a cup of coffee

    e the number of trout in a lake   **f** the number of hairs on a cat

    g the length of a horse's mane   **h** the height of a skyscraper.

2 For each scenario:

    i Identify the random variable being considered.

    ii State whether the variable is continuous or discrete.

    iii Give possible values for the random variable.

    a To measure the rainfall over a 24-hour period in Singapore, water is collected in a rain gauge.

    b To investigate the stopping distance for a tyre with a new tread pattern, a braking experiment is carried out.

    c To check the reliability of a new type of light switch, switches are repeatedly turned off and on until they fail.

3 Suppose the spinners alongside are spun, and X is the sum of the numbers.

   a Explain why X is a discrete random variable.

   b State the possible values of X.

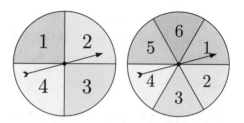

4 In the finals series of a baseball championship, the first team to win 4 games wins the championship. Let X represent the number of games played in the finals series.

   a State the possible values of X.

   b What value(s) of X correspond to the series lasting:

     i exactly 5 games   **ii** at least 6 games?

5 A supermarket has four checkouts A, B, C, and D. Management checks the weighing devices at each checkout. The random variable X is the number of weighing devices which are accurate.

   a What values can X have?

   b List the possible outcomes and the corresponding values of X.

   c What value(s) of X correspond to:

     i exactly two devices being accurate   **ii** at least two devices being accurate?

6 Suppose three coins are tossed simultaneously. Let X be the number of heads that result.

   a State the possible values of X.

   b List the possible outcomes and the corresponding values of X.

   c Are the possible values of X equally likely to occur? Explain your answer.

B   DISCRETE PROBABILITY DISTRIBUTIONS

For any random variable, there is a corresponding **probability distribution** which describes the probability that the variable will take a particular value.

The probability that the variable X takes value x is denoted $P(X = x)$.

> If X is a random variable with possible values $\{x_1, x_2, x_3, ..., x_n\}$ and corresponding probabilities $\{p_1, p_2, p_3, ..., p_n\}$ such that $P(X = x_i) = p_i$, $i = 1, ..., n$, then:
>
> - $0 \leqslant p_i \leqslant 1$ for all $i = 1, ..., n$
>
> - $\displaystyle\sum_{i=1}^{n} p_i = p_1 + p_2 + p_3 + ... + p_n = 1$
>
> - $\{p_1, ..., p_n\}$ describes the **probability distribution** of X.

For example, suppose X is the number of heads obtained when 2 coins are tossed. The possible values for X are $\{0, 1, 2\}$ with corresponding probabilities $\{\frac{1}{4}, \frac{1}{2}, \frac{1}{4}\}$. We see that $0 \leqslant p_i \leqslant 1$ for each value of i, and that the probabilities add up to 1.

We can display this probability distribution in a **table** or a **graph**.

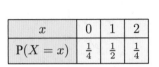

x	0	1	2
$P(X = x)$	$\frac{1}{4}$	$\frac{1}{2}$	$\frac{1}{4}$

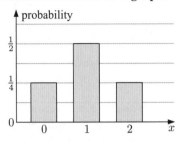

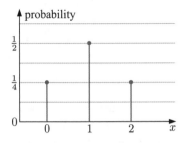

UNIFORM DISCRETE RANDOM VARIABLES

If the possible values x_1, x_2, ..., x_n of a discrete random variable X all have the same probability $\dfrac{1}{n}$ of occurring, then X is a **uniform discrete random variable**.

An example of a uniform discrete random variable is the result X when a die is rolled. The possible values of X are 1, 2, 3, 4, 5, and 6, and each value has probability $\frac{1}{6}$ of occurring.

By contrast, if two dice are rolled, the sum of the resulting numbers Y is *not* a uniform discrete random variable.

THE MODE AND MEDIAN

The **mode** of a discrete probability distribution is the most frequently occurring value of the variable. This is the data value x_i whose probability p_i is the highest.

The **median** of the distribution corresponds to the 50th percentile. If the possible values $\{x_1, x_2, ..., x_n\}$ are listed in ascending order, the median is the value x_j when the cumulative sum $p_1 + p_2 + ... + p_j$ reaches 0.5 .

Example 2 ◀)) **Self Tutor**

A magazine store recorded the number of magazines purchased by its customers in one week. 23% purchased one magazine, 38% purchased two, 21% purchased three, 13% purchased four, and 5% purchased five. Let X be the number of magazines sold to a randomly selected customer.

  a State the possible values of X.   **b** Construct a probability table for X.

  c Graph the probability distribution.   **d** Find the mode and median of X.

---

a $X = 1, 2, 3, 4,$ or 5

b

x	1	2	3	4	5
$P(X = x)$	0.23	0.38	0.21	0.13	0.05

c

d Customers are most likely to buy 2 magazines, so this is the mode of X.

Now $p_1 = 0.23$

and $p_1 + p_2 = 0.23 + 0.38 = 0.61$

Since $p_1 + p_2 \geqslant 0.5$, the median is 2 magazines.

We can also describe the probability distribution of a discrete random variable using a **probability mass function** $P(x) = P(X = x)$. The domain of the probability mass function is the set of possible values of the variable, and the range is the set of values in the probability distribution.

Example 3   ◀) **Self Tutor**

Show that $P(x) = \dfrac{x^2 + 1}{34}$, $x = 1, 2, 3, 4$ is a valid probability mass function.

$P(1) = \frac{2}{34}$, $P(2) = \frac{5}{34}$, $P(3) = \frac{10}{34}$, $P(4) = \frac{17}{34}$

All of these values obey $0 \leqslant P(x_i) \leqslant 1$, and $\displaystyle\sum_{i=1}^{n} P(x_i) = \frac{2}{34} + \frac{5}{34} + \frac{10}{34} + \frac{17}{34} = 1$

$\therefore$ $P(x)$ is a valid probability mass function.

EXERCISE 20B

1   **a** State whether each of the following is a valid probability distribution:

i

x	1	2	3	4
$P(X = x)$	0.2	0.4	0.15	0.25

ii

x	0	1	2	3
$P(X = x)$	0.2	0.3	0.4	0.2

iii

x	0	1	2	3	4
$P(X = x)$	0.2	0.2	0.2	0.2	0.2

iv

x	2	3	4	5
$P(X = x)$	0.3	0.4	0.5	−0.2

b For which of the probability distributions in **a** is X a uniform random variable?

2 Find k in each of these probability distributions:

a

x	0	1	2
$P(X = x)$	0.3	k	0.5

b

x	0	1	2	3
$P(X = x)$	k	$2k$	$3k$	k

3 Consider the probability distribution alongside.

x	0	1	2	3
$P(X = x)$	0.1	0.25	0.45	a

a Find the value of a.

b Is X a uniform discrete random variable? Explain your answer.

c State the mode of the distribution.

d Find $P(X \geqslant 2)$.

4 The probability distribution for Jason scoring X home runs in each game during his baseball career is given in the following table:

x	0	1	2	3	4	5
$P(x)$	a	0.3333	0.1088	0.0084	0.0007	0.0000

  a State the value of $P(2)$.

  b Find the value of a. Explain what this number means.

  c Find the value of $P(1) + P(2) + P(3) + P(4) + P(5)$. Explain what this means.

  d Draw a graph of $P(x)$ against x.

  e Find the mode and median of the distribution.

5 A policeman inspected the safety of tyres on cars passing through a checkpoint. The number of tyres X which needed replacing on each car followed the probability distribution below.

x	0	1	2	3	4
$P(X = x)$	0.68	0.2	0.06	k	0.02

  a Find the value of k.　　　　　　**b** Find the mode of the distribution.

  c Find $P(X > 1)$, and interpret this value.

6 Let X be the result when the spinner alongside is spun.

  a Display the probability distribution of X in a table.

  b Graph the probability distribution.

  c Find the mode and median of the distribution.

  d Find $P(X \leqslant 3)$.

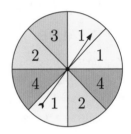

7 100 people were surveyed about the number of bedrooms in their house. 24 people had one bedroom, 35 people had two bedrooms, 27 people had three bedrooms, and 14 people had four bedrooms. Let X be the number of bedrooms a randomly selected person has in their house.

  a State the possible values of X.　　　**b** Construct a probability table for X.

  c Find the mode and median of the distribution.

8 A group of 25 basketballers took shots from the free throw line until they scored a goal. 12 of the players only needed one shot, 7 players took two shots, 2 players took three shots, and the rest took four shots. Let X be the number of shots a randomly selected player needs to score a goal.

  a State the possible values of X.　　　**b** Construct a probability table for X.

  c Find the mode and median of the distribution.

9 Show that the following are valid probability mass functions:

  a $P(x) = \dfrac{x+1}{10}$ for $x = 0,\ 1,\ 2,\ 3$　　　**b** $P(x) = \dfrac{6}{11x}$ for $x = 1,\ 2,\ 3$.

10 Find k for the following probability mass functions:

  a $P(x) = k(x+2)$ for $x = 1,\ 2,\ 3$　　　**b** $P(x) = \dfrac{k}{x+1}$ for $x = 0,\ 1,\ 2,\ 3$.

11 A discrete random variable X has the probability mass function $P(x) = \dfrac{4x - x^2}{a}$ for $x = 0, 1, 2, 3$.

    a Find the value of a.   **b** Find $P(X = 1)$.

    c Find the mode of the distribution.

12 The discrete random variable X has probability mass function $P(x) = a\left(\frac{1}{3}\right)^{x-1}$, $x = 1, 2, 3, ...$

    a Find the sum of the infinite geometric series $\sum\limits_{i=1}^{\infty} \left(\frac{1}{3}\right)^{i-1}$.

    b Hence find the value of a.

13 A discrete random variable X has probability mass function $P(x) = a\left(\frac{2}{5}\right)^x$, $x = 0, 1, 2, 3, ...$ Find the value of a.

C   EXPECTATION

We have already seen how probabilities can be used to predict the number of times we *expect* an event to occur when an experiment is repeated many times.

We can consider the **expected value** or **expectation** of a random variable in a similar way.

EXPECTED VALUE

When the spinner alongside is spun, players are awarded the resulting number of points. On average, how many points can we *expect* to be awarded per spin?

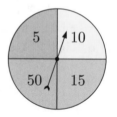

For every 4 spins, we would expect that on average, each score will be spun once. The total score in this case would be $50 + 15 + 10 + 5 = 80$, which is an average of $\frac{80}{4} = 20$ points per spin.

Alternatively, we can write the average score as

$\frac{1}{4}(50 + 15 + 10 + 5)$

$= \frac{1}{4} \times 50 + \frac{1}{4} \times 15 + \frac{1}{4} \times 10 + \frac{1}{4} \times 5$

$= 20$ points.

> It is impossible to score 20 points on any given spin, but over many spins we *expect* an average of 20 points per spin.

Notice that each score is multiplied by its probability of occurring.

For a random variable X with possible values $x_1, x_2, x_3, ..., x_n$ and associated probabilities $p_1, p_2, ..., p_n$, the **expected value** of X is

$$\mathbf{E}(X) = \sum_{i=1}^{n} x_i p_i$$

$$= x_1 p_1 + x_2 p_2 + ... + x_n p_n$$

$E(X)$ is the **mean** of the probability distribution of X. It is sometimes denoted μ.

Example 4   ◀️ **Self Tutor**

Consider the magazine store from **Example 2**.

Find the expected number of magazines bought by each customer. Explain what this represents.

The probability table is:

x_i	1	2	3	4	5
p_i	0.23	0.38	0.21	0.13	0.05

In **Example 2** we found the mode and median for this distribution.

$$E(X) = \sum_{i=1}^{n} x_i p_i$$
$$= 1(0.23) + 2(0.38) + 3(0.21) + 4(0.13) + 5(0.05)$$
$$= 2.39$$

In the long term, the average number of magazines purchased per customer is 2.39.

EXERCISE 20C.1

1 Find $E(X)$ for the following probability distributions:

a

x_i	1	2	3
p_i	0.4	0.5	0.1

b

x_i	0	1	2	3	4
p_i	0.1	0.2	0.15	0.2	0.35

c

x_i	0	2	5	10
p_i	0.2	0.35	0.27	0.18

d

x_i	10	15	30	60
p_i	$\frac{1}{4}$	$\frac{1}{3}$	$\frac{1}{12}$	$\frac{1}{3}$

2 Consider the probability distribution alongside.

a Find the value of a.

b Find the mode of the distribution.

c Find the mean μ of the distribution.

x	1	3	5
$P(X = x)$	$\frac{2}{5}$	a	$\frac{1}{10}$

3 When the spinner alongside is spun, players are awarded the resulting number of points. In the long term, how many points can we expect to be awarded per spin?

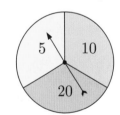

4 When Ernie goes fishing, he catches 0, 1, 2, or 3 fish, with the probabilities shown.
On average, how many fish would you expect Ernie to catch on a fishing trip?

Number of fish	0	1	2	3
Probability	0.17	0.28	0.36	0.19

5 Each time Pam visits the library, she borrows either 1, 2, 3, 4, or 5 books, with the probabilities shown.

Number of books	1	2	3	4	5
Probability	0.16	0.15	a	0.28	0.16

a Find the value of a.   **b** Find the mode of the distribution.

c On average, how many books does Pam borrow per visit?

6 Lachlan randomly selects a ball from a bag containing 5 red balls, 2 green balls, and 1 white ball. He is then allowed to take a particular number of lollies from a jar according to the colour of the ball.

Find the average number of lollies that Lachlan can expect to receive.

Colour	Number of lollies
Red	4
Green	6
White	10

7 When ten-pin bowler Jenna bowls her first bowl of a frame, she always knocks down at least 8 pins. $\frac{1}{3}$ of the time she knocks down 8 pins, and $\frac{2}{5}$ of the time she knocks down 9 pins.

   a Find the probability that she knocks down all 10 pins on the first bowl.

   b On average, how many pins does Jenna knock down with her first bowl?

8 Given that $E(X) = 2.5$, find a and b.

x	1	2	3	4
$P(X = x)$	0.3	a	b	0.2

9 When Brad's soccer team plays an offensive strategy, they win 30% of the time and lose 55% of the time. When they play a defensive strategy, they win 20% of the time and lose 30% of the time.

On the league table, teams are awarded 3 points for a win, 1 point for a draw, and no points for a loss.

   a Find the probability that Brad's team will draw a match under each strategy.

   b Calculate the expected number of points per game under each strategy.

   c In the long run, is it better for the team to play an offensive or defensive strategy?

   d Should the strategy change if teams are awarded 4 points instead of 3 points for a win?

10 Every Thursday, Zoe meets her friends in the city for dinner. There are two car parks nearby, the costs for which are shown below:

Car park A

Time	Cost
0 - 1 hour	$7
1 - 2 hours	$12
2 - 3 hours	$15
3 - 4 hours	$19

Car park B

Time	Cost
0 - 1 hour	$6.50
1 - 2 hours	$11
2 - 3 hours	$16
3 - 4 hours	$18.50

Zoe's dinner takes 1 - 2 hours 20% of the time, 2 - 3 hours 70% of the time, and 3 - 4 hours 10% of the time.

   a Which car park is cheapest for Zoe if she stays:

   i 1 - 2 hours   **ii** 2 - 3 hours   **iii** 3 - 4 hours?

   b When Zoe parks her car, she does not know how long she will stay. Which car park do you recommend for her? Explain your answer.

11 An insurance policy covers a $20 000 sapphire ring against theft and loss. If the ring is stolen then the insurance company will pay the policy owner in full. If the ring is lost then they will pay the owner $8000. From past experience, the insurance company knows that the probability of theft is 0.0025, and the probability of loss is 0.03. How much should the company charge to cover the ring in order that their expected return is $100?

FAIR GAMES

In gambling, the **expected gain** of the player from each game is the expected return or payout from the game, less the amount it cost them to play.

A game is said to be **fair** if the expected gain is zero.

> Suppose X represents the gain of a player from each game.
> The game is **fair** if $E(X) = 0$.

DISCUSSION

Would you expect a gambling game to be "fair"?

Example 5
◀)) **Self Tutor**

In a game of chance, a player spins a square spinner labelled 1, 2, 3, 4. The player wins an amount of money according to the table alongside.

Number	1	2	3	4
Winnings	$1	$2	$5	$8

a Find the expected return for one spin of the spinner.

b Find the expected *gain* of the player if it costs $5 to play each game.

c Discuss whether you would recommend playing this game.

---

a Let Y denote the return or payout from each spin.

Each outcome is equally likely, so the probability for each outcome is $\frac{1}{4}$

∴ the expected return $= E(Y) = \frac{1}{4} \times 1 + \frac{1}{4} \times 2 + \frac{1}{4} \times 5 + \frac{1}{4} \times 8 = \$4.$

b Let X denote the *gain* of the player from each game.

Since it costs $5 to play the game, the expected gain $= E(X) = E(Y) - \$5$
$$= \$4 - \$5$$
$$= -\$1$$

c Since $E(X) \neq 0$, the game is not fair. In particular, since $E(X) = -\$1$, we expect the player to lose $1 on average with each spin. We would not recommend that a person play the game.

EXERCISE 20C.2

1 A dice game costs $2 to play. If an odd number is rolled, the player receives $3. If an even number is rolled, the player receives $1.

Determine whether the game is fair.

2   A man rolls a regular six-sided die. He wins the number of dollars shown on the uppermost face.

   a   Find the expected return from one roll of the die.

   b   Find the expected *gain* if it costs $4 to play the game.

   c   Would you advise the man to play many games?

3   A roulette wheel has 18 red numbers, 18 black numbers, and 1 green number. Each number has an equal chance of occurring. I place a bet of $2 on red. If a red is spun, I receive my $2 back plus another $2. Otherwise I lose my $2.

   a   Calculate the expected gain from this bet.

   b   If the same bet is made 100 times, what is the expected result?

4   A person pays $5 to play a game with a pair of coins. If two heads appear then $10 is won. If a head and a tail appear then $3 is won. If two tails appear then $1 is won.

Let X be the gain of the person from each game. Find the expected value of X.

5   In a carnival game, a player randomly selects a ticket from a box of tickets numbered 1 to 20. If the selected number is a multiple of 3, the player wins 5 tokens. If the selected number is a multiple of 10 the player wins 10 tokens.

   a   Calculate the probability of a player winning:

      i   5 tokens   **ii**   10 tokens.

   b   Let X be the number of tokens won from playing this game. Find the expected value of X.

   c   If it costs 3 tokens to play the game, would you recommend playing the game many times? Explain your answer.

6   A person selects a disc from a bag containing 10 black discs, 4 blue discs, and 1 gold disc. They win $1 for a black disc, $5 for a blue disc, and $20 for the gold disc. The game costs $4 to play.

   a   Calculate the expected gain for this game, and hence show that the game is not fair.

   b   To make the game fair, the prize money for selecting the gold disc is increased. Find the new prize money for selecting the gold disc.

7   At a charity event there is a money-raising game involving a pair of ordinary dice. The game costs $a to play. When the two dice are rolled, their sum is described by the variable X. A sum which is less than 4 or between 7 and 9 inclusive gives a return of $\$\frac{a}{3}$. A result between 4 and 6 inclusive gives a return of $7. A result of 10 or more gives a return of $21.

   a   Determine $P(X \leqslant 3)$, $P(4 \leqslant X \leqslant 6)$, $P(7 \leqslant X \leqslant 9)$, and $P(X \geqslant 10)$.

   b   Show that the expected gain of a player is given by $\frac{1}{6}(35 - 5a)$ dollars.

   c   What value would a need to have for the game to be "fair"?

   d   Explain why the organisers would not let a be 4.

   e   The organisers set $a = 9$ for the event, and the game is played 2406 times. Estimate the amount of money raised by this game.

8 In a fundraising game "Lucky 11", a player selects 3 cards without replacement from a box containing 5 red, 4 blue, and 3 green cards.

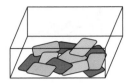

The player wins $11 if the cards drawn are all the same colour *or* are one of each colour.

If the organiser of the game wants to make an average of $1 per game, how much should they charge to play it?

ACTIVITY   GREEDY PIGS

In this Activity, we will play a variant of the dice game **Greedy Pigs**. We will use expected value to find a strategy for playing the game.

In each turn of the game, a player rolls a die a number of times, accumulating points according to the numbers rolled. After each roll, the player can either end their turn and "bank" the points accumulated so far, or continue rolling in an attempt to score more points. However, if the player rolls a 1, the player loses all of the points accumulated on that turn, and their turn is over.

What to do:

1 Play the game in pairs, so that each player has 20 turns.
Which player scored the most points in total? Discuss the strategies you used during the game. Did your strategy change during the game?

2 Expected value can be used to find a strategy that, *on average*, will maximise a player's score.

  a Explain why it would not be sensible to:
    i stop while you have scored less than 5 points
    ii keep going if you have scored over 50 points.

  b Suppose you have scored 10 points so far in your turn. Let X be the gain or loss from rolling again.
    i Construct a probability distribution for X.
    ii Show that $\mathrm{E}(X)$ is positive.
    iii What does $\mathrm{E}(X)$ tell us about whether we should roll again at 10 points?

  c Find the lowest score at which, on average, it is not beneficial to continue rolling. Hence describe a strategy that will maximise your score in the long term.

  d Can you think of situations where this strategy may not be the best strategy for winning the game?

3 How would the strategy for maximising your score change if your turn ended when a 6 was rolled, rather than a 1?

THE BINOMIAL DISTRIBUTION

Suppose X = the number of blues which result from spinning this spinner *once*.

The probability distribution of X is:

x	0	1
$P(X = x)$	$\frac{1}{4}$	$\frac{3}{4}$

Now suppose we spin the spinner n times and count the number of blues that result. The probability that we get a blue is the same for each spin, and each spin is independent of every other spin. This is an example of a **binomial experiment**.

> In a **binomial experiment**:
> - there are a fixed number of **independent trials**
> - there are only *two* possible results for each trial:
>   **success** if some event occurs, or **failure** if the event does not occur
> - the probability of success is the same for each trial.
>
> If X is the number of successes in a binomial experiment with n trials, each with probability of success p, then X is a **binomial random variable.**

THE PROBABILITY DISTRIBUTION OF A BINOMIAL RANDOM VARIABLE

Consider the spinner above with 3 blue sectors and 1 white sector. Suppose a "success" is a blue result and let X be the number of "successes" in 3 spins of the spinner. X is a binomial random variable with $n = 3$ and $p = \frac{3}{4}$, and can take the values 0, 1, 2, or 3.

To help determine the probability distribution of X, we first draw a tree diagram and find the probabilities associated with each possible outcome. We let B represent blue and W represent white.

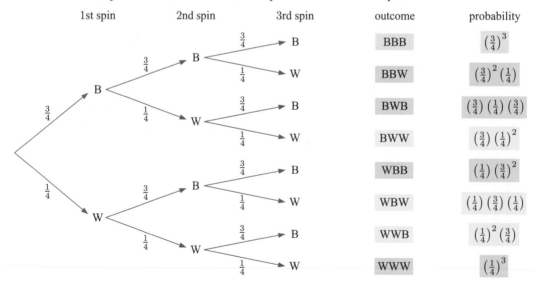

The outcomes have been shaded according to the value of X.

The probabilities associated with each value of X are:

$P(X = 0) = P(WWW)$

$\qquad = \left(\frac{1}{4}\right)^3$ {outcome shaded green}

$P(X = 1) = P(BWW \text{ or } WBW \text{ or } WWB)$

$\qquad = \left(\frac{3}{4}\right)\left(\frac{1}{4}\right)^2 + \left(\frac{1}{4}\right)\left(\frac{3}{4}\right)\left(\frac{1}{4}\right) + \left(\frac{1}{4}\right)^2\left(\frac{3}{4}\right)$

$\qquad = ③ \times \left(\frac{3}{4}\right)\left(\frac{1}{4}\right)^2$ {outcomes shaded yellow}

$P(X = 2) = P(BBW \text{ or } BWB \text{ or } WBB)$

$\qquad = \left(\frac{3}{4}\right)^2\left(\frac{1}{4}\right) + \left(\frac{3}{4}\right)\left(\frac{1}{4}\right)\left(\frac{3}{4}\right) + \left(\frac{1}{4}\right)\left(\frac{3}{4}\right)^2$

$\qquad = 3 \times \left(\frac{3}{4}\right)^2\left(\frac{1}{4}\right)$ {outcomes shaded red}

$P(X = 3) = P(BBB)$

$\qquad = \left(\frac{3}{4}\right)^3$ {outcome shaded blue}

Notice that for any particular value of X, each outcome with this property will have the same probability of occurring. The *order* in which blues and whites appear does not matter.

In **Chapter 1** we saw that $\ {}^nC_r = \binom{n}{r} = \dfrac{n!}{r!(n-r)!}\ $ is the number of ways in which we can obtain r successes from n trials, ignoring order.

For example, the circled factor ③ is the number of ways of getting 1 success out of 3 trials, or $\binom{3}{1}$.

We can use this notation to write:

$P(X = 0) = \left(\frac{1}{4}\right)^3 \qquad = \binom{3}{0}\left(\frac{3}{4}\right)^0\left(\frac{1}{4}\right)^3 \approx 0.0156$

$P(X = 1) = 3\left(\frac{1}{4}\right)^2\left(\frac{3}{4}\right)^1 = \binom{3}{1}\left(\frac{3}{4}\right)^1\left(\frac{1}{4}\right)^2 \approx 0.1406$

$P(X = 2) = 3\left(\frac{1}{4}\right)^1\left(\frac{3}{4}\right)^2 = \binom{3}{2}\left(\frac{3}{4}\right)^2\left(\frac{1}{4}\right)^1 \approx 0.4219$

$P(X = 3) = \left(\frac{3}{4}\right)^3 \qquad = \binom{3}{3}\left(\frac{3}{4}\right)^3\left(\frac{1}{4}\right)^0 \approx 0.4219$

So, $P(X = x) = \binom{3}{x}\left(\frac{3}{4}\right)^x\left(\frac{1}{4}\right)^{3-x}$ where $x = 0,\ 1,\ 2,\ 3$.

The sum of the probabilities $\qquad P(X = 0) + P(X = 1) + P(X = 2) + P(X = 3)$

$\qquad\qquad = \left(\frac{1}{4}\right)^3 + 3\left(\frac{1}{4}\right)^2\left(\frac{3}{4}\right) + 3\left(\frac{1}{4}\right)\left(\frac{3}{4}\right)^2 + \left(\frac{3}{4}\right)^3$

which is the binomial expansion of $\left(\frac{1}{4} + \frac{3}{4}\right)^3$.

Evaluating, $\left(\frac{1}{4} + \frac{3}{4}\right)^3 = 1$ which must be the case since all possibilities are covered.

Suppose X is a binomial random variable with n independent trials and probability of success p. The probability mass function of X is:

$$P(x) = P(X = x) = \underbrace{\binom{n}{x}}\ \underbrace{p^x(1-p)^{n-x}} \quad \text{where } x = 0,\ 1,\ 2,\ ....,\ n.$$

"~" reads "is distributed as".

number of ways x successes
can be ordered amongst the
n trials

probability of obtaining x successes
and $n - x$ failures in a particular
order

The probability distribution of X is called the **binomial distribution**, and we write $X \sim B(n,\ p)$.

Example 6   ◄)) **Self Tutor**

a Expand $\left(\frac{9}{10} + \frac{1}{10}\right)^5$.

b An archer has a 90% chance of hitting a target with each arrow. If 5 arrows are fired, determine the chance of hitting the target:
   i twice only   ii at most 3 times.

a $\left(\frac{9}{10} + \frac{1}{10}\right)^5$

$$= \sum_{k=0}^{5} \binom{5}{k}\left(\frac{9}{10}\right)^k\left(\frac{1}{10}\right)^{5-k}$$

$$= \left(\frac{1}{10}\right)^5 + 5\left(\frac{9}{10}\right)\left(\frac{1}{10}\right)^4 + 10\left(\frac{9}{10}\right)^2\left(\frac{1}{10}\right)^3 + 10\left(\frac{9}{10}\right)^3\left(\frac{1}{10}\right)^2 + 5\left(\frac{9}{10}\right)^4\left(\frac{1}{10}\right) + \left(\frac{9}{10}\right)^5$$

b The probability of success with each arrow is $p = \frac{9}{10}$.

Let X be the number of arrows that hit the target.

The expansion in a gives the probability distribution for X.

$$\underbrace{\left(\frac{1}{10}\right)^5}_{\substack{\text{P}(X=0) \\ \text{5 misses}}} + \underbrace{5\left(\frac{9}{10}\right)\left(\frac{1}{10}\right)^4}_{\substack{\text{P}(X=1) \\ \text{1 hit} \\ \text{4 misses}}} + \underbrace{10\left(\frac{9}{10}\right)^2\left(\frac{1}{10}\right)^3}_{\substack{\text{P}(X=2) \\ \text{2 hits} \\ \text{3 misses}}} + \underbrace{10\left(\frac{9}{10}\right)^3\left(\frac{1}{10}\right)^2}_{\substack{\text{P}(X=3) \\ \text{3 hits} \\ \text{2 misses}}} + \underbrace{5\left(\frac{9}{10}\right)^4\left(\frac{1}{10}\right)}_{\substack{\text{P}(X=4) \\ \text{4 hits} \\ \text{1 miss}}} + \underbrace{\left(\frac{9}{10}\right)^5}_{\substack{\text{P}(X=5) \\ \text{5 hits}}}$$

i P(hits twice only) $= \text{P}(X = 2)$

$$= 10\left(\frac{9}{10}\right)^2\left(\frac{1}{10}\right)^3$$

$$= 0.0081$$

ii P(hits at most 3 times) $= \text{P}(X \leqslant 3)$

$$= \text{P}(X = 0) + \text{P}(X = 1) + \text{P}(X = 2) + \text{P}(X = 3)$$

$$= \left(\frac{1}{10}\right)^5 + 5\left(\frac{9}{10}\right)\left(\frac{1}{10}\right)^4 + 10\left(\frac{9}{10}\right)^2\left(\frac{1}{10}\right)^3 + 10\left(\frac{9}{10}\right)^3\left(\frac{1}{10}\right)^2$$

$$\approx 0.0815$$

EXERCISE 20D

1 For which of these probability experiments does the binomial distribution apply? Explain your answers.

   a A coin is thrown 100 times. The variable is the number of heads.

   b One hundred coins are each thrown once. The variable is the number of heads.

   c A box contains 5 blue and 3 red marbles. I draw out 5 marbles one at a time, replacing each marble before the next is drawn. The variable is the number of red marbles drawn.

   d A box contains 5 blue and 3 red marbles. I draw out 5 marbles without replacement. The variable is the number of red marbles drawn.

   e A large bin contains ten thousand bolts, 1% of which are faulty. I draw a sample of 10 bolts from the bin. The variable is the number of faulty bolts.

2 a Expand $(p + q)^4$.

   b If a coin is tossed *four* times, what is the probability of getting:
      i 4 heads   ii 3 heads   iii 2 heads?

3 a Expand $(p+q)^5$.

   b If *five* coins are tossed simultaneously, what is the probability of getting:

     i 4 heads and 1 tail in any order

     ii 2 heads and 3 tails in any order

     iii 4 heads and then 1 tail?

4 a Expand $\left(\frac{2}{3}+\frac{1}{3}\right)^4$.

   b A box of chocolates contains strawberry creams and almond centres in the ratio $2:1$. Four chocolates are selected at random, with replacement. Find the probability of getting:

     i all strawberry creams

     ii two of each type

     iii at least 2 strawberry creams.

5 a Expand $\left(\frac{3}{4}+\frac{1}{4}\right)^5$.

   b In New Zealand in 1946 there were two different coins of value one florin. These were "normal" kiwis and "flat back" kiwis, in the ratio $3:1$. From a very large batch of 1946 florins, five were selected at random with replacement. Find the probability that:

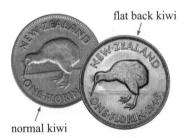

flat back kiwi

normal kiwi

     i two were "flat backs"

     ii at least 3 were "flat backs"

     iii at most 3 were "normal" kiwis.

6 The probability mass function for $X \sim B(n,\,p)$ is $P(x) = \binom{n}{x} p^x (1-p)^{n-x}$.

   a Use the binomial theorem to show that $\displaystyle\sum_{x=0}^{n} P(x) = 1$.

   b *Hence* explain why $0 \leqslant P(x) \leqslant 1$ for all $x = 0, 1, ..., n$.

   c What do **a** and **b** tell you about $P(x)$?

INVESTIGATION 1   THE GRAPH OF A BINOMIAL DISTRIBUTION

In this Investigation we will explore the graph of a binomial distribution and how its shape varies with changes to n and p.

What to do:

1 Click on the icon to access the demonstration. It shows the graph of the binomial distribution for $X \sim B(n,\,p)$. Set $n = 25$ and $p = 0.1$.

DEMO

   a What is the mode of X?

   b Describe the shape of the distribution.

2 Use the slider to change the value of p. Describe how the *shape* of the distribution changes as p changes.

3 Reset p to 0.1. Use the slider to change the value of n.

How does this affect the shape of the distribution? What happens to the shape of the binomial distribution as the number of trials n increases?

E | USING TECHNOLOGY TO FIND BINOMIAL PROBABILITIES

We can quickly calculate binomial probabilities using a graphics calculator.

For example:

GRAPHICS CALCULATOR INSTRUCTIONS

- To find the probability $P(X = k)$ that the variable takes the value k, we use the **binomial probability function**.

- To find the probability that the variable takes a *range* of values, such as $P(X \leqslant k)$ or $P(X \geqslant k)$, we use the **binomial cumulative probability function**.

Some calculator models, such as the **TI-84 Plus CE**, only allow you to calculate $P(X \leqslant k)$. To find the probability $P(X \geqslant k)$ for these models, it is often easiest to find the complement $P(X \leqslant k - 1)$ and use $P(X \geqslant k) = 1 - P(X \leqslant k - 1)$.

Example 7 | ◀)) Self Tutor

72% of union members are in favour of a certain change to their conditions of employment. A random sample of five members is taken. Find the probability that:

a three members are in favour of the change in conditions

b at least three members are in favour of the changed conditions.

Let X denote the number of members in the sample in favour of the change.

$n = 5$, so $X = 0, 1, 2, 3, 4,$ or $5,$ and $p = 72\% = 0.72$

$\therefore$ $X \sim B(5, 0.72)$.

a $P(X = 3) = \binom{5}{3}(0.72)^3(0.28)^2 \approx 0.293$

Casio fx-CG50	TI-84 Plus CE	TI-*n*spire
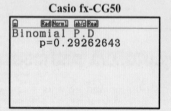	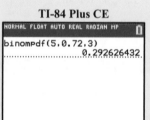	

b $P(X \geqslant 3) \approx 0.862$

Casio fx-CG50	TI-84 Plus CE	TI-*n*spire
	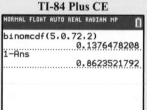	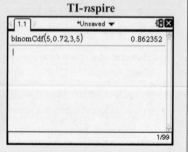

EXERCISE 20E

1   5% of electric light bulbs are defective at manufacture. 6 bulbs are randomly tested, with each one being replaced before the next is chosen. Determine the probability that:

    a two are defective
        b at least one is defective.

2   Records show that 6% of the items assembled on a production line are faulty. A random sample of 12 items is selected with replacement. Find the probability that:

    a none will be faulty
        b at most one will be faulty

    c at least two will be faulty
        d less than four will be faulty.

3   The local bus service does not have a good reputation. The 8 am bus will run late on average two days out of every five. For any week of the year taken at random, find the probability of the 8 am bus being on time:

    a all 7 days
        b only on Monday

    c on any 6 days
        d on at least 4 days.

4   In a multiple choice test there are 10 questions. Each question has 5 choices, one of which is correct. Raj knows absolutely nothing about the subject, and guesses each answer at random. Given that the pass mark is 70%, determine the probability that he will pass.

5   An infectious flu virus is spreading through a school. The probability of a randomly selected student having the flu next week is 0.3. Mr C has a class of 25 students.

    a Calculate the probability that 2 or more students from Mr C's class will have the flu next week.

    b If more than 20% of the students have the flu next week, a class test will have to be cancelled. What is the probability that the test will be cancelled?

6   During a season, a basketball player has an 85% success rate in shooting from the free throw line. In one match the basketballer has 20 shots from the free throw line.
Find the probability that the basketballer is successful with:

    a all 20 throws
        b at least 18 throws

    c between 14 and 17 (inclusive) throws.

7   Martina beats Jelena in 2 games out of 3 at tennis. What is the probability that Jelena wins a set of tennis 6 games to 4?
Hint: What does the score after 9 games need to be?

8   A fair coin is tossed 200 times. Find the probability of obtaining:

    a between 90 and 110 (inclusive) heads
        b more than 95 but less than 105 heads.

9   **a** Find the probability of rolling double sixes with a pair of dice.

    b Suppose a pair of dice is rolled 500 times. Find the probability of rolling between 10 and 20 (inclusive) double sixes.

10 Shelley must pass through 15 traffic lights on her way to work. She has probability 0.6 of being stopped at any given traffic light. If she is stopped at more than 11 traffic lights, she will be late for work.

   a Find the probability that Shelley will be late for work on a given day.

   b Find the probability that Shelley is on time for work each day of a 5 day week.

   c Shelley wants to increase the probability in **b** to at least 80%. She decides to leave home a little earlier, so she must now be stopped at more than 12 traffic lights in order to be late. Has Shelley achieved her goal? Justify your answer.

11 A hot water unit relies on 20 solar components for its power, and will operate provided at least one of its 20 components is working. The probability that an individual solar component will fail in a year is 0.85, and the failure of each individual component is independent of the others.

   a Find the probability that the hot water unit will fail within one year.

   b Find the smallest number of solar components required to ensure that a hot water service like this one is operating at the end of one year with a probability of at least 0.98 .

F   THE MEAN AND STANDARD DEVIATION OF A BINOMIAL DISTRIBUTION

INVESTIGATION 2   THE MEAN AND STANDARD DEVIATION OF A BINOMIAL DISTRIBUTION

In this Investigation we will use a calculator to calculate the mean and standard deviation of several binomial distributions. A spreadsheet can also be used to speed up the process.

GRAPHICS CALCULATOR INSTRUCTIONS

What to do:

1 We will first calculate the mean and standard deviation for the variable $X \sim B(30, 0.25)$.

   a Enter the possible values for X from $x = 0$ to $x = 30$ into **List 1**, and their corresponding binomial probabilities $P(X = x) = \binom{30}{x}(0.25)^x(0.75)^{30-x}$ into **List 2**.

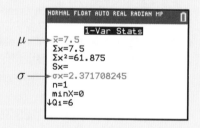

   b Calculate the descriptive statistics for the distribution. You should obtain the results in the screenshot.

2 Copy and complete the following table for distributions with other values of n and p.

	$p = 0.1$	$p = 0.25$	$p = 0.5$	$p = 0.7$
$n = 10$				
$n = 30$		$\mu = 7.5$ $\sigma \approx 2.3717$		
$n = 50$				

3 Compare your values with the formulae $\mu = np$ and $\sigma = \sqrt{np(1-p)}$.

From this **Investigation** you should have observed the following results:

> Suppose X is a binomial random variable with parameters n and p, so $X \sim B(n, p)$.
>
> - The **mean** of X is $\mu = np$.
> - The **variance** of X is $\sigma^2 = np(1 - p)$.
> - The **standard deviation** of X is $\sigma = \sqrt{np(1 - p)}$.

Click on this icon to see a proof for the mean of the binomial distribution.

PROOF

Example 8   ◀)) **Self Tutor**

A fair die is rolled twelve times, and X is the number of sixes that result.
Find the mean, variance, and standard deviation of X.

This is a binomial distribution with $n = 12$ and $p = \frac{1}{6}$, so $X \sim B(12, \frac{1}{6})$.

$$\mu = np \qquad\qquad \sigma^2 = np(1 - p) \qquad \text{and} \qquad \sigma = \sqrt{\sigma^2}$$
$$= 12 \times \tfrac{1}{6} \qquad\qquad = 12 \times \tfrac{1}{6} \times \tfrac{5}{6} \qquad\qquad\qquad = \sqrt{\tfrac{5}{3}}$$
$$= 2 \qquad\qquad\qquad = \tfrac{5}{3} \qquad\qquad\qquad\qquad \approx 1.291$$

We expect a six to be rolled 2 times, with variance $\frac{5}{3}$ and standard deviation 1.291.

EXERCISE 20F

1 Suppose $X \sim B(6, p)$. For each of the following cases:
  i Find the mean and standard deviation of X.
  ii Graph the distribution using a column graph.
  iii Comment on the shape of the distribution.

  a $p = 0.5$ **b** $p = 0.2$ **c** $p = 0.8$

2 A coin is tossed 10 times and X is the number of heads which occur. Find the mean and variance of X.

3 Bolts produced by a machine vary in quality. The probability that a given bolt is defective is 0.04. Random samples of 30 bolts are taken from the week's production.

  a If X is the number of defective bolts in a sample, find the mean and standard deviation of X.
  b If Y is the number of non-defective bolts in a sample, find the mean and standard deviation of Y.

4 A city restaurant knows that 13% of reservations are not honoured, which means the group does not arrive. Suppose the restaurant receives 30 reservations. Let the random variable X be the number of groups that do not arrive. Find the mean and standard deviation of X.

5 A new drug has a 75% probability of curing a patient within one week. Suppose 38 patients are treated using this drug. Let X be the number of patients who are cured within a week.

  a Find the mean μ and standard deviation σ of X.   **b** Find $P(\mu - \sigma < X < \mu + \sigma)$.

6 Let X be the number of heads which occur when a coin is tossed 100 times, and Y be the number of ones which occur when a die is rolled 300 times.

  a Show that the mean of both distributions is 50.

  b Calculate the standard deviation of each distribution.

  c Which variable do you think is more likely to lie between 45 and 55 (inclusive)? Explain your answer.

  d Find: **i** $P(45 \leqslant X \leqslant 55)$ **ii** $P(45 \leqslant Y \leqslant 55)$

REVIEW SET 20A

1 Determine whether the following variables are discrete or continuous:

  a the number of attempts to pass a driving test

  b the length of time before a phone loses its battery charge

  c the number of phone calls made before a salesperson has sold 3 products.

2 **a** State whether each of the following is a valid probability distribution:

i

x	1	2	3
$P(X = x)$	0.6	0.25	0.15

ii

x	0	2	5	10
$P(X = x)$	0.3	0.5	0.1	0.2

iii

x	0	1	2	3
$P(X = x)$	0.4	−0.2	0.35	0.45

iv

x	2	3	4	5
$P(X = x)$	0.25	0.25	0.25	0.25

v

x	2	3
$P(X = x)$	0.7	0.3

vi

x	0	1
$P(X = x)$	0.28	0.72

  b For which of the probability distributions in **a** is X a uniform discrete random variable?

3 $P(X = x) = \dfrac{a}{x^2 + 1}$, $x = 0, 1, 2, 3$ is a probability mass function.

  a Find the value of a.   **b** Find $P(X \geqslant 1)$.

4 A random variable X has the probability mass function $P(x)$ described in the table.

x	0	1	2	3	4
$P(x)$	0.10	0.30	0.45	0.10	k

  a Find k.

  b Find $P(X \geqslant 3)$.

  c Find the mode of the distribution.

  d Find the expected value $E(X)$ for the distribution.

5 Three green balls and two yellow balls are placed in a hat. Two balls are randomly drawn without replacement, and X is the number of green balls drawn.

  a Explain why X is a discrete random variable.

  b State the possible values of X.

  c Construct a probability table for X.

  d Find the expected number of green balls drawn.

6 The faces of a die are labelled 1, 3, 3, 4, 6, 6. Let X be the result when the die is rolled. Find the expected value of X.

7   Lakshmi rolls a regular six-sided die. She wins twice the number of dollars as the number rolled.

   a   How much does Lakshmi expect to win from one roll of the die?

   b   If it costs $8 to play the game, would you advise Lakshmi to play many games? Explain your answer.

8   Suppose X is the number of marsupials entering a park at night. It is suspected that X has a probability mass function $P(x) = a(x^2 - 8x)$ where $x = 0, 1, 2, 3, ..., 8$.

   a   Find the constant a.

   b   Find the expected number of marsupials entering the park on a given night.

9   **a**   Expand $\left(\frac{4}{5} + \frac{1}{5}\right)^5$.

   b   With every attempt, Jack has an 80% chance of kicking a goal. In one quarter of a match he has 5 kicks for goal. Determine the probability that he scores:

   i   3 goals then misses twice   **ii**   3 goals and misses twice.

10   Consider the two spinners illustrated:

pentagonal   square
spinner   spinner
$\frac{1}{4}$ → R

$\frac{3}{5}$ → R
                     → R'

→ R'
     → R
     → R'

   a   Copy and complete the tree diagram which shows all possible results when the two spinners are spun together.

   b   Calculate the probability that exactly one red will occur.

   c   The pair of spinners is now spun 10 times. Let X be the number of times that exactly one red occurs.

   i   State the distribution of X.

   ii   Write down expressions for $P(X = 1)$ and $P(X = 9)$. Hence determine which of these outcomes is more likely.

11   Ruben has an 80% chance of waking up early enough to get to school on time each weekday. Let X be the number of days that Ruben arrives at school on time over a 10 week long school term.
Calculate:

   a   the mean of X **b**   the standard deviation of X.

12   A school volleyball team has 9 players, each of whom has a 75% chance of coming to any given game. The team needs at least 6 players to avoid forfeiting the game.

   a   Find the probability that for a randomly chosen game, the team will:

   i   have all of its players   **ii**   have to forfeit the game.

   b   The team plays 30 games for the season. How many games would you expect the team to forfeit?

13 It is observed that 3% of all batteries produced by a company are defective.

    a For a random sample of 20 batteries, calculate the probability that:

        i none are defective   **ii** at least one is defective.

    b Let X be the number of defectives in a random sample of n batteries.

        i Write down an expression for $P(X = 0)$.

        ii Calculate the smallest value of n such that $P(X \geqslant 1) \geqslant 0.3$.

REVIEW SET 20B

1 Sally's number of hits in each softball match has the probability distribution shown.

x	0	1	2	3	4	5
$P(X = x)$	0.07	0.14	k	0.46	0.08	0.02

    a State clearly what the random variable represents.

    b Find: **i** k **ii** $P(X \geqslant 2)$ **iii** $P(1 \leqslant X \leqslant 3)$

    c Find the mode and median number of hits.

2 Show that the following are valid probability mass functions:

    a $P(x) = \dfrac{e^x}{1 + e}$, $x = 0, 1$ **b** $P(x) = \dfrac{x^2 + x}{40}$, $x = 1, 2, 3, 4$

    c $P(x) = \log\left(\dfrac{x + 1}{x}\right)$, $x = 1, 2, 3, ..., 9$

3 The probability distribution of a random variable X is graphed alongside. Find:

    a the mode of X

    b the median of X

    c the expected value of X.

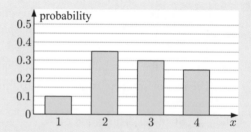

4 $P(X = x) = \frac{1}{3} \times a^{x-1}$, $x = 1, 2, 3, ...$ is a probability mass function.

    a Show that $a = \frac{2}{3}$.

    b Explain why the mode of the distribution is 1.

5 The probabilities of Naomi and Rosslyn hitting each section of an archery target are shown alongside.

    a On a single shot, who is more likely to score:

        i 10 points

        ii at least 6 points?

    b In the long run, who would you expect to score more points per shot?

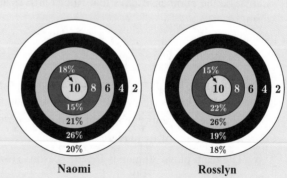

Naomi   Rosslyn

6 The numbers from 1 to 20 are written on tickets and placed in a bag. A person draws out a number at random. The person wins $3 if the number is even, $6 if the number is a square number, and $9 if the number is both even and square.

   a Calculate the probability that the player wins:

     i $3   **ii** $6   **iii** $9

   b How much should be charged to play the game so that it is fair?

7 Suppose X has the probability distribution alongside.
Given that $E(X) = 2.8$, find a and b.

x_i	1	2	3	4
p_i	0.2	a	0.3	b

8 When a biased coin is tossed twice, the probability of getting two heads is 0.64.

   a What is the probability of tossing a head with a single toss?

   b If the coin is tossed 10 times, determine the probability of obtaining:

     i exactly 6 heads   **ii** at least 6 heads.

9 A 6-sided and 4-sided die are rolled simultaneously. Let X be the number of twos rolled.

   a Explain why X is not a binomial random variable.

   b Find the probability distribution of X.

   c Find the mean of X.

10 Caleb is thrown a baseball 4 times. Let X be the number of times Caleb catches the ball. The probability distribution of X is:

x	0	1	2	3	4
$P(X = x)$	0.1	0.2	0.3	0.3	0.1

   a Find $E(X)$.

   b Let Y be the number of times Caleb *drops* the ball. Find $E(Y)$.

11 The spinner alongside is spun 20 times. Let X be the number of threes spun.

   a Explain why X is a binomial random variable.

   b Find the mean and standard deviation of X.

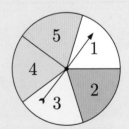

12 24% of visitors to a museum make voluntary donations. On a certain day the museum has 175 visitors.

   a Find the expected number of donations.

   b Find the probability that:

     i less than 40 visitors make a donation

     ii between 50 and 60 (inclusive) visitors make a donation.

13 Suvi plays a game involving 2 coins and a set of bowling pins. The coins are flipped and the number of heads that result is the number of attempts she gets to knock down the pins. If she knocks all of the pins down on a given attempt, it is called a "strike".

Suvi wins a prize worth $10 multiplied by the number of strikes she gets. On each attempt, the probability that Suvi gets a strike is $\frac{1}{3}$.

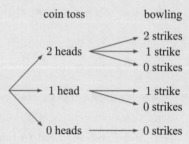

a Copy and complete this tree diagram of possible outcomes.

b Let X be the number of strikes that Suvi gets. Find the probability distribution of X.

c Calculate Suvi's expected return per game.

d Find Suvi's expected gain if the game costs $5 to play. Would you advise her to play the game many times?

Chapter 21

The normal distribution

Contents:

OPENING PROBLEM

A salmon breeder is interested in the distribution of the *weight of female adult salmon, w*.

He catches hundreds of female adult fish and records their weights in a frequency table with class intervals $3 \leqslant w < 3.1$ kg, $3.1 \leqslant w < 3.2$ kg, $3.2 \leqslant w < 3.3$ kg, and so on.

The mean weight is 4.73 kg, and the standard deviation is 0.53 kg.

Things to think about:

a Which of these do you think is the most likely distribution for the weights of the female adult salmon?

A

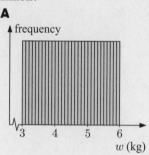

B

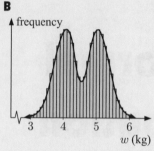

C

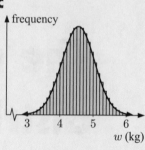

b How can we use the mean and standard deviation to estimate the proportion of salmon that weigh:

   i more than 6 kg   **ii** between 4 kg and 6 kg?

c How can we find the weight which:

   i 90% of salmon weigh less than   **ii** 25% of salmon weigh more than?

In the previous Chapter we looked at discrete random variables and examined binomial probability distributions where the random variable X could take the non-negative integer values $x = 0, 1, 2, 3, 4,$ ...., n for some finite $n \in \mathbb{N}$.

For a **continuous random variable** X, x can take any real value within some reasonable domain. There are infinitely many values X can take, and even if a measuring device enabled us to measure X exactly, the measurements of X from any two members of the population would never be *identical*. This means that the probability that X is exactly equal to any particular value is zero.

> For a continuous variable X, $P(X = x) = 0$ for all x.

For example, the probability that an egg will weigh *exactly* 72.9 g is zero. If you were to weigh an egg on scales that measure to the nearest 0.1 g, a reading of 72.9 g means the weight lies somewhere between 72.85 g and 72.95 g. No matter how accurate your scales are, you can only ever know the weight of an egg within a range.

So, for a continuous variable X, we can only talk about the probability that a measured value lies in an **interval**.

Remembering that $P(X = x) = 0$ for all x,
$P(c \leqslant X \leqslant d) = P(c < X \leqslant d) = P(c \leqslant X < d) = P(c < X < d)$.

Since $P(X = x) = 0$ for all x, we cannot use a probability mass function to describe the distribution. Instead we use a function called a **probability density function** or **distribution curve**.

The value of the function is not a probability. Rather, probabilities are found by calculating areas under the probability density function curve for a particular interval.

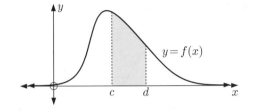

For a continuous random variable X, the **probability density function** is a function $f(x)$ such that $f(x) \geqslant 0$ on its entire domain.

The probability that X lies in the interval $c \leqslant X \leqslant d$ is $P(c \leqslant X \leqslant d) = \displaystyle\int_{c}^{d} f(x)\,dx$.

If the domain of the function is $a \leqslant x \leqslant b$, then $\displaystyle\int_{a}^{b} f(x)\,dx = 1$.

DISCUSSION

What does the *value* of a probability density function at a particular point represent?

A INTRODUCTION TO THE NORMAL DISTRIBUTION

In this Chapter, we consider variables with **symmetrical, bell-shaped** distribution curves. We call this a **normal distribution**. It is the most important distribution in statistics.

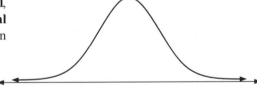

The normal distribution arises in nature when many different factors affect the value of the variable.

For example, consider the apples harvested from an apple orchard. They do not all have the same weight. This variation may be due to genetic factors, the soil, the amount of sunlight reaching the leaves and fruit, weather conditions, and so on.

The result is that most of the fruit will have weights centred about the mean weight, and there will be fewer apples that are much heavier or much lighter than this mean.

Some examples of quantities that may be normally distributed or approximately normally distributed are:

- the heights of 16 year old boys
- the lengths of adult sharks
- the yields of corn or wheat

- the volumes of liquid in soft drink cans
- the weights of peaches in a harvest
- the life times of batteries

EXERCISE 21A.1

1 Which of the following appear to be normal distribution curves?

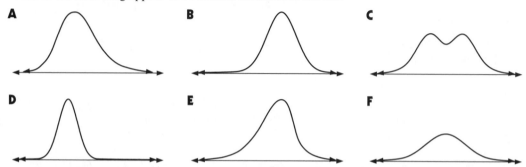

2 Explain why it is likely that the following variables will be normally distributed:

   a the diameter of wooden rods cut using a lathe

   b scores for tests taken by a large population

   c the amount of time a student takes to walk to school each day.

3 Discuss whether the following variables are likely to be normally distributed. Sketch a graph to illustrate the possible distribution of each variable.

   a the ages of people at a football match

   b the distances recorded by a long jumper

   c the numbers drawn in a lottery

   d the lengths of carrots in a supermarket

   e the amounts of time passengers spend waiting in a queue at an airport

   f the numbers of brown eggs in a sample of cartons which each contain a dozen eggs

   g the numbers of children in families living in Cardiff, Wales

   h the heights of buildings in a city.

THE NORMAL DISTRIBUTION CURVE

Although all normal distributions have the same general bell-shaped curve, the exact location and shape of the curve is determined by:

- the **mean** μ which measures the **centre** of the distribution

- the **standard deviation** σ which measures the **spread** of the distribution.

If X is a normally distributed random variable with mean μ and standard deviation σ, we write $X \sim N(\mu, \sigma^2)$.

We say that μ and σ are the **parameters** of the distribution.

The probability density function of X is:

$$f(x) = \frac{1}{\sigma\sqrt{2\pi}} e^{-\frac{1}{2}\left(\frac{x-\mu}{\sigma}\right)^2}, \quad \text{for } x \in \mathbb{R}$$

The graph of this function is called the **normal distribution curve** or just **normal curve**.

$\sim$ is read "is distributed as".

| INVESTIGATION 1 | **PROPERTIES OF THE NORMAL CURVE** |

In this Investigation, we will look at some interesting properties of the normal distribution curve

$f(x) = \dfrac{1}{\sigma\sqrt{2\pi}}\, e^{-\frac{1}{2}\left(\frac{x-\mu}{\sigma}\right)^2}$ with the help of **graphing software** and **calculus**.

What to do:

1 Click on the icon to explore the normal distribution curve and how it changes when μ and σ are altered.

DEMO

  a What effects do variations in μ and σ have on the curve? How do these relate to what μ and σ represent?

  b Does the curve have a line of symmetry? If so, what is it?

  c Is the function ever negative? Why is this important?

  d Discuss the behaviour of the normal curve as $x \to \pm\infty$.

  e What do you think happens to the *area* under the curve as you change μ and σ?

2 For a general normal curve, use calculus to find and classify the:

  a stationary point   **b** inflection points.

3 Sketch a normal distribution curve to illustrate your answers to **2**.

From the **Investigation**, you should have found that:

- The normal curve is symmetrical about the vertical line $x = \mu$.
- $f(x) > 0$ for all x.
- The x-axis is a horizontal asymptote.
- The maximum occurs at $x = \mu$.

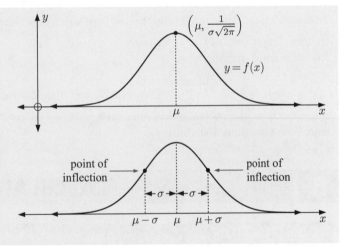

- The points of inflection occur at $x = \mu \pm \sigma$, so the standard deviation is the horizontal distance from the line of symmetry $x = \mu$ to a point of inflection.

EXERCISE 21A.2

1 Match each pair of parameters with the correct normal distribution curve:

  a $\mu = 5, \ \sigma = 2$
  b $\mu = 15, \ \sigma = 0.5$
  c $\mu = 5, \ \sigma = 1$
  d $\mu = 15, \ \sigma = 3$

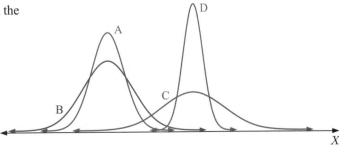

2 Sketch the following normal distributions on the same set of axes.

Distribution	Mean (mL)	Standard deviation (mL)
A	25	5
B	30	2
C	21	10

3 Consider the distribution curve of $X \sim N(\mu, \sigma^2)$ where $\mu = 4$ and $\sigma = 3$ shown:

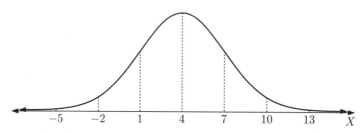

Copy the above graph, and on the same set of axes sketch the distribution curve for:

a $N(\mu + 2, \sigma^2)$ **b** $N(\mu, (2\sigma)^2)$ **c** $N(\mu + 2, (2\sigma)^2)$

d $N\left(\mu - 1, \left(\dfrac{\sigma}{3}\right)^2\right)$ **e** $N\left(3 + \mu, \dfrac{\sigma^2}{4}\right)$

PRINTABLE
GRAPH

HISTORICAL NOTE

The normal distribution was first characterised by **Carl Friedrich Gauss** in 1809 as a way to rationalise his **method of least squares** for linear regression.

In fact, the normal distribution curve is a special case of the **Gaussian function** which has the form:

$$f(x) = ae^{-\frac{1}{2}\left(\frac{x-b}{c}\right)^2}$$ where a, b, and c are constants.

Since the normal distribution has such strong ties to Gauss, it is sometimes called the **Gaussian distribution**.

Carl Friedrich Gauss

B   CALCULATING PROBABILITIES

INVESTIGATION 2   PROPORTIONS FROM A NORMAL DISTRIBUTION

In this Investigation we find the proportions of normally distributed data which lie within σ, 2σ, and 3σ of the mean.

What to do:

1 Click on the icon to run a demonstration which randomly generates 1000 data values from a normal distribution with mean μ and standard deviation σ. Set $\mu = 0$ and $\sigma = 1$.

DEMO

2 Find the endpoints of the interval:

a $\mu - \sigma$ to $\mu + \sigma$ **b** $\mu - 2\sigma$ to $\mu + 2\sigma$ **c** $\mu - 3\sigma$ to $\mu + 3\sigma$

3 Use the frequency table provided to find the proportion of data values which lie between:

    a $\mu - \sigma$ and $\mu + \sigma$ **b** $\mu - 2\sigma$ and $\mu + 2\sigma$ **c** $\mu - 3\sigma$ and $\mu + 3\sigma$

4 Repeat **2** and **3** for values of μ and σ of your choosing. Summarise your answers in a table like the one below.

μ	σ	$\mu - \sigma$ to $\mu + \sigma$		$\mu - 2\sigma$ to $\mu + 2\sigma$		$\mu - 3\sigma$ to $\mu + 3\sigma$	
		Interval	*Proportion*	*Interval*	*Proportion*	*Interval*	*Proportion*
0	1	$-1 \leqslant X \leqslant 1$					

5 What do you notice about the proportion of data values in each interval?

6 To more accurately calculate proportions from a normal distribution, we can integrate the normal probability density function. However, we cannot easily write an antiderivative for

$$f(x) = \frac{1}{\sigma\sqrt{2\pi}} e^{-\frac{1}{2}\left(\frac{x-\mu}{\sigma}\right)^2}, \quad \text{so we calculate definite integrals numerically using technology.}$$

    a Suppose X is normally distributed with $\mu = 0$ and $\sigma = 1$. Use the **graphing package** to help you estimate the following probabilities with an appropriate definite integral:

GRAPHING PACKAGE

        i $P(\mu - \sigma \leqslant X \leqslant \mu + \sigma)$ **ii** $P(\mu - 2\sigma \leqslant X \leqslant \mu + 2\sigma)$

        iii $P(\mu - 3\sigma \leqslant X \leqslant \mu + 3\sigma)$

    b Repeat **a** for each of the values of μ and σ that you chose in **4**. How do the definite integrals compare to your proportions from the simulation?

    c Does changing the mean and standard deviation of a normal distribution change the proportion of the population that lies within 1, 2, or 3 standard deviations of the mean?

From the **Investigation**, you should have found that:

For any population that is normally distributed with mean μ and standard deviation σ:

- approximately **0.68** or **68%** of the population will lie between $\mu - \sigma$ and $\mu + \sigma$
- approximately **0.95** or **95%** of the population will lie between $\mu - 2\sigma$ and $\mu + 2\sigma$
- approximately **0.997** or **99.7%** of the population will lie between $\mu - 3\sigma$ and $\mu + 3\sigma$.

The proportion of data values that lie within different ranges relative to the mean are:

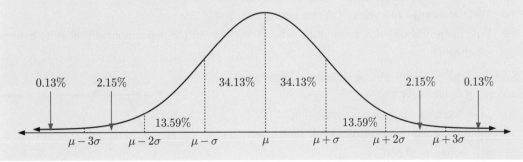

For any variable that is normally distributed, we can use the mean and standard deviation to estimate the proportion of data that will lie in a given interval. This proportion tells us the probability that a randomly selected member of the population will be in that interval.

Example 1   ◄)) **Self Tutor**

A sample of cans of peaches was taken from a warehouse, and the contents of each can was weighed. The sample mean was 486 g with standard deviation 6 g.

State the proportion of cans that weigh:

  a between 480 g and 486 g   **b** more than 492 g.

For a manufacturing process such as this, the distribution of weights is approximately normal.

a

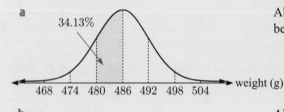

About 34.13% of the cans are expected to weigh between 480 g and 486 g.

b

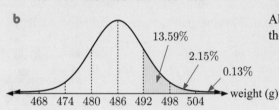

About 13.59% + 2.15% + 0.13% = 15.87% of the cans are expected to weigh more than 492 g.

> The probability of randomly selecting a can which weighs more than 492 g is approximately 0.1587.

EXERCISE 21B.1

1 Suppose X is normally distributed with mean 30 and standard deviation 5.

  a State the value which is:
    i 2 standard deviations above the mean   **ii** 1 standard deviation below the mean.

  b Describe the following values in terms of the number of standard deviations above or below the mean:
    i 35   **ii** 20   **iii** 45

  c Draw a curve to illustrate the distribution of X.

  d What proportion of values of X are between 25 and 30?

  e Find the probability that a randomly selected member of the population will measure between 35 and 40.

2 Suppose the variable X is normally distributed according to the curve shown.

  a State the mean and standard deviation of X.

  b Find the proportion of values of X which are:
    i between 20 and 24
    ii between 12 and 16
    iii greater than 28.

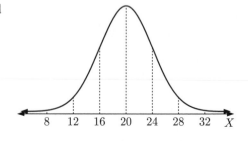

3 A school's Grade 12 students sat for a Mathematics examination. Their marks were approximately normally distributed with mean 75 and standard deviation 8.

a Copy and complete this bell-shaped curve, assigning scores to the markings on the horizontal axis.

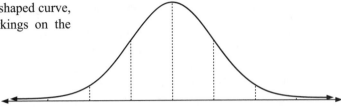

b What proportion of students would you expect to have scored:

    i more than 83   **ii** less than 59   **iii** between 67 and 91?

4 State the probability that a randomly selected, normally distributed value:

    a lies within one standard deviation either side of the mean

    b is more than two standard deviations above the mean.

Example 2   **◀)) Self Tutor**

The chest measurements of 18 year old male rugby players are normally distributed with mean 95 cm and standard deviation 8 cm.

a From a group of 200 18 year old male rugby players, how many would you expect to have a chest measurement between 87 cm and 111 cm?

b Find the value of k such that approximately 16% of chest measurements are below k cm.

a About $34.13\% + 34.13\% + 13.59\% = 81.85\%$ of the rugby players have a chest measurement between 87 cm and 111 cm.
So, we would expect 81.85% of $200 \approx 164$ of the rugby players to have a chest measurement between 87 cm and 111 cm.

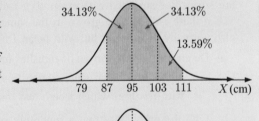

b Approximately 16% of data lies more than one standard deviation below the mean.
$\therefore$ k is σ below the mean μ
$\therefore$ $k = 95 - 8$
    $= 87$

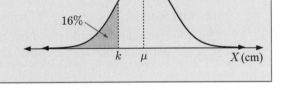

---

5 The height of female students at a university is normally distributed with mean 170 cm and standard deviation 8 cm.

    a Find the percentage of female students whose height is:

        i between 162 cm and 170 cm   **ii** between 170 cm and 186 cm.

    b Find the probability that a randomly chosen female student has a height:

        i less than 154 cm   **ii** greater than 162 cm.

    c From a group of 500 female university students, how many would you expect to be between 178 cm and 186 cm tall?

    d Estimate the value of k such that 16% of the female students are taller than k cm.

6 The weights of the 545 babies born at a maternity hospital last year were normally distributed with mean 3.0 kg and standard deviation 200 grams. Estimate the number that weighed:

    a less than 3.2 kg   **b** between 2.8 kg and 3.4 kg.

7 An industrial machine fills an average of 20 000 bottles each day with standard deviation 2000 bottles. Assuming that production is normally distributed and the year comprises 260 working days, estimate the number of working days on which:

    a under 18 000 bottles are filled

    b over 16 000 bottles are filled

    c between 18 000 and 24 000 bottles are filled.

8 Two hundred lifesavers competed in a swimming race. Their times were normally distributed with mean 10 minutes 30 seconds and standard deviation 15 seconds. Estimate the number of competitors who completed the race in a time:

    a longer than 11 minutes   **b** less than 10 minutes 15 seconds

    c between 10 minutes 15 seconds and 10 minutes 45 seconds.

9 The weights of Jason's oranges are normally distributed. 84% of the crop weighs more than 152 grams and 16% weighs more than 200 grams.

    a Find μ and σ for the crop.

    b What percentage of the oranges weigh between 152 grams and 224 grams?

10 When a particular variety of radish is grown without fertiliser, the weights of the radishes produced are normally distributed with mean 40 g and standard deviation 10 g.
When these radishes are grown in the same conditions but with fertiliser added, their weights are also normally distributed, but with mean 140 g and standard deviation 40 g.

    a Determine the proportion of radishes grown:

        i without fertiliser which weigh less than 50 grams

        ii with fertiliser which weigh less than 60 grams.

    b Find the probability that a randomly selected radish weighs between 20 g and 60 g, if it is grown:

        i with fertiliser   **ii** without fertiliser.

    c One radish grown with fertiliser and one radish grown without fertiliser are selected at random. Find the probability that *both* radishes weigh more than 60 g.

USING TECHNOLOGY

When calculating normal distribution probabilities, we have so far only considered numbers that are a whole number of standard deviations from the mean.

To calculate other probabilities, we could use definite integrals of the normal probability density function. However, this function does not have an indefinite integral, so we need to use a numerical approximation. Your **graphics calculator** has built-in functions to calculate these integrals.

GRAPHICS
CALCULATOR
INSTRUCTIONS

Example 3

◀)) **Self Tutor**

The variable X is normally distributed with mean 40 and standard deviation 10. Find:

a $P(37 < X < 48)$ 　　　　**b** $P(X > 45)$ 　　　　**c** $P(X < 26)$

Illustrate your answers.

a To find $P(37 < X < 48)$, we set the lower bound to 37 and the upper bound to 48.

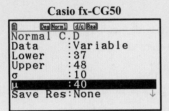 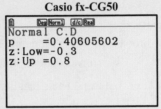 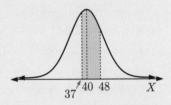

$P(37 < X < 48) \approx 0.406$

b To find $P(X > 45)$, we use a very high value such as 10^{99} to represent the upper bound.

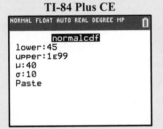 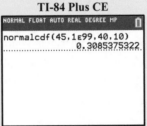 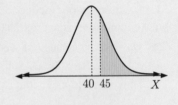

$P(X > 45) \approx 0.309$

c To find $P(X < 26)$, we use a very low value such as -10^{99} to represent the lower bound.

 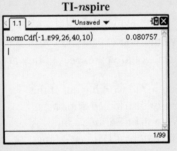 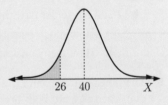

$P(X < 26) \approx 0.081$

EXERCISE 21B.2

1 Suppose X is normally distributed with mean 60 and standard deviation 5. Find:

a $P(60 \leqslant X \leqslant 65)$ 　　　　**b** $P(62 \leqslant X \leqslant 67)$

c $P(X \geqslant 64)$ 　　　　**d** $P(X \leqslant 68)$

e $P(X \leqslant 61)$ 　　　　**f** $P(57.5 \leqslant X \leqslant 62.5)$

Illustrate your answers.

> A continuous random variable X can never be *exactly* 64, so $P(X \geqslant 64) = P(X > 64)$.

2 Suppose X is normally distributed with mean 37 and standard deviation 7.

   a Use technology to find $P(X > 40)$.

   b Hence find $P(37 \leqslant X \leqslant 40)$ without technology.

3 A machine produces metal bolts. The lengths of these bolts have a normal distribution with mean 19.8 cm and standard deviation 0.3 cm.

If a bolt is selected at random from the machine, find the probability that it will have a length between 19.7 cm and 20 cm.

4 The speed of cars passing a supermarket is normally distributed with mean 46.3 km h^{-1} and standard deviation 7.4 km h^{-1}. Find the probability that a randomly selected car is travelling:

   a between 50 and 65 km h^{-1} **b** slower than 60 km h^{-1} **c** faster than 50 km h^{-1}.

5 Eels are washed onto a beach after a storm. Their lengths have a normal distribution with mean 41 cm and standard deviation 5.5 cm.

   a If an eel is randomly selected, find the probability that it is at least 50 cm long.

   b Find the percentage of eels measuring between 40 cm and 50 cm long.

   c How many eels from a sample of 200 would you expect to measure at least 45 cm in length?

6 Max's customers put money for charity into a collection box on the front counter of his shop. The weekly collection is approximately normally distributed with mean \$40 and standard deviation \$6.

   a On what percentage of weeks would Max expect to collect:

     i between \$30 and \$50   **ii** at least \$50?

   b How much money would you expect Max to collect in two years?

7 The amount of petrol bought by customers at a petrol station is normally distributed with mean 36 L and standard deviation 7 L.

   a What percentage of customers buy:

     i less than 28 L of petrol   **ii** between 30 L and 40 L of petrol?

   b On a particular day, the petrol station has 600 customers.

     i How much petrol would you expect the petrol station to sell on this day?

     ii How many customers would you expect to buy at least 44 L of petrol?

8 The times Enrique and Damien spend working out at the gym each day are both normally distributed with mean 45 minutes. The standard deviation of Enrique's times is 9 minutes, and the standard deviation of Damien's times is 6 minutes.

   a On what percentage of days does:

     i Enrique spend between 32 and 40 minutes at the gym

     ii Damien spend less than 55 minutes at the gym?

   b Tomorrow, who do you think is more likely to spend:

     i at least 1 hour at the gym

     ii between 40 minutes and 50 minutes at the gym?

   Explain your answers.

   c Perform calculations to check your answers to **b**.

Example 4   ◀)) **Self Tutor**

The times taken by students to complete a puzzle are normally distributed with mean 28.3 minutes and standard deviation 3.6 minutes. Calculate the probability that:

a a randomly selected student took at least 30 minutes to complete the puzzle

b out of 10 randomly selected students, 5 or fewer of them took at least 30 minutes to complete the puzzle.

a Let X denote the time for a student to complete the puzzle.

$X \sim N(28.3, 3.6^2)$

$\therefore \ P(X \geqslant 30) \approx 0.318\,38$

≈ 0.318

b Let Y denote the number of students who took at least 30 minutes to complete the puzzle.

$Y \sim B(10, 0.318\,38)$

$\therefore \ P(Y \leqslant 5) \approx 0.938$

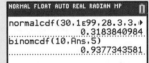

> $B(n, p)$ is the binomial distribution with n independent trials, each with probability of success p.

9 Apples from a grower's crop were normally distributed with mean 173 grams and standard deviation 34 grams. Apples weighing less than 130 grams were too small to sell.

a Find the percentage of apples from this crop which were too small to sell.

b Find the probability that in a picker's basket of 100 apples, more than 10 apples were too small to sell.

10 People found to have high blood pressure are prescribed a course of tablets. They have their blood pressure checked at the end of 4 weeks. The drop in blood pressure over the period is normally distributed with mean 5.9 units and standard deviation 1.9 units.

a Find the proportion of people who show a drop of more than 4 units.

b Eight people taking the course of tablets are selected at random. Find the probability that at least six of them will show a drop in blood pressure of more than 4 units.

HISTORICAL NOTE

The French scholar **Pierre-Simon, Marquis de Laplace** (1749 - 1827) was the first to calculate $\int_{-\infty}^{\infty} e^{-x^2}\, dx = \sqrt{\pi}$. Using this result, it can be shown that $\int_{-\infty}^{\infty} f(x)\, dx = 1$ where $f(x)$ is the normal probability density function.

So, although we cannot calculate normal probabilities exactly with integration, we know and can prove that the total area under the normal curve is 1.

C   THE STANDARD NORMAL DISTRIBUTION

Suppose a random variable X is normally distributed with mean μ and standard deviation σ.

For each value of x we can calculate a **z-score** using the algebraic transformation $z = \dfrac{x - \mu}{\sigma}$.

This algebraic transformation is known as the **Z-transformation**.

INVESTIGATION 3   z-SCORES

In this Investigation we consider how the z-scores for a distribution are themselves distributed.

What to do:

1   Consider the x-values: 1, 2, 2, 3, 3, 3, 3, 4, 4, 4, 4, 4, 5, 5, 5, 5, 6, 6, 7.

   a   Draw a histogram of the x-values to check that the distribution is approximately normal.

   b   Find the mean μ and standard deviation σ of the x-values.

   c   Calculate the z-score for each x-value.

   d   Find the mean and standard deviation of the z-scores.

2   Click on the icon to access a demo which randomly generates data values from a normal distribution with given mean and standard deviation. The z-score of each data value is calculated, and histograms of the original data and the z-scores are also shown.

DEMO

   a   Generate samples using various values of μ and σ of your choosing.

   b   Record the mean and standard deviation of the z-scores in a table like the one below.

	x-values		z-scores
Mean	Standard deviation	Mean	Standard deviation

   c   How does the histogram of the z-scores generally compare with the histogram of the x-values?

   d   What conclusions can you make about the *distribution* of the z-scores?

From the **Investigation**, you should have found that the z-scores were normally distributed with mean 0 and standard deviation 1.

$$\text{If } X \sim N(\mu, \sigma^2) \text{ and } Z = \frac{X - \mu}{\sigma} \text{ then } Z \sim N(0, 1^2).$$

No matter what the parameters μ and σ of the original X-distribution are, we always end up with the same Z-distribution, $Z \sim N(0, 1^2)$.

Click on the icon to see why the Z-transformation works.

THE Z-TRANSFORMATION

The distribution $Z \sim N(0, 1^2)$ is called the **standard normal distribution** or **Z-distribution**.

The diagram below shows how z-scores are related to a general normal curve:

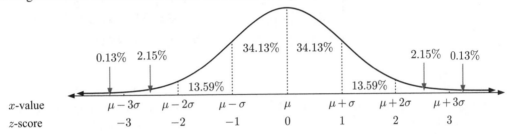

x-value	$\mu - 3\sigma$	$\mu - 2\sigma$	$\mu - \sigma$	μ	$\mu + \sigma$	$\mu + 2\sigma$	$\mu + 3\sigma$
z-score	-3	-2	-1	0	1	2	3

Notice that the value of the z-score corresponds to the coefficient of σ in the x-value.

The **z-score** of x is the number of standard deviations x is from the mean.

For example:

- if $z = 1.84$, then x is 1.84 standard deviations to the *right* of the mean
- if $z = -0.273$, then x is 0.273 standard deviations to the *left* of the mean.

z-scores are particularly useful when comparing two populations with different μ and σ. However, these comparisons will only be reasonable if both distributions are approximately normal.

Example 5   ◀ⓘ **Self Tutor**

Kelly scored 73% in History, where the class mean was 68% and the standard deviation was 10.2%. In Mathematics she scored 66%, where the class mean was 62% and the standard deviation was 6.8%.

In which subject did Kelly perform better compared with the rest of her class?

Assume the scores for both subjects were normally distributed.

Kelly's z-score for History $= \dfrac{73 - 68}{10.2} \approx 0.490$

Kelly's z-score for Mathematics $= \dfrac{66 - 62}{6.8} \approx 0.588$

Kelly's result in Mathematics was 0.588 standard deviations above the mean, whereas her result in History was 0.490 standard deviations above the mean.

$\therefore$ Kelly's result in Mathematics was better compared to her class, even though her percentage was lower.

EXERCISE 21C.1

1 In Emma's classes, the exam results for each subject are normally distributed with the mean μ and standard deviation σ shown in the table.

Subject	Emma's score	μ	σ
English	48	40	4.4
Mandarin	81	60	9
Geography	84	55	18
Biology	68	50	20
Mathematics	84	50	15

  a Find the z-score for each of Emma's scores.

  b Arrange Emma's subjects from best to worst in terms of the z-scores.

  c Explain why the z-scores are a reasonable way to compare Emma's performances with the rest of her class.

2

Subject	Sergio's score	μ	σ
Physics	73%	78%	10.8%
Chemistry	77%	72%	11.6%
Mathematics	76%	74%	10.1%
German	91%	86%	9.6%
Biology	58%	62%	5.2%

The table alongside shows Sergio's results in his final examinations, along with the class means and standard deviations.

  a Find Sergio's z-score for each subject.

  b Hence arrange Sergio's performances in each subject from best to worst.

3 At a swimming competition, Frederick competed in the 50 m freestyle, 100 m backstroke, 200 m breaststroke, and 100 m butterfly events. His times are summarised in the table, along with the event means and standard deviations.

Event	Time (seconds)	μ (seconds)	σ (seconds)
50 m freestyle	32.1	27.8	2.2
100 m backstroke	53.5	58.1	4.3
200 m breaststroke	140.0	143.7	6.4
100 m butterfly	59.6	57.7	5.5

  a Calculate the z-scores for each of Frederick's times.

  b Explain why in this case a lower z-score indicates a better performance.

  c Hence arrange Frederick's performances in each event from best to worst.

CALCULATING PROBABILITIES USING THE Z-DISTRIBUTION

Consider the variables $X \sim N(\mu, \sigma^2)$ and $Z \sim N(0, 1^2)$.

For any $x_1, x_2 \in \mathbb{R}$, $x_1 < x_2$, with corresponding z-scores $z_1 = \dfrac{x_1 - \mu}{\sigma}$ and $z_2 = \dfrac{x_2 - \mu}{\sigma}$:

- $P(X \geqslant x_1) = P(Z \geqslant z_1)$

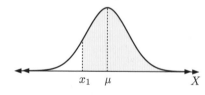
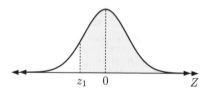

- $P(X \leqslant x_1) = P(Z \leqslant z_1)$

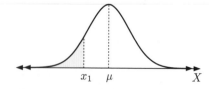
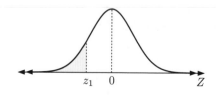

- $P(x_1 \leqslant X \leqslant x_2) = P(z_1 \leqslant Z \leqslant z_2)$

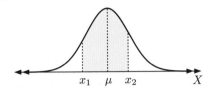

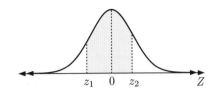

Example 6   ◀️) **Self Tutor**

Use technology to illustrate and calculate:

  a $P(-0.41 \leqslant Z \leqslant 0.67)$ **b** $P(Z \leqslant 1.5)$ **c** $P(Z > 0.84)$

$Z \sim N(0, 1^2)$

a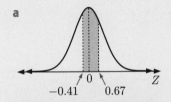

b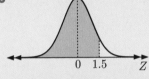

c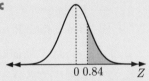

```
NORMAL FLOAT AUTO REAL RADIAN MP
normalcdf(-0.41,0.67,0,1)
                    0.407668162
```

```
NORMAL FLOAT AUTO REAL RADIAN MP
normalcdf(-1E99,1.5,0,1)
                    0.9331927713
```

```
NORMAL FLOAT AUTO REAL RADIAN MP
normalcdf(0.84,1E99,0,1)
                    0.2004541388
```

$P(-0.41 \leqslant Z \leqslant 0.67)$
≈ 0.408

$P(Z \leqslant 1.5) \approx 0.933$

$P(Z > 0.84) \approx 0.200$

EXERCISE 21C.2

1 Consider the normal distribution curve below.

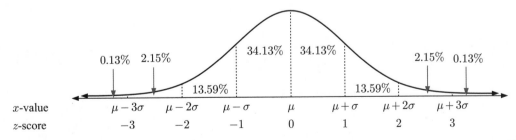

Use the diagram to calculate the following probabilities. In each case sketch the
Z-distribution and shade in the region of interest.

**PRINTABLE
CURVES**

  a $P(-1 < Z < 1)$ **b** $P(-1 \leqslant Z \leqslant 3)$ **c** $P(-1 < Z < 0)$

  d $P(Z < 2)$ **e** $P(-1 < Z)$ **f** $P(Z \geqslant 1)$

2 Given $X \sim N(\mu, \sigma^2)$ and $Z \sim N(0, 1^2)$, determine the values of a and b such that:

   a $P(\mu - \sigma < X < \mu + 2\sigma) = P(a < Z < b)$

   b $P(\mu - 0.5\sigma < X < \mu) = P(a < Z < b)$

   c $P(0 \leqslant Z \leqslant 3) = P(\mu - a\sigma \leqslant X \leqslant \mu + b\sigma)$

3 If $Z \sim N(0, 1^2)$, find the following probabilities using technology. In each case sketch the region under consideration.

   a $P(0.5 \leqslant Z \leqslant 1)$ **b** $P(-0.86 \leqslant Z \leqslant 0.32)$ **c** $P(-2.3 \leqslant Z \leqslant 1.5)$

   d $P(Z \leqslant 1.2)$ **e** $P(Z \leqslant -0.53)$ **f** $P(Z \geqslant 1.3)$

   g $P(Z \geqslant -1.4)$ **h** $P(Z > 4)$ **i** $P(-0.5 < Z < 0.5)$

   j $P(-1.960 \leqslant Z \leqslant 1.960)$ **k** $P(-1.645 \leqslant Z \leqslant 1.645)$ **l** $P(|Z| > 1.645)$

4 **a** Suppose X is normally distributed with mean μ and standard deviation σ.

     i Explain why $P(\mu - 3\sigma < X < \mu + 2\sigma) = P(-3 < Z < 2)$.

     ii Hence find $P(\mu - 3\sigma < X < \mu + 2\sigma)$.

   b For a random variable $X \sim N(\mu, \sigma^2)$, find:

     i $P(\mu - 2\sigma < X < \mu + 1.5\sigma)$ **ii** $P(\mu - 2.5\sigma < X < \mu - 0.5\sigma)$

5 Suppose X is normally distributed with mean $\mu = 58.3$ and standard deviation $\sigma = 8.96$.

   a Let the z-score of $x_1 = 50.6$ be z_1 and the z-score of $x_2 = 68.9$ be z_2.

     i Calculate z_1 and z_2.   **ii** Find $P(z_1 \leqslant Z \leqslant z_2)$.

   b Check your answer by calculating $P(50.6 \leqslant X \leqslant 68.9)$ directly using technology.

HISTORICAL NOTE

The normal distribution has two parameters μ and σ, whereas the standard normal distribution has no parameters. This means that a unique table of probabilities can be constructed for the standard normal distribution.

Before graphics calculators and computer packages, it was impossible to calculate probabilities for a general normal distribution $N(\mu, \sigma^2)$ directly.

Instead, all data was transformed using the Z-transformation, and the standard normal distribution table was consulted for the required probabilities.

D   QUANTILES

Consider a population of crabs where the length of a shell, X mm, is normally distributed with mean 70 mm and standard deviation 10 mm.

A biologist wants to protect the population by allowing only the largest 5% of crabs to be harvested. He therefore wants to know what length corresponds to the 95th percentile of crabs.

To answer this question we need to find k such that $P(X \leqslant k) = 0.95$.

The number k is known as a **quantile**. In this case it is the 95% quantile.

When finding quantiles, we are given a probability and are asked to calculate the corresponding measurement. This is the *inverse* of finding probabilities, so we use the **inverse normal function** on our calculator.

GRAPHICS
CALCULATOR
INSTRUCTIONS

Example 7   ◀)) **Self Tutor**

A population of crabs has shell length X mm. X is normally distributed with mean 70 and standard deviation 10. Find k for which $P(X < k) = 0.95$.

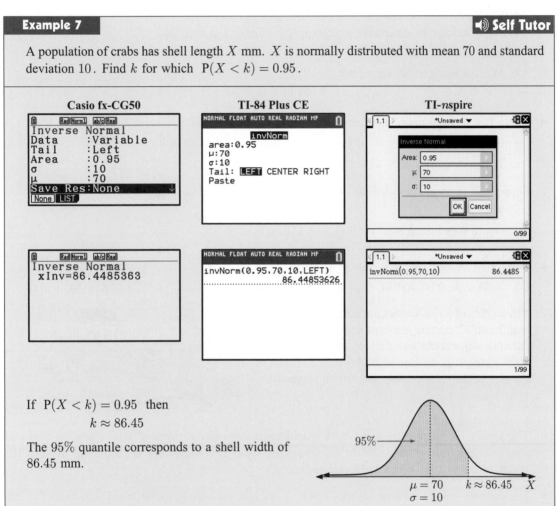

If $P(X < k) = 0.95$ then
$$k \approx 86.45$$

The 95% quantile corresponds to a shell width of 86.45 mm.

When using the **HP Prime** or **TI-*n*spire** calculators, we must always use the area to the *left* of k. Therefore, to find k such that $P(X > k) = 0.7$, we instead find k such that $P(X < k) = 1 - 0.7 = 0.3$.

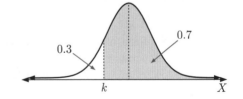

EXERCISE 21D.1

1 Suppose X is normally distributed with mean 20 and standard deviation 3. Illustrate with a sketch and find k such that:

a $P(X \leqslant k) = 0.3$ **b** $P(X \leqslant k) = 0.9$ **c** $P(X \leqslant k) = 0.5$

d $P(X > k) = 0.2$ **e** $P(X < k) = 0.62$ **f** $P(X \geqslant k) = 0.13$

2 Suppose Z has the standard normal distribution. Illustrate with a sketch and find k such that:

   a $P(Z \leqslant k) = 0.81$ **b** $P(Z \leqslant k) = 0.58$ **c** $P(Z \leqslant k) = 0.17$

   d $P(Z \geqslant k) = 0.95$ **e** $P(Z \geqslant k) = 0.9$ **f** $P(Z \geqslant k) = 0.41$

3 Suppose X is normally distributed with mean 30 and standard deviation 5, and $P(X \leqslant a) = 0.57$.

   a Using a diagram, determine whether a is greater or less than 30.

   b Use technology to find a.

   c Without using technology, find:

        i $P(X \geqslant a)$ **ii** $P(30 \leqslant X \leqslant a)$

4 Given that X is normally distributed with mean 15 and standard deviation 3, find k such that:

   a $P(X < k) = 0.2$ **b** $P(X > k) = 0.1$

   c $P(15 - k < X < 15 + k) = 0.9$

5 Suppose X is normally distributed with mean 80 and standard deviation 10.

   a Find $P(X \leqslant 72)$.

   b Hence find k such that $P(72 \leqslant X \leqslant k) = 0.1$.

6 Given that $X \sim N(45, 8^2)$, find a such that:

   a $P(35 \leqslant X \leqslant a) = 0.25$ **b** $P(a \leqslant X \leqslant 50) = 0.15$ **c** $P(a \leqslant X \leqslant 54) = 0.6$

7 The lengths of a fish species are normally distributed with mean 35 cm and standard deviation 8 cm. The fisheries department has decided that the smallest 10% of the fish are not to be harvested. What is the size of the smallest fish that can be harvested?

8 The lengths of screws produced by a machine are normally distributed with mean 75 mm and standard deviation 0.1 mm. 1% of the screws are rejected because they are too long. What is the length of the smallest screw to be rejected?

9 The volumes of cool drink in bottles filled by a machine are normally distributed with mean 503 mL and standard deviation 0.5 mL. 1% of the bottles are rejected because they are underfilled, and 2% are rejected because they are overfilled. They are otherwise kept for sale. Find, correct to 1 decimal place, the range of volumes in the bottles that are kept.

10 Abbey goes for a morning walk as long as the temperature is not too cold and not too hot. The morning temperatures are normally distributed with mean $20°C$ and standard deviation $5°C$. Given that the lower limit of Abbey's walking temperatures is $11°C$, and that she goes for a walk 95% of the time, find the upper limit of Abbey's walking temperatures.

FINDING AN UNKNOWN MEAN OR STANDARD DEVIATION

> We always need to convert to z-scores if we are trying to find an unknown mean μ or standard deviation σ.

Example 8 ◀)) **Self Tutor**

The weights of an adult scallop population are known to be normally distributed with a standard deviation of 5.9 g. If 15% of scallops weigh less than 58.2 g, find the mean weight of the population.

Let the mean weight of the population be μ g.

If X g denotes the weight of an adult scallop, then $X \sim N(\mu, 5.9^2)$.

$$P(X \leqslant 58.2) = 0.15$$

$$\therefore \ P\left(Z \leqslant \frac{58.2 - \mu}{5.9}\right) = 0.15$$

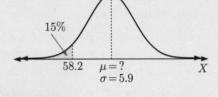

Using the inverse normal function for $N(0, 1^2)$,

```
NORMAL FLOAT AUTO REAL RADIAN MP
invNorm(0.15,0,1)
                    -1.03643338
```

Since we do not know μ we cannot use the inverse normal function directly.

$$\frac{58.2 - \mu}{5.9} \approx -1.0364$$

$$\therefore \ 58.2 - \mu \approx -6.1$$

$$\mu \approx 64.3$$

So, the mean weight is approximately 64.3 g.

Example 9 ◀)) **Self Tutor**

Find the mean and standard deviation of a normally distributed random variable X for which $P(X \leqslant 20) = 0.1$ and $P(X \geqslant 29) = 0.15$.

$X \sim N(\mu, \sigma^2)$ where we have to find μ and σ.

We start by finding z_1 and z_2 which correspond to $x_1 = 20$ and $x_2 = 29$.

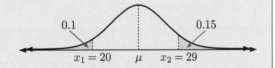

Now $P(X \leqslant x_1) = 0.1$ and $P(X \leqslant x_2) = 0.85$

$\therefore \ P\left(Z \leqslant \frac{20 - \mu}{\sigma}\right) = 0.1$ $\therefore \ P\left(Z \leqslant \frac{29 - \mu}{\sigma}\right) = 0.85$

$\therefore \ z_1 = \frac{20 - \mu}{\sigma} \approx -1.282$ {technology} $\therefore \ z_2 = \frac{29 - \mu}{\sigma} \approx 1.036$ {technology}

$\therefore \ 20 - \mu \approx -1.282\sigma$ .... (1) $\therefore \ 29 - \mu \approx 1.036\sigma$ .... (2)

Solving (1) and (2) simultaneously we get $\mu \approx 25.0$ and $\sigma \approx 3.88$.

EXERCISE 21D.2

1 Suppose X is normally distributed with standard deviation 6, and that $P(X < 40) = 0.2$.

   a Would you expect the mean of X to be greater or less than 40? Explain your answer.

   b Find the mean of X.

2 Suppose X is normally distributed with mean 15 and $P(X > 20) = 0.1$. Find the standard deviation of X.

3 The IQs of students at a school are normally distributed with a standard deviation of 15. If 20% of the students have an IQ higher than 125, find the mean IQ of students at the school.

4 The distances an athlete jumps are normally distributed with mean 5.2 m. If 15% of the athlete's jumps are less than 5 m, what is the standard deviation?

5 The weekly income of a bakery is normally distributed with mean €6100. If the weekly income exceeds €6000 85% of the time, what is the standard deviation?

6 The arrival times of buses at a depot are normally distributed with standard deviation 5 minutes. If 10% of the buses arrive before 3:55 pm, find the mean arrival time of buses at the depot.

7 Find the mean and standard deviation of a normally distributed random variable X for which $P(X \geqslant 35) = 0.32$ and $P(X \leqslant 8) = 0.26$.

8 **a** Find the mean and standard deviation of a normally distributed random variable X for which $P(X \geqslant 80) = 0.1$ and $P(X \leqslant 30) = 0.15$.

   b In a Mathematics examination it was found that 10% of the students scored at least 80, and 15% scored 30 or less. Assuming the scores are normally distributed, what percentage of students scored more than 50?

9 The diameters of pistons manufactured by a company are normally distributed. Only those pistons whose diameters lie between 3.994 cm and 4.006 cm are acceptable.

   a Find the mean and the standard deviation of the distribution if 4% of the pistons are rejected as being too small, and 5% are rejected as being too large.

   b Determine the probability that the diameter of a randomly chosen piston measures between 3.997 cm and 4.003 cm.

10 Circular metal tokens are used to operate a washing machine in a laundromat. The diameters of the tokens are normally distributed, and only tokens with diameters between 1.94 and 2.06 cm will operate the machine. In the manufacturing process, 2% of the tokens were made too small, and 3% were made too large.

   a Find the mean and standard deviation of the distribution.

   b Find the probability that at most one token out of a randomly selected sample of 20 will not operate the machine.

   c Jake has 3 tokens. Find the probability that they all have diameter greater than 2 cm.

GAME

Click on the icon to play a card game for the normal distribution.

CARD GAME

INVESTIGATION 4 — THE NORMAL APPROXIMATION TO THE BINOMIAL DISTRIBUTION

In the previous Chapter, we saw how the **binomial distribution** arises from considering the number of "successes" in a fixed number of independent trials of an experiment.

> Suppose $X \sim B(n, p)$ is the number of successes in n independent trials, each with probability of success p. The probability of getting x successes is:
>
> $$P(X = x) = \binom{n}{x} p^x (1 - p)^{n-x} \quad \text{where } x = 0, 1, 2, ..., n$$

You will have used this formula to calculate probabilities for binomial random variables in cases where the number of trials n is relatively small. As n increases, the probability becomes more difficult to calculate. This is because the binomial coefficient $\binom{n}{x} = \dfrac{n!}{x!(n - x)!}$ becomes very large.

What to do:

1 Click on the icon to access a demonstration which draws the probability distribution of $X \sim B(n, p)$.

DEMO

  a Set $p = 0.5$ and use the sliders to change the value of n. Describe what happens to the distribution of X as n increases.

  b Repeat **a** for p equal to:

    i 0.25   **ii** 0.1   **iii** 0.75   **iv** 0.9

    Comment on your observations.

  c Do you think that it would be *reasonable* to approximate the binomial distribution with a normal distribution? Explain your answer.

  d What should be the mean and standard deviation of this normal distribution?

2 Consider $X \sim B(50, 0.2)$ and its normal approximation $X_{\text{norm}} \sim N(\mu, \sigma^2)$.

  a Write down expressions for μ and σ.

  b Suppose we want to calculate the probability of 15 successes. The diagram alongside shows part of the probability distribution of X with the normal distribution curve of X_{norm} drawn over the top. Explain why $P(X = 15) \approx P(14.5 \leqslant X_{\text{norm}} \leqslant 15.5)$.

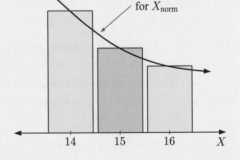

normal curve for X_{norm}

  c Describe how you would estimate the following using the normal approximation:

    i $P(X \leqslant 10)$ **ii** $P(X < 25)$

    iii $P(10 \leqslant X < 25)$

3 It is known that 2% of tyres manufactured by a company are unfit for sale. A quality inspector randomly sampled 500 tyres. Use a normal approximation to estimate the probability that at least 10 tyres in the sample will be unfit for sale.

REVIEW SET 21A

1 Discuss whether the following variables will be normally distributed:

   a the time students take to read a novel

   b the amount spent on groceries at a supermarket.

2 The amount of juice Simon can squeeze from his lemons is normally distributed with mean 35 mL and standard deviation 5 mL.

   a Copy and complete this curve.

   b What percentage of the lemons will produce:

     i between 25 mL and 35 mL of juice

     ii at least 45 mL of juice?

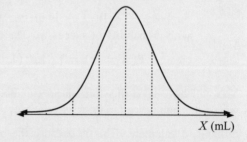

X (mL)

3 Sketch, on the same set of axes, the standard normal distribution $Z \sim N(0, 1^2)$ and the normal curves $N(3, 2^2)$, $N(5, 2^2)$, and $N(1, 4^2)$.

4 The average height of 17 year old boys is normally distributed with mean 179 cm and standard deviation 8 cm. Calculate the percentage of 17 year old boys whose heights are:

   a more than 195 cm   **b** between 171 cm and 187 cm

   c between 163 cm and 195 cm.

5 The weight of the edible part of a batch of Coffin Bay oysters is normally distributed with mean 38.6 grams and standard deviation 6.3 grams.

   a Find the percentage of oysters that weigh between 30 g and 40 g.

   b From a sample of 200 oysters, how many would you expect to weigh more than 50 g?

6 The results of a test are normally distributed. The z-score of Harri's test score is -2.

   a Interpret this z-score with regard to the mean and standard deviation of the test scores.

   b What percentage of students obtained a better score than Harri?

   c The mean test score was 61 and Harri's actual score was 47. Find the standard deviation of the test scores.

7 A random variable X is normally distributed with mean 20.5 and standard deviation 4.3. Find:

   a $P(X \geqslant 22)$ **b** $P(18 \leqslant X \leqslant 22)$ **c** k such that $P(X \leqslant k) = 0.3$.

8 The distribution of weights in grams of bags of sugar filled by a machine is $X \sim N(503, 2^2)$. Bags less than 500 grams are considered underweight.

   a What percentage of bags are underweight?

   b If a quality inspector randomly selects 20 bags, what is the probability that 2 or fewer bags are underweight?

9 The life of a Xenon-brand battery is normally distributed with mean 33.2 weeks and standard deviation 2.8 weeks.

   a Find the probability that a randomly selected battery will last at least 35 weeks.

   b For how many weeks can the manufacturer expect the batteries to last before 8% of them fail?

10 Suppose X is normally distributed with mean 25 and standard deviation 6. Find k such that:

   a $P(X \leqslant k) = 0.7$ **b** $P(X \geqslant k) = 0.4$ **c** $P(20 \leqslant X \leqslant k) = 0.3$

11 A random variable X is normally distributed with standard deviation 2.83. Find the probability that a randomly selected score from X will differ from the mean by less than 4.

12 The distribution curve shown corresponds to
$X \sim N(\mu, \sigma^2)$. Area $A =$ Area $B = 0.2$.

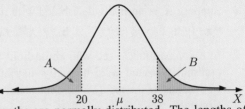

   a Find μ and σ.

   b Calculate:

   i $P(X \leqslant 35)$ **ii** $P(23 \leqslant X \leqslant 30)$

13 Machines A and B both produce nails whose lengths are normally distributed. The lengths of nails from machine A have mean 50.2 mm and standard deviation 1.1 mm. The lengths of nails from machine B have mean 50.6 mm and standard deviation 0.8 mm. Nails which are longer than 52 mm or shorter than 48 mm are rejected.

   a Find the probability of randomly selecting a nail that has to be rejected from:

   i machine A   **ii** machine B.

   b A quality inspector randomly selects a nail from a randomly chosen machine. Find the probability that the nail was made by machine A *given* that it should be rejected.

REVIEW SET 21B

1 Sketch these normal distributions on the same set of axes:

Distribution	Mean (cm)	Standard deviation (cm)
A	22	2
B	20	4
C	25	7

2 The variable X is normally distributed with graph shown.

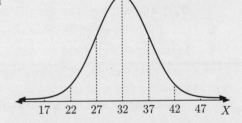

   a State the mean and standard deviation of X.

   b What percentage of values of X are:

   i between 27 and 32

   ii less than 37

   iii greater than 42?

3 The contents of soft drink cans are normally distributed with mean 327 mL and standard deviation 4.2 mL.

   a Find the percentage of cans with contents:

   i less than 318.6 mL   **ii** between 322.8 mL and 339.6 mL.

   b Find the probability that a randomly selected can contains between 327 mL and 331.2 mL.

4 The arm lengths of 18 year old females are normally distributed with mean 64 cm and standard deviation 4 cm.

   a Find the percentage of 18 year old females whose arm lengths are:

   i between 61 cm and 73 cm   **ii** greater than 57 cm.

   b Find the probability that a randomly chosen 18 year old female has an arm length in the range 50 cm to 65 cm.

   c The arm lengths of 70% of the 18 year old females are more than x cm. Find the value of x.

5 The random variable Z has the standard normal distribution $N(0, 1^2)$. Find the value of k for which $P(-k \leqslant Z \leqslant k) = 0.95$.

6 Suppose X is normally distributed with mean 50 and standard deviation 7. Find:

    a $P(46 \leqslant X \leqslant 55)$ **b** $P(X \geqslant 60)$ **c** k such that $P(X > k) = 0.23$.

7 In a competition to see who could hold their breath underwater the longest, the times in the preliminary round were normally distributed with mean 150 seconds and standard deviation 12 seconds. If the top 15% of contestants went through to the finals, what time was required to advance?

8 For $X \sim N(12, 2^2)$, find a such that:

    a $P(X < a) = 0.07$ **b** $P(X > a) = 0.2$ **c** $P(a \leqslant X \leqslant 11) = 0.1$

9 X is normally distributed with standard deviation 2.1. Let $Z \sim N(0, 1^2)$.
Given that $P(X > 5.4) = P(Z > -1.7)$, find the mean of X.

10 A normally distributed random variable X has the distribution curve shown. Its mean is 50, and $P(X < 90) \approx 0.975$.
Find the shaded area.

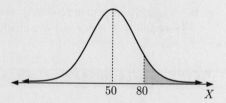

11 On an ostrich farm the weights of the birds are found to be normally distributed. The weights of the females have mean 78.6 kg and standard deviation 5.03 kg. The weights of the males have mean 91.3 kg and standard deviation 6.29 kg.

    a Find the probability that a randomly selected:

        i male will weigh less than 80 kg   **ii** female will weigh less than 80 kg

        iii female will weigh between 70 and 80 kg.

    b 20% of females weigh less than k kg. Find k.

    c The middle 90% of the males weigh between a kg and b kg. Find the values of a and b.

    d In one field there are 82% females and 18% males. One of these ostriches is selected at random.
    Calculate the probability that the ostrich weighs less than 80 kg.

12 The weight of an apple in an apple harvest is normally distributed with mean 300 grams and standard deviation 50 grams. Only apples with weights between 250 grams and 350 grams are considered fit for sale.

    a Find the percentage of apples fit for sale.

    b In a sample of 100 apples, what is the probability that at least 75 are fit for sale?

13 Giovanni and Beppe are both carrot farmers. The lengths of Giovanni's carrots are normally distributed with mean 22 cm and standard deviation 3.4 cm. The lengths of Beppe's carrots are also normally distributed, with mean 23.5 cm and standard deviation 4.2 cm.

    a Find the probability that a carrot is longer than 20 cm, given it comes from:

        i Giovanni's farm   **ii** Beppe's farm.

    b A buyer randomly selects a carrot from each farmer's crop. Calculate the probability that *neither* carrot is longer than 20 cm.

ANSWERS

EXERCISE 1A

1 **a** 2 **b** 6 **c** 24 **d** 120 **e** 720 **f** 3 628 800

2 **a** 4! **b** 7! **c** $\frac{6!}{4!}$ **d** $\frac{8!}{5!}$ **e** $\frac{10!}{6!}$ **f** $\frac{15!}{11!}$

   g $\frac{9!}{3!6!}$ **h** $\frac{13!}{4!9!}$ **i** $\frac{15!}{5!10!}$

3 **a** 7 **b** 56 **c** 132 **d** 120 **e** 45 **f** 4950

4 **a** $n,\ n \geqslant 1$ **b** $(n+2)(n+1),\ n \geqslant 0$

   c $(n+1)n,\ n \geqslant 1$

EXERCISE 1B

1 **a** $p^3 + 3p^2q + 3pq^2 + q^3$ **b** $x^3 + 3x^2 + 3x + 1$

   c $x^3 - 9x^2 + 27x - 27$ **d** $8 + 12x + 6x^2 + x^3$

   e $27x^3 - 27x^2 + 9x - 1$ **f** $8x^3 + 60x^2 + 150x + 125$

   g $8a^3 - 12a^2b + 6ab^2 - b^3$ **h** $27x^3 - 9x^2 + x - \frac{1}{27}$

   i $8x^3 + 12x + \frac{6}{x} + \frac{1}{x^3}$ **j** $x\sqrt{x} - 3x + 3\sqrt{x} - 1$

   k $x^6 + 6x^4 + 12x^2 + 8$ **l** $x^6 - 3x^2 + \frac{3}{x^2} - \frac{1}{x^6}$

2 **a** $1 + 4x + 6x^2 + 4x^3 + x^4$

   b $p^4 - 4p^3q + 6p^2q^2 - 4pq^3 + q^4$

   c $x^4 - 8x^3 + 24x^2 - 32x + 16$

   d $81 - 108x + 54x^2 - 12x^3 + x^4$

   e $1 + 8x + 24x^2 + 32x^3 + 16x^4$

   f $16x^4 - 96x^3 + 216x^2 - 216x + 81$

   g $16x^4 + 32x^3b + 24x^2b^2 + 8xb^3 + b^4$

   h $x^4 + 4x^2 + 6 + \frac{4}{x^2} + \frac{1}{x^4}$

   i $16x^4 - 32x^2 + 24 - \frac{8}{x^2} + \frac{1}{x^4}$

3 **a** **i** $a^3 - 3a^2b + 3ab^2 - b^3$

   ii $a^4 - 4a^3b + 6a^2b^2 - 4ab^3 + b^4$

   b The terms are the same, except for their signs. The signs in the expansions of $(a+b)^3$ and $(a+b)^4$ are all positive, whereas the signs in the expansions of $(a-b)^3$ and $(a-b)^4$ start with a positive and then alternate $(a > 0,\ b > 0)$.

4 **a** 1 5 10 10 5 1

   b $(a+b)^5 = a^5 + 5a^4b + 10a^3b^2 + 10a^2b^3 + 5ab^4 + b^5$

   c **i** $x^5 + 10x^4 + 40x^3 + 80x^2 + 80x + 32$

   ii $1 - 5x + 10x^2 - 10x^3 + 5x^4 - x^5$

   iii $1 + 10x + 40x^2 + 80x^3 + 80x^4 + 32x^5$

   iv $x^5 - 10x^4y + 40x^3y^2 - 80x^2y^3 + 80xy^4 - 32y^5$

   v $x^{10} + 5x^8 + 10x^6 + 10x^4 + 5x^2 + 1$

   vi $x^5 - 5x^3 + 10x - \frac{10}{x} + \frac{5}{x^3} - \frac{1}{x^5}$

5 **a** 1 6 15 20 15 6 1

   b $(a+b)^6 = a^6 + 6a^5b + 15a^4b^2 + 20a^3b^3 + 15a^2b^4$
   $+ 6ab^5 + b^6$

   c **i** $x^6 + 12x^5 + 60x^4 + 160x^3 + 240x^2 + 192x + 64$

   ii $64x^6 - 192x^5 + 240x^4 - 160x^3 + 60x^2 - 12x + 1$

   iii $x^6 + 6x^4 + 15x^2 + 20 + \frac{15}{x^2} + \frac{6}{x^4} + \frac{1}{x^6}$

6 **a** $7 + 5\sqrt{2}$ **b** $161 + 72\sqrt{5}$ **c** $232 - 164\sqrt{2}$

7 **a** $64 + 192x + 240x^2 + 160x^3 + 60x^4 + 12x^5 + x^6$

   b 65.944 160 601 201

8 **a** $2x^5 + 11x^4 + 24x^3 + 26x^2 + 14x + 3$

   b $8x^4 + 4x^3 - 6x^2 - 5x - 1$

9 **a** 270 **b** 4320

EXERCISE 1C

1 **a** $1^{11} + \binom{11}{1}(2x)^1 + \binom{11}{2}(2x)^2 + \ldots + \binom{11}{10}(2x)^{10} + (2x)^{11}$

   b $(3x)^{15} + \binom{15}{1}(3x)^{14}\left(\frac{2}{x}\right)^1 + \binom{15}{2}(3x)^{13}\left(\frac{2}{x}\right)^2 + \ldots$
   $\ldots + \binom{15}{14}(3x)^1\left(\frac{2}{x}\right)^{14} + \left(\frac{2}{x}\right)^{15}$

   c $(2x)^{20} + \binom{20}{1}(2x)^{19}\left(-\frac{3}{x}\right)^1 + \binom{20}{2}(2x)^{18}\left(-\frac{3}{x}\right)^2 + \ldots$
   $\ldots + \binom{20}{19}(2x)^1\left(-\frac{3}{x}\right)^{19} + \left(-\frac{3}{x}\right)^{20}$

2 **a** $T_6 = \binom{15}{5}(2x)^{10}5^5$ **b** $T_4 = \binom{9}{3}(x^2)^6y^3$

   c $T_{10} = \binom{17}{9}x^8\left(-\frac{2}{x}\right)^9$ **d** $T_9 = \binom{21}{8}(2x^2)^{13}\left(-\frac{1}{x}\right)^8$

4 **a** $T_{r+1} = \binom{8}{r}x^{8-r}2^r$ **b** 448

5 **a** $T_{r+1} = \binom{7}{r}x^{7-r}b^r$ **b** $b = -2$

6 **a** $\binom{15}{5}2^5$ **b** $\binom{9}{3}(-3)^3$

7 **a** $\binom{10}{5}3^5 2^5$ **b** $\binom{6}{3}2^3(-3)^3$ **c** $\binom{6}{3}2^3(-3)^3$

   d $\binom{12}{4}2^8(-1)^4$

8 $T_3 = \binom{6}{2}(-2)^2 x^8 y^8$ **9** $n = 9,\ T_4 = 84x^3$

10 $a = 2$

11 **a** $\binom{6}{3}(-3)^3 + 4\binom{6}{2}(-3)^2 = 0$ **b** $\binom{8}{6} = 28$

   c $2\binom{9}{3}3^6 x^6 - \binom{9}{4}3^5 x^6 = 91\,854x^6$

12 $n = 6$ and $k = -2$

13 **a**
```
        1   1
      1   2   1
    1   3   3   1
  1   4   6   4   1
1   5   10   10   5   1
```
   b **i** 2

   ii 4

   iii 8

   iv 16

   v 32

   c The sum of the numbers in row n of Pascal's triangle is 2^n.

   e **i** **Hint:** Let $x = 1$, in the expansion of $(1+x)^n$.

   ii **Hint:** Let $x = -1$, in the expansion of $(1+x)^n$.

   f $\sum_{r=0}^{n} 2^r \binom{n}{r} = 3^n$

14 **a** $(3+x)^n = 3^n + \binom{n}{1}3^{n-1}x + \binom{n}{2}3^{n-2}x^2 +$
   $\binom{n}{3}3^{n-3}x^3 + \ldots + \binom{n}{n-1}3^1 x^{n-1} + x^n$

   b 4^n

REVIEW SET 1A

1 **a** 8! **b** $\frac{10!}{7!}$ **2** **a** $n(n-1),\ n \geqslant 2$ **b** $n+2$

3 **a** $x^3 + 9x^2 + 27x + 27$

   b $x^5 - 10x^4 + 40x^3 - 80x^2 + 80x - 32$

4 **a** $\binom{9}{4}(2x)^5 3^4$ **b** $\binom{12}{7}(3x)^5\left(-\frac{1}{x}\right)^7$

5 **a** $170 + 78\sqrt{3}$ **b** $x^5 - x^4 - 6x^3 + 14x^2 - 11x + 3$

6 64.964 808

7 $(a+b)^6 = a^6 + 6a^5b + 15a^4b^2 + 20a^3b^3 + 15a^2b^4 + 6ab^5 + b^6$

   a $x^6 - 18x^5 + 135x^4 - 540x^3 + 1215x^2 - 1458x + 729$

   b $64 + \frac{192}{x} + \frac{240}{x^2} + \frac{160}{x^3} + \frac{60}{x^4} + \frac{12}{x^5} + \frac{1}{x^6}$

8 $\binom{12}{6}2^6(-3)^6$ **9** $8\binom{6}{2} - 6\binom{6}{1} = 84$ **10** $c = 3$

11 **a** $2^n + \binom{n}{1}2^{n-1}x^1 + \binom{n}{2}2^{n-2}x^2 + \binom{n}{3}2^{n-3}x^3 + \ldots.$

.... $+ \binom{n}{n-1}2^1x^{n-1} + x^n$

b 3^n **Hint:** Let $x = 1$ in **a**.

12 $a = \pm 4$

REVIEW SET 1B

1 **a** 72   **b** 56   **2** **a** $\dfrac{7!}{3!}$ **b** $\dfrac{11!}{3!8!}$

3 **a** $x^3 - 6x^2y + 12xy^2 - 8y^3$

b $81x^4 + 216x^3 + 216x^2 + 96x + 16$

4 $\binom{6}{3}2^35^3 = 20\,000$ **5** $\binom{6}{4}2^2(-1)^4 = 60$

6 **a** $792 - 560\sqrt{2}$ **b** $8x^4 + 36x^3 + 42x^2 + 19x + 3$

7 **a** $(2x)^{10} + \binom{10}{1}(2x)^9(-7)^1 + \binom{10}{2}(2x)^8(-7)^2 + \ldots.$

.... $+ \binom{10}{9}(2x)^1(-7)^9 + (-7)^{10}$

b $(3x)^{13} + \binom{13}{1}(3x)^{12}\left(\frac{4}{x}\right)^1 + \binom{13}{2}(3x)^{11}\left(\frac{4}{x}\right)^2 + \ldots.$

.... $+ \binom{13}{12}(3x)^1\left(\frac{4}{x}\right)^{12} + \left(\frac{4}{x}\right)^{13}$

8 $(-4)^{10} = 1\,048\,576$

9 **a** $\binom{9}{2}3^7 = 78\,732$ **b** $\binom{9}{6}3^3 = 2268$

10 $k = -\frac{1}{4}$, $n = 16$ **11** $k = 180$ **12** $q = \pm\sqrt{\frac{3}{35}}$

EXERCISE 2A

1 **a, c, d**, and **f** are quadratic functions.

2 **a** $y = -3$ **b** $y = -16$ **c** $y = 16$ **d** $y = -12$

3 **a** $y = x^2 - 3x + 1$

x	-2	-1	0	1	2
y	11	5	1	-1	-1

b $y = x^2 + 2x - 5$

x	-2	-1	0	1	2
y	-5	-6	-5	-2	3

c $y = 2x^2 - x + 3$

x	-4	-2	0	2	4
y	39	13	3	9	31

d $y = -3x^2 + 2x + 4$

x	-4	-2	0	2	4
y	-52	-12	4	-4	-36

4 **a** no   **b** yes   **c** yes   **d** yes   **e** no   **f** yes

5 **a** $x = -1$ or -2 **b** $x = 2$ **c** $x = 1$ or 5
d $x = -3$ or $\frac{1}{2}$ **e** $x = -6$ or 1   **f** no real solutions

EXERCISE 2B.1

1 **a**   **b**

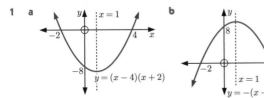

c 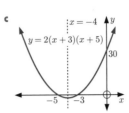   **d**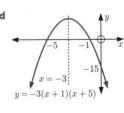

e 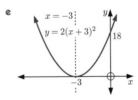   **f**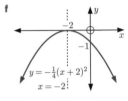

2 **a C**   **b E**   **c B**   **d F**   **e G**   **f H**
g I   **h A**   **i D**

3 **a** 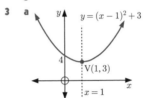   **b**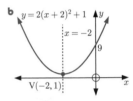

c 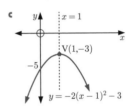   **d**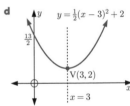

e 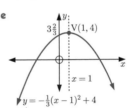   **f**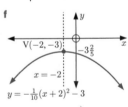

4 **a G**   **b A**   **c E**   **d B**   **e I**   **f C**
g D   **h F**   **i H**

EXERCISE 2B.2

1 **a** $y = (x-1)^2 + 2$ **b** $y = (x+2)^2 - 6$

c $y = (x-2)^2 - 4$ **d** $y = \left(x + \frac{3}{2}\right)^2 - \frac{9}{4}$

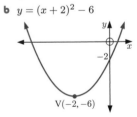

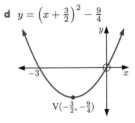

e $y = \left(x + \frac{5}{2}\right)^2 - \frac{33}{4}$

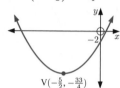

V$\left(-\frac{5}{2}, -\frac{33}{4}\right)$

f $y = \left(x - \frac{3}{2}\right)^2 - \frac{1}{4}$

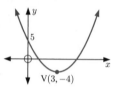

V$\left(\frac{3}{2}, -\frac{1}{4}\right)$

g $y = (x - 3)^2 - 4$

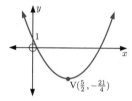

V$(3, -4)$

h $y = (x + 4)^2 - 18$

V$(-4, -18)$

i $y = \left(x - \frac{5}{2}\right)^2 - \frac{21}{4}$

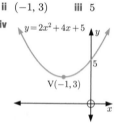

V$\left(\frac{5}{2}, -\frac{21}{4}\right)$

2 a i $y = 2(x + 1)^2 + 3$
  ii $(-1, 3)$ **iii** 5
  iv

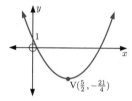

$y = 2x^2 + 4x + 5$

V$(-1, 3)$

b i $y = 2(x - 2)^2 - 5$
  ii $(2, -5)$ **iii** 3
  iv

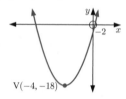

$y = 2x^2 - 8x + 3$

V$(2, -5)$

c i $y = 2\left(x - \frac{3}{2}\right)^2 - \frac{7}{2}$
  ii $\left(\frac{3}{2}, -\frac{7}{2}\right)$ **iii** 1
  iv

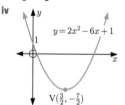

$y = 2x^2 - 6x + 1$

V$\left(\frac{3}{2}, -\frac{7}{2}\right)$

d i $y = 3(x - 1)^2 + 2$
  ii $(1, 2)$ **iii** 5
  iv

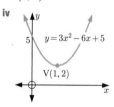

$y = 3x^2 - 6x + 5$

V$(1, 2)$

e i $y = -(x - 2)^2 + 6$
  ii $(2, 6)$ **iii** 2
  iv

V$(2, 6)$

$y = -x^2 + 4x + 2$

f i $y = -2\left(x + \frac{5}{4}\right)^2 + \frac{49}{8}$
  ii $\left(-\frac{5}{4}, \frac{49}{8}\right)$ **iii** 3
  iv

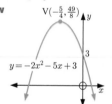

V$\left(-\frac{5}{4}, \frac{49}{8}\right)$

$y = -2x^2 - 5x + 3$

---

1 a i $(2, -2)$ **ii** minimum turning point
  b i $(-1, -4)$ **ii** minimum turning point
  c i $(0, 4)$ **ii** minimum turning point
  d i $(0, 1)$ **ii** maximum turning point
  e i $(-2, -15)$ **ii** minimum turning point
  f i $(-2, -5)$ **ii** maximum turning point
  g i $\left(-\frac{3}{2}, -\frac{11}{2}\right)$ **ii** minimum turning point
  h i $\left(\frac{5}{2}, -\frac{19}{2}\right)$ **ii** minimum turning point
  i i $\left(1, -\frac{9}{2}\right)$ **ii** maximum turning point
  j i $(14, -43)$ **ii** minimum turning point

2 a i $x = 4$
   ii $(4, -9)$
   iii x-intercepts $1, 7$,
      y-intercept 7
   iv

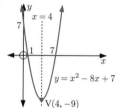

$x = 4$

$y = x^2 - 8x + 7$

V$(4, -9)$

b i $x = -3$
   ii $(-3, 1)$
   iii x-int. $-2, -4$,
      y-intercept -8
   iv

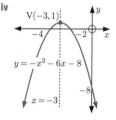

V$(-3, 1)$

$y = -x^2 - 6x - 8$

$x = -3$

c i $x = 3$
   ii $(3, 9)$
   iii x-intercepts $0, 6$,
      y-intercept 0
   iv

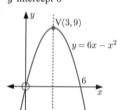

V$(3, 9)$

$y = 6x - x^2$

$x = 3$

d i $x = \frac{3}{2}$
   ii $\left(\frac{3}{2}, \frac{1}{4}\right)$
   iii x-intercepts $1, 2$,
      y-intercept -2
   iv

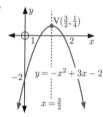

V$\left(\frac{3}{2}, \frac{1}{4}\right)$

$y = -x^2 + 3x - 2$

$x = \frac{3}{2}$

e i $x = -1$
   ii $(-1, -26)$
   iii x-int. $-1 \pm \sqrt{13}$,
      y-intercept -24
   iv $y = 2x^2 + 4x - 24$

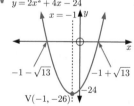

$x = -1$

$-1 - \sqrt{13}$ $-1 + \sqrt{13}$

-24

V$(-1, -26)$

f i $x = \frac{2}{3}$
   ii $\left(\frac{2}{3}, \frac{1}{3}\right)$
   iii x-intercepts $\frac{1}{3}, 1$,
      y-intercept -1
   iv

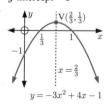

V$\left(\frac{2}{3}, \frac{1}{3}\right)$

$\frac{1}{3}$ 1

$x = \frac{2}{3}$

$y = -3x^2 + 4x - 1$

g   **i** $x = \frac{5}{4}$

    ii $(\frac{5}{4}, -\frac{9}{8})$

    iii x-intercepts $\frac{1}{2}$, 2,
       y-intercept 2

    iv

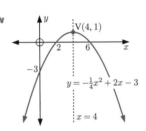

h   **i** $x = 1$

    ii $(1, -9)$

    iii x-intercepts $-\frac{1}{2}$, $\frac{5}{2}$,
       y-intercept -5

    iv

i   **i** $x = 4$

   ii $(4, 1)$

   iii x-intercepts 2, 6,
     y-intercept -3

   iv

EXERCISE 2C

1   **a** $\Delta = 9$ which is > 0, graph cuts x-axis twice; is concave up.

   b $\Delta = 12$ which is > 0, graph cuts x-axis twice; is concave up.

   c $\Delta = -12$ which is < 0, graph lies entirely below the x-axis; is concave down, negative definite.

   d $\Delta = 57$ which is > 0, graph cuts x-axis twice; is concave up.

   e $\Delta = 0$, graph touches x-axis; is concave up.

   f $\Delta = 17$ which is > 0, graph cuts x-axis twice; is concave down.

   g $\Delta = 121$ which is > 0, graph cuts x-axis twice; is concave up.

   h $\Delta = 25$ which is > 0, graph cuts x-axis twice; is concave down.

   i $\Delta = 0$, graph touches x-axis; is concave up.

2   **a** concave up

   b $\Delta = 17$ which is > 0
     $\therefore$ cuts x-axis twice

   c x-intercepts
     ≈ 0.22 and 2.28

   d y-intercept is 1

   e

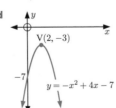

3   **a** $\Delta = -12$ which is < 0
     $\therefore$ does not cut x-axis

   b negative definite, since
     $a < 0$ and $\Delta < 0$

   c vertex is $(2, -3)$,
     y-intercept is -7

   d

4   **a** $a = 2$ which is > 0 and $\Delta = -40$ which is < 0
     $\therefore$ positive definite.

   b $a = -2$ which is < 0 and $\Delta = -23$ which is < 0
     $\therefore$ negative definite.

   c $a = 1$ which is > 0 and $\Delta = -15$ which is < 0
     $\therefore$ positive definite so $x^2 - 3x + 6 > 0$ for all x.

   d $a = -1$ which is < 0 and $\Delta = -8$ which is < 0
     $\therefore$ negative definite so $4x - x^2 - 6 < 0$ for all x.

5

Constant	a	b	c	d	e	f	Δ_1	Δ_2
Sign	$+$	$-$	$+$	$-$	$+$	0	$-$	$+$

6   **a**   **i** $k < \frac{9}{4}$ **ii** $k = \frac{9}{4}$ **iii** $k > \frac{9}{4}$

   b   **i** $k < 4$, $k \neq 0$ **ii** $k = 4$ **iii** $k > 4$

   c   **i** $k > -\frac{4}{3}$, $k \neq -1$ **ii** $k = -\frac{4}{3}$ **iii** $k < -\frac{4}{3}$

7 $a = 3$ which is > 0 and $\Delta = k^2 + 12$ which is always > 0
     $\{$as $k^2 \geqslant 0$ for all $k\}$ $\therefore$ cannot be positive definite.

8 $k = -2$, the graph touches the x-axis in this case.

EXERCISE 2D

1   **a** $y = 2(x-1)(x-2)$ **b** $y = 3(x-2)^2$

   c $y = (x-1)(x-3)$ **d** $y = -(x-3)(x+1)$

   e $y = -3(x-1)^2$ **f** $y = -2(x+2)(x-3)$

2   **a** $y = \frac{3}{2}(x-2)(x-4)$ **b** $y = -\frac{1}{2}(x+4)(x-2)$

   c $y = -\frac{4}{3}(x+3)^2$

3   **a** $y = 3x^2 - 18x + 15$ **b** $y = -4x^2 + 6x + 4$

   c $y = -x^2 + 6x - 9$ **d** $y = 4x^2 + 16x + 16$

   e $y = \frac{3}{2}x^2 - 6x + \frac{9}{2}$ **f** $y = -\frac{1}{3}x^2 + \frac{2}{3}x + 5$

4   **a** $y = -(x-2)^2 + 4$ **b** $y = 2(x-2)^2 - 1$

   c $y = \frac{1}{3}(x+3)^2 - 4$ **d** $y = -2(x-3)^2 + 8$

   e $y = \frac{2}{3}(x-4)^2 - 6$ **f** $y = -\frac{5}{9}(x+2)^2 + 5$

   g $y = -2(x-2)^2 + 3$ **h** $y = \frac{3}{2}(x+4)^2 + 3$

   i $y = 2(x-\frac{1}{2})^2 - \frac{3}{2}$

5 $y = 3$

EXERCISE 2E

1   **a** $(1, 7)$ and $(2, 8)$ **b** $(4, 5)$ and $(-3, -9)$

   c $(3, 0)$ (touching)   **d** graphs do not meet

2   **a** $(0.586, 5.59)$ and $(3.41, 8.41)$

   b $(3, -4)$ (touching)   **c** graphs do not meet

   d $(-2.56, -18.8)$ and $(1.56, 1.81)$

3   **a** $(-1, 1)$ and $(2, 4)$ **b**

   c $x < -1$ or $x > 2$

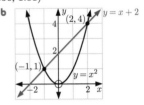

4   **a** $(-2, -3)$ and
     $(1, 0)$ **b**

   c $x < -2$ or $x > 1$

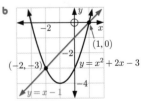

5   **a** $(1, 4)$ **b**

   c $x \in \mathbb{R}$, $x \neq 1$

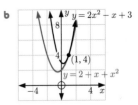

6 a $x = -4$ or 1 **b**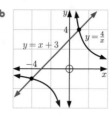

c $x < -4$ or
$0 < x < 1$

7 $c = -9$ **8** $m = 0$ or -8 **9** -1 or 11

10 a $c < -9$
b example: $c = -10$

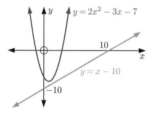

12 a $c > -2$ **b** $c = -2$ **c** $c < -2$

13 Hint: A straight line through $(0, 3)$ will have an equation of the form $y = mx + 3$.

14 $b = 8$, $c = -14$

EXERCISE 2F

1 7 and -5 or -7 and 5 **2** 5 or $\frac{1}{5}$ **3** 14
4 18 and 20 or -18 and -20
5 15 and 17 or -15 and -17 **6** 15 sides   **7** ≈ 3.48 cm
8 b 6 cm by 6 cm by 7 cm   **9** ≈ 11.2 cm square
10 no   **12** ≈ 61.8 km h^{-1} **13** 32 elderly citizens
14 a $y = -\frac{8}{9}x^2 + 8$
b No, as the tunnel is only 4.44 m high when it is the same width as the truck.
15 a $h = -5(t - 2)^2 + 80$ **b** 75 m   **c** 6 seconds

EXERCISE 2G

1 a min. -1, when $x = 1$ **b** max. 8, when $x = -1$
c max. $8\frac{1}{3}$, when $x = \frac{1}{3}$ **d** min. $-1\frac{1}{8}$, when $x = -\frac{1}{4}$
e min. $4\frac{15}{16}$, when $x = \frac{1}{8}$ **f** max. $6\frac{1}{8}$, when $x = \frac{7}{4}$
2 a 40 refrigerators   **b** €4000
4 500 m by 250 m   **5 c** 100 m by 112.5 m
6 a $41\frac{2}{3}$ m by $41\frac{2}{3}$ m   **b** 50 m by $31\frac{1}{4}$ m
7 a 50 m   **b** 30 m   **8 b** $3\frac{1}{8}$ units
9 a $y = 6 - \frac{3}{4}x$ **b** 3 cm by 4 cm

EXERCISE 2H.1

1 a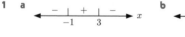
b

c
d

e
f

2 a
b

c
d

2 e
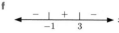
f

g
h

i

3 a
b

c
d

e
f

4 a
b

c
d

e
f

g
h

i

5 a
b

c
d

e
f

EXERCISE 2H.2

1 a $-5 \leqslant x \leqslant 2$ **b** $-3 \leqslant x \leqslant 2$ **c** no solutions
d all $x \in \mathbb{R}$ **e** $-\frac{1}{2} < x < 3$ **f** $-\frac{3}{2} < x < 4$
2 a $x \leqslant 0$ or $x \geqslant 1$ **b** $-\frac{2}{3} < x < 0$ **c** $x \neq -2$
d $-5 \leqslant x \leqslant 3$ **e** $x < -2$ or $x > 6$ **f** $-4 < x < 1$
3 a $x \leqslant 0$ or $x \geqslant 3$ **b** $-2 < x < 2$
c $x \leqslant -\sqrt{2}$ or $x \geqslant \sqrt{2}$ **d** $-3 \leqslant x \leqslant 7$
e $x < 5$ or $x > 6$ **f** $x < -6$ or $x > 7$
g $x \leqslant -1$ or $x \geqslant \frac{3}{2}$ **h** no solutions
i $-\frac{3}{2} < x < \frac{1}{3}$ **j** $x < -\frac{4}{3}$ or $x > 4$
k $x \neq 1$ **l** $\frac{1}{3} \leqslant x \leqslant \frac{1}{2}$
m $x < -\frac{1}{6}$ or $x > 1$ **n** $x \leqslant -\frac{1}{4}$ or $x \geqslant \frac{2}{3}$
o $x < \frac{3}{2}$ or $x > 3$
4 a **i** $k < -8$ or $k > 0$ **ii** $k = -8$ or 0
  iii $-8 < k < 0$
b **i** $-1 < k < 1$, $k \neq 0$ **ii** $k = -1$ or 1
  iii $k < -1$ or $k > 1$

c **i** $k < -6$ or $k > 2$ **ii** $k = -6$ or $k = 2$
iii $-6 < k < 2$

5 **a** **i** $k < -2$ or $k > 6$ **ii** $k = -2$ or $k = 6$
iii $-2 < k < 6$

b **i** $k < -\frac{13}{9}$ or $k > 3$ **ii** $k = -\frac{13}{9}$ or $k = 3$
iii $-\frac{13}{9} < k < 3$

c **i** $-\frac{4}{3} < k < 0$, $k \neq -1$ **ii** $k = -\frac{4}{3}$ or $k = 0$
iii $k < -\frac{4}{3}$ or $k > 0$

6 **a** $m > 3$ **b** $m < -1$

7 **a** $m < -1$ or $m > 7$ **b** $m = -1$ or $m = 7$
c $-1 < m < 7$

REVIEW SET 2A

1 **a**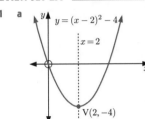

b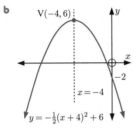

2 **a** $y = 3x^2 - 24x + 48$ **b** $y = \frac{2}{5}x^2 + \frac{16}{5}x + \frac{37}{5}$

3 maximum $= 5$ when $x = 1$

4 $(4, 4)$ and $(-3, 18)$ **5** $k < -3\frac{1}{8}$

6 **a** $m = \frac{9}{8}$ **b** $m < \frac{9}{8}$ **c** $m > \frac{9}{8}$ **7** $\frac{6}{5}$ or $\frac{5}{6}$

8 **Hint:** Let the line have equation $y = mx + 10$.

9 **a** $y = 2(x + \frac{3}{2})^2 - \frac{15}{2}$ **b**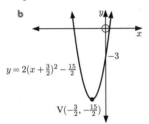

10 **a** $y = \frac{20}{9}(x - 2)^2 - 20$ **b** $y = -\frac{2}{7}(x - 1)(x - 7)$
c $y = \frac{2}{9}(x + 3)^2$

11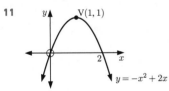

12 $\frac{1}{2}$ **13** $k < 1$

14 **a** **i** $\Delta > 0$ **ii** $a < 0$
b **i** $A(-m, 0)$, $B(-n, 0)$ **ii** $x = \dfrac{-m - n}{2}$

15 $y = -4x^2 + 4x + 24$ **16** $m = -5$ or 19

17 21 m

18 **a** 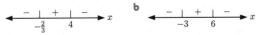   **b**

19 **a** $x < -2$ or $x > 3$ **b** $-1 \leqslant x \leqslant 5$
c $x < -\frac{5}{2}$ or $x > 2$

20 **a** $k < 6 - 2\sqrt{5}$ or $k > 6 + 2\sqrt{5}$ **b** $k = 6 \pm 2\sqrt{5}$
c $6 - 2\sqrt{5} < k < 6 + 2\sqrt{5}$

REVIEW SET 2B

1 **a** $x = 2$ **d**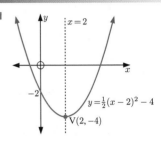
b $(2, -4)$
c -2

2 $x = \frac{4}{3}$, $V(\frac{4}{3}, 12\frac{1}{3})$

3 **a** $\Delta = 65$, the graph cuts the x-axis twice   **b** $\Delta = 97$, the graph cuts the x-axis twice

4 **a** $a < 0$, $\Delta > 0$, neither
b $a > 0$, $\Delta < 0$, positive definite

5 $y = -6(x - 2)^2 + 25$

6 **a** $x = -1$ **d**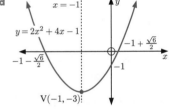
b $(-1, -3)$
c x-int. $-1 \pm \frac{\sqrt{6}}{2}$
y-intercept -1

7 **a** $y = -\frac{2}{5}(x + 5)(x - 1)$ **b** $(-2, 3\frac{3}{5})$, $x = -2$

8 **a** $c > -6$
b example: $c = -2$, $(-1, -5)$ and $(3, 7)$

9 **a** minimum $= 5\frac{2}{3}$ when $x = -\frac{2}{3}$
b maximum $= 5\frac{1}{8}$ when $x = -\frac{5}{4}$

10 **a** $y = 3x^2 - 3x - 18$ **b** -18 **c** $(\frac{1}{2}, -18\frac{3}{4})$

11 **a** $m = -2$, $n = 4$ **b** $k = 7$

12 ≈ 13.5 cm square

13 **a** $x = -4$ or 0 **b**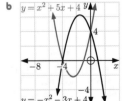
c $x < -4$ or $x > 0$

14 **a** $a > 0$ {graph opens upwards}
b $b < 0$ {$x = -\dfrac{b}{2a} > 0$ is x-coordinate of vertex}
c $c < 0$ {y-intercept is negative}
d $\Delta > 0$ {two x-intercepts $\therefore$ two real roots}

15 a i $y = (x+2)^2 - 1$ **b i** $y = (x+1)^2 - 4$
   ii $y = (x+3)(x+1)$ **ii** $y = (x+3)(x-1)$
   iii   **iii**

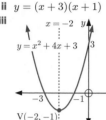   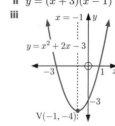

c i $y = 2(x-2)^2 - 18$ **d i** $y = -(x-3)^2 + 16$
   ii $y = 2(x-5)(x+1)$ **ii** $y = -(x-7)(x+1)$
   iii   **iii**

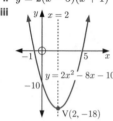   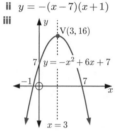

16 a $k = \pm 12$ **b** $(0, 4)$

17 b $37\frac{1}{2}$ m by $33\frac{1}{3}$ m   **c** 1250 m^2

18 a
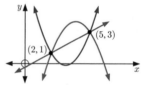

19 a $0 < x < \frac{3}{4}$ **b** $x \leqslant -1$ or $x \geqslant \frac{5}{2}$
   c $x \leqslant \frac{1}{3}$ or $x \geqslant \frac{3}{2}$

20 a $-\frac{25}{2} < m < \frac{1}{2}$, $m \neq 0$ **b** $m = -\frac{25}{2}$ or $m = \frac{1}{2}$
   c $m < -\frac{25}{2}$ or $m > \frac{1}{2}$

EXERCISE 3A

1 a Is a function, since for any value of x there is at most one value of y.
   b Is a function, since for any value of x there is at most one value of y.
   c Is not a function. If $x^2 + y^2 = 9$, then $y = \pm\sqrt{9 - x^2}$. So, for example, for $x = 2$, $y = \pm\sqrt{5}$.

2 a function   **b** function   **c** function
   d not a function   **e** not a function   **f** function
   g function   **h** not a function

3 No, because a vertical line (the y-axis) would cut the relation more than once.

4 No. A vertical line is not a function. It will not pass the "vertical line" test.

5 Not a function as a 2 year old child could pay $0 or $20.

6 a $y^2 = x$ is a relation but not a function.
   $y = x^2$ is a function (and a relation).
   $y^2 = x$ has a horizontal axis of symmetry (the x-axis).
   $y = x^2$ has a vertical axis of symmetry (the y-axis).
   Both $y^2 = x$ and $y = x^2$ pass through $(0, 0)$ and $(1, 1)$.
   $y^2 = x$ is a rotation of $y = x^2$ clockwise through $90°$ about the origin *or* $y^2 = x$ is a reflection of $y = x^2$ in the line $y = x$.
   b i The part of $y^2 = x$ in the first quadrant.
   ii $y = \sqrt{x}$ is a function as any vertical line cuts the graph at most once.

7 a Both curves are functions since any vertical line will cut each curve at most once.
   b $y = \sqrt[3]{x}$

EXERCISE 3B

1 a 2   **b** 8   **c** −1   **d** −13   **e** 1
2 a 2   **b** 2   **c** −16   **d** −68   **e** $\frac{17}{4}$
3 a −3   **b** 3   **c** 3   **d** −3   **e** $\frac{15}{2}$
4 a i 1   **ii** −1   **b** $x = -4$
5 a i $-\frac{7}{2}$ **ii** $-\frac{3}{4}$ **iii** $-\frac{4}{9}$ **b** $x = 4$ **c** $x = \frac{9}{5}$
6 a $7 - 3a$ **b** $7 + 3a$ **c** $-3a - 2$ **d** $7 - 6a$
   e $1 - 3x$ **f** $7 - 3x - 3h$
7 a $2x^2 + 19x + 43$ **b** $2x^2 - 11x + 13$
   c $2x^2 - 3x - 1$ **d** $2x^4 + 3x^2 - 1$
   e $18x^2 + 9x - 1$ **f** $2x^2 + (4h + 3)x + 2h^2 + 3h - 1$
8 a $9x^2$ **b** $\frac{x^2}{4}$ **c** $3x^2$ **d** $2x^2 - 4x + 7$
9 a $-\frac{1}{x}$ **b** $\frac{2}{x}$ **c** $\frac{2+3x}{x}$ **d** $\frac{2x+1}{x-1}$
10 f is the function which converts x into $f(x)$ whereas $f(x)$ is the value of the function at any value of x.
11 Note: Other answers are possible.

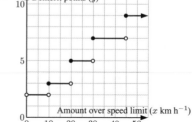

12 $f(x) = -2x + 5$
13 a $P(3) = 35$. There are 35 L of petrol in the tank after 3 minutes.
   b $t = 4.5$ After $4\frac{1}{2}$ minutes there are 50 L of petrol in the tank.
   c 5 L
14 a $H(30) = 800$. After 30 minutes the balloon is 800 m high.
   b $t = 20$ or 70. After 20 minutes and after 70 minutes the balloon is 600 m high.
   c $0 \leqslant t \leqslant 80$ **d** 0 m to 900 m
15 $a = 3$, $b = -2$ **16** $a = 3$, $b = -1$, $c = -4$
17 a $V(4) = 5400$; $V(4)$ is the value of the photocopier in pounds after 4 years.
   b $t = 6$. After 6 years the value of the photocopier is £3600.
   c £9000   **d** $0 \leqslant t \leqslant 10$

EXERCISE 3C

1 a

graph: Demerit points (y) vs Amount over speed limit (x km h^{-1})

b Domain is $\{x \mid x > 0\}$, Range is $\{y \mid y = 2, 3, 5, 7,$ or $9\}$

2 **a** At any moment in time there can be only one temperature, so the graph is a function.

  b Domain is $\{t \mid 0 \leqslant t \leqslant 30\}$, Range is $\{T \mid 15 \leqslant T \leqslant 25\}$

3 **a** Domain is $\{x \mid x \geqslant -1\}$, Range is $\{y \mid y \leqslant 3\}$

  b Domain is $\{x \mid -1 < x \leqslant 5\}$, Range is $\{y \mid 1 < y \leqslant 3\}$

  c Domain is $\{x \mid x \neq 2\}$, Range is $\{y \mid y \neq -1\}$

  d Domain is $\{x \mid x \in \mathbb{R}\}$, Range is $\{y \mid 0 < y \leqslant 2\}$

  e Domain is $\{x \mid x \in \mathbb{R}\}$, Range is $\{y \mid y \geqslant -1\}$

  f Domain is $\{x \mid x \in \mathbb{R}\}$, Range is $\{y \mid y \leqslant \frac{25}{4}\}$

  g Domain is $\{x \mid x \geqslant -4\}$, Range is $\{y \mid y \geqslant -3\}$

  h Domain is $\{x \mid x \in \mathbb{R}\}$, Range is $\{y \mid y > -2\}$

  i Domain is $\{x \mid x \neq \pm 2\}$,
  Range is $\{y \mid y \leqslant -1 \text{ or } y > 0\}$

4 **a** true   **b** false   **c** true   **d** true

5 **a** $\{y \mid y \geqslant 0\}$ **b** $\{y \mid y \leqslant 0\}$ **c** $\{y \mid y \geqslant 2\}$

  d $\{y \mid y \leqslant 0\}$ **e** $\{y \mid y \leqslant 1\}$ **f** $\{y \mid y \geqslant 3\}$

  g $\{y \mid y \geqslant -\frac{9}{4}\}$ **h** $\{y \mid y \leqslant 9\}$ **i** $\{y \mid y \leqslant \frac{25}{12}\}$

6 **a** $\{x \mid x \geqslant 0\}$ **b**

x	0	1	4	9	16
$f(x)$	0	1	2	3	4

  c
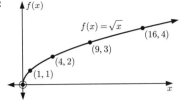

  d $\{y \mid y \geqslant 0\}$

7 **a** Domain is $\{x \mid x \geqslant -6\}$, Range is $\{y \mid y \geqslant 0\}$

  b Domain is $\{x \mid x \neq 0\}$, Range is $\{y \mid y > 0\}$

  c Domain is $\{x \mid x \neq -1\}$, Range is $\{y \mid y \neq 0\}$

  d Domain is $\{x \mid x > 0\}$, Range is $\{y \mid y < 0\}$

  e Domain is $\{x \mid x \neq 3\}$, Range is $\{y \mid y \neq 0\}$

  f Domain is $\{x \mid x \leqslant 4\}$, Range is $\{y \mid y \geqslant 0\}$

8 **a**
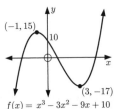

$f(x) = x^3 - 3x^2 - 9x + 10$

Domain is $\{x \mid x \in \mathbb{R}\}$,
Range is $\{y \mid y \in \mathbb{R}\}$

  b
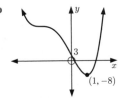

$f(x) = x^4 + 4x^3 - 16x + 3$

Domain is $\{x \mid x \in \mathbb{R}\}$,
Range is $\{y \mid y \geqslant -8\}$

  c
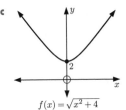

$f(x) = \sqrt{x^2 + 4}$

Domain is $\{x \mid x \in \mathbb{R}\}$,
Range is $\{y \mid y \geqslant 2\}$

  d
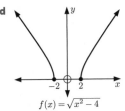

$f(x) = \sqrt{x^2 - 4}$

Domain is $\{x \mid x \leqslant -2$
  or $x \geqslant 2\}$,
Range is $\{y \mid y \geqslant 0\}$

e
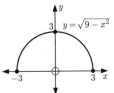

Domain is
$\{x \mid -3 \leqslant x \leqslant 3\}$,
Range is $\{y \mid 0 \leqslant y \leqslant 3\}$

f
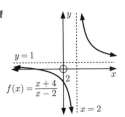

$f(x) = \dfrac{x+4}{x-2}$

Domain is $\{x \mid x \neq 2\}$,
Range is $\{y \mid y \neq 1\}$

g
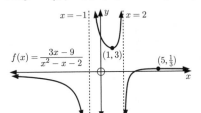

$f(x) = \dfrac{3x-9}{x^2-x-2}$

Domain is $\{x \mid x \neq -1 \text{ or } 2\}$,
Range is $\{y \mid y \leqslant \frac{1}{3} \text{ or } y \geqslant 3\}$

h
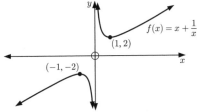

$f(x) = x + \dfrac{1}{x}$

Domain is $\{x \mid x \neq 0\}$,
Range is $\{y \mid y \leqslant -2 \text{ or } y \geqslant 2\}$

i
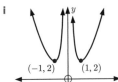

$f(x) = x^2 + \dfrac{1}{x^2}$

Domain is $\{x \mid x \neq 0\}$,
Range is $\{y \mid y \geqslant 2\}$

j
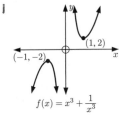

$f(x) = x^3 + \dfrac{1}{x^3}$

Domain is $\{x \mid x \neq 0\}$,
Range is $\{y \mid y \leqslant -2$
  or $y \geqslant 2\}$

k
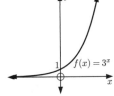

Domain is $\{x \mid x \in \mathbb{R}\}$,
Range is $\{y \mid y > 0\}$

l
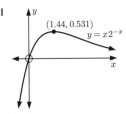

Domain is $\{x \mid x \in \mathbb{R}\}$,
Range is $\{y \mid y \leqslant 0.531\}$

9 a

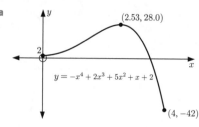

$y = -x^4 + 2x^3 + 5x^2 + x + 2$

(2.53, 28.0)

(4, −42)

Range is $\{y \mid -42 \leqslant y \leqslant 28.0\}$

b

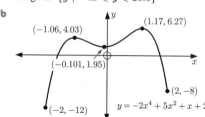

(−1.06, 4.03)   (1.17, 6.27)

(−0.101, 1.95)

(2, −8)

(−2, −12) $y = -2x^4 + 5x^2 + x + 2$

Range is $\{y \mid -12 \leqslant y \leqslant 6.27\}$

c

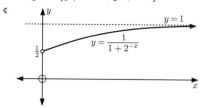

$y = 1$

$y = \dfrac{1}{1 + 2^{-x}}$

$\frac{1}{2}$

Range is $\{y \mid \frac{1}{2} < y < 1\}$

EXERCISE 3D.1

1 a

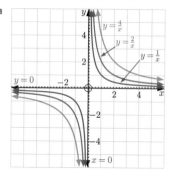

$y = \frac{4}{x}$ $y = \frac{2}{x}$ $y = \frac{1}{x}$ $y = 0$ $x = 0$

b i As k becomes larger the graphs move further from the origin.
ii quadrants 1 and 3   **iii**

2 a

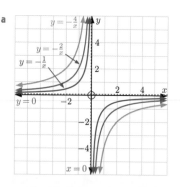

$y = -\frac{4}{x}$ $y = -\frac{2}{x}$ $y = -\frac{1}{x}$ $y = 0$ $x = 0$

b i As $|k|$ becomes larger, the graphs move further from the origin.
ii quadrants 2 and 4   **iii**

3 a $\{x \mid x \neq 0\}$ **b** $\{y \mid y \neq 0\}$ **c** $x = 0$ **d** $y = 0$

4 a $y = \dfrac{6}{x}$ **b** $y = \dfrac{15}{x}$ **c** $y = -\dfrac{36}{x}$

EXERCISE 3D.2

1 a i vertical asymptote $x = 2$, horizontal asymptote $y = 0$
ii Domain is $\{x \mid x \neq 2\}$, Range is $\{y \mid y \neq 0\}$
iii no x-intercept, y-intercept $-\frac{3}{2}$
iv as $x \to 2^-$, $f(x) \to -\infty$
as $x \to 2^+$, $f(x) \to \infty$
as $x \to -\infty$, $f(x) \to 0^-$
as $x \to \infty$, $f(x) \to 0^+$
v

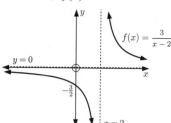

$f(x) = \dfrac{3}{x-2}$ $y = 0$ $-\frac{3}{2}$ $x = 2$

b i vertical asymptote $x = 3$, horizontal asymptote $y = 2$
ii Domain is $\{x \mid x \neq 3\}$, Range is $\{y \mid y \neq 2\}$
iii x-intercept $\frac{5}{2}$, y-intercept $\frac{5}{3}$
iv as $x \to 3^-$, $f(x) \to -\infty$
as $x \to 3^+$, $f(x) \to \infty$
as $x \to -\infty$, $f(x) \to 2^-$
as $x \to \infty$, $f(x) \to 2^+$
v

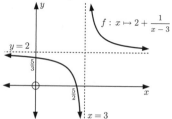

$f : x \mapsto 2 + \dfrac{1}{x-3}$ $y = 2$ $\frac{5}{3}$ $\frac{5}{2}$ $x = 3$

c i vertical asymptote $x = -1$, horizontal asymptote $y = 2$
ii Domain is $\{x \mid x \neq -1\}$, Range is $\{y \mid y \neq 2\}$
iii x-intercept $\frac{1}{2}$, y-intercept -1
iv as $x \to -1^-$, $f(x) \to \infty$
as $x \to -1^+$, $f(x) \to -\infty$
as $x \to -\infty$, $f(x) \to 2^+$
as $x \to \infty$, $f(x) \to 2^-$
v

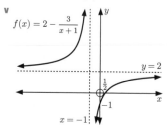

$f(x) = 2 - \dfrac{3}{x+1}$ $y = 2$ $\frac{1}{2}$ -1 $x = -1$

2 a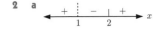

b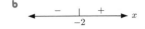

c

3 a

b

c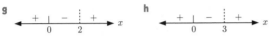

d

e

f

g

h

4 a i vertical asymptote is $x = 1$
ii x-intercept 0, y-intercept 0
iii $f(x) = 1 + \dfrac{1}{x-1}$, horizontal asymptote is $y = 1$
iv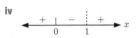

v as $x \to 1^-$, $f(x) \to -\infty$
as $x \to 1^+$, $f(x) \to \infty$
as $x \to -\infty$, $f(x) \to 1^-$
as $x \to \infty$, $f(x) \to 1^+$
vi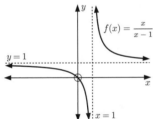

$f(x) = \dfrac{x}{x-1}$

$y = 1$

$x = 1$

b i vertical asymptote is $x = 2$
ii x-intercept -3, y-intercept $-\frac{3}{2}$
iii $f(x) = 1 + \dfrac{5}{x-2}$, horizontal asymptote is $y = 1$
iv

v as $x \to 2^-$, $f(x) \to -\infty$
as $x \to 2^+$, $f(x) \to \infty$
as $x \to -\infty$, $f(x) \to 1^-$
as $x \to \infty$, $f(x) \to 1^+$
vi

$f : x \mapsto \dfrac{x+3}{x-2}$

$y = 1$

$x = 2$

c i vertical asymptote is $x = -2$
ii x-intercept $\frac{1}{3}$, y-intercept $-\frac{1}{2}$
iii $f(x) = 3 - \dfrac{7}{x+2}$, horizontal asymptote is $y = 3$
iv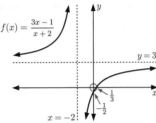

v as $x \to -2^-$, $f(x) \to \infty$
as $x \to -2^+$, $f(x) \to -\infty$
as $x \to -\infty$, $f(x) \to 3^+$
as $x \to \infty$, $f(x) \to 3^-$
vi

$f(x) = \dfrac{3x-1}{x+2}$

$y = 3$

$x = -2$

d i vertical asymptote is $x = 3$
ii x-intercept $-\frac{1}{2}$, y-intercept $\frac{1}{3}$
iii $f(x) = -2 - \dfrac{7}{x-3}$, horizontal asymptote is $y = -2$
iv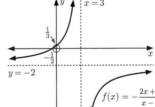

v as $x \to 3^-$, $f(x) \to \infty$
as $x \to 3^+$, $f(x) \to -\infty$
as $x \to -\infty$, $f(x) \to -2^+$
as $x \to \infty$, $f(x) \to -2^-$
vi

$x = 3$

$y = -2$

$f(x) = -\dfrac{2x+1}{x-3}$

e i vertical asymptote is $x = 3$
ii x-intercept -2, y-intercept $\frac{4}{3}$
iii $f(x) = -2 + \dfrac{10}{3-x}$, horizontal asymptote is $y = -2$
iv

v as $x \to 3^-$, $f(x) \to \infty$
as $x \to 3^+$, $f(x) \to -\infty$
as $x \to -\infty$, $f(x) \to -2^+$
as $x \to \infty$, $f(x) \to -2^-$

vi

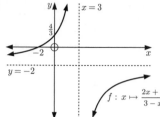

$f : x \mapsto \dfrac{2x + 4}{3 - x}$

f i vertical asymptote is $x = \frac{1}{2}$

ii x-intercept -3, y-intercept -3

iii $f(x) = \frac{1}{2} + \dfrac{7}{4x - 2}$, horizontal asymptote is $y = \frac{1}{2}$

iv

v as $x \to \frac{1}{2}^{-}$, $f(x) \to -\infty$

as $x \to \frac{1}{2}^{+}$, $f(x) \to \infty$

as $x \to -\infty$, $f(x) \to \frac{1}{2}^{-}$

as $x \to \infty$, $f(x) \to \frac{1}{2}^{+}$

vi

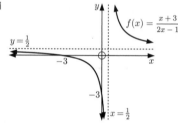

$f(x) = \dfrac{x + 3}{2x - 1}$

5 a Domain is $\{x \mid x \neq -\frac{d}{c}\}$

b vertical asymptote is $x = -\dfrac{d}{c}$

c x-intercept is $-\dfrac{b}{a}$, $a \neq 0$, y-intercept is $\dfrac{b}{d}$, $d \neq 0$

d $\dfrac{ax + b}{cx + d} = \dfrac{\frac{a}{c}(cx + d) - \frac{ad}{c} + b}{cx + d}$ and so on

As $|x| \to \infty$, $\dfrac{b - \frac{ad}{c}}{cx + d} \to 0$.

$\therefore$ the horizontal asymptote is $y = \dfrac{a}{c}$.

EXERCISE 3E

1 a $5 - 2x$ **b** $-2x - 2$ **c** 11 **d** -2

2 a $-2 - 2x^2$ **b** $1 + 4x^2$ **c** -10 **d** -4

3 a $-4x^2 - 16x - 13$ **b** $10 - 2x^2$ **c** 14 **d** $-\frac{73}{16}$

4 a $25x - 42$ **b** $\sqrt{8}$ **c** -7 **d** 2

5 a i $x^2 - 6x + 10$ **ii** $2 - x^2$ **b** $x = \pm\frac{1}{\sqrt{2}}$

6 a $(f \circ g)(x) = 9 - \sqrt{x^2 + 4}$

Domain is $\{x \mid x \in \mathbb{R}\}$, Range is $\{y \mid y \leqslant 7\}$

b 53

c $(f \circ f)(x) = 9 - \sqrt{9 - \sqrt{x}}$

Domain is $\{x \mid 0 \leqslant x \leqslant 81\}$, Range is $\{y \mid 6 \leqslant y \leqslant 9\}$

7 a $-6x - 9$ **b** $x = -1$

8 a i $1 - 9x^2$ **ii** $1 + 6x - 3x^2$ **b** $x = -\frac{1}{9}$

9 a $(f \circ g)(x) = \dfrac{1}{x - 3}$

Domain is $\{x \mid x \neq 3\}$, Range is $\{y \mid y \neq 0\}$

b $(f \circ g)(x) = -\dfrac{1}{x^2 + 3x + 2}$

Domain is $\{x \mid x \neq -1, \ x \neq -2\}$
Range is $\{y \mid y \geqslant 4, \ y < 0\}$

10 a Let $x = 0$, $\therefore$ $b = d$ and so

$$ax + b = cx + b$$
$$\therefore \ ax = cx \quad \text{for all } x$$

Let $x = 1$, $\therefore$ $a = c$

b $(f \circ g)(x) = [2a]x + [2b + 3] = 1x + 0$ for all x

$\therefore$ $2a = 1$ and $2b + 3 = 0$

c Yes, $\{(g \circ f)(x) = [2a]x + [3a + b]\}$

11 a $(f \circ g)(x) = \sqrt{1 - x^2}$

b Domain is $\{x \mid -1 \leqslant x \leqslant 1\}$, Range is $\{y \mid 0 \leqslant y \leqslant 1\}$

12 a $R_g \cap D_f \neq \varnothing$

b Domain is $\{x \mid x \in D_g, \ g(x) \in D_f\}$

EXERCISE 3F

1 a i

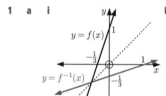

ii, iii $f^{-1}(x) = \dfrac{x - 1}{3}$

b i

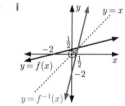

ii, iii $f^{-1}(x) = 4x - 2$

2 a i $f^{-1}(x) = \dfrac{x - 5}{2}$

ii

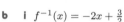

b i $f^{-1}(x) = -2x + \frac{3}{2}$

ii

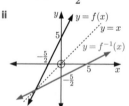

c i $f^{-1}(x) = x - 3$

ii

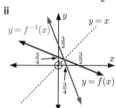

3 a

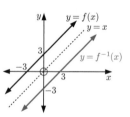

f:
Domain is $\{x \mid -2 \leqslant x \leqslant 0\}$
Range is $\{y \mid 0 \leqslant y \leqslant 5\}$

f^{-1}:
Domain is $\{x \mid 0 \leqslant x \leqslant 5\}$
Range is $\{y \mid -2 \leqslant y \leqslant 0\}$

b

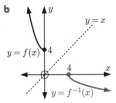

f:
Domain is $\{x \mid x \leqslant 0\}$
Range is $\{y \mid y \geqslant 4\}$

f^{-1}:
Domain is $\{x \mid x \geqslant 4\}$
Range is $\{y \mid y \leqslant 0\}$

c

f:
Domain is $\{x \mid x \in \mathbb{R}\}$
Range is $\{y \mid y \in \mathbb{R}\}$

f^{-1}:
Domain is $\{x \mid x \in \mathbb{R}\}$
Range is $\{y \mid y \in \mathbb{R}\}$

d

f:
Domain is $\{x \mid x \in \mathbb{R}\}$
Range is $\{y \mid y > 0\}$

f^{-1}:
Domain is $\{x \mid x > 0\}$
Range is $\{y \mid y \in \mathbb{R}\}$

e

f:
Domain is $\{x \mid x \in \mathbb{R}\}$
Range is $\{y \mid y \in \mathbb{R}\}$

f^{-1}:
Domain is $\{x \mid x \in \mathbb{R}\}$
Range is $\{y \mid y \in \mathbb{R}\}$

f

f:
Domain is $\{x \mid x \in \mathbb{R}\}$
Range is $\{y \mid y \in \mathbb{R}\}$

f^{-1}:
Domain is $\{x \mid x \in \mathbb{R}\}$
Range is $\{y \mid y \in \mathbb{R}\}$

4 $(f^{-1})^{-1}(x) = 2x - 5 = f(x)$

5 f is $y = 3 - x$ $\therefore$ f^{-1} is $x = 3 - y$
$\therefore$ $y = 3 - x$
$\therefore$ $f(x) = f^{-1}(x)$ and the function is its own inverse.

6 a $\{(2, 1), (4, 2), (5, 3)\}$ **b** inverse does not exist
c $\{(1, 2), (0, -1), (2, 0), (3, 1)\}$
d $\{(-1, -1), (0, 0), (1, 1)\}$

7 Range is $\{y \mid -2 \leqslant y < 3\}$ **8**

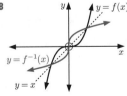

9 f is $y = \dfrac{1}{x}$, $x \neq 0$ $\therefore$ f^{-1} is $x = \dfrac{1}{y}$
$\therefore$ $y = \dfrac{1}{x}$
$\therefore$ $f = f^{-1}$
$\therefore$ f is self-inverse.

10 a The inverse function must also be a function and must therefore satisfy the vertical line test, which it can only do if the original function satisfies the horizontal line test.
b i is the only one.

11 $f : x \mapsto x^2 - 4$ is many-to-one so it does not satisfy the horizontal line test. $\therefore$ it does not have an inverse.

12 a $f^{-1}(x) = -\sqrt{x}$ **b**

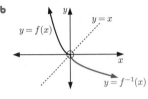

13 a $g^{-1}(x) = 8 - 2x$ **b** $x = 10$ **d** $x = 3$

14 $(f^{-1} \circ g^{-1})(x) = \dfrac{x + 3}{8}$ and $(g \circ f)^{-1}(x) = \dfrac{x + 3}{8}$

15 a

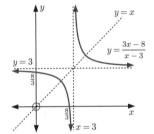

$y = \dfrac{3x - 8}{x - 3}$ is symmetrical about $y = x$

$\therefore$ $f^{-1}(x) = \dfrac{3x - 8}{x - 3} = f(x)$

b $f^{-1}(x) = \dfrac{3x - 8}{x - 3}$

16 a B is $(f(x), x)$

EXERCISE 3G

1 a

b

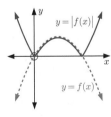

2 a

b

c

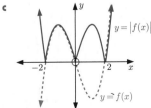

d

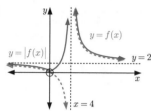

3 a

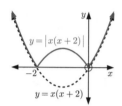

b

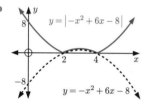

4 a   **b**

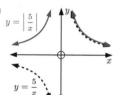   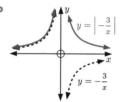

REVIEW SET 3A

1 a i Domain is $\{x \mid x \in \mathbb{R}\}$ **ii** Range is $\{y \mid y > -4\}$
   iii yes, it is a function
  b i Domain is $\{x \mid x \in \mathbb{R}\}$ **ii** Range is $\{y \mid y = 2\}$
   iii yes, it is a function
  c i Domain is $\{x \mid x \in \mathbb{R}\}$
   ii Range is $\{y \mid y \leqslant -1 \text{ or } y \geqslant 1\}$
   iii no, not a function
  d i Domain is $\{x \mid x \in \mathbb{R}\}$
   ii Range is $\{y \mid -5 \leqslant y \leqslant 5\}$ **iii** yes, it is a function

2 a 0   **b** -15 **c** $-\frac{5}{4}$

3 a i 2   **ii** 0   **b** $x = -1$ **4** $a = -6$, $b = 13$

5 a $10 - 6x$ **b** $x = 2$

6 Domain is $\{t \mid 0 \leqslant t \leqslant 140\}$,
   Range is $\{N \mid 70 \leqslant N \leqslant 110\}$

7 a $x = 0$ **b**
  c Domain is $\{x \mid x \neq 0\}$
   Range is $\{y \mid y < 0\}$

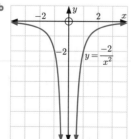

8 a $f(-3) = (-3)^2 = 9$, $g(-\frac{4}{3}) = 1 - 6(-\frac{4}{3}) = 9$
  b $x = -4$

9 a Domain is $\{x \mid x \geqslant -4\}$,   Range is $\{y \mid y \geqslant 0\}$
  b Domain is $\{x \mid x \in \mathbb{R}\}$,   Range is $\{y \mid y \leqslant 1\}$
  c Domain is $\{x \mid x \in \mathbb{R}\}$,   Range is $\{y \mid y \geqslant -\frac{1}{8}\}$

10 a $y = -\dfrac{20}{x}$ **b** $y = \dfrac{60}{x}$

11

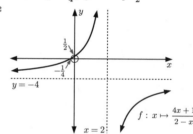

12 a vertical asymptote $x = 2$,   horizontal asymptote $y = -4$
  b Domain is $\{x \mid x \neq 2\}$,   Range is $\{y \mid y \neq -4\}$
  c

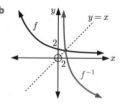

   as $x \to 2^-$, $f(x) \to \infty$ as $x \to -\infty$, $f(x) \to -4^+$
   as $x \to 2^+$, $f(x) \to -\infty$ as $x \to \infty$, $f(x) \to -4^-$
  d x-intercept $-\frac{1}{4}$, y-intercept $\frac{1}{2}$
  e

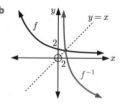

$$f: x \mapsto \frac{4x+1}{2-x}$$

13 a $2x^2 + 1$ **b** $4x^2 - 12x + 11$ **c** -1

14 a $6x - 3$ **b** $x = 1$

15 a $1 - 2\sqrt{x}$ **b** $\sqrt{1-2x}$ **c** 3   **16** $a = 1$, $b = -1$

17 a   **b**

18 a $f^{-1}(x) = \dfrac{x-2}{4}$ **b** $f^{-1}(x) = \dfrac{3-4x}{5}$

19 $(f^{-1} \circ h^{-1})(x) = (h \circ f)^{-1}(x) = x - 2$

20 a

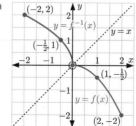

b Range is $\{y \mid 0 \leqslant y \leqslant 2\}$

c **i** $x = \sqrt{3}$ **ii** $x = -\frac{1}{2}$

21 **a**

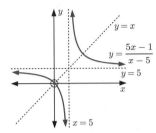

$y = \dfrac{5x - 1}{x - 5}$ is symmetrical about $y = x$

$\therefore$ f is a self-inverse function.

b $f^{-1}(x) = \dfrac{5x - 1}{x - 5}$ and $f(x) = \dfrac{5x - 1}{x - 5}$

$\therefore$ $f = f^{-1}$ $\therefore$ f is a self-inverse function.

22 **a** -4 **b** 1

23 **a**

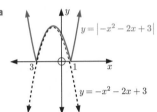

b

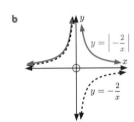

REVIEW SET 3B

1 **a** Domain is $\{x \mid x \in \mathbb{R}\}$,   Range is $\{y \mid y \geqslant -4\}$
b Domain is $\{x \mid x \geqslant -2\}$,   Range is $\{y \mid 1 \leqslant y < 3\}$
c Domain is $\{x \mid x \in \mathbb{R}\}$,   Range is $\{y \mid y = -1, 1, \text{ or } 2\}$

2 **a** $x^2 - x - 2$ **b** $16x^2 - 12x$

3 **a** **i** Domain is $\{x \mid x \in \mathbb{R}\}$,   Range is $\{y \mid y \geqslant -5\}$
ii x-intercepts -1 and 5, y-intercept $-\frac{25}{9}$
iii is a function
b **i** Domain is $\{x \mid x \in \mathbb{R}\}$,   Range is $\{y \mid y = 1 \text{ or } -3\}$
ii no x-intercepts, y-intercept 1
iii is a function

4 **a** is a function   **b** is not a function

5 **a** **i** -4 **ii** $-\frac{1}{2}$ **iii** 2 **b** $x = -2$
c $\dfrac{3x - 4}{x + 1}$ **d** $x = -9$

6 **a** 12 **b** $x = \pm 1$

7 **a** Domain is $\{x \mid x \neq \frac{1}{2}\}$,   Range is $\{y \mid y \neq 10\}$
b Domain is $\{x \mid x \geqslant -7\}$,   Range is $\{y \mid y \geqslant 0\}$

8 **a**

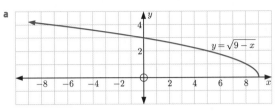

b It is a function.
c Domain is $\{x \mid x \leqslant 9\}$,   Range is $\{y \mid y \geqslant 0\}$

9 $a = 1$, $b = -6$, $c = 5$

10

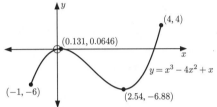

Range is $\{y \mid -6.88 \leqslant y \leqslant 4\}$

11 **a**

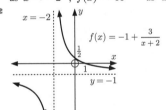

b

12 **a** vertical asymptote is $x = -2$,
horizontal asymptote is $y = -1$
b Domain is $\{x \mid x \neq -2\}$,   Range is $\{y \mid y \neq -1\}$
c x-intercept is 1, y-intercept is $\frac{1}{2}$
d as $x \to -2^-$, $f(x) \to -\infty$ as $x \to -\infty$, $f(x) \to -1^-$
as $x \to -2^+$, $f(x) \to \infty$ as $x \to \infty$, $f(x) \to -1^+$
e

13 **a** $-4x^2 + 4x + 2$ **b** $5 - 2x^2$ **c** 2

14 $(f \circ g)(x) = \dfrac{1}{(x^2 - 4x + 3)^2}$

Domain is $\{x \mid x \neq 3, \ x \neq 1\}$,   Range is $\{y \mid y > 0\}$

15 **a** **i** $6x^2 - 3x + 5$ **ii** $18x^2 + 57x + 45$
b $x = -\frac{5}{11}$

16 **a**

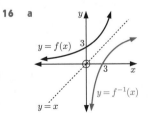

b

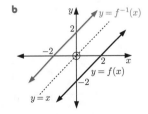

17 **a** $f^{-1}(x) = \dfrac{7 - x}{4}$ **b** $f^{-1}(x) = \dfrac{5x - 3}{2}$

18 a

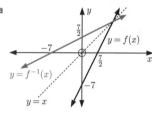

b $f^{-1}(x) = \dfrac{x+7}{2}$

19 $(f^{-1} \circ h^{-1})(x) = (h \circ f)^{-1}(x) = \dfrac{4x+6}{15}$

20 a $(g \circ f)(x) = \dfrac{2}{3x+1}$ **b** $x = -\frac{1}{2}$

c i vertical asymptote $x = -\frac{1}{3}$,
horizontal asymptote $y = 0$

ii

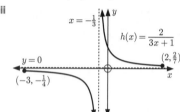

iii Range is $\{y \mid y \leqslant -\frac{1}{4} \text{ or } y \geqslant \frac{2}{7}\}$

21 16

22 a $a = 2, \ b = -1$
b Domain is $\{x \mid x \neq 2\}$, Range is $\{y \mid y \neq -1\}$

23 a $\dfrac{3x}{x-2}$ **b** $\dfrac{2x+1}{x-1}$

24 a

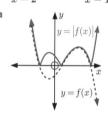

b

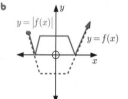

EXERCISE 4A

1 a

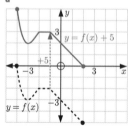

b

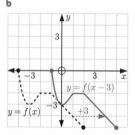

c

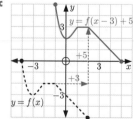

2 a

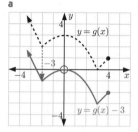

b

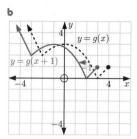

c

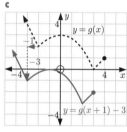

d

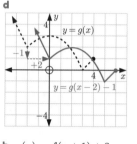

3 a $g(x) = f(x-4)$ **b** $g(x) = f(x+1) + 3$

4 a $g(x) = 2x - 1$ **b** $g(x) = 3x + 2$
 c $g(x) = -x^2 + 5x - 4$ **d** $g(x) = x^2 - 6x + 4$

5 a

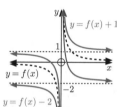

b

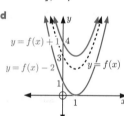

c

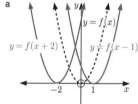

d

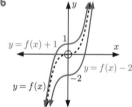

6 a

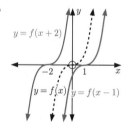

b

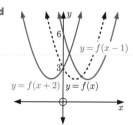

c

d

7 a

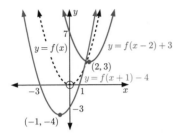

b

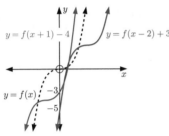

c

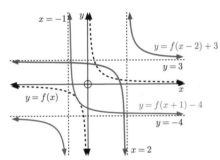

d

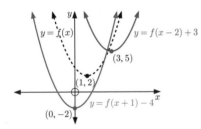

8 $(1, -9)$

9 a y-intercept is -1 **b** x-intercepts are -2 and 5
   c inconclusive

10 $g(x) = x^2 - 8x + 17$

11 a i $(3, 2)$ **ii** $(0, 11)$ **iii** $(5, 6)$
   b i $(-2, 4)$ **ii** $(-5, 25)$ **iii** $\left(-1\frac{1}{2}, 2\frac{1}{4}\right)$

EXERCISE 4B

1 a

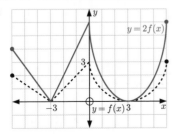

b

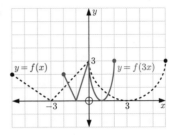

2 a

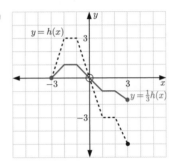

b

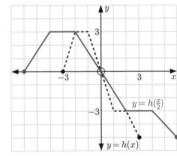

3 a $g(x) = 2f(x)$ **b** $g(x) = f\left(\frac{x}{3}\right)$ **4** cm

5 a

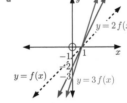

b

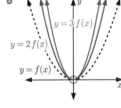

c

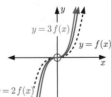

d

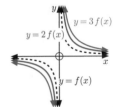

6 a

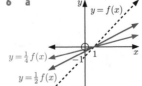

b

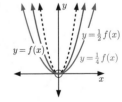

c

d
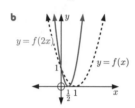

7 a
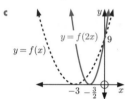

b

c
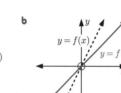

8 a
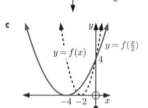

b

c

9 a $(2, 25)$ b $(-25, -15)$

10 a $g(x) = 2x^2 + 4$ b $g(x) = 5 - x$
  c $g(x) = \frac{1}{4}x^3 + 2x^2 - \frac{1}{2}$ d $g(x) = 8x^2 + 2x - 3$

11
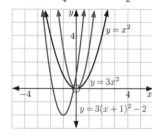

$y = x^2$ is transformed to $y = 3(x + 1)^2 - 2$ by vertically stretching with scale factor 3 and then translating through $\begin{pmatrix} -1 \\ -2 \end{pmatrix}$.

12
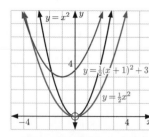

$y = x^2$ is transformed to $y = \frac{1}{2}(x + 1)^2 + 3$ by vertically stretching with scale factor $\frac{1}{2}$ and then translating through $\begin{pmatrix} -1 \\ 3 \end{pmatrix}$.

13
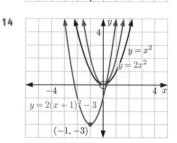

$y = x^2$ is transformed to $y = 2(x - \frac{3}{2})^2 + 1$ by vertically stretching with scale factor 2 and then translating through $\begin{pmatrix} \frac{3}{2} \\ 1 \end{pmatrix}$.

14

$y = x^2$ is transformed to $y = 2(x + 1)^2 - 3$ by vertically stretching with scale factor 2 and then translating through $\begin{pmatrix} -1 \\ -3 \end{pmatrix}$.

15 a Horizontally stretching with scale factor $\frac{1}{2}$, then vertically stretching with scale factor 3.
  b i $(\frac{3}{2}, -15)$ ii $(\frac{1}{2}, 6)$ iii $(-1, 3)$
  c i $(4, \frac{1}{3})$ ii $(-6, \frac{2}{3})$ iii $(-14, 1)$

16 a $y = \dfrac{1}{2x}$ b $y = \dfrac{3}{x}$ c $y = \dfrac{1}{x + 3}$
  d $y = 4 + \dfrac{1}{x} = \dfrac{4x + 1}{x}$

17 a $g(x) = \dfrac{3}{x - 1} - 1 = \dfrac{-x + 4}{x - 1}$
  b vertical asymptote $x = 1$, horizontal asymptote $y = -1$
  c Domain is
     $\{x \mid x \neq 1\}$
     Range is
     $\{y \mid y \neq -1\}$
  d
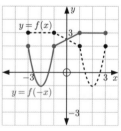

EXERCISE 4C

1 a
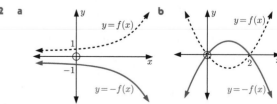
  b

2 a   b

c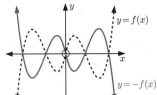

3 a 　**b**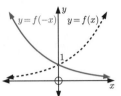

c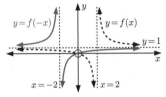

4 a 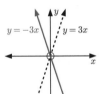　**b**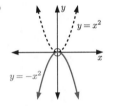

c 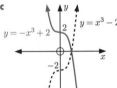　**d**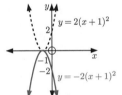

5 a i $f(-x) = -2x + 1$　ii $f(-x) = x^2 - 2x + 1$
iii $f(-x) = -x^3$

b i 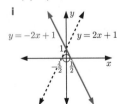　ii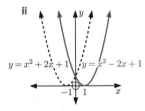

iii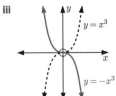

6 $g(x) = x^4 + 2x^3 - 3x^2 - 5x - 7$

7 a i $(3, 0)$　ii $(2, 1)$　iii $(-3, -2)$
b i $(7, 1)$　ii $(-5, 0)$　iii $(-3, 2)$

8 a i $(-2, -1)$　ii $(0, 3)$　iii $(1, 2)$
b i $(-5, -4)$　ii $(0, 3)$　iii $(-2, 3)$
9 a A reflection in the y-axis and a reflection in the x-axis.
b $(-3, 7)$　**c** $(5, 1)$
10 a A reflection in the x-axis.
b A vertical stretch with scale factor 3.
c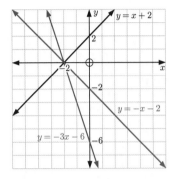

11 a A reflection in the y-axis.
b A horizontal stretch with scale factor 2.
c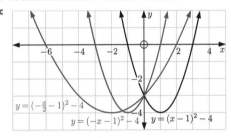

12 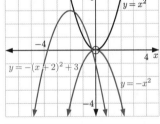　$y = x^2$ is transformed to $y = -(x+2)^2 + 3$ by reflecting in the x-axis and then translating through $\begin{pmatrix} -2 \\ 3 \end{pmatrix}$.

13 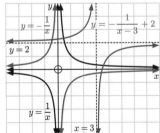　$y = \frac{1}{x}$ is transformed to $y = -\frac{1}{x-3} + 2$ by reflecting in the x-axis and then translating through $\begin{pmatrix} 3 \\ 2 \end{pmatrix}$.

EXERCISE 4D

1 a 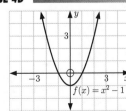　x-intercepts are ± 1, y-intercept is -1

b   **i**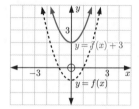

$y = f(x)$ has been translated 3 units upwards.

ii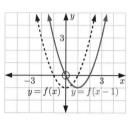

$y = f(x)$ has been translated 1 unit to the right.

iii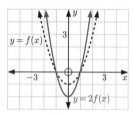

$y = f(x)$ has been vertically stretched with scale factor 2.

iv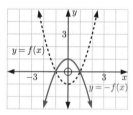

$y = f(x)$ has been reflected in the x-axis.

2   **a**   **i** A vertical stretch with scale factor 3.
            ii $g(x) = 3f(x)$
    b   **i** A translation through $\begin{pmatrix} 0 \\ -2 \end{pmatrix}$.
            ii $g(x) = f(x) - 2$
    c   **i** A vertical stretch with scale factor $\frac{1}{2}$.
            ii $g(x) = \frac{1}{2}f(x)$
    d   **i** A reflection in the y-axis.   **ii** $g(x) = f(-x)$

3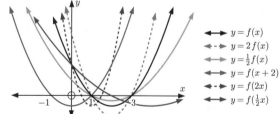

4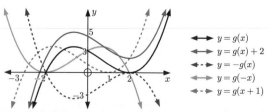

5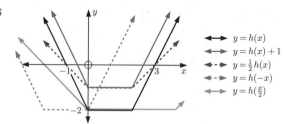

6   **a** x-intercepts are -1 and β, y-intercept is $-\beta$

b, c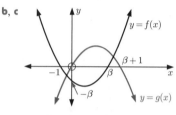

7   **a** $f(-x - 4) - 1$ **b** $f(-x + 4) - 1$
    c $\frac{1}{2}f(x + 2) + \frac{1}{2}$ **d** $\frac{1}{2}f(x + 2) + 1$

8   **a** A reflection in the x-axis, then a translation through $\begin{pmatrix} -1 \\ 3 \end{pmatrix}$.

    b A horizontal stretch with scale factor 2, then a translation through $\begin{pmatrix} 0 \\ -7 \end{pmatrix}$.

    c A horizontal stretch with scale factor $\frac{1}{3}$, then a translation through $\begin{pmatrix} 1 \\ 0 \end{pmatrix}$.

    d A vertical stretch with scale factor 2, a horizontal stretch with scale factor 4, then a translation through $\begin{pmatrix} 4 \\ -1 \end{pmatrix}$.

    e A vertical stretch with scale factor 2, a horizontal stretch with scale factor $\frac{1}{3}$, then a translation through $\begin{pmatrix} 1 \\ 5 \end{pmatrix}$.

    f A reflection in the x-axis, a vertical stretch with scale factor 4, a horizontal stretch with scale factor 2, then a translation through $\begin{pmatrix} -3 \\ -1 \end{pmatrix}$.

9   **a** The graph is stretched vertically with scale factor $|a|$, and reflected in the x-axis. It is then translated h units horizontally and k units vertically.

    b The function has shape ⌒ after it is reflected in the x-axis.
    The function has vertex (h, k), and y-intercept $ah^2 + k$.

REVIEW SET 4A

1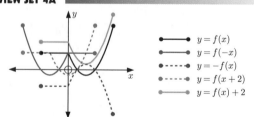

2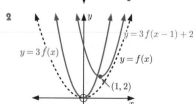

3 a $g(x) = 4x - 10$ **b** $g(x) = 5x^2 + 30$

c $g(x) = -3x - 5$ **d** $g(x) = \frac{2}{9}x^2 - \frac{1}{3}x + 4$

e $g(x) = -x^3$

4

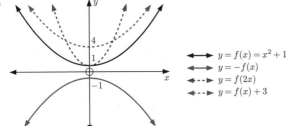

5 $g(x)$ is the result of transforming $f(x)$ 3 units to the left and 4 units down.

∴ domain of $g(x)$ is $\{x \mid -5 \leqslant x \leqslant 0\}$

range of $g(x)$ is $\{y \mid -5 \leqslant y \leqslant 3\}$.

6 a $g(x) = (x - 1)^2 + 8$

b i $\{y \mid y \geqslant 4\}$ **ii** $\{y \mid y \geqslant 8\}$

7 $g(x) = 3x^2 + 5x + 9$

8 a i $y = 3x + 8$ **ii** $y = 3x + 8$

b $f(x + k) = a(x + k) + b = ax + b + ak = f(x) + ak$

9 a $-f(x + 2) + 3$ **b** $2f(x - 4) - 2$

10 a x-intercepts -9 and -3

b x-intercepts -5 and 1, y-intercept -9

c x-intercepts -10 and 2, y-intercept -3

d x-intercepts -5 and 1, y-intercept 3

11 a $g(x) = \dfrac{2x - 3}{x - 1}$ **d**

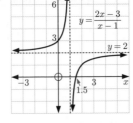

b vertical asymptote $x = 1$,

horizontal asymptote $y = 2$

c Domain is $\{x \mid x \neq 1\}$

Range is $\{y \mid y \neq 2\}$

12

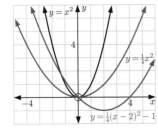

$y = x^2$ is transformed to $y = \frac{1}{4}(x - 2)^2 - 1$ by vertically stretching with scale factor $\frac{1}{4}$ and then translating through $\begin{pmatrix} 2 \\ -1 \end{pmatrix}$.

REVIEW SET 4B

1 a

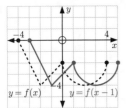

b

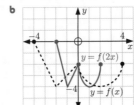

c

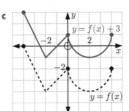

d

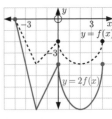

e

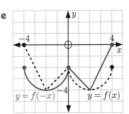

f

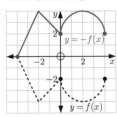

2 a $g(x) = 3x - x^2$ **b** $g(x) = 16 - x$

c $g(x) = \frac{1}{12}x + 2$

3

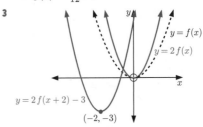

4 $g(x) = -x^2 - 6x - 7$

5

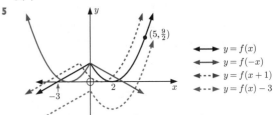

6

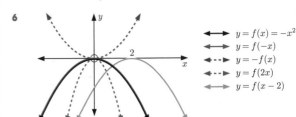

7 a

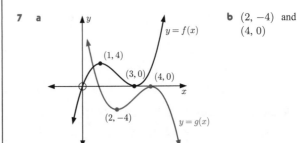

b $(2, -4)$ and $(4, 0)$

8 $y = -2x^2 + 5x - 3$

9

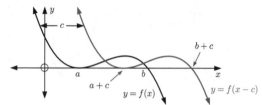

10 $(1, 6)$

11 **a** A vertical stretch with scale factor 2, then a translation through $\begin{pmatrix} -1 \\ 3 \end{pmatrix}$.

b A horizontal stretch with scale factor $\frac{3}{2}$, a reflection in the x-axis, then a translation through $\begin{pmatrix} 0 \\ -6 \end{pmatrix}$.

c A reflection in the y-axis, a vertical stretch with scale factor $\frac{1}{3}$, then a translation through $\begin{pmatrix} 0 \\ 2 \end{pmatrix}$.

12 **a**

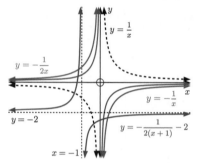

b A reflection in the x-axis, a vertical stretch with scale factor $\frac{1}{2}$, then a translation through $\begin{pmatrix} -1 \\ -2 \end{pmatrix}$.

c $y = \dfrac{-4x - 5}{2x + 2}$

Domain is $\{x \mid x \neq -1\}$,   Range is $\{y \mid y \neq -2\}$

EXERCISE 5A

1 **a** $2^{\frac{1}{5}}$ **b** $2^{-\frac{1}{5}}$ **c** $2^{\frac{3}{2}}$ **d** $2^{\frac{5}{2}}$ **e** $2^{-\frac{1}{3}}$
   f $2^{\frac{4}{3}}$ **g** $2^{\frac{3}{2}}$ **h** $2^{\frac{3}{2}}$ **i** $2^{-\frac{4}{3}}$ **j** $2^{-\frac{3}{2}}$

2 **a** $3^{\frac{1}{3}}$ **b** $3^{-\frac{1}{3}}$ **c** $3^{\frac{1}{4}}$ **d** $3^{\frac{3}{2}}$ **e** $3^{-\frac{5}{2}}$

3 **a** $7^{\frac{1}{3}}$ **b** $3^{\frac{3}{4}}$ **c** $2^{\frac{4}{5}}$ **d** $2^{\frac{5}{8}}$ **e** $7^{\frac{2}{7}}$
   f $7^{-\frac{1}{3}}$ **g** $3^{-\frac{3}{4}}$ **h** $2^{-\frac{5}{6}}$ **i** $2^{-\frac{5}{3}}$ **j** $7^{-\frac{2}{7}}$

4 **a** $x^{\frac{1}{2}}$ **b** $x^{\frac{3}{2}}$ **c** $x^{-\frac{1}{2}}$ **d** $x^{\frac{5}{2}}$ **e** $x^{-\frac{3}{2}}$

5 **a** ≈ 2.28 **b** ≈ 0.435 **c** ≈ 1.68 **d** ≈ 1.93
   e ≈ 0.523

6 **a** $\sqrt[3]{5}$ **b** $\frac{1}{\sqrt{3}}$ **c** $9\sqrt{3}$ **d** $m\sqrt{m}$ **e** $x^3\sqrt{x}$

7 **a** 8   **b** 32   **c** 8   **d** 125   **e** 4
   f $\frac{1}{2}$ **g** $\frac{1}{27}$ **h** $\frac{1}{16}$ **i** $\frac{1}{81}$ **j** $\frac{1}{25}$

EXERCISE 5B

1 **a** 1   **b** x **c** $x^{\frac{1}{2}}$ or $\sqrt{x}$

2 **a** $x^5 + 2x^4 + x^2$ **b** $2^{2x} + 2^x$ **c** $x + 1$
   d $7^{2x} + 2(7^x)$ **e** $2(3^x) - 1$ **f** $x^2 + 2x + 3$

g $1 + 5(2^{-x})$ **h** $5^x + 1$ **i** $x^{\frac{3}{2}} + x^{\frac{1}{2}} + 1$
j $3^{2x} + 5(3^x) + 1$ **k** $2x^{\frac{3}{2}} - x^{\frac{1}{2}} + 5$ **l** $2^{3x} - 3(2^{2x}) - 1$

3 **a** $2^{2x} + 2^{x+1} - 3$ **b** $3^{2x} + 7(3^x) + 10$
   c $5^{2x} - 6(5^x) + 8$ **d** $2^{2x} + 6(2^x) + 9$
   e $3^{2x} - 2(3^x) + 1$ **f** $4^{2x} + 14(4^x) + 49$
   g $x - 4$ **h** $4^x - 9$ **i** $x - \frac{1}{x}$ **j** $x^2 + 4 + \frac{4}{x^2}$
   k $7^{2x} - 2 + 7^{-2x}$ **l** $25 - 10(2^{-x}) + 2^{-2x}$

4 **a** $5^x(5^x + 1)$ **b** $10(3^n)$ **c** $7^n(1 + 7^{2n})$
   d $5(5^n - 1)$ **e** $6(6^{n+1} - 1)$ **f** $16(4^n - 1)$
   g $2^n(2^n - 8)$ **h** $5(2^{n-1})$ **i** $9(2^{2n-1})$

5 **a** $(3^x + 2)(3^x - 2)$ **b** $(2^x + 5)(2^x - 5)$
   c $(4 + 3^x)(4 - 3^x)$ **d** $(5 + 2^x)(5 - 2^x)$
   e $(3^x + 2^x)(3^x - 2^x)$ **f** $(2^x + 3)^2$
   g $(3^x + 5)^2$ **h** $(2^x - 7)^2$ **i** $(5^x - 2)^2$

6 **a** $(2^x + 1)(2^x - 2)$ **b** $(3^x + 3)(3^x - 2)$
   c $(2^x - 3)(2^x - 4)$ **d** $(2^x + 3)(2^x + 6)$
   e $(2^x + 4)(2^x - 5)$ **f** $(3^x + 2)(3^x + 7)$
   g $(3^x + 5)(3^x - 1)$ **h** $(5^x + 2)(5^x - 1)$
   i $(7^x - 4)(7^x - 3)$

7 **a** 2^n **b** 10^a **c** 3^b **d** $\dfrac{1}{5^n}$ **e** 5^x
   f $(\frac{3}{4})^a$ **g** $(\frac{8}{3})^k$ **h** 5   **i** 5^n

8 **a** $3^m + 1$ **b** $1 + 6^n$ **c** $4^n + 2^n$ **d** $4^x - 1$
   e 6^n **f** 5^n **g** 4   **h** $2^n - 1$ **i** $\frac{1}{2}$

9 **a** $n\,2^{n+1}$ **b** -3^{n-1}

EXERCISE 5C

1 **a** $x = 5$ **b** $x = 2$ **c** $x = 4$ **d** $x = 0$
   e $x = -1$ **f** $x = \frac{1}{2}$ **g** $x = -3$ **h** $x = 2$
   i $x = -3$ **j** $x = -4$ **k** $x = 2$ **l** $x = 1$

2 **a** $x = \frac{5}{3}$ **b** $x = -\frac{3}{2}$ **c** $x = -\frac{3}{2}$ **d** $x = -\frac{1}{2}$
   e $x = -\frac{2}{3}$ **f** $x = -\frac{5}{4}$ **g** $x = \frac{3}{2}$ **h** $x = \frac{5}{2}$
   i $x = \frac{1}{8}$ **j** $x = \frac{9}{2}$ **k** $x = -4$ **l** $x = -4$
   m $x = 0$ **n** $x = \frac{7}{2}$ **o** $x = -2$ **p** $x = -6$

3 **a** $x = \frac{1}{7}$ **b** has no solutions   **c** $x = \frac{5}{2}$

4 **a** $x = 3$ **b** $x = 2$ **c** $x = -1$ **d** $x = 2$
   e $x = -2$ **f** $x = -2$

5 **a** $x = 1$ or 2 **b** $x = 1$ **c** $x = 1$ or 2
   d $x = 1$ **e** $x = 2$ **f** $x = 0$

EXERCISE 5D

1 **a** **i** ≈ 1.4 **ii** ≈ 1.7 **iii** ≈ 2.8 **iv** ≈ 0.4
   b **i** $x \approx 1.6$ **ii** $x \approx -0.7$
   c $y = 2^x$ has a horizontal asymptote of $y = 0$.

2 **a** C   **b** B   **c** E   **d** A   **e** D

3 **a**   **b**

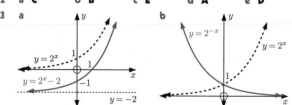

c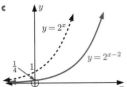

d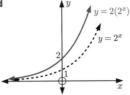

4 a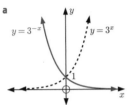

b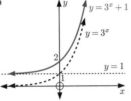

c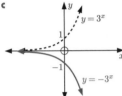

d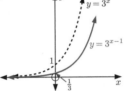

5 a $y = 0$ **b** $y = -1$ **c** $y = 3$ **d** $y = 2$
e $y = 0$ **f** $y = -4$

6 a i -1 **ii** 7 **iii** $-\frac{17}{9} = -1\frac{8}{9}$ **b** $y = -2$

c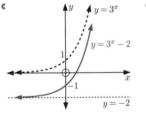

d Domain is $\{x \mid x \in \mathbb{R}\}$
Range is $\{y \mid y > -2\}$

7 a i 7 **ii** $\frac{19}{4} = 4\frac{3}{4}$ **iii** 16 **b** $y = 4$

c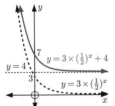

d Domain is $\{x \mid x \in \mathbb{R}\}$
Range is $\{y \mid y > 4\}$

8 a i $\frac{7}{8}$ **ii** 0 **iii** -7 **b** $y = 1$

c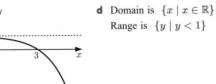

d Domain is $\{x \mid x \in \mathbb{R}\}$
Range is $\{y \mid y < 1\}$

9 a i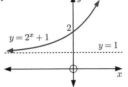

ii Domain is $\{x \mid x \in \mathbb{R}\}$
Range is $\{y \mid y > 1\}$
iii $y \approx 3.67$

iv as $x \to \infty$, $y \to \infty$
as $x \to -\infty$, $y \to 1^+$
v $y = 1$

b i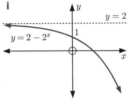

ii Domain is $\{x \mid x \in \mathbb{R}\}$
Range is $\{y \mid y < 2\}$
iii $y \approx -0.665$

iv as $x \to \infty$, $y \to -\infty$
as $x \to -\infty$, $y \to 2^-$
v $y = 2$

c i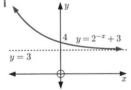

ii Domain is $\{x \mid x \in \mathbb{R}\}$
Range is $\{y \mid y > 3\}$
iii $y \approx 3.38$

iv as $x \to \infty$, $y \to 3^+$
as $x \to -\infty$, $y \to \infty$
v $y = 3$

d i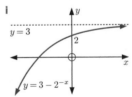

ii Domain is $\{x \mid x \in \mathbb{R}\}$
Range is $\{y \mid y < 3\}$
iii $y \approx 2.62$

iv as $x \to \infty$, $y \to 3^-$ **v** $y = 3$
as $x \to -\infty$, $y \to -\infty$

10 a $a = 5$, $b = -10$ **b** $y = 310$

11 a $(0, 2.5)$ **b** $a = 1.5$ **c** $y = 3.5$

12 a $x \approx 3.46$ **b** $x \approx 2.46$ **c** $x \approx 1.16$
d $x \approx -0.738$ **e** $x \approx 1.85$ **f** $x \approx 0.0959$
g $x \approx 6.03$ **h** $x \approx 50.0$ **i** $x \approx 31.0$

EXERCISE 5E.1

1 a 100 grams
b i ≈ 131 g
ii ≈ 197 g
iii ≈ 507 g

c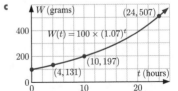

2 a $P_0 = 50$
b i ≈ 76 possums   **ii** ≈ 141 possums
iii ≈ 396 possums

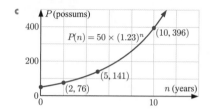

d ≈ 11 years   e ≈ 11.1 years

3 a $B_0 = 12$ bears   b ≈ 138 bears
   c $\approx 239\%$ d ≈ 23.0 years

4 a 4 people   b 393 people   c ≈ 19.9 days

5 a i V_0 ii $2V_0$ b 100%
   c $\approx 183\%$ increase, it is the percentage increase in reaction
      speed from $20°C$ to $50°C$.

6 a $A(t) = 5000 \times (1.1)^t$ b i £6050   ii £8052.55

   c   d ≈ 4.93 years

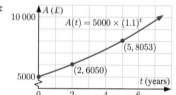

EXERCISE 5E.2

1 a 250 g   b i ≈ 112 g   ii ≈ 50.4 g   iii ≈ 22.6 g

   c

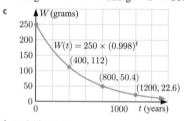

   d ≈ 346 years

2 a $100°C$
   b i $\approx 80.9°C$ ii $\approx 75.4°C$ iii $\approx 33.3°C$

   c

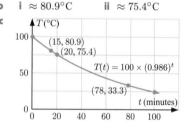

3 a 1000 g
   b i ≈ 809 g   ii ≈ 120 g   iii $\approx 6.06 \times 10^{-7}$ g

   c

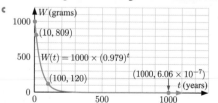

   d ≈ 217 years   e $1000(1 - 0.979^t)$ grams

4 a $P(t) = 400 \times (0.92)^t$
   b i 368 orangutans   ii ≈ 264 orangutans

c

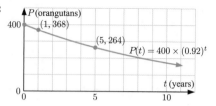

d ≈ 8.31 years, or ≈ 8 years 4 months

5 a $L_0 = 10$ units   b ≈ 2.77 units   c ≈ 17.9 m
   d between ≈ 23.5 m and ≈ 44.9 m

6 a $24\,000   b $r = 0.85$ c ≈ 7 years

7 a i $22°C$ ii $6°C$ iii $-2°C$

   b

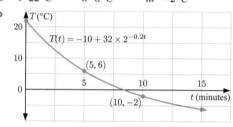

   c ≈ 8.39 min or ≈ 8 min 23 s
   d No, as $32 \times 2^{-0.2t} > 0$ for any value of t.

8 a W_0 b $\approx 12.9\%$ c 45 000 years

EXERCISE 5F

1

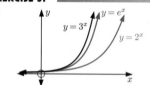

The graph of $y = e^x$ lies
between $y = 2^x$ and
$y = 3^x$.

2

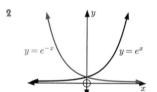

One is the other reflected
in the y-axis.

3 p

4 a $e^x > 0$ for all x
   b i $y \approx 4.12 \times 10^{-9}$ ii $y \approx 9.70 \times 10^8$

5 a ≈ 7.39 b ≈ 20.1 c ≈ 2.01 d ≈ 1.65
   e ≈ 0.368

6 a $e^{\frac{1}{2}}$ b $e^{-\frac{1}{2}}$ c e^{-2} d $e^{\frac{3}{2}}$

7 a ≈ 10.074 b $\approx 0.099\,261$ c ≈ 125.09
   d $\approx 0.007\,994\,5$ e ≈ 41.914 f ≈ 42.429
   g ≈ 3540.3 h $\approx 0.006\,342\,4$

8 a $e^{2x} + 2e^x + 1$ b $1 - e^{2x}$ c $1 - 3e^x$

9 a $e^x(e^x + 1)$ b $(e^x + 4)(e^x - 4)$ c $(e^x - 6)(e^x - 2)$

10 a

![Graph showing f(x)=e^x, g(x)=e^{x-2}, h(x)=e^x+3, and y=3, with point ≈0.135]

b Domain of f, g, and h is $\{x \mid x \in \mathbb{R}\}$
Range of f is $\{y \mid y > 0\}$,   Range of g is $\{y \mid y > 0\}$
Range of h is $\{y \mid y > 3\}$

11 a

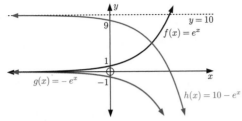

b Domain of f, g, and h is $\{x \mid x \in \mathbb{R}\}$
Range of f is $\{y \mid y > 0\}$,   Range of g is $\{y \mid y < 0\}$
Range of h is $\{y \mid y < 10\}$

c For f: as $x \to \infty$, $y \to \infty$
as $x \to -\infty$, $y \to 0^+$
For g: as $x \to \infty$, $y \to -\infty$
as $x \to -\infty$, $y \to 0^-$
For h: as $x \to \infty$, $y \to -\infty$
as $x \to -\infty$, $y \to 10^-$

12 a **i** 2 g
ii ≈ 2.57 g
iii ≈ 4.23 g
iv ≈ 40.2 g

b

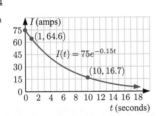

13 a $x = \frac{1}{2}$ **b** $x = -4$

14 a **i** ≈ 64.6 amps
ii ≈ 16.7 amps
c ≈ 28.8 seconds

b

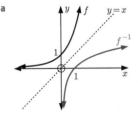

15 a

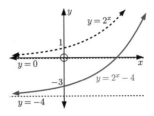

b Domain of f^{-1} is
$\{x \mid x > 0\}$
Range of f^{-1} is
$\{y \mid y \in \mathbb{R}\}$

16 $e^1 \approx \displaystyle\sum_{i=0}^{19} \frac{1}{i!} 1^i \approx 2.718\,281\,828$

REVIEW SET 5A

1 a 4   **b** $\frac{1}{9}$ **c** $\frac{1}{3}$

2 a $x = -2$ **b** $x = \frac{3}{4}$ **c** $x = -\frac{1}{4}$

3 a **i** ≈ 2.2 **ii** ≈ 0.6
b **i** $x \approx 1.45$ **ii** $x \approx -0.6$ **iii** $x \approx 1.1$

4 a $1 + e^{2x}$ **b** $2^{2x} + 10(2^x) + 25$ **c** $x - 49$

5 a $x = 5$ **b** $x = -4$ **6** $k = \frac{3}{2}$

7 a 3   **b** 24   **c** $\frac{3}{4}$

8

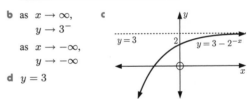

9 a

x	-2	-1	0	1	2
y	$-4\frac{8}{9}$	$-4\frac{2}{3}$	-4	-2	4

b as $x \to \infty$,
$y \to \infty$
as $x \to -\infty$,
$y \to -5^+$

c

d $y = -5$

10 a

x	-2	-1	0	1	2
y	-1	1	2	$2\frac{1}{2}$	$2\frac{3}{4}$

b as $x \to \infty$,
$y \to 3^-$
as $x \to -\infty$,
$y \to -\infty$

c

d $y = 3$

11 a

b For $f(x)$: domain is $\{x \mid x \in \mathbb{R}\}$,   range is $\{y \mid y > 0\}$
For $g(x)$: domain is $\{x \mid x \in \mathbb{R}\}$,   range is $\{y \mid y > 0\}$
For $h(x)$: domain is $\{x \mid x \in \mathbb{R}\}$,   range is $\{y \mid y < 3\}$

c For $f(x)$: as $x \to \infty$, $f(x) \to \infty$
as $x \to -\infty$, $f(x) \to 0^+$
For $g(x)$: as $x \to \infty$, $g(x) \to \infty$
as $x \to -\infty$, $g(x) \to 0^+$
For $h(x)$: as $x \to \infty$, $h(x) \to -\infty$
as $x \to -\infty$, $h(x) \to 3^-$

12 a $80°$C
b **i** $\approx 26.8°$C
ii $\approx 9.00°$C
iii $\approx 3.02°$C
d ≈ 12.8 min

c

13 a $A(t) = 10 \times (1.15)^t$
b **i** 13.225 m^2 **ii** ≈ 20.1 m^2

c

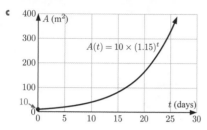

$A(t) = 10 \times (1.15)^t$

d ≈ 24.3 days

REVIEW SET 5B

1 **a** ≈ 3.95 **b** ≈ 0.517 **c** ≈ 3.16

2 **a** $9 - 6e^x + e^{2x}$ **b** $x - 2 - x^{-1}$ **c** $2^x + 1$

3 **a** $8(3^x)$ **b** $(2^x - 4)(2^x + 3)$ **c** $(e^x + 5)(e^x - 3)$

4 **a** $x = 4$ **b** $x = -4$ **c** $x = 0$ or 2

5 **a** **i** ≈ 2.3 **ii** ≈ 0.2 **b** $x \approx 0.8$

6 **a** $\frac{1}{\sqrt{2}} + 1 \approx 1.71$ **b** $a = -1$

7 **a**

x	-2	-1	0	1	2
y	15.8	6.44	3	1.74	1.27

b as $x \to \infty$, $y \to 1^+$

as $x \to -\infty$, $y \to \infty$

d $y = 1$

c

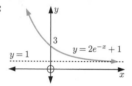

$y = 2e^{-x} + 1$

$y = 1$

8 **a** C   **b** E   **c** A   **d** B   **e** D

9 **a** **i** 81   **ii** $\frac{1}{3}$ **b** $k = 9$

10 **a** y^2 **b** y^{-1} **c** $\frac{1}{\sqrt{y}}$ or $y^{-\frac{1}{2}}$

11 **a** clock: £525,   vase: £428

b clock: $V(t) = 500 \times (1.05)^t$

vase: $V(t) = 400 \times (1.07)^t$

c clock $\approx$ £1039.46,   vase $\approx$ £1103.61 $\therefore$ the vase

d $500 \times (1.05)^t = 400 \times (1.07)^t$ and solve for t;

$t \approx 11.8$ years

12 **a** 1500 g

b **i** ≈ 90.3 g

ii ≈ 5.44 g

d ≈ 386 years

c

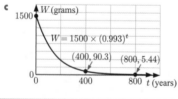

$W = 1500 \times (0.993)^t$

$(400, 90.3)$ $(800, 5.44)$

EXERCISE 6A

1 **a** 4   **b** -3 **c** 1   **d** 0   **e** $\frac{1}{2}$ **f** $\frac{1}{3}$

g $-\frac{1}{4}$ **h** $1\frac{1}{2}$ **i** $\frac{2}{3}$ **j** $1\frac{1}{2}$ **k** $1\frac{1}{3}$ **l** $3\frac{1}{2}$

2 **a** n **b** $a + 2$ **c** $1 - m$ **d** $a - b$

3 **a** $100 < 237 < 1000$ **b** ≈ 2.37

$\therefore \ \log 100 < \log 237 < \log 1000$

$\therefore \ 2 < \log 237 < 3$

4 **a** $-1 < \log(0.6) < 0$ **b** ≈ -0.22

5 **a** ≈ 1.88 **b** ≈ 2.06 **c** ≈ 0.48 **d** ≈ 2.92

e ≈ -0.40 **f** ≈ 3.51 **g** ≈ -2.10 **h** does not exist

6 **a** $x > 1$ **b** $x = 1$ **c** $0 < x < 1$ **d** $x \leqslant 0$

7 **a** $\approx 10^{0.7782}$ **b** $\approx 10^{1.7782}$ **c** $\approx 10^{3.7782}$

d $\approx 10^{-0.2218}$ **e** $\approx 10^{-2.2218}$ **f** $\approx 10^{1.1761}$

g $\approx 10^{3.1761}$ **h** $\approx 10^{0.1761}$ **i** $\approx 10^{-0.8239}$

j $\approx 10^{-3.8239}$

8 **a** **i** ≈ 0.477 **ii** ≈ 2.477

b $\log 300 = \log(3 \times 10^2) = \log(10^{\log 3} \times 10^2) = ...$

9 **a** **i** ≈ 0.699 **ii** ≈ -1.301

b $\log 0.05 = \log(5 \times 10^{-2}) = \log(10^{\log 5} \times 10^{-2}) = ...$

10 **a** $x = 100$ **b** $x = 10$ **c** $x = 1$

d $x = \frac{1}{10}$ **e** $x = \sqrt{10}$ **f** $x = \frac{1}{\sqrt{10}}$

g $x = 10\,000$ **h** $x = 0.000\,01$ **i** $x \approx 6.84$

j $x \approx 140$ **k** $x \approx 0.0419$ **l** $x \approx 0.000\,631$

EXERCISE 6B

1 **a** $10^2 = 100$ **b** $10^4 = 10\,000$ **c** $10^{-1} = 0.1$

d $10^{\frac{1}{2}} = \sqrt{10}$ **e** $2^3 = 8$ **f** $3^2 = 9$

g $2^{-2} = \frac{1}{4}$ **h** $3^{1.5} = \sqrt{27}$ **i** $5^{-\frac{1}{2}} = \frac{1}{\sqrt{5}}$

2 **a** $\log_4 64 = 3$ **b** $\log_5 25 = 2$

c $\log_7 49 = 2$ **d** $\log_2 64 = 6$

e $\log_2\left(\frac{1}{8}\right) = -3$ **f** $\log_{10}(0.01) = -2$

g $\log_2\left(\frac{1}{2}\right) = -1$ **h** $\log_3\left(\frac{1}{27}\right) = -3$

3 **a** 5   **b** -2 **c** $\frac{1}{2}$ **d** 2   **e** 6   **f** 7

g 2   **h** 3   **i** -3 **j** $\frac{1}{2}$ **k** 2   **l** $\frac{1}{2}$

m 5   **n** $\frac{1}{3}$ **o** $\frac{1}{3}$ **p** $\frac{3}{2}$ **q** 0   **r** 1

s -1 **t** $\frac{3}{4}$ **u** $-\frac{1}{2}$ **v** $\frac{5}{2}$ **w** $-\frac{3}{2}$ **x** $-\frac{3}{4}$

4 **a** 2   **b** -1 **c** $\frac{1}{2}$ **d** 3   **e** $\frac{1}{4}$ **f** $\frac{3}{2}$

g -2 **h** $-\frac{1}{2}$ **i** $\frac{5}{2}$

5 **a** $x = 8$ **b** $x = 2$ **c** $x = 3$ **d** $x = 14$

6 $\log_b a = \frac{1}{x}$

EXERCISE 6C

1 **a** $\log 16$ **b** $\log 20$ **c** $\log 8$ **d** $\log\left(\frac{p}{m}\right)$

e 1   **f** $\log 2$ **g** 3   **h** 2

i $\log 24$ **j** 1   **k** 0   **l** $\log 28$

2 **a** $\log 700$ **b** $\log\left(\frac{2}{5}\right)$ **c** $\log_2 6$

d $\log_3\left(\frac{5}{9}\right)$ **e** $\log 200$ **f** $\log(0.005)$

g $\log(10^t \times w)$ **h** $\log_m\left(\frac{40}{m^2}\right)$ **i** $\log_5\left(\frac{5}{2}\right)$

3 **a** $\log 96$ **b** $\log 72$ **c** $\log 8$ **d** $\log_3\left(\frac{25}{8}\right)$

e 1   **f** $\log\left(\frac{1}{2}\right)$ **g** $\log 20$ **h** $\log 25$ **i** $\log_n\left(\frac{n^2}{10}\right)$

4 **a** 2   **b** $\frac{3}{2}$ **c** 3   **d** $\frac{1}{2}$ **e** -2 **f** $-\frac{3}{2}$

5 For example, for **a**, $\log 9 = \log(3^2) = 2\log 3$.

7 **a** $p + q$ **b** $2q + r$ **c** $2p + 3q$ **d** $r + \frac{1}{2}q - p$

e $r - 5p$ **f** $p - 2q$

8 **a** $x + z$ **b** $z + 2y$ **c** $x + z - y$ **d** $2x + \frac{1}{2}y$

e $3y - \frac{1}{2}z$ **f** $2z + \frac{1}{2}y - 3x$

9 **a** 0.86   **b** 2.15   **c** 1.075

10 $\log 384$ **11** $4 + \log_2 45$

EXERCISE 6D

1 **a** 2   **b** 4   **c** $\frac{3}{2}$ **d** 0   **e** -1
   f $\frac{1}{3}$ **g** -2 **h** $-\frac{1}{2}$

2 **a** 3   **b** 9   **c** $\frac{1}{5}$ **d** $\frac{1}{4}$ **e** a
   f $1 + a$ **g** $a + b$ **h** ab

3 **a** ≈ 2.485 **b** ≈ 4.220 **c** ≈ 0.336
   d ≈ -0.357 **e** ≈ 6.215

4 x does not exist such that $e^x = -2$ or 0 since $e^x > 0$ for all $x \in \mathbb{R}$.

5 **a** $\approx e^{1.7918}$ **b** $\approx e^{4.0943}$ **c** $\approx e^{8.6995}$
   d $\approx e^{-0.5108}$ **e** $\approx e^{-5.1160}$ **f** $\approx e^{2.7081}$
   g $\approx e^{7.3132}$ **h** $\approx e^{0.4055}$ **i** $\approx e^{-1.8971}$
   j $\approx e^{-8.8049}$

6 **a** $x \approx 20.1$ **b** $x = e$ **c** $x = 1$
   d $x \approx 0.368$ **e** $x \approx 0.006\,74$ **f** $x \approx 2.30$
   g $x \approx 8.54$ **h** $x \approx 0.0370$

7 **a** **i** x **ii** x **b** They are inverses of each other.

8 **a** $\ln 45$ **b** $\ln 5$ **c** $\ln 4$ **d** $\ln 24$
   e $\ln 1 = 0$ **f** $\ln 30$ **g** $\ln(4e)$ **h** $\ln\left(\frac{6}{e}\right)$
   i $\ln 20$ **j** $\ln(4e^2)$ **k** $\ln\left(\frac{20}{e^2}\right)$ **l** $\ln 1 = 0$

9 **a** $\ln 972$ **b** $\ln 200$ **c** $\ln 1 = 0$ **d** $\ln 16$
   e $\ln 6$ **f** $\ln\left(\frac{1}{3}\right)$ **g** $\ln\left(\frac{1}{2}\right)$ **h** $\ln 2$
   i $\ln 16$ **j** $\ln(16e^2)$ **k** $\ln\left(\frac{3}{e}\right)$ **l** $\ln\left(\frac{\sqrt{e}}{8}\right)$

10 For example, for **a**, $\ln 27 = \ln(3^3) = 3 \ln 3$.

EXERCISE 6E

1 **a** $\log y = x \log 2$ **b** $\log y = \log 20 + 3 \log b$
   c $\log M = \log a + 4 \log d$ **d** $\log T = \log 5 + \frac{1}{2} \log d$
   e $\log R = \log b + \frac{1}{2} \log l$ **f** $\log Q = \log a - n \log b$
   g $\log y = \log a + x \log b$ **h** $\log F = \log 20 - \frac{1}{2} \log n$
   i $\log L = \log a + \log b - \log c$
   j $\log N = \frac{1}{2} \log a - \frac{1}{2} \log b$
   k $\log S = \log 200 + t \log 2$ **l** $\log y = m \log a - n \log b$

2 **a** $D = 2e$ **b** $F = \frac{5}{t}$ **c** $P = \sqrt{x}$ **d** $M = b^2 c$
   e $B = \frac{m^3}{n^2}$ **f** $N = \frac{1}{\sqrt[3]{p}}$ **g** $P = 10x^3$ **h** $Q = \frac{a^2}{x}$

3 **a** $D = ex$ **b** $F = \frac{e^2}{p}$ **c** $P = \sqrt{x}$
   d $M = e^3 y^2$ **e** $B = \frac{t^3}{e}$ **f** $N = \frac{1}{\sqrt[3]{g}}$
   g $Q \approx 8.66 x^3$ **h** $D \approx 0.518 n^{0.4}$

4 **a** $\log_2 y = \log_2 3 + x$ **b** $x = \log_2\left(\frac{y}{3}\right)$
   c **i** $x = 0$ **ii** $x = 2$ **iii** $x \approx 3.32$

5 **a** $x = 9$ **b** $x = 2$ or 4 **c** $x = 25\sqrt{5}$
   d $x = 200$ **e** $x = 5$ **f** $x = 3$

6 **a** $2^x = 7$ **b** $\log(2^x) = \log 7$
                                 $\therefore \; x \log 2 = \log 7$
               $\therefore \; x = \log_2 7 = \frac{\log 7}{\log 2} \approx 2.81$

7 **a** Taking the logarithm in base a of both sides, $x = \log_a b$.
   b $\log(a^x) = \log b$ **c** Using **b**, $x \log a = \log b$
              $\therefore \; x = \frac{\log b}{\log a}$
       and using part **a**, $x = \log_a b = \frac{\log b}{\log a}$

EXERCISE 6F

1 **a** ≈ 1.77 **b** ≈ 5.32 **c** ≈ 3.23
   d ≈ -10.3 **e** ≈ -2.46 **f** ≈ 5.42

2 2   **4** **a** $x = 16$ **b** $x = \sqrt[3]{5} \approx 1.71$ **5** $\frac{8}{x}$

EXERCISE 6G

1 **a** $16 < 20 < 32 \Rightarrow 2^4 < 20 < 2^5$ **b** $x = \frac{\log 20}{\log 2}$
   c $x \approx 4.32$

2 **a** 3 and 4   **b** $x = \frac{\log 40}{\log 3}$ **c** $x \approx 3.36$

3 **a** **i** $x = \frac{1}{\log 2}$ **ii** $x \approx 3.32$
   b **i** $x = \frac{\log 20}{\log 3}$ **ii** $x \approx 2.73$
   c **i** $x = \frac{\log 50}{\log 4}$ **ii** $x \approx 2.82$
   d **i** $x = 4$ **ii** $x = 4$
   e **i** $x = -\frac{1}{\log\left(\frac{3}{4}\right)}$ **ii** $x \approx 8.00$
   f **i** $x = \log(0.000\,015)$ **ii** $x \approx -4.82$

4 **a** $x \approx 2.29$ **b** $x \approx 5.13$ **c** $x \approx 0.194$

5 **a** $x = \ln 10$ **b** $x = \ln 1000$ **c** $x = \ln(0.15)$
   d $x = 2 \ln 5$ **e** $x = \frac{1}{2} \ln 18$ **f** $x = 0$

6 **a** $x = \frac{\log 25}{\log 2}$ **b** $x = \frac{\log\left(\frac{20}{7}\right)}{\log(1.5)}$ **c** $x = \frac{\log(0.6)}{\log(0.8)}$
   d $x = -\frac{\log(0.03)}{\log 2}$ **e** $x = \frac{10 \log\left(\frac{10}{3}\right)}{\log 5}$ **f** $x = 4 \ln 8$

7 **a** $x = \frac{\log 3}{\log 5}$ **b** $x = -\frac{\log 8}{\log 3}$ **c** $x = -1$

8 **a** $x = \ln 2$ **b** $x = 0$ **c** $x = \ln 2$ or $\ln 3$ **d** $x = 0$
   e $x = \ln 4$ **f** $x = \ln\left(\frac{3+\sqrt{5}}{2}\right)$ or $\ln\left(\frac{3-\sqrt{5}}{2}\right)$

9 **a** $(\ln 3, 3)$ **b** $(\ln 2, 5)$ **c** $(0, 2)$ and $(\ln 5, -2)$

10 **a** ≈ 2.37 years   **b** ≈ 8.36 years

11 **a** ≈ 3.90 hours   **b** ≈ 15.5 hours

12 **a, b** see graph below

$\therefore$ approximately 2.8 weeks.

13 In ≈ 5.86 years or ≈ 5 years 10 months.   **14** 9 years

15 a $\dfrac{8.4\%}{12} = 0.7\% = 0.007, \quad r = 1 + 0.007 = 1.007$

    b after 74 months

16 a ≈ 17.3 years   **b** ≈ 92.2 years   **c** ≈ 115 years

17 Hint: $0.1 \times I_0 = I_0 \times 2^{-0.02t}$

        $\therefore \; 0.1 = 2^{-0.02t}$ and solve for t using logarithms.

18 Hint: Set $V = 40$, solve for t.

19 a

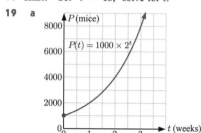

   b ≈ 4.32 weeks

   c $t = \dfrac{\log P - 3}{\log 2}$

20 a

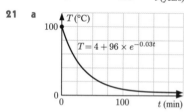

   b $t = \dfrac{3 - \log W}{0.04 \log 2}$

   c   **i** $t \approx 141$ years

       ii $t \approx 498$ years

21 a

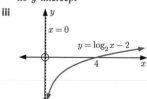

   b $t = \dfrac{\ln 96 - \ln(T - 4)}{0.03}$

   c   **i** ≈ 50.7 minutes   **ii** ≈ 152 minutes

22 $t = \dfrac{-5 \log\left(1 - \frac{v}{60}\right)}{\log 2}$ s

23 a decreasing   **b**   **i** 3900 m s^{-1} **ii** $\approx 2600 \text{ m s}^{-1}$

   c ≈ 11.8 s

EXERCISE 6H

1 a   **i** Domain is $\{x \mid x > 0\}$,   Range is $\{y \mid y \in \mathbb{R}\}$

     ii vertical asymptote is $x = 0$, x-intercept 4,

       no y-intercept

     iii

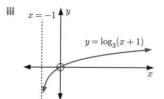

     iv $x = 2$ **v** $f^{-1}(x) = 2^{x+2}$

   b   **i** Domain is $\{x \mid x > -1\}$,   Range is $\{y \mid y \in \mathbb{R}\}$

     ii vertical asymptote is $x = -1$, x and y-intercepts 0

     iii

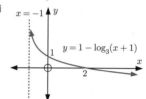

     iv $x = -\frac{2}{3}$ **v** $f^{-1}(x) = 3^x - 1$

   c   **i** Domain is $\{x \mid x > -1\}$,   Range is $\{y \mid y \in \mathbb{R}\}$

     ii vertical asymptote is $x = -1$, x-intercept 2,

       y-intercept 1

     iii

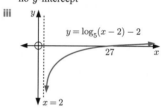

     iv $x = 8$ **v** $f^{-1}(x) = 3^{1-x} - 1$

   d   **i** Domain is $\{x \mid x > 2\}$,   Range is $\{y \mid y \in \mathbb{R}\}$

     ii vertical asymptote is $x = 2$, x-intercept 27,

       no y-intercept

     iii

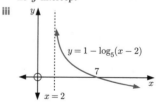

     iv $x = 7$ **v** $f^{-1}(x) = 5^{x+2} + 2$

   e   **i** Domain is $\{x \mid x > 2\}$,   Range is $\{y \mid y \in \mathbb{R}\}$

     ii vertical asymptote is $x = 2$, x-intercept 7,

       no y-intercept

     iii

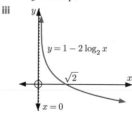

     iv $x = 27$ **v** $f^{-1}(x) = 5^{1-x} + 2$

   f   **i** Domain is $\{x \mid x > 0\}$,   Range is $\{y \mid y \in \mathbb{R}\}$

     ii vertical asymptote is $x = 0$, x-intercept $\sqrt{2}$,

       no y-intercept

     iii

     iv $x = 2$ **v** $f^{-1}(x) = 2^{\frac{1-x}{2}}$

2 a   **i** A translation through $\begin{pmatrix} 0 \\ -4 \end{pmatrix}$.

ii Domain is $\{x \mid x > 0\}$, Range is $\{y \mid y \in \mathbb{R}\}$

iii vertical asymptote is $x = 0$, x-intercept e^4, no y-intercept

iv

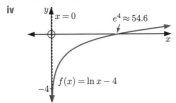

v $f^{-1}(x) = e^{x+4}$

b i A translation through $\begin{pmatrix} 1 \\ 2 \end{pmatrix}$.

ii Domain is $\{x \mid x > 1\}$, Range is $\{y \mid y \in \mathbb{R}\}$

iii vertical asymptote is $x = 1$, x-intercept $1 + e^{-2}$, no y-intercept

iv

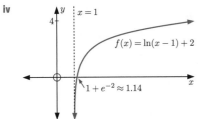

v $f^{-1}(x) = e^{x-2} + 1$

c i A vertical stretch with scale factor 3, then a translation through $\begin{pmatrix} 0 \\ -1 \end{pmatrix}$.

ii Domain is $\{x \mid x > 0\}$, Range is $\{y \mid y \in \mathbb{R}\}$

iii vertical asymptote is $x = 0$, x-intercept $e^{\frac{1}{3}}$, no y-intercept

iv

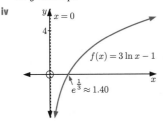

v $f^{-1}(x) = e^{\frac{x+1}{3}}$

3 a A is $y = \ln x$ as its x-intercept is 1.

b

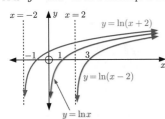

c $y = \ln x$ has vertical asymptote $x = 0$
$y = \ln(x - 2)$ has vertical asymptote $x = 2$
$y = \ln(x + 2)$ has vertical asymptote $x = -2$

4 $y = \ln(x^2) = 2\ln x$, so she is correct.
This is because the y-values are twice as large for $y = \ln(x^2)$ as they are for $y = \ln x$.

5 a

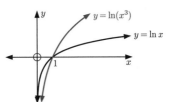

b

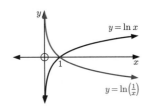

c

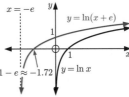

d

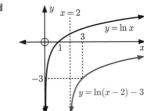

e

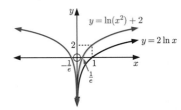

6 a $b^2 x$ **b** $2\ln b + x$ **c** $x = \dfrac{2\ln b}{b^2 - 1}$

7 $f^{-1}(x) = \frac{1}{2}\ln x$

a $(f^{-1} \circ g)(x) = \frac{1}{2}\ln(2x - 1)$

b $(g \circ f)^{-1}(x) = \frac{1}{2}\ln\left(\dfrac{x+1}{2}\right)$

REVIEW SET 6A

1 a $\frac{1}{2}$ **b** $-\frac{1}{3}$ **c** $a + b + 1$

2 a 3 **b** 8 **c** -2 **d** $\frac{1}{2}$ **e** 0

  f $\frac{1}{4}$ **g** -1 **h** $\frac{1}{2}$, $k > 0$, $k \neq 1$

3 a ≈ 1.431 **b** ≈ -0.237 **c** ≈ 2.602 **d** ≈ 3.689

4 a $\ln 144$ **b** $\ln\left(\frac{3}{2}\right)$ **c** $\ln\left(\dfrac{25}{e}\right)$ **d** $\ln 3$

5 a $\log 144$ **b** $\log_2\left(\frac{16}{9}\right)$ **c** $\log_4 80$

6 a $2A + 2B$ **b** $A + 3B$ **c** $3A + \frac{1}{2}B$

  d $\frac{1}{2}(A + B)$ **e** $4B - 2A$ **f** $3A - 2B$

7 **a** $\log M = \log a + n \log b$ **b** $\log T = \log 5 - \frac{1}{2} \log l$
   c $\log G = 2 \log a + \log b - \log c$

8 **a** $x \approx 5.19$ **b** $x \approx 4.29$ **c** $x \approx -0.839$

9 **a** $x = \ln 3$ **b** $x = \ln 3$ or $\ln 4$

10 **a** $P = TQ^{1.5}$ **b** $M = \dfrac{e^{1.2}}{\sqrt{N}}$

11 **a** $x = 0$ or $\ln\left(\frac{2}{3}\right)$ **b** $x = e^2$

12 **a** $x = \frac{1}{8}$ **b** $x \approx 82.7$ **c** $x \approx 0.0316$

13 **a** **i** $x = \dfrac{\log 50}{\log 2}$ **ii** $x \approx 5.64$

   b **i** $x = \dfrac{\log 4}{\log 7}$ **ii** $x \approx 0.71$

   c **i** $x = \dfrac{-2}{\log(0.6)}$ **ii** $x \approx 9.02$

14 $\log_a\left(\dfrac{1}{b}\right) = -x$ **15 Hint:** $2^{4x} - 5 \times 2^{3x} = 0$

16 **a** $x = e^5$ **b** $x = e^{-\frac{2}{3}}$ **c** $x = \ln 400$
   d $x = \dfrac{\ln 11 - 1}{2}$ **e** $x = 2\ln 30$

17 **b** $\frac{1}{3}\ln\left(\frac{7}{2}\right)$

18 **a** A translation through $\begin{pmatrix} -2 \\ -2 \end{pmatrix}$.
   b Domain is $\{x \mid x > -2\}$, Range is $\{y \mid y \in \mathbb{R}\}$
   c vertical asymptote is $x = -2$, x-intercept is 7,
      y-intercept is ≈ -1.37
   d $g^{-1}(x) = 3^{x+2} - 2$
   e

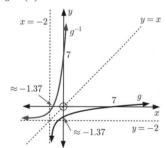

19 **a** ≈ 13.9 weeks   **b** ≈ 41.6 weeks   **c** ≈ 138 weeks

20 **a** ≈ 4.96 years or ≈ 4 years $11\frac{1}{2}$ months   **b** $\approx 74.9\%$

21 **a** **i** Domain is $\{x \mid x > -4\}$, Range is $\{y \mid y \in \mathbb{R}\}$
      ii vertical asymptote is $x = -4$, x-intercept -2,
         y-intercept 1
      iii

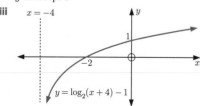

   b **i** Domain is $\{x \mid x > 0\}$, Range is $\{y \mid y \in \mathbb{R}\}$
      ii vertical asymptote is $x = 0$, x-intercept e^{-2},
         no y-intercept

      iii

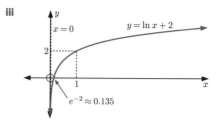

22 **a**

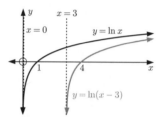

   b

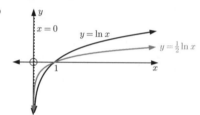

23 **a** 9   **b** $\ln 5$

1 **a** $\frac{3}{2}$ **b** $\frac{2}{3}$ **c** $a + b$

2 **a** 7   **b** -3 **c** $-\frac{1}{2}$

3 **a** $\approx 10^{1.5051}$ **b** $\approx 10^{-2.8861}$ **c** $\approx 10^{-4.0475}$

4 **a** $\frac{3}{2}$ **b** -3 **c** $2x$ **d** $1 - x$

5 **a** $\frac{2}{3}$ **b** $\frac{6}{5}$ **c** 8

6 **a** x^4 **b** 5   **c** $\frac{1}{2}$ **d** $3x$ **e** $-x$ **f** $\log x$

7 **a** $\approx e^{2.9957}$ **b** $\approx e^{8.0064}$ **c** $\approx e^{-2.5903}$

8 **a** **i** $x = \dfrac{\log 7}{\log 5}$ **ii** $x \approx 1.21$

   b **i** $x = -\dfrac{1}{\log 2}$ **ii** $x \approx -3.32$

9 **a** $\ln 3$ **b** $\ln 4$ **c** $\ln 125$

10 **a** $x = \dfrac{\ln 70}{2}$ **b** $x = \dfrac{\log\left(\frac{11}{3}\right)}{\log 1.3}$ **c** $x = \dfrac{10\log\left(\frac{16}{5}\right)}{3\log 2}$

11 $x = 1$

12 **a** $\log P = \log 3 + x \log b$ **b** $\log m = 3 \log n - 2 \log p$

13 Hint: Use the change of base rule.

14 **a** $T = \dfrac{x^2}{y}$ **b** $K = n\sqrt{t}$

15 **a** $5\ln 2$ **b** $3\ln 5$ **c** $6\ln 3$

16

	$y = \log_2 x$	$y = \ln(x + 5)$
Domain	$x > 0$	$x > -5$
Range	$y \in \mathbb{R}$	$y \in \mathbb{R}$

17 **a** $(2^x + 4)(2^x - 5)$ **b** $x = \dfrac{\log 5}{\log 2}$

c i $x = \dfrac{1}{p}$ **ii** $x = \dfrac{1}{3p+1}$

18 a $g^{-1}(x) = \ln\left(\dfrac{x+5}{2}\right)$

b

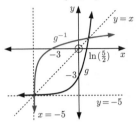

c Domain of g is $\{x \mid x \in \mathbb{R}\}$, Range is $\{y \mid y > -5\}$
Domain of g^{-1} is $\{x \mid x > -5\}$, Range is $\{y \mid y \in \mathbb{R}\}$

d g has horizontal asymptote $y = -5$,
x-intercept is $\ln\left(\frac{5}{2}\right) \approx 0.916$, y-intercept is -3
g^{-1} has vertical asymptote $x = -5$,
x-intercept is -3, y-intercept is ≈ 0.916

19 Hint: Set $T = 40$, and solve for t.

20 a 2500 g   **b** ≈ 3288 years   **c** $\approx 42.3\%$

21 a $x = \dfrac{2\log 9}{\log 5}$ **b** $x = \ln 30$ **c** $x = \dfrac{1 - \ln 2}{3}$

22 a

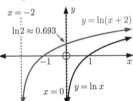

b

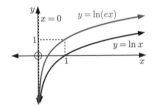

23 a

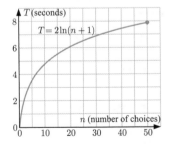

b i ≈ 3.58 seconds   **ii** ≈ 5.55 seconds
c ≈ 1.34 seconds longer

EXERCISE 7A

1 a $\dfrac{\pi}{2}$ **b** $\dfrac{\pi}{3}$ **c** $\dfrac{\pi}{6}$ **d** $\dfrac{\pi}{10}$ **e** $\dfrac{\pi}{20}$
  f $\dfrac{3\pi}{4}$ **g** $\dfrac{5\pi}{4}$ **h** $\dfrac{3\pi}{2}$ **i** 2π **j** 4π
  k $\dfrac{7\pi}{4}$ **l** 3π **m** $\dfrac{\pi}{5}$ **n** $\dfrac{4\pi}{9}$ **o** $\dfrac{23\pi}{18}$

2 a $\approx 0.641^c$ **b** $\approx 2.39^c$ **c** $\approx 5.55^c$ **d** $\approx 3.83^c$
  e $\approx 6.92^c$

3 a $36°$ **b** $108°$ **c** $135°$ **d** $10°$ **e** $20°$
  f $140°$ **g** $18°$ **h** $27°$ **i** $210°$ **j** $22.5°$

4 a $\approx 114.59°$ **b** $\approx 87.66°$ **c** $\approx 49.68°$
  d $\approx 182.14°$ **e** $\approx 301.78°$

5 a F   **b B**   **c D**   **d A**   **e E**   **f C**

6 a

Degrees	0	45	90	135	180	225	270	315	360
Radians	0	$\frac{\pi}{4}$	$\frac{\pi}{2}$	$\frac{3\pi}{4}$	π	$\frac{5\pi}{4}$	$\frac{3\pi}{2}$	$\frac{7\pi}{4}$	2π

b

Deg.	0	30	60	90	120	150	180	210	240	270	300	330	360
Rad.	0	$\frac{\pi}{6}$	$\frac{\pi}{3}$	$\frac{\pi}{2}$	$\frac{2\pi}{3}$	$\frac{5\pi}{6}$	π	$\frac{7\pi}{6}$	$\frac{4\pi}{3}$	$\frac{3\pi}{2}$	$\frac{5\pi}{3}$	$\frac{11\pi}{6}$	2π

EXERCISE 7B

1 a 7 cm   **b** 12 cm   **c** ≈ 13.0 m
2 a 6 cm²   **b** 48 cm²   **c** ≈ 8.21 cm²
3 a arc length ≈ 49.5 cm, area ≈ 223 cm²
  b arc length ≈ 23.0 cm, area ≈ 56.8 cm²
4 a $\approx 0.686^c$ **b** 0.6^c
5 a $\theta = 0.75^c$, area $= 24$ cm²
  b $\theta = 1.68^c$, area $= 21$ cm²
  c $\theta \approx 2.32^c$, area $= 126.8$ cm²
6 a ≈ 3.15 m   **b** ≈ 9.32 m²
7 a ≈ 5.91 cm   **b** ≈ 18.9 cm
8 a $\alpha \approx 0.3218^c$ **b** $\theta \approx 2.498^c$ **c** ≈ 387 m²
9 a $\theta = \frac{\pi}{3}$ **b** 6 cm
10 a ≈ 11.7 cm   **b** $r \approx 11.7$ **c** ≈ 37.7 cm   **d** $\theta \approx 3.23^c$
11 ≈ 25.9 cm   **12 b** ≈ 2 h 24 min   **13** ≈ 227 m²
14 a 4 cm   **b i** ≈ 2.16 cm²   **ii** ≈ 29.3 cm²

EXERCISE 7C

1

θ (degrees)	0°	90°	180°	270°	360°	450°
θ (radians)	0	$\frac{\pi}{2}$	π	$\frac{3\pi}{2}$	2π	$\frac{5\pi}{2}$
sine	0	1	0	-1	0	1
cosine	1	0	-1	0	1	0
tangent	0	undef.	0	undef.	0	undef.

2 a i $A(\cos 26°, \sin 26°)$, $B(\cos 146°, \sin 146°)$,
      $C(\cos 199°, \sin 199°)$
    ii $A(0.899, 0.438)$, $B(-0.829, 0.559)$,
      $C(-0.946, -0.326)$
  b i $A(\cos 123°, \sin 123°)$, $B(\cos 251°, \sin 251°)$,
      $C(\cos(-35°), \sin(-35°))$
    ii $A(-0.545, 0.839)$, $B(-0.326, -0.946)$,
      $C(0.819, -0.574)$

3 a i $\dfrac{1}{\sqrt{2}} \approx 0.707$ **ii** $\dfrac{\sqrt{3}}{2} \approx 0.866$

b

θ (degrees)	30°	45°	60°	135°	150°	240°	315°
θ (radians)	$\frac{\pi}{6}$	$\frac{\pi}{4}$	$\frac{\pi}{3}$	$\frac{3\pi}{4}$	$\frac{5\pi}{6}$	$\frac{4\pi}{3}$	$\frac{7\pi}{4}$
sine	$\frac{1}{2}$	$\frac{1}{\sqrt{2}}$	$\frac{\sqrt{3}}{2}$	$\frac{1}{\sqrt{2}}$	$\frac{1}{2}$	$-\frac{\sqrt{3}}{2}$	$-\frac{1}{\sqrt{2}}$
cosine	$\frac{\sqrt{3}}{2}$	$\frac{1}{\sqrt{2}}$	$\frac{1}{2}$	$-\frac{1}{\sqrt{2}}$	$-\frac{\sqrt{3}}{2}$	$-\frac{1}{2}$	$\frac{1}{\sqrt{2}}$
tangent	$\frac{1}{\sqrt{3}}$	1	$\sqrt{3}$	-1	$-\frac{1}{\sqrt{3}}$	$\sqrt{3}$	-1

4 a

Quadrant	Degree measure	Radian measure	$\cos\theta$	$\sin\theta$	$\tan\theta$
1	$0° < \theta < 90°$	$0 < \theta < \frac{\pi}{2}$	+ve	+ve	+ve
2	$90° < \theta < 180°$	$\frac{\pi}{2} < \theta < \pi$	−ve	+ve	−ve
3	$180° < \theta < 270°$	$\pi < \theta < \frac{3\pi}{2}$	−ve	−ve	+ve
4	$270° < \theta < 360°$	$\frac{3\pi}{2} < \theta < 2\pi$	+ve	−ve	−ve

b **i** 1 and 4   **ii** 2 and 3   **iii** 3   **iv** 2

5 a $\cos 400° = \cos(360 + 40)° = \cos 40°$

b $\sin\frac{5\pi}{7} = \sin\left(\frac{5\pi}{7} + 2\pi\right) = \sin\frac{19\pi}{7}$

c $\tan\frac{13\pi}{8} = \tan\left(\frac{13\pi}{8} - 3\pi\right) = \tan\left(-\frac{11\pi}{8}\right)$

6 B and D   **7 B and E**

8 a **i** ≈ 0.985 **ii** ≈ 0.985 **iii** ≈ 0.866 **iv** ≈ 0.866
   v 0.5   **vi** 0.5   **vii** ≈ 0.707 **viii** ≈ 0.707

b $\sin(180° - \theta) = \sin\theta$ **c** $\sin(\pi - \theta) = \sin\theta$

d The points have the same y-coordinate.

e **i** $135°$ **ii** $129°$ **iii** $\frac{2\pi}{3}$ **iv** $\frac{5\pi}{6}$

9 a **i** ≈ 0.342 **ii** ≈ -0.342 **iii** 0.5
   iv -0.5 **v** ≈ 0.906 **vi** ≈ -0.906
   vii ≈ 0.174 **viii** ≈ -0.174

b $\cos(180° - \theta) = -\cos\theta$ **c** $\cos(\pi - \theta) = -\cos\theta$

d The x-coordinates of the points have the same magnitude but are opposite in sign.

e **i** $140°$ **ii** $161°$ **iii** $\frac{4\pi}{5}$ **iv** $\frac{3\pi}{5}$

10 $\tan(\pi - \theta) = -\tan\theta$

11 a ≈ 0.6820 **b** ≈ 0.8572 **c** ≈ -0.7986
   d ≈ 0.9135 **e** ≈ 0.9063 **f** ≈ -0.6691

12 a

θ^c	$\sin\theta$	$\sin(-\theta)$	$\cos\theta$	$\cos(-\theta)$
0.75	≈ 0.682	≈ -0.682	≈ 0.732	≈ 0.732
1.772	≈ 0.980	≈ -0.980	≈ -0.200	≈ -0.200
3.414	≈ -0.269	≈ 0.269	≈ -0.963	≈ -0.963
6.25	≈ -0.0332	≈ 0.0332	≈ 0.999	≈ 0.999
-1.17	≈ -0.921	≈ 0.921	≈ 0.390	≈ 0.390

b $\sin(-\theta) = -\sin\theta$, $\cos(-\theta) = \cos\theta$

c Q has coordinates $(\cos(-\theta), \sin(-\theta))$ or
$(\cos\theta, -\sin\theta)$ (since it is the reflection of P in the x-axis)
$\therefore$ $\cos(-\theta) = \cos\theta$ and $\sin(-\theta) = -\sin\theta$

d $\cos(2\pi - \theta) = \cos(-\theta) = \cos\theta$
$\sin(2\pi - \theta) = \sin(-\theta) = -\sin\theta$

e $\tan(2\pi - \theta) = -\tan\theta$

13 a The angle between [OP] and the positive x-axis is $\left(\frac{\pi}{2} - \theta\right)$.
$\therefore$ P is $\left(\cos\left(\frac{\pi}{2} - \theta\right),\ \sin\left(\frac{\pi}{2} - \theta\right)\right)$

b **i** In $\triangle$OXP, $\sin\theta = \dfrac{XP}{OP} = \dfrac{XP}{1}$
   $\therefore$ $XP = \sin\theta$
  ii In $\triangle$OXP, $\cos\theta = \dfrac{OX}{OP} = \dfrac{OX}{1}$
   $\therefore$ $OX = \cos\theta$

c **i** $\cos\left(\frac{\pi}{2} - \theta\right) = XP = \sin\theta$
  ii $\sin\left(\frac{\pi}{2} - \theta\right) = OX = \cos\theta$

d **i** $\cos\frac{\pi}{5} = \sin\left(\frac{\pi}{2} - \frac{\pi}{5}\right) = \sin\frac{3\pi}{10} \approx 0.809$
  ii $\sin\frac{\pi}{8} = \cos\left(\frac{\pi}{2} - \frac{\pi}{8}\right) = \cos\frac{3\pi}{8} \approx 0.383$

e $\tan\left(\frac{\pi}{2} - \theta\right) = \dfrac{1}{\tan\theta}$

EXERCISE 7D

1

	a	b	c	d	e
$\sin\theta$	$\frac{1}{\sqrt{2}}$	$\frac{1}{\sqrt{2}}$	$-\frac{1}{\sqrt{2}}$	0	$-\frac{1}{\sqrt{2}}$
$\cos\theta$	$\frac{1}{\sqrt{2}}$	$-\frac{1}{\sqrt{2}}$	$\frac{1}{\sqrt{2}}$	-1	$-\frac{1}{\sqrt{2}}$
$\tan\theta$	1	-1	-1	0	1

2

	a	b	c	d	e
$\sin\beta$	$\frac{1}{2}$	$\frac{\sqrt{3}}{2}$	$-\frac{1}{2}$	$-\frac{\sqrt{3}}{2}$	$-\frac{1}{2}$
$\cos\beta$	$\frac{\sqrt{3}}{2}$	$-\frac{1}{2}$	$-\frac{\sqrt{3}}{2}$	$\frac{1}{2}$	$\frac{\sqrt{3}}{2}$
$\tan\beta$	$\frac{1}{\sqrt{3}}$	$-\sqrt{3}$	$\frac{1}{\sqrt{3}}$	$-\sqrt{3}$	$-\frac{1}{\sqrt{3}}$

3 a $\cos\frac{2\pi}{3} = -\frac{1}{2}$, $\sin\frac{2\pi}{3} = \frac{\sqrt{3}}{2}$, $\tan\frac{2\pi}{3} = -\sqrt{3}$

b $\cos\left(-\frac{\pi}{4}\right) = \frac{1}{\sqrt{2}}$, $\sin\left(-\frac{\pi}{4}\right) = -\frac{1}{\sqrt{2}}$, $\tan\left(-\frac{\pi}{4}\right) = -1$

4 a $\cos\frac{\pi}{2} = 0$, $\sin\frac{\pi}{2} = 1$ **b** $\tan\frac{\pi}{2}$ is undefined

5 a $\frac{3}{4}$ **b** $\frac{1}{4}$ **c** 3   **d** $\frac{1}{4}$ **e** $-\frac{1}{4}$ **f** 1
  g $\sqrt{2}$ **h** $\frac{1}{2}$ **i** $\frac{1}{2}$ **j** 2   **k** -1 **l** $-\sqrt{3}$

6 a $\frac{\pi}{6}, \frac{5\pi}{6}$ **b** $\frac{\pi}{3}, \frac{2\pi}{3}$ **c** $\frac{\pi}{4}, \frac{7\pi}{4}$
  d $\frac{2\pi}{3}, \frac{4\pi}{3}$ **e** $\frac{3\pi}{4}, \frac{5\pi}{4}$ **f** $\frac{4\pi}{3}, \frac{5\pi}{3}$

7 a $\frac{\pi}{4}, \frac{5\pi}{4}$ **b** $\frac{3\pi}{4}, \frac{7\pi}{4}$ **c** $\frac{\pi}{3}, \frac{4\pi}{3}$
  d $0, \pi, 2\pi$ **e** $\frac{\pi}{6}, \frac{7\pi}{6}$ **f** $\frac{2\pi}{3}, \frac{5\pi}{3}$

8 a $\frac{\pi}{6}, \frac{11\pi}{6}, \frac{13\pi}{6}, \frac{23\pi}{6}$ **b** $\frac{7\pi}{6}, \frac{11\pi}{6}, \frac{19\pi}{6}, \frac{23\pi}{6}$ **c** $\frac{3\pi}{2}, \frac{7\pi}{2}$

9 a $\theta = \frac{\pi}{3}, \frac{5\pi}{3}$ **b** $\theta = \frac{\pi}{3}, \frac{2\pi}{3}$ **c** $\theta = \pi$
  d $\theta = \frac{\pi}{2}$ **e** $\theta = \frac{3\pi}{4}, \frac{5\pi}{4}$ **f** $\theta = \frac{\pi}{2}, \frac{3\pi}{2}$
  g $\theta = 0, \pi, 2\pi$ **h** $\theta = \frac{\pi}{4}, \frac{3\pi}{4}, \frac{5\pi}{4}, \frac{7\pi}{4}$
  i $\theta = \frac{5\pi}{6}, \frac{11\pi}{6}$ **j** $\theta = \frac{\pi}{3}, \frac{2\pi}{3}, \frac{4\pi}{3}, \frac{5\pi}{3}$

10 a $\theta = k\pi,\ k \in \mathbb{Z}$ **b** $\theta = \frac{\pi}{2} + k\pi,\ k \in \mathbb{Z}$

EXERCISE 7E

1 a $\cos\theta = \pm\frac{\sqrt{3}}{2}$ **b** $\cos\theta = \pm\frac{2\sqrt{2}}{3}$ **c** $\cos\theta = \pm 1$
  d $\cos\theta = 0$

2 a $\sin\theta = \pm\frac{3}{5}$ **b** $\sin\theta = \pm\frac{\sqrt{7}}{4}$ **c** $\sin\theta = 0$
  d $\sin\theta = \pm 1$

3 a $\sin\theta = \frac{\sqrt{5}}{3}$ **b** $\cos\theta = -\frac{\sqrt{21}}{5}$ **c** $\cos\theta = \frac{4}{5}$
  d $\sin\theta = -\frac{12}{13}$

4 a $\tan\theta = -\frac{1}{2\sqrt{2}}$ **b** $\tan\theta = -2\sqrt{6}$ **c** $\tan\theta = \frac{1}{\sqrt{2}}$
  d $\tan\theta = -\frac{\sqrt{7}}{3}$

5 a $\sin\theta = \frac{2}{\sqrt{13}}$, $\cos\theta = \frac{3}{\sqrt{13}}$ **b** $\sin\theta = \frac{4}{5}$, $\cos\theta = -\frac{3}{5}$
  c $\sin\theta = -\sqrt{\frac{5}{14}}$, $\cos\theta = -\frac{3}{\sqrt{14}}$
  d $\sin\theta = -\frac{12}{13}$, $\cos\theta = \frac{5}{13}$

6 $\sin\theta = \dfrac{-k}{\sqrt{k^2 + 1}}$, $\cos\theta = \dfrac{-1}{\sqrt{k^2 + 1}}$

EXERCISE 7F

1 **a** $\theta \approx 76.0°$ or $256°$ **b** $\theta \approx 33.9°$ or $326.1°$
   c $\theta \approx 36.9°$ or $143.1°$ **d** $\theta = 90°$ or $270°$
   e $\theta \approx 81.5°$ or $261.5°$ **f** $\theta \approx 83.2°$ or $276.8°$

2 **a** $\theta \approx 0.322$ or 3.46 **b** $\theta \approx 1.13$ or 5.16
   c $\theta \approx 0.656$ or 2.49 **d** $\theta \approx 1.32$ or 4.97
   e $\theta \approx 0.114$ or 3.26 **f** $\theta \approx 0.167$ or 2.97

3 **a** $\theta \approx 1.82$ or 4.46 **b** $\theta = 0, \pi,$ or 2π
   c $\theta \approx 1.88$ or 5.02 **d** $\theta \approx 3.58$ or 5.85
   e $\theta \approx 0.876$ or 4.02 **f** $\theta \approx 0.674$ or 5.61
   g $\theta \approx 0.0910$ or 3.05 **h** $\theta \approx 2.19$ or 4.10

4 **a** $\theta \approx -95.7°$ or $95.7°$ **b** $\theta \approx 53.1°$ or $126.9°$
   c $\theta \approx -56.3°$ or $123.7°$ **d** $\theta \approx -36.9°$ or $36.9°$
   e $\theta \approx -39.8°$ or $140.2°$ **f** $\theta \approx -140.5°$ or $-39.5°$

EXERCISE 7G

1 **a** $y = \sqrt{3}\,x$ **b** $y = x$ **c** $y = -\frac{1}{\sqrt{3}}x$

2 **a** $y = \sqrt{3}\,x + 2$ **b** $y = -\sqrt{3}\,x$ **c** $y = \frac{1}{\sqrt{3}}x - 2$

3 **a** $\theta \approx 1.25$ **b** $\theta \approx -0.983$ **c** $\theta \approx -0.381$

4 **a** $\theta \approx 23.2°$ **b** $\theta \approx 117°$ **c** $\theta \approx -11.3°$

REVIEW SET 7A

1 **a** $\frac{2\pi}{3}$ **b** $\frac{5\pi}{4}$ **c** $\frac{5\pi}{6}$ **d** 3π

2 **a** $72°$ **b** $225°$ **c** $140°$ **d** $330°$

3

4 **a** $(0.766, -0.643)$ **b** $(-0.956, 0.292)$
   c $(0.778, 0.629)$

5 12 cm   **6** **a** $\frac{\pi}{3}$ **b** $15°$ **c** $84°$

7 **a** ≈ 0.358 **b** ≈ -0.035 **c** ≈ 0.259 **d** ≈ 1.072

8 **a** $\cos 360° = 1,\ \sin 360° = 0$
   b $\cos(-\pi) = -1,\ \sin(-\pi) = 0$

9 **a** $\sin\frac{2\pi}{3} = \frac{\sqrt{3}}{2},\ \cos\frac{2\pi}{3} = -\frac{1}{2},\ \tan\frac{2\pi}{3} = -\sqrt{3}$
   b $\sin\frac{8\pi}{3} = \frac{\sqrt{3}}{2},\ \cos\frac{8\pi}{3} = -\frac{1}{2},\ \tan\frac{8\pi}{3} = -\sqrt{3}$

10 **a** **i** $60°$ **ii** $\frac{\pi}{3}$ **b** $\frac{\pi}{3}$ cm   **c** $\frac{\pi}{6}$ cm^2

11 $\tan x = \frac{1}{\sqrt{15}}$ **12** $\sin\theta = \pm\frac{\sqrt{7}}{4}$

13 **a** $\frac{\sqrt{3}}{2}$ **b** 0 **c** $\frac{1}{2}$ **14** **a** $\frac{2}{\sqrt{13}}$ **b** $-\frac{3}{\sqrt{13}}$

15 perimeter $= 12$ cm, area $= 8$ cm^2 **16** $\tan\theta = \frac{\sqrt{6}}{\sqrt{11}}$

17 **a** $\theta \approx 0.841$ or 5.44 **b** $\theta \approx 3.39$ or 6.03
   c $\theta \approx 1.25$ or 4.39

18 **a** $y = \frac{1}{\sqrt{3}}x$ **b** $y = \sqrt{3}\,x + 3$

REVIEW SET 7B

1 **a** $\approx 1.239^c$ **b** $\approx 2.175^c$ **c** $\approx -2.478^c$

2 **a** $\approx 171.89°$ **b** $\approx 83.65°$ **c** $\approx 24.92°$
   d $\approx -302.01°$

3 ≈ 111 cm^2

4 $M(\cos 73°, \sin 73°) \approx (0.292, 0.956)$
   $N(\cos 190°, \sin 190°) \approx (-0.985, -0.174)$
   $P(\cos 307°, \sin 307°) \approx (0.602, -0.799)$

5 $\approx 103°$ **6** radius ≈ 8.79 cm, area ≈ 81.0 cm^2

7 **a** $\cos\frac{3\pi}{2} = 0,\ \sin\frac{3\pi}{2} = -1$
   b $\cos\left(-\frac{\pi}{2}\right) = 0,\ \sin\left(-\frac{\pi}{2}\right) = -1$

8 **a** $\sin(\pi - p) = m$ **b** $\sin(p + 2\pi) = m$
   c $\cos p = \sqrt{1 - m^2}$ **d** $\tan p = \dfrac{m}{\sqrt{1 - m^2}}$

9 **a** $150°, 210°$ **b** $45°, 135°$ **c** $120°, 300°$

10 **a** $\theta = \pi$ **b** $\theta = \frac{\pi}{3}, \frac{2\pi}{3}, \frac{4\pi}{3}, \frac{5\pi}{3}$

11 **a** $133°$ **b** $\frac{14\pi}{15}$ **c** $174°$

12 perimeter ≈ 34.1 cm, area ≈ 66.5 cm^2

14 **a** $\frac{\sqrt{7}}{4}$ **b** $-\frac{\sqrt{7}}{3}$ **c** $\frac{3}{4}$

15 **a** $2\frac{1}{2}$ **b** $1\frac{1}{2}$ **c** $-\frac{1}{2}$ **d** 3

17 **a** $\theta \approx 0.322$ **b** $\theta \approx 1.95$

EXERCISE 8A

1 **a** periodic   **b** periodic   **c** periodic   **d** not periodic
   e periodic   **f** periodic   **g** not periodic   **h** not periodic

2 **a**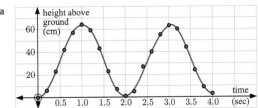

   b A curve can be fitted to the data.
   c The data is periodic.
     i $y = 32$ (approximately)   **ii** ≈ 64 cm
     iii ≈ 2 seconds   **iv** ≈ 32 cm

3 **a**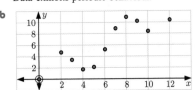

   Data exhibits periodic behaviour.
   b

   Not enough information to say data is periodic.

EXERCISE 8B

1 **a** 0
   b **i** $\theta = 0, \pi, 2\pi, 3\pi, 4\pi$ **ii** $\theta = \frac{3\pi}{2}, \frac{7\pi}{2}$
     iii $\theta = \frac{\pi}{6}, \frac{5\pi}{6}, \frac{13\pi}{6}, \frac{17\pi}{6}$ **iv** $\theta = \frac{\pi}{3}, \frac{2\pi}{3}, \frac{7\pi}{3}, \frac{8\pi}{3}$
   c **i** $0 < \theta < \pi,\ 2\pi < \theta < 3\pi$
     ii $\pi < \theta < 2\pi,\ 3\pi < \theta < 4\pi$
   d $\{y \mid -1 \leqslant y \leqslant 1\}$

2 **a** 1
   b **i** $\theta = \frac{\pi}{2}, \frac{3\pi}{2}, \frac{5\pi}{2}, \frac{7\pi}{2}$ **ii** $\theta = 0, 2\pi, 4\pi$
     iii $\theta = \frac{2\pi}{3}, \frac{4\pi}{3}, \frac{8\pi}{3}, \frac{10\pi}{3}$ **iv** $\theta = \frac{3\pi}{4}, \frac{5\pi}{4}, \frac{11\pi}{4}, \frac{13\pi}{4}$

c i $0 \leqslant \theta < \frac{\pi}{2}$, $\frac{3\pi}{2} < \theta < \frac{5\pi}{2}$, $\frac{7\pi}{2} < \theta \leqslant 4\pi$

   ii $\frac{\pi}{2} < \theta < \frac{3\pi}{2}$, $\frac{5\pi}{2} < \theta < \frac{7\pi}{2}$

d $\{y \mid -1 \leqslant y \leqslant 1\}$

EXERCISE 8C

1 a vertical translation 1 unit downwards
   b horizontal translation $\frac{\pi}{4}$ units to the right
   c vertical stretch, scale factor 2
   d horizontal stretch, scale factor $\frac{1}{4}$
   e horizontal stretch, scale factor 4
   f translation $\frac{\pi}{3}$ units right and 2 units upwards

2 a vertical stretch, scale factor $\frac{1}{2}$
   b reflection in the x-axis
   c translation $\frac{\pi}{6}$ units left and 2 units downwards

3 a $\frac{2\pi}{5}$ **b** $\frac{10\pi}{3}$ **c** 2   **d** $\frac{2\pi}{3}$ **e** 6π **f** 100

4 a $b = \frac{2}{5}$ **b** $b = 3$ **c** $b = \frac{1}{6}$ **d** $b = \frac{\pi}{2}$ **e** $b = \frac{\pi}{50}$

5 a maximum 4, minimum -4 **b** maximum 8, minimum 2
   c maximum -2, minimum -6

6 a 4   **b** $\frac{2\pi}{3}$ **c** $\{y \mid -2 \leqslant y \leqslant 6\}$

7 $|a|$ = amplitude, $b = \dfrac{2\pi}{\text{period}}$, c = horizontal translation,

   d = vertical translation

8 a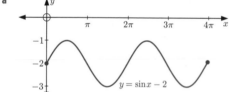

   b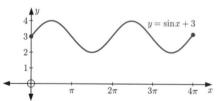

   c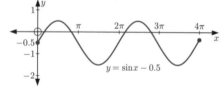

   d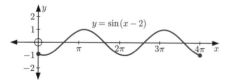

   e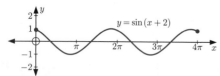

f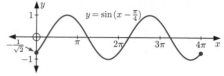

g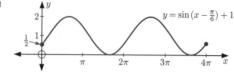

h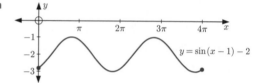

i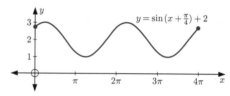

j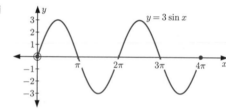

k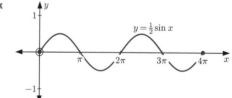

l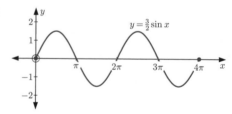

m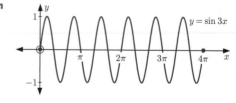

n

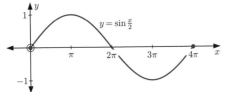

o

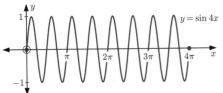

9 a

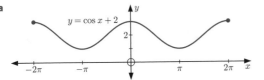

b

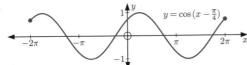

c

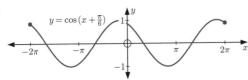

d

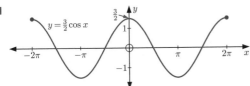

e

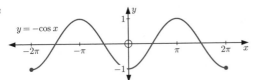

f

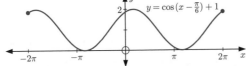

g

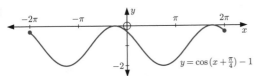

h

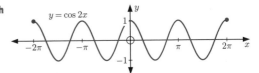

i

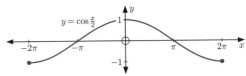

10 a

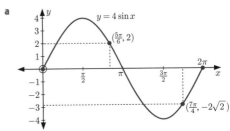

    b **i** $y = 2$ **ii** $y = -2\sqrt{2} \approx -2.83$

11 **a** $d > 3$ **b** $d < -3$ **c** $-3 < d < 3$

12 **a** A horizontal stretch with scale factor $\frac{1}{3}$, then a vertical stretch with scale factor 2.

    b A vertical stretch with scale factor 2, then a reflection in the x-axis.

    c A vertical stretch with scale factor 3, then a translation 5 units downwards.

    d A horizontal stretch with scale factor $\frac{1}{2}$, then a translation $\frac{\pi}{6}$ units left.

13 a

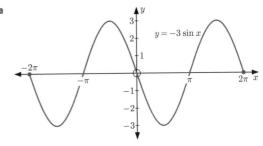

b

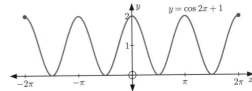

c

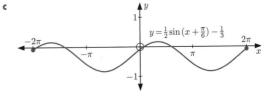

d

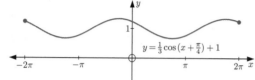

$$y = \tfrac{1}{3}\cos\left(x + \tfrac{\pi}{4}\right) + 1$$

e

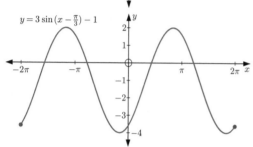

$$y = 3\sin\left(x - \tfrac{\pi}{3}\right) - 1$$

f

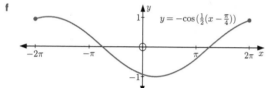

$$y = -\cos\left(\tfrac{1}{2}\left(x - \tfrac{\pi}{4}\right)\right)$$

14 a b, c, d **b** c, d **c** a, d

15 a $a = 4,\ d = 1$ **b** $a = -2,\ d = 3$ **c** $a = \tfrac{1}{3},\ d = \tfrac{4}{3}$

16 a $y = \sin x - 2$ **b** $y = \sin 3x$ **c** $y = \sin\left(x + \tfrac{\pi}{2}\right)$

　　d $y = 2\sin x + 1$ **e** $y = 4\sin\tfrac{x}{2} - 1$ **f** $y = 6\sin\tfrac{2\pi x}{5}$

17 a $y = 2\cos 2x$ **b** $y = \cos\tfrac{x}{2} + 2$ **c** $y = -5\cos\tfrac{\pi x}{3}$

EXERCISE 8D.1

1 a

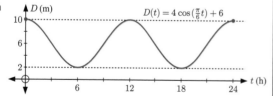

$$T(t) = 6\sin\left(\tfrac{\pi}{12}t\right) + 26$$

　　b i $26°$C   **ii** $29°$C   **c** $32°$C, at 6 pm

2 a

$$D(t) = 4\cos\left(\tfrac{\pi}{6}t\right) + 6$$

D (m) graph

　　b highest $= 10$ m, at midnight, midday, and midnight the next day

　　　　lowest $= 2$ m, at 6 am and 6 pm

　　c no (water height is 4 m)

3 a

$$H(t) = 15\cos\left(\tfrac{\pi}{30}t\right) + 150$$

H (cm) graph

　　b 15 cm

　　c i ≈ 160.0 cm   **ii** ≈ 138.9 cm   **iii** ≈ 158.8 cm

　　　iv ≈ 138.9 cm

4 a

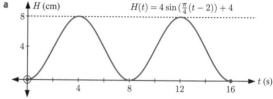

$$H(t) = 4\sin\left(\tfrac{\pi}{4}(t - 2)\right) + 4$$

　　b 4 cm

　　c no (ball diameter is 4.28 cm, gate height is ≈ 3.07 cm)

5 $T(t) = 5.2\sin\left(\tfrac{\pi}{12}(t - 8)\right) + 10.6$ °C

6 $H(t) = 0.6\cos\left(\tfrac{5\pi}{31}(t - 1.5)\right) + 0.76$ m

7 a

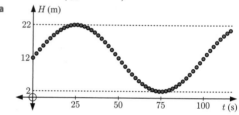

　　b

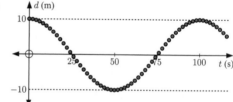

　　c Both graphs are periodic with an amplitude of 10 m and a period of 100 s. The graphs differ by a horizontal translation of 25 s and the principal axis is also translated by 12 m.

　　d i $H(t) = 10\sin\left(\tfrac{\pi}{50}t\right) + 12$ m

　　　ii $d(t) = 10\sin\left(\tfrac{\pi}{50}(t + 25)\right)$ m

　　　Note: The function of horizontal displacement of the light will be different depending on how the coordinate system is defined.

8 a $H(t) = 7\sin\left(\tfrac{5\pi}{31}(t - 5.9)\right) + 9.2$ m

　　b

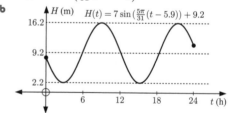

$$H(t) = 7\sin\left(\tfrac{5\pi}{31}(t - 5.9)\right) + 9.2$$

9 a $H(t) = 6\cos\left(\tfrac{\pi}{6}t\right)$ **b** $d(t) = 12\sin 2\pi t$

EXERCISE 8D.2

1 a

T (°C) scatter plot

b The data appears to be periodic.

c **i** $b \approx \frac{\pi}{6}$ **ii** $a \approx 6.5$ **iii** $d \approx 20.5$ **iv** $c \approx 4.5$

d Using technology, $T \approx 6.15 \sin(0.575t - 2.69) + 20.4$.
Our model was a reasonable fit.

2 **a** $T \approx 4.5 \cos\left(\frac{\pi}{6}(t-2)\right) + 11.5$

b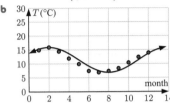

c Using technology, $T \approx 4.29 \cos(0.533t - 0.805) + 11.2$.

3 **a** $T \approx 9.5 \sin\left(\frac{\pi}{6}(t-10.5)\right) - 9.5$

b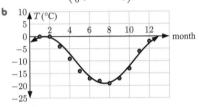

c The model is a reasonable fit, but not perfect.

4 **a**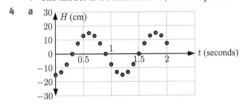

b $H \approx 15.0 \sin(5.24t - 1.57) + 0.000\,170$ **c** ≈ 14.5 cm
d The spring will not oscillate indefinitely at the same rate.

EXERCISE 8E

1 **a** A horizontal translation $\frac{\pi}{2}$ units to the right.
b A vertical stretch with scale factor 4.
c A horizontal stretch with scale factor $\frac{2}{\pi}$.
d A horizontal stretch with scale factor $\frac{1}{2}$, then a translation 1 unit downwards.
e A vertical stretch with scale factor $\frac{1}{2}$, then a reflection in the x-axis.
f A translation 2 units upwards.

2 **a** $\frac{\pi}{3}$ **b** 4π **c** 1 **d** 2 **e** $\frac{3\pi}{2}$ **f** $\frac{\pi}{n}$

3 **a** **i** $\frac{k\pi}{2}, \ k \in \mathbb{Z}$ **ii** $x = \frac{\pi}{4} + \frac{k\pi}{2}, \ k \in \mathbb{Z}$

b **i** $\frac{2\pi}{3} + k\pi, \ k \in \mathbb{Z}$ **ii** $x = \frac{\pi}{6} + k\pi, \ k \in \mathbb{Z}$

c **i** $\frac{\pi}{6} + 2k\pi, \ k \in \mathbb{Z}$ **ii** $x = \frac{7\pi}{6} + 2k\pi, \ k \in \mathbb{Z}$

4 **a**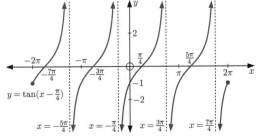

b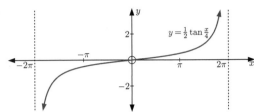

c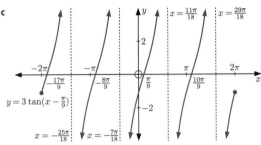

5 $p = \frac{1}{2}, \quad q = 1$ **6** $a = \frac{3}{2}, \quad b = -\frac{2\pi}{15} + \frac{2k\pi}{3}, \quad k \in \mathbb{Z}$

7 **a** A vertical stretch with scale factor 2, then a translation $\frac{\pi}{4}$ units left and 1 unit downwards.

b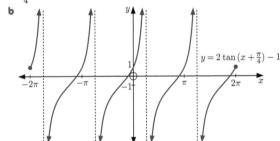

8 **a** **i** $(f \circ g)(x) = \tan\left(2x - \frac{\pi}{2}\right)$
ii $(g \circ f)(x) = 2 \tan x - \frac{\pi}{2}$

b **i** $\frac{1}{\sqrt{3}}$ **ii** $-\frac{\pi}{2}$

c **i** period $\frac{\pi}{2}$, vertical asymptotes $x = \frac{k\pi}{2}, \ k \in \mathbb{Z}$
ii period π, vertical asymptotes $x = \frac{\pi}{2} + k\pi, \ k \in \mathbb{Z}$

d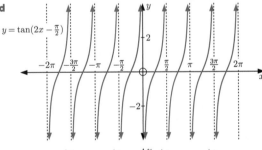

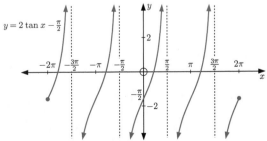

REVIEW SET 8A

1 a not periodic   **b** periodic
2 a minimum 0, maximum 2   **b** minimum -2, maximum 2
3 a 10π **b** $\frac{\pi}{2}$ **c** 4π **d** $\frac{\pi}{3}$

4

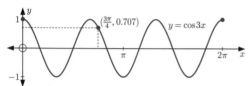

Function	Period	Amplitude	Range
$y = -3\sin\frac{x}{4} + 1$	8π	3	$-2 \leqslant y \leqslant 4$
$y = 3\cos\pi x$	2	3	$-3 \leqslant y \leqslant 3$

5 a

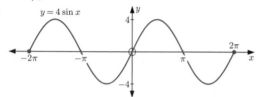

b $y = \frac{1}{\sqrt{2}} \approx 0.707$

6 a

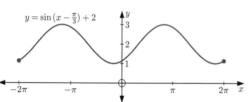

b

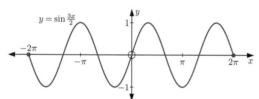

c

d

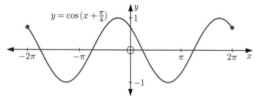

e

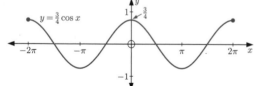

f

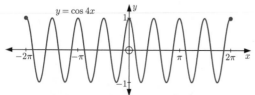

7 a A vertical stretch with scale factor 3, then a horizontal stretch with scale factor $\frac{1}{2}$.
b A translation $\frac{\pi}{3}$ units right and 1 unit downwards.
8 a $y = -4\cos 2x$ **b** $y = \cos\frac{\pi x}{4} + 2$
9 a

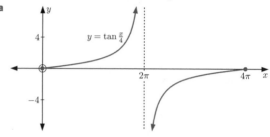

b

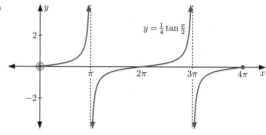

10 a A horizontal stretch with scale factor $\frac{1}{3}$, then a vertical translation 2 units upwards.
b $\frac{\pi}{3}$
c

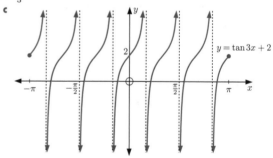

11 a $a = 7$, $b = \frac{\pi}{8}$, $c = 1$, $d = 10$
b $g(x) = 14\sin\left(\frac{\pi}{8}(x-3)\right) + 14$
12 a

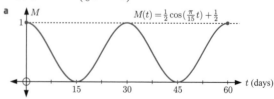

b i 0.75   **ii** 0.25   **iii** ≈ 0.835 **iv** ≈ 0.165
c once every 30 days   **d** January 16, February 15
13 a $T(t) = 3.7\sin\left(\frac{\pi}{12}(t-8.5)\right) + 10.4$ °C
b

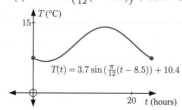

14 a maximum: $-5°C$, minimum: $-79°C$

b ≈ 700 Mars days   **c** $T \approx 37\sin(0.008\,98n) - 42$

d

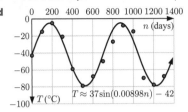

e Using technology,
$T \approx 36.5\sin(0.009\,01n - 0.0903) - 43.2$.
Our model fits the data well.

REVIEW SET 8B

1 a The function repeats itself over and over in a horizontal direction, in intervals of length 8 units.

b i 8   **ii** 5   **iii** -1

2 a A translation $\frac{\pi}{4}$ units left and 1 unit upwards.

b A horizontal stretch with scale factor $\frac{1}{3}$.

3 a 6π **b** $\frac{\pi}{4}$

4 a $b = \frac{1}{3}$ **b** $b = 24$ **c** $b = \frac{2\pi}{9}$

5 a minimum -8, maximum 2   **b** minimum $\frac{2}{3}$, maximum $1\frac{1}{3}$

6 a $y = 5$ **b** $y = -4$

7 a

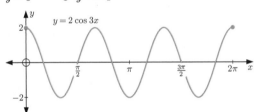

b

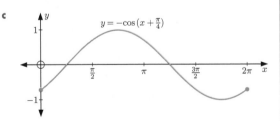

c

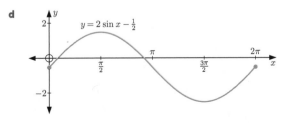

d

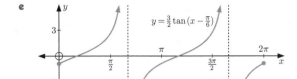

e

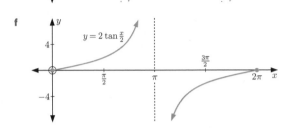

f

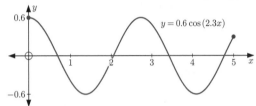

8 a $y = 4\sin x + 6$ **b** $y = 4\cos\left(x - \frac{\pi}{2}\right) + 6$

9

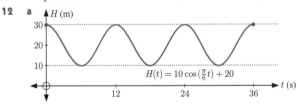

10 $a = \frac{3}{2}$, $b = -\frac{1}{2}$

11 a A reflection in the x-axis, then a horizontal stretch with scale factor $\frac{1}{2}$.

b A vertical stretch with scale factor 2, then a horizontal stretch with scale factor 2, then a translation $\frac{\pi}{2}$ units right and $\frac{1}{2}$ unit upwards.

12 a

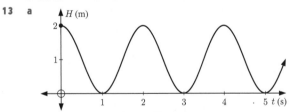

b 20 m   **c** 10 m   **d** 12 seconds

13 a

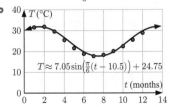

b $H(t) = \sin(\pi(t - 1.5)) + 1$

14 a $a \approx 7.05$, $b \approx \frac{\pi}{6}$, $c \approx 10.5$, $d \approx 24.75$

b

$T \approx 7.05\sin\left(\frac{\pi}{6}(t - 10.5)\right) + 24.75$

c Using technology, $T \approx 7.20 \sin(0.488t + 1.08) + 24.7$. The model fits reasonably well but not perfectly.

EXERCISE 9A.1

1 **a** $x \approx 0.3, 2.8, 6.6, 9.1, 12.9$ **b** $x \approx 5.9, 9.8, 12.2$
  c $x \approx 0.3, 2.8$ **d** $x \approx 3.8, 5.6$

2 **a** $x \approx 1.2, 5.1, 7.4$ **b** $x \approx 4.4, 8.2, 10.7$
  c $x \approx 5.2$ **d** $x \approx 2.5, 3.8$

3 **a** $x \approx 0.4, 1.2, 3.5, 4.3, 6.7, 7.5, 9.8, 10.6, 13.0, 13.7$
  b $x \approx 1.7, 3.0, 4.9, 6.1, 8.0, 9.3, 11.1, 12.4, 14.3, 15.6$
  c $x \approx 3.2, 4.6$ **d** $x \approx 1.6, 3.1, 4.8, 6.2$

4 **a** $x \approx 1.1, 4.2, 7.4$ **b** $x \approx 2.2, 5.3$
  c $x \approx 1.3, 4.4$ **d** $x \approx 2.0$

EXERCISE 9A.2

1 **a** $x \approx 0.446, 2.70, 6.73, 8.98$
  b $x \approx 2.52, 3.76, 8.80, 10.0$
  c $x \approx 0.588, 3.73, 6.87, 10.0$

2 **a** $x \approx -0.644, 0.644$ **b** $x \approx -4.56, -1.42, 1.72, 4.87$
  c $x \approx -2.76, -0.384, 3.53$

3 **a** $x \approx 1.08, 4.35$ **b** $x \approx 0.666, 2.48$

4 $x \approx -0.951, 0.234, 5.98$

EXERCISE 9A.3

1 **a** $x = \frac{\pi}{3}$ or $\frac{5\pi}{3}$ **b** $x = \frac{5\pi}{4}$ or $\frac{7\pi}{4}$ **c** $x = \frac{\pi}{6}$ or $\frac{7\pi}{6}$
  d $x = \frac{3\pi}{2}$ **e** $x = \frac{\pi}{2}$ or $\frac{3\pi}{2}$ **f** $x = 0, \pi,$ or 2π

2 **a** $x = \frac{\pi}{3}$ or $\frac{2\pi}{3}$ **b** $x = \pi$ **c** $x = \frac{\pi}{4}$ or $\frac{5\pi}{4}$

3 **a** $x = \frac{2\pi}{3}, \frac{4\pi}{3}, \frac{8\pi}{3},$ or $\frac{10\pi}{3}$ **b** $x = \frac{\pi}{4}, \frac{3\pi}{4}, \frac{9\pi}{4},$ or $\frac{11\pi}{4}$
  c $x = \frac{\pi}{4}, \frac{5\pi}{4}, \frac{9\pi}{4},$ or $\frac{13\pi}{4}$

4 **a** $x = -\frac{2\pi}{3}, -\frac{\pi}{3}, \frac{4\pi}{3},$ or $\frac{5\pi}{3}$
  b $x = -\frac{5\pi}{4}, -\frac{3\pi}{4}, \frac{3\pi}{4},$ or $\frac{5\pi}{4}$
  c $x = -\frac{5\pi}{4}, -\frac{\pi}{4}, \frac{3\pi}{4},$ or $\frac{7\pi}{4}$

5 **a** $x = \frac{\pi}{6}, \frac{5\pi}{6}, \frac{7\pi}{6},$ or $\frac{11\pi}{6}$ **b** $x = \frac{\pi}{2}$ or $\frac{3\pi}{2}$
  c $x = \frac{\pi}{3}, \frac{2\pi}{3}, \frac{4\pi}{3},$ or $\frac{5\pi}{3}$

6 **a** $0 \leqslant 2x \leqslant 4\pi$ **b** $0 \leqslant \frac{x}{4} \leqslant \frac{\pi}{2}$
  c $\frac{\pi}{2} \leqslant x + \frac{\pi}{2} \leqslant \frac{5\pi}{2}$ **d** $-\frac{\pi}{6} \leqslant x - \frac{\pi}{6} \leqslant \frac{11\pi}{6}$
  e $-\frac{\pi}{2} \leqslant 2\left(x - \frac{\pi}{4}\right) \leqslant \frac{7\pi}{2}$ **f** $-2\pi \leqslant -x \leqslant 0$

7 **a** $-3\pi \leqslant 3x \leqslant 3\pi$ **b** $-\frac{\pi}{4} \leqslant \frac{x}{4} \leqslant \frac{\pi}{4}$
  c $-\frac{3\pi}{2} \leqslant x - \frac{\pi}{2} \leqslant \frac{\pi}{2}$ **d** $-\frac{3\pi}{2} \leqslant 2x + \frac{\pi}{2} \leqslant \frac{5\pi}{2}$
  e $-2\pi \leqslant -2x \leqslant 2\pi$ **f** $0 \leqslant \pi - x \leqslant 2\pi$

8 **a** $x = \frac{\pi}{3}, \frac{5\pi}{3},$ or $\frac{7\pi}{3}$
  b $x = \frac{\pi}{6}, \frac{5\pi}{6}, \frac{7\pi}{6}, \frac{11\pi}{6}, \frac{13\pi}{6},$ or $\frac{17\pi}{6}$
  c $x = 0, \frac{4\pi}{3},$ or 2π

9 **a** $x = \frac{7\pi}{12}, \frac{11\pi}{12}, \frac{19\pi}{12},$ or $\frac{23\pi}{12}$
  b $x = \frac{\pi}{18}, \frac{11\pi}{18}, \frac{13\pi}{18}, \frac{23\pi}{18}, \frac{25\pi}{18},$ or $\frac{35\pi}{18}$
  c $x = \frac{\pi}{6}, \frac{2\pi}{3}, \frac{7\pi}{6},$ or $\frac{5\pi}{3}$ **d** $x = \frac{\pi}{2}$ or $\frac{3\pi}{2}$
  e $x = \frac{4\pi}{3}$ **f** $x = \frac{3\pi}{4}$

10 **a** $x = \frac{\pi}{9}, \frac{2\pi}{9}, \frac{4\pi}{9}, \frac{5\pi}{9}, \frac{7\pi}{9}, \frac{8\pi}{9}, \frac{10\pi}{9}, \frac{11\pi}{9}, \frac{13\pi}{9}, \frac{14\pi}{9},$ $\frac{16\pi}{9},$ or $\frac{17\pi}{9}$

b $x = \frac{\pi}{4}, \frac{3\pi}{4}, \frac{5\pi}{4},$ or $\frac{7\pi}{4}$ **c** $x = \frac{\pi}{3}$ or $\frac{5\pi}{3}$

11 **a** $x = \frac{3\pi}{4}$ or $\frac{7\pi}{4}$ **b** $x = \frac{\pi}{12}, \frac{5\pi}{12}, \frac{3\pi}{4}, \frac{13\pi}{12}, \frac{17\pi}{12},$ or $\frac{7\pi}{4}$
  c $x = \frac{\pi}{6}, \frac{2\pi}{3}, \frac{7\pi}{6},$ or $\frac{5\pi}{3}$

12 **a** $x = -\frac{5\pi}{3}, -\pi, \frac{\pi}{3},$ or π **b** $x = 0, \frac{3\pi}{2},$ or 2π
  c $x = 0, \frac{\pi}{4}, \frac{\pi}{2}, \frac{3\pi}{4},$ or π **d** $x = 0, \frac{\pi}{6}, \pi, \frac{7\pi}{6},$ or 2π

13 **a** $b = \frac{1}{3}, \ d = 2$ **b** $a = -2, \ b = \frac{1}{2}$
  c $b = 4, \ d = -1$ **d** $b = \frac{1}{2}, \ d = -4$

14 $x = \frac{\pi}{3}$ or $\frac{4\pi}{3}$
  a $x = \frac{\pi}{2}$ or $\frac{3\pi}{2}$
  b $x = \frac{\pi}{12}, \frac{\pi}{3}, \frac{7\pi}{12}, \frac{5\pi}{6}, \frac{13\pi}{12}, \frac{4\pi}{3}, \frac{19\pi}{12},$ or $\frac{11\pi}{6}$
  c $x = \frac{\pi}{3}, \frac{2\pi}{3}, \frac{4\pi}{3},$ or $\frac{5\pi}{3}$

15 **a** $x = 0, \frac{\pi}{6}, \frac{5\pi}{6}, \pi,$ or 2π **b** $x = \frac{\pi}{3}, \frac{\pi}{2}, \frac{3\pi}{2},$ or $\frac{5\pi}{3}$
  c $x = 0, \frac{2\pi}{3}, \frac{4\pi}{3},$ or 2π **d** $x = \frac{7\pi}{6}, \frac{3\pi}{2},$ or $\frac{11\pi}{6}$
  e $x = \frac{\pi}{3}, \frac{2\pi}{3}, \frac{4\pi}{3},$ or $\frac{5\pi}{3}$

EXERCISE 9B

1 **a** **i** 7500 grasshoppers **ii** $\approx 10\,300$ grasshoppers
  b $10\,500$ grasshoppers, when $t = 4$ weeks
  c **i** at $t = 1\frac{1}{3}$ weeks and $6\frac{2}{3}$ weeks
   ii at $t = 9\frac{1}{3}$ weeks
  d $2.51 \leqslant t \leqslant 5.49$

2 **a** **i** 12 metres **ii** 2 metres **b** 100 seconds
  c at approximately 6.55, 43.5, 107, and 143 seconds

3 **a** 1 m above ground **b** at $t = 1\frac{1}{2}$ min **c** 3 min
  d

$$H(t) = 20 - 19 \cos \frac{2\pi t}{3}$$

  e $0.570 \leqslant t \leqslant 2.43$ min

4 **a** 400 water buffalo
  b **i** 577 water buffalo **ii** 400 water buffalo
  c 650, which is the maximum population.
  d 150, after 3 years **e** $t \approx 0.262$ years

5 **a** **i** true **ii** true **b** 116.8 cents L^{-1}
  c on the 5th, 11th, 19th, and 25th days
  d 98.6 cents L^{-1} on the 1st and 15th days

6 **a** $H(t) = 3 \cos\left(\frac{\pi}{2}t\right) + 4$ **b** $t \approx 1.46$ s

EXERCISE 9C.1

1 **a** $2 \sin \theta$ **b** $3 \cos \theta$ **c** $2 \sin \theta$ **d** $\sin \theta$
  e $-2 \tan \theta$ **f** $-3 \cos^2 \theta$

2 **a** $2 \tan x$ **b** $\tan^2 x$ **c** $\sin x$ **d** $\cos x$
  e $5 \sin x$ **f** $\dfrac{2}{\cos x}$

3 **a** $2 \cos \theta$ **b** $-\tan \theta$ **c** 0 **d** $-\tan \theta$
  e $\dfrac{1}{\tan \theta}$ **f** $2 \cos \theta$ **g** $\tan \theta$ **h** $\tan \theta$
  i $2 \tan \theta$

EXERCISE 9C.2

1 a 3   **b** -2 **c** -1 **d** $3\cos^2\theta$
  e $4\sin^2\theta$ **f** $\cos\theta$ **g** $-\sin^2\theta$ **h** $-\cos^2\theta$
  i $-2\sin^2\theta$ **j** 1 **k** $\sin\theta$ **l** $\sin\theta$

2 a $1 + 2\sin\theta + \sin^2\theta$ **b** $\sin^2\alpha - 4\sin\alpha + 4$
  c $\dfrac{1}{\cos^2\alpha} - 2\tan\alpha$ **d** $1 + 2\sin\alpha\cos\alpha$
  e $1 - 2\sin\beta\cos\beta$ **f** $-4 + 4\cos\alpha - \cos^2\alpha$

3 a $-\sin^2 x\tan^2 x$ **b** 13

EXERCISE 9C.3

1 a $(1 + \sin\theta)(1 - \sin\theta)$ **b** $(\sin\alpha + \cos\alpha)(\sin\alpha - \cos\alpha)$
  c $(\tan\alpha + 1)(\tan\alpha - 1)$ **d** $\sin\beta(2\sin\beta - 1)$
  e $\cos\phi(2 + 3\cos\phi)$ **f** $3\sin\theta(\sin\theta - 2)$
  g $(\tan\theta + 3)(\tan\theta + 2)$ **h** $(2\cos\theta + 1)(\cos\theta + 3)$
  i $(3\cos\alpha + 1)(2\cos\alpha - 1)$ **j** $\tan\alpha(3\tan\alpha - 2)$
  k $(2\sin x + \cos x)(\sin x + 3\cos x)$

2 a $x = \frac{\pi}{6}, \frac{5\pi}{6}$, or $\frac{3\pi}{2}$ **b** no real solutions
  c $x = \frac{\pi}{6}$ or $\frac{5\pi}{6}$

3 a $1 + \sin\alpha$ **b** $\tan\beta - 1$ **c** $\cos\phi - \sin\phi$
  d $\cos\phi + \sin\phi$ **e** $\dfrac{1}{\sin\alpha - \cos\alpha}$ **f** $\dfrac{\cos\theta}{2}$

EXERCISE 9D

2 a $\frac{24}{25}$ **b** $-\frac{7}{25}$ **c** $-\frac{24}{7}$ **3 a** $-\frac{7}{9}$ **b** $\frac{1}{9}$

4 a $\cos\alpha = -\frac{\sqrt{5}}{3}$ **b** $\sin 2\alpha = \frac{4\sqrt{5}}{9}$

5 a $\sin\beta = -\frac{\sqrt{21}}{5}$ **b** $\sin 2\beta = -\frac{4\sqrt{21}}{25}$

6 a $\frac{1}{3}$ **b** $\frac{2\sqrt{2}}{3}$ **7 a** $-\frac{1}{\sqrt{3}}$ **b** $\frac{\sqrt{2}}{\sqrt{3}}$

9 a $\sin 2\alpha$ **b** $2\sin 2\alpha$ **c** $\frac{1}{2}\sin 2\alpha$ **d** $\cos 2\beta$
  e $-\cos 2\phi$ **f** $\cos 2N$ **g** $-\cos 2M$ **h** $\cos 2\alpha$
  i $-\cos 2\alpha$ **j** $\sin 4A$ **k** $\sin 6\alpha$ **l** $\cos 8\theta$
  m $-\cos 6\beta$ **n** $\cos 10\alpha$ **o** $-\cos 6D$ **p** $\cos 4A$
  q $\cos\alpha$ **r** $-2\cos 6P$

10 $\frac{3}{2}$

12 a $x = 0, \frac{2\pi}{3}, \pi, \frac{4\pi}{3}$, or 2π **b** $x = \frac{\pi}{2}$ or $\frac{3\pi}{2}$
  c $x = 0, \pi$, or 2π

14 $\theta = -\frac{11\pi}{12}, -\frac{7\pi}{12}, \frac{\pi}{12}$, or $\frac{5\pi}{12}$

15 a $x = 0, \frac{2\pi}{3}, \frac{4\pi}{3}$, or 2π **b** $x = \frac{\pi}{3}$ or $\frac{5\pi}{3}$
  c $x = \frac{\pi}{2}, \frac{7\pi}{6}$, or $\frac{11\pi}{6}$
  d $x = 0, \frac{\pi}{6}, \frac{\pi}{2}, \frac{5\pi}{6}, \pi, \frac{7\pi}{6}, \frac{3\pi}{2}, \frac{11\pi}{6}$, or 2π
  e $x = \frac{\pi}{4}$ **f** $x = \frac{\pi}{6}$ or $\frac{5\pi}{6}$

16 a C_1 is $y = \cos x$, C_2 is $y = \cos 2x + 1$
  b $A(\frac{\pi}{3}, \frac{1}{2})$, $B(\frac{\pi}{2}, 0)$, $C(\frac{3\pi}{2}, 0)$, $D(\frac{5\pi}{3}, \frac{1}{2})$

REVIEW SET 9A

1 a $x \approx 2.0, 4.3, 8.3, 10.6$ **b** $x \approx 0.5, 5.8, 6.7, 12.1$

2 a $x \approx 0.392, 2.75, 6.68$ **b** $x \approx 5.42$

3 a $x \approx 1.12, 5.17, 7.40$ **b** $x \approx 0.184, 4.62$

4 a $x = \frac{7\pi}{6}$ or $\frac{11\pi}{6}$ **b** $x = \frac{\pi}{4}$ or $\frac{7\pi}{4}$
  c $x = \frac{\pi}{3}, \frac{2\pi}{3}, \frac{4\pi}{3}$, or $\frac{5\pi}{3}$

5 a $x = \frac{\pi}{8}, \frac{3\pi}{8}, \frac{5\pi}{8}, \frac{7\pi}{8}, \frac{9\pi}{8}, \frac{11\pi}{8}, \frac{13\pi}{8}$, or $\frac{15\pi}{8}$
  b $x = \frac{3\pi}{2}$ **c** $x = \frac{\pi}{6}, \frac{5\pi}{6}, \frac{7\pi}{6}$, or $\frac{11\pi}{6}$

6 a $x = 0, \frac{3\pi}{2}, 2\pi, \frac{7\pi}{2}$, or 4π **b** $x = \frac{\pi}{6}, \frac{2\pi}{3}, \frac{7\pi}{6}$, or $\frac{5\pi}{3}$

7 a 5000 beetles   **b** smallest 3000, largest 7000
  c $0.5 < t < 2.5$ and $6.5 < t \leqslant 8$

8 a $\cos\theta$ **b** $-\sin\theta$ **c** $\cos\theta$
  d $1 - \cos\theta$ **e** $\dfrac{1}{\sin\alpha + \cos\alpha}$ **f** $-\dfrac{\cos\alpha}{2}$

9 a $-\frac{\sqrt{7}}{4}$ **b** $\frac{3\sqrt{7}}{8}$ **c** $-\frac{1}{8}$

11 a $x = 0, \pi, 2\pi$ **b** $x = \frac{\pi}{3}, \frac{5\pi}{3}$ **12 c** $x = \frac{16}{3}$

REVIEW SET 9B

1 a $x \approx -6.1, -3.4$ **b** $x \approx 0.8$

2 a $x \approx 1.27, 5.02$ **b** $x \approx 1.09, 2.05$

3 a $x \approx 1.33, 4.47, 7.61$ **b** $x \approx 5.30$
  c $x \approx 2.83, 5.97, 9.11$

4 a $x = \frac{4\pi}{9}, \frac{5\pi}{9}, \frac{10\pi}{9}, \frac{11\pi}{9}, \frac{16\pi}{9}$, or $\frac{17\pi}{9}$ **b** $x = \frac{5\pi}{3}$
  c $x = \frac{\pi}{12}, \frac{7\pi}{12}, \frac{13\pi}{12}$, or $\frac{19\pi}{12}$

5 a $x = -\frac{\pi}{2}$ or $\frac{\pi}{2}$ **b** $x = -\frac{2\pi}{3}, -\frac{\pi}{6}, \frac{\pi}{3}$, or $\frac{5\pi}{6}$
  c $x = -\frac{2\pi}{3}, -\frac{\pi}{3}, \frac{\pi}{3}$, or $\frac{2\pi}{3}$

6 a $\frac{4\pi}{9}, \frac{5\pi}{9}, \frac{10\pi}{9}, \frac{11\pi}{9}, \frac{16\pi}{9}, \frac{17\pi}{9}$ **b** $\frac{3\pi}{4}, \frac{7\pi}{4}, \frac{11\pi}{4}$

7 a 28 milligrams per m^3 **b** 8:00 am Monday

8 a $\cos\theta$ **b** $-\sin\theta$ **c** $5\cos^2\theta$ **d** $-\cos\theta$

9 a $\frac{120}{169}$ **b** $\frac{119}{169}$ **11** $\theta = \frac{\pi}{3}$ **12** 1.5 m

EXERCISE 10A

1 a The cat is not black.   **b** x is not prime.
  c The tree is not deciduous.

2 a False, x may be -3.   **b** True, $3^2 = 9$.
  c False, $x^2 = 9$ does not imply that $x = 3$.

3 a True, as the square root of any positive number is real.
  b False: for example, $\sqrt{0} = 0 \in \mathbb{R}$ but 0 is not positive.
  c False, $\sqrt{x} \in \mathbb{R} \not\Rightarrow x$ is positive.

4 a "If Socrates is an animal, then Socrates is a cat."   **b** false

5 a equivalent   **b** not equivalent

6 We need to turn cards D and 3. We do not need to turn cards K and 7.

EXERCISE 10B

1 b If $x^2 - x - 6 = 0$ then $x = -2$ or 3.

2 Hint: Use Pythagoras' theorem.

4 Hint: Let the middle number be x.

6 Hint: $(a - b)^2 \geqslant 0$ for all $a, b \in \mathbb{R}$.

7 Hint: $\sin 2\theta = 2\sin\theta\cos\theta$

8 Hint: The 3-digit number "abc" has value $100a + 10b + c$.

9 a $4x^2 = 3x \not\Rightarrow 4x = 3$
  b $(x + 3)(2 - x) = 4 \not\Rightarrow x + 3 = 4 \vee 2 - x = 4$

EXERCISE 10C

1 a Hint: $(a + b)^2 - (a - b)^2$
    $= [a + b + (a - b)][a + b - (a - b)]$

2 a $= 14$

3 Hint: $(x-y)^5 + (x-y)^3 = (x-y)^3[(x-y)^2 + 1]$

4 **a** $n^4 + 4$ **b** $n = \pm 1$

5 **b** **i** 121 and 81   **ii** 676 and 576

6 **a** $(a-b)(a+b) = b(a-b) \not\Rightarrow a+b = b$
$2a = a \not\Rightarrow 2 = 1$

b $\dfrac{4x-40}{6-x} = \dfrac{4x-40}{13-x} \not\Rightarrow 6-x = 13-x$

7 **a** $6x - 12 = 3(x-2) \not\Rightarrow 6x - 12 + 3(x-2) = 0$
b $x(x-6) = 3(-3) \not\Rightarrow x = 3 \ \lor \ x - 6 = -3$

8 **b** No, $\dfrac{1}{n+1} + \dfrac{1}{n^2+n}$ is undefined for $n = 0, -1$ while
$\dfrac{1}{n}$ is only undefined for $n = 0$.

EXERCISE 10D

1 Hint: Let $x = 0.\overline{9}$, $\therefore \ 10x = 9.\overline{9} = 9 + x$ and so on.

3 Hint: $u_1 = 4 - \sqrt{2}$, $r = \dfrac{1}{3 - \sqrt{2}}$

6 Hint: Let the 2 odd integers be $2a + 1$ and $2b + 1$, $a, b \in \mathbb{Z}$.

7 Hint: Let $p = 2a + 1$, $q = 2b + 1$, $a, b \in \mathbb{Z}$.

REVIEW SET 10A

3 **a** The boy does not have blue eyes.
b x is not larger than 4.

4 **a** True, by definition.
b False, the period of f may be $\dfrac{p}{2}$ or $\dfrac{p}{3}$, and so on.
c False, $f(x + p) = f(x)$ for all $x \not\Rightarrow f$ is periodic with period p.

5 Hint: $(3a - b)^2 \geqslant 0$ for all $a, b \in \mathbb{R}$.

6 **b** **ii** The LHS is undefined for $\theta = \dfrac{(2n+1)\pi}{2}$, $n \in \mathbb{Z}$
while the RHS is defined for all $\theta \in \mathbb{R}$.

8 **a** **i** 9, composite   **ii** 35, composite
iii 91, composite   **iv** 189, composite
c For all $k \in \mathbb{Z}^+$, $k^3 + (k+1)^3$ will always have factors $(2k+1)$ and $(k^2 + k + 1)$ and is hence composite.

REVIEW SET 10B

2 Hint: $(\sqrt{a} - \sqrt{b})^2 \geqslant 0$

3 **a** true   **b** If $\sin x$ is positive then x is acute.   **c** false

4 **a** not equivalent   **b** not equivalent

5 Hint: $k^3 + k^2 - k - 1 = (k^2 - 1)(k + 1)$

6 Hint: Divide the triangle into 3 smaller triangles, then find the sum of their areas.

7 Hint: "ab" has value $10a + b$, "ba" has value $10b + a$.

8 $\left(3 - \dfrac{5}{2}\right)^2 = \left(2 - \dfrac{5}{2}\right)^2 \not\Rightarrow 3 - \dfrac{5}{2} = 2 - \dfrac{5}{2}$

EXERCISE 11A.1

1 **a** Yes. The distance increases by the same amount each time interval.
b

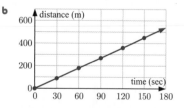

c 3 m per s

2 **a** Yes. The height increases by the same amount each time interval.
b 5 cm per week

3 **a** 3   **b** -2 **c** $-\dfrac{1}{4}$ **4** $\dfrac{5}{2}$

EXERCISE 11A.2

1 **a** No. The graph is not a straight line.
b **i** 60 km per hour   **ii** 100 km per hour

2 **a** 100 m per hour   **b** 100 m per hour (downwards)

3 **a** $\dfrac{1}{2}$ **b** $\dfrac{2}{5}$ **c** $-\dfrac{5}{4}$ **d** -2

4 **a** **i** 3   **ii** 2.5   **iii** 2.1   **iv** 2.01   **v** 2.001
b The average rate of change approaches 2.

EXERCISE 11B

1 **a** 0.5 m s^{-1} **b** 2 m s^{-1} **2** **a** 1   **b** 4
3 **a, b**   **c** -2

6 **a** -3 **b** 5   **c** -1 **d** 6   **e** -4 **f** -8
g 1   **h** 2   **i** 5

EXERCISE 11C.1

1 **a** 7   **b** 7   **c** 11   **d** 16   **e** 0   **f** 5

2 **a** 5   **b** 7   **c** c

3 **a** -2 **b** 7   **c** -1

4 As $x \neq 0$, we can cancel the xs, to give
$$\lim_{x \to 0} \frac{x}{x} = \lim_{x \to 0} 1 = 1$$

5 **a**

x	$\dfrac{x^2-4}{x-2}$
1.9	3.9
1.99	3.99
1.999	3.999
1.9999	3.9999
1.99999	3.99999

x	$\dfrac{x^2-4}{x-2}$
2.1	4.1
2.01	4.01
2.001	4.001
2.0001	4.0001
2.00001	4.00001

b $\lim\limits_{x \to 2} \dfrac{x^2-4}{x-2} = 4$

EXERCISE 11C.2

1 **a** **i** as $x \to 0^-$, $f(x) \to -\infty$
as $x \to 0^+$, $f(x) \to \infty$
as $x \to -\infty$, $f(x) \to 0^-$
as $x \to \infty$, $f(x) \to 0^+$
vertical asymptote $x = 0$, horizontal asymptote $y = 0$
ii $\lim\limits_{x \to -\infty} f(x) = 0$, $\lim\limits_{x \to \infty} f(x) = 0$

b **i** as $x \to -3^-$, $f(x) \to \infty$
as $x \to -3^+$, $f(x) \to -\infty$
as $x \to -\infty$, $f(x) \to 3^+$
as $x \to \infty$, $f(x) \to 3^-$
vertical asymptote $x = -3$,
horizontal asymptote $y = 3$

ii $\lim\limits_{x\to-\infty} f(x) = 3$, $\lim\limits_{x\to\infty} f(x) = 3$

c **i** as $x\to-\frac{2}{3}^{-}$, $f(x)\to-\infty$

as $x\to-\frac{2}{3}^{+}$, $f(x)\to\infty$

as $x\to-\infty$, $f(x)\to-\frac{2}{3}^{-}$

as $x\to\infty$, $f(x)\to-\frac{2}{3}^{+}$

vertical asymptote $x=-\frac{2}{3}$,

horizontal asymptote $y=-\frac{2}{3}$

ii $\lim\limits_{x\to-\infty} f(x) = -\frac{2}{3}$, $\lim\limits_{x\to\infty} f(x) = -\frac{2}{3}$

d **i** as $x\to 1^{-}$, $f(x)\to\infty$,

as $x\to 1^{+}$, $f(x)\to-\infty$,

as $x\to-\infty$, $f(x)\to-1^{+}$

as $x\to\infty$, $f(x)\to-1^{-}$

vertical asymptote $x=1$,

horizontal asymptote $y=-1$

ii $\lim\limits_{x\to-\infty} f(x) = -1$, $\lim\limits_{x\to\infty} f(x) = -1$

2 **a**

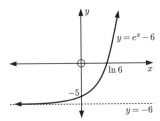

b **i** $\lim\limits_{x\to-\infty} (e^x - 6) = -6$

$y = -6$ is a horizontal asymptote of $y = e^x - 6$.

ii $\lim\limits_{x\to\infty} (e^x - 6)$ does not exist

3 **a** $\lim\limits_{x\to-\infty} (2e^{-x} - 3)$ does not exist

b $\lim\limits_{x\to\infty} (2e^{-x} - 3) = -3$

4 **a**

x	xe^{-x}
10	$\approx 0.000\,454$
50	$\approx 9.64 \times 10^{-21}$
100	$\approx 3.72 \times 10^{-42}$
200	$\approx 2.77 \times 10^{-85}$

b $\lim\limits_{x\to\infty} xe^{-x} = 0$

c yes

EXERCISE 11D

1 **a** $(3+h)^2$

b $\dfrac{(3+h)^2 - 9}{(3+h) - 3} = 6 + h$ for $h \neq 0$

c **i** 7   **ii** 6.5   **iii** 6.1   **iv** 6.01   **d** 6

2 **a** **i** 2   **ii** 8

b

x-coordinate	Gradient of tangent to $f(x) = x^2$
1	2
2	4
3	6
4	8

c $2a$

3 **a** 5   **b** 3   **c** −1   **d** 4

EXERCISE 11E

1 **a** $f(0) = 4$ **b** $f'(0) = -1$ **2** $f'(2) = 1$

3 **a** positive   **b** negative   **c** negative   **d** positive

4 **a** **i** $f'(-2) = -3$

At $x = -2$, the derivative function is -3, *or* the gradient of the tangent to $y = f(x)$ at the point where $x = -2$ is -3.

ii $f'(0) = 1$

At $x = 0$, the derivative function is 1, *or* the gradient of the tangent to $y = f(x)$ at the point where $x = 0$ is 1.

b

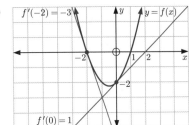

5 **c**

EXERCISE 11F

1 **a** $f'(x) = 1$ **b** $f'(x) = 0$ **c** $f'(x) = 3x^2$

2 **a** $f'(x) = 2$ **b** $f'(x) = 2x - 3$ **c** $f'(x) = -2x + 5$

3 **a** $\dfrac{dy}{dx} = -1$ **b** $\dfrac{dy}{dx} = 4x + 1$ **c** $\dfrac{dy}{dx} = 3x^2 - 4x$

4 **a** 12   **b** 108

5 **a** $f'(x) = -\dfrac{1}{x^2}$

b $f'(-1) = -1$; the tangent at the point where $x = -1$ has gradient -1.

$f'(3) = -\frac{1}{9}$; the tangent at the point where $x = 3$ has gradient $-\frac{1}{9}$.

6 **a** **i** 3   **ii** −1   **b** $f'(x) = -2x + 3$

c $f'(0) = 3$, $f'(2) = -1$

7 **a** $\dfrac{dy}{dx} = 3x^2 - 3$ **b** $(-1, 2)$ and $(1, -2)$

8 **a** $f'(x) = 4x + 2$ **c**

b $(-1, -12)$

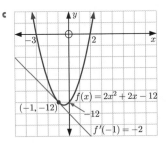

9 **a** $f'(x) = -\frac{1}{2}x + 1$

b $f'(-2) = 2$, $f'(3) = -\frac{1}{2}$

Gradients of tangents are 2 and $-\frac{1}{2}$, and $2 \times -\frac{1}{2} = -1$

$\therefore$ tangents are perpendicular.

10 **a**

$f(x)$	$f'(x)$
x^1	1
x^2	$2x$
x^3	$3x^2$
x^4	$4x^3$
x^{-1}	$-x^{-2}$
x^0	0

b If $f(x) = x^n$, then $f'(x) = nx^{n-1}$.

REVIEW SET 11A

1 $\frac{4}{3}$

2 a Yes. The height increases by the same amount each time interval.
  b 1.6 m s^{-1}

3 a -1 **b** -1 **c** 8

4 a

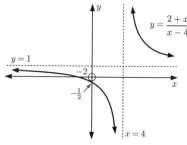

$y = \dfrac{2+x}{x-4}$

$y = 1$

b as $x \to 4^-$, $y \to -\infty$,   as $x \to -\infty$, $y \to 1^-$,
  as $x \to 4^+$, $y \to \infty$,   as $x \to \infty$, $y \to 1^+$,
  vertical asymptote $x = 4$, horizontal asymptote $y = 1$

c $\lim\limits_{x \to -\infty} \dfrac{2+x}{x-4} = 1$, $\lim\limits_{x \to \infty} \dfrac{2+x}{x-4} = 1$

5 b

h	$\dfrac{f(3+h) - f(3)}{h}$
0.1	12.2
0.01	12.02
0.001	12.002
0.0001	12.0002

c $\lim\limits_{h \to 0} \dfrac{f(3+h) - f(3)}{h} = 12$
  The gradient of the tangent to $y = 2x^2$ at $(3, 18)$ is 12.

6 $f'(3) = -\frac{1}{2}$ **7 a** $f'(x) = 2x + 2$ **b** $\dfrac{dy}{dx} = -6x$

8 a $\dfrac{dy}{dx} = 4x$ **b** gradient $= 16$ **c** $x = -3$

9 a $f'(x) = 3x^2 - 6x$
  b $f'(-1) = 9$, $f'(3) = 9$
  Gradients of tangents are both 9.
  $\therefore$ the tangents are parallel.

REVIEW SET 11B

1 $\frac{1}{2}$ **2 a** $2°C$ per hour   **b** $-2\frac{1}{2}°C$ per hour

3 a -3 **b** 3 **c** -1

4 a

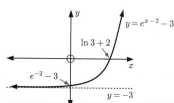

$y = e^{x-2} - 3$

$\ln 3 + 2$

$e^{-2} - 3$

$y = -3$

b i $\lim\limits_{x \to -\infty} (e^{x-2} - 3) = -3$
  ii $\lim\limits_{x \to \infty} (e^{x-2} - 3)$ does not exist

5 a negative   **b** positive   **c** positive   **d** negative

6 a, b

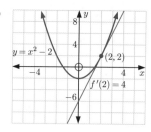

$y = x^2 - 2$

$(2, 2)$

$f'(2) = 4$

c 4

7 a $f'(x) = 4x^3 - 2$
  b $f'(-2) = -34$
  The gradient of $f'(x)$ at the point where $x = -2$ is -34.

8 a $\dfrac{dy}{dx} = 2x + 5$ **b** $(-4, -6)$

9 a i 447.2 m   **ii** 432.8 m   **b** $f'(t) = -9.6t$
  c i 9.6 m s^{-1} **ii** 19.2 m s^{-1}

EXERCISE 12A

1 a $3x^2$ **b** $8x^7$ **c** $11x^{10}$ **d** 6
  e $6x^2$ **f** $14x$ **g** $15x^4$ **h** $30x^5$
  i 5 **j** $2x$ **k** $2x + 1$ **l** $2x + 3$
  m $4x + 1$ **n** $6x - 7$ **o** $-4x$ **p** $2x^3 - 12x$
  q $3x^2 - 8x + 6$ **r** $6x^2 + 1$ **s** $-1 - 12x^2$ **t** $\frac{3}{5}x^2 - 7x$

2 a $-\dfrac{2}{x^3}$ **b** $-\dfrac{5}{x^6}$ **c** $-\dfrac{3}{x^2}$ **d** $-\dfrac{12}{x^4}$ **e** $\dfrac{28}{x^5}$
  f $2 - \dfrac{6}{x^3}$ **g** $2x + \dfrac{6}{x^2}$ **h** $\dfrac{6}{x^4}$ **i** $-\dfrac{4}{x^3} - \dfrac{36}{x^5}$
  j $3 + \dfrac{1}{x^2} - \dfrac{4}{x^3}$ **k** $\dfrac{16}{x^3} - \dfrac{12}{x^4}$ **l** $-\dfrac{2}{5x^3}$
  m $4 + \dfrac{1}{4x^2}$ **n** $2x - \dfrac{4}{x^2}$ **o** $-\dfrac{2}{x^2} + \dfrac{10}{x^3}$

3 a $\dfrac{1}{2\sqrt{x}}$ **b** $\dfrac{1}{3\sqrt[3]{x^2}}$ **c** $\dfrac{-1}{2x\sqrt{x}}$
  d $3x^2 - \dfrac{1}{4\sqrt{x}}$ **e** $-\dfrac{2}{x^3} + \dfrac{3}{\sqrt{x}}$ **f** $2 - \dfrac{1}{2\sqrt{x}}$
  g $\dfrac{3}{2}\sqrt{x}$ **h** $\dfrac{-3}{2x^2\sqrt{x}}$ **i** $4x + \dfrac{3}{2x\sqrt{x}}$
  j $-\dfrac{1}{2x\sqrt{x}} + \dfrac{4}{x^2}$ **k** $\dfrac{1}{2\sqrt{x}} - \dfrac{5}{2x\sqrt{x}}$ **l** $-\dfrac{7}{2x\sqrt{x}} - \dfrac{3\sqrt{x}}{2}$
  m $6x - \dfrac{3\sqrt{x}}{2}$ **n** $\dfrac{-10}{x^3\sqrt{x}}$ **o** $2 + \dfrac{9}{2x^2\sqrt{x}}$
  p $\dfrac{5\sqrt[3]{x^2}}{3} - \dfrac{2}{3\sqrt[3]{x}} - \dfrac{2}{3x\sqrt[3]{x}}$

4 a $\dfrac{dy}{dx} = 2\pi x$ **b** $\dfrac{dy}{dx} = 6x + \dfrac{16}{x^3}$ **c** $\dfrac{dy}{dx} = \dfrac{3}{\sqrt{x}} - \dfrac{5}{x^2}$
  d $\dfrac{dy}{dx} = 12\pi x^2$ **e** $\dfrac{dy}{dx} = 7.5x^2 - 2.8x$
  f $\dfrac{dy}{dx} = 10$ **g** $\dfrac{dy}{dx} = 2x - 1$ **h** $\dfrac{dy}{dx} = 12x - 1$
  i $\dfrac{dy}{dx} = 2x - 10$ **j** $\dfrac{dy}{dx} = 8x - 4$
  k $\dfrac{dy}{dx} = 6x^2 - 6x - 5$ **l** $\dfrac{dy}{dx} = \dfrac{3}{2}\sqrt{x} - \dfrac{3}{\sqrt{x}} - \dfrac{9}{2x\sqrt{x}}$

5 a $\dfrac{dy}{dt} = 2t^3 - \dfrac{1}{3}$ **b** $\dfrac{dy}{dt} = 3t^{-\frac{3}{2}} = \dfrac{3}{t\sqrt{t}}$

c $\dfrac{dT}{dt} = \frac{1}{3}t^{-\frac{2}{3}} + 4t^{-3} = \dfrac{1}{3\sqrt[3]{t^2}} + \dfrac{4}{t^3}$

d $\dfrac{dP}{du} = -5u^{-2} - 15u^{\frac{1}{2}} = -\dfrac{5}{u^2} - 15\sqrt{u}$

6 a 4 **b** 22 **c** $-\frac{16}{729}$ **d** -7 **e** $\frac{3}{2}$
f $\frac{13}{4}$ **g** $\frac{1}{8}$ **h** -11

7 a $b = 3, \ c = -4$ **b** $b = 2, \ c = -3$

8 $\dfrac{dy}{dx} = 4 + \dfrac{3}{x^2}, \ \dfrac{dy}{dx}$ is the gradient function of $y = 4x - \dfrac{3}{x}$
from which the gradient of the tangent at any point can be found.

9 a $\{x \mid x > 0\}$ **b** $f'(x) = \dfrac{1}{2\sqrt{x}} + \dfrac{2}{x\sqrt{x}}$
c $\{x \mid x > 0\}$
d $f'(1) = 2.5$ The gradient of the tangent to the curve
$f(x) = \sqrt{x} - \dfrac{4}{\sqrt{x}}$ at $x = 1$ is 2.5.

10 a $\dfrac{dS}{dt} = 4t + 4 \ \text{ms}^{-1}, \ \dfrac{dS}{dt}$ is the instantaneous rate of
change in the car's position at the time t.
b When $t = 3, \ \dfrac{dS}{dt} = 16 \ \text{ms}^{-1}$. This is the instantaneous
rate of change in position at the time $t = 3$ seconds.

11 When $x = 1000, \ \dfrac{dC}{dx} = 7$. When 1000 toasters per week are
being produced, the cost of production is increasing by £7 per
toaster.

EXERCISE 12B.1

1 a $g(f(x)) = (2x + 7)^2$ **b** $g(f(x)) = 2x^2 + 7$
c $g(f(x)) = \sqrt{3 - 4x}$ **d** $g(f(x)) = 3 - 4\sqrt{x}$
e $g(f(x)) = \dfrac{2}{x^2 + 3}$ **f** $g(f(x)) = \dfrac{4}{x^2} + 3$

2 Note: There may be other answers.
a $g(x) = x^3, \ f(x) = 3x + 10$
b $g(x) = x^5, \ f(x) = 7 - 2x$
c $g(x) = \dfrac{1}{x}, \ f(x) = 2x + 4$
d $g(x) = \sqrt{x}, \ f(x) = x^2 - 3x$
e $g(x) = \dfrac{1}{x^4}, \ f(x) = 5x - 1$
f $g(x) = \dfrac{10}{x^3}, \ f(x) = 3x - x^2$

EXERCISE 12B.2

1 a $u^{-2}, \ u = 2x - 1$ **b** $u^{\frac{1}{2}}, \ u = x^2 - 3x$
c $2u^{-\frac{1}{2}}, \ u = 2 - x^2$ **d** $u^{\frac{1}{3}}, \ u = x^3 - x^2$
e $4u^{-3}, \ u = 3 - x$ **f** $10u^{-1}, \ u = x^2 - 3$

2 a $\dfrac{dy}{dx} = 4(2x + 3) = 8x + 12$ **b** $\dfrac{dy}{dx} = 8x + 12$

3 a $\dfrac{dy}{dx} = 8(4x - 5)$ **b** $\dfrac{dy}{dx} = 2(5 - 2x)^{-2}$
c $\dfrac{dy}{dx} = \frac{1}{2}(3x - x^2)^{-\frac{1}{2}}(3 - 2x)$
d $\dfrac{dy}{dx} = -12(1 - 3x)^3$ **e** $\dfrac{dy}{dx} = -18(5 - x)^2$
f $\dfrac{dy}{dx} = \frac{1}{3}(2x^3 - x^2)^{-\frac{2}{3}}(6x^2 - 2x)$

g $\dfrac{dy}{dx} = -60(5x - 4)^{-3}$

h $\dfrac{dy}{dx} = 5(x^2 - 5x + 8)^4(2x - 5)$

i $\dfrac{dy}{dx} = 6\left(x^2 - \dfrac{2}{x}\right)^2\left(2x + \dfrac{2}{x^2}\right)$

4 a $-\frac{1}{\sqrt{3}}$ **b** -18 **c** -8 **d** -4 **e** $-\frac{3}{32}$ **f** 0

5 $a = 3, \ b = 1$ **6** $a = 2, \ b = 1$ **7** $a = 2, \ b = 3$

8 a $\dfrac{dy}{dx} = 3x^2, \ \dfrac{dx}{dy} = \frac{1}{3}y^{-\frac{2}{3}}$ **Hint:** Substitute $y = x^3$
b $\dfrac{dy}{dx} \times \dfrac{dx}{dy} = \dfrac{dy}{dy}$ {chain rule} $= 1$

EXERCISE 12C

1 a $f'(x) = 2x - 1$ **b** $f'(x) = 4x + 2$
c $f'(x) = 2x(x + 1)^{\frac{1}{2}} + \frac{1}{2}x^2(x + 1)^{-\frac{1}{2}}$
d $f'(x) = 2x + 2$
e $f'(x) = (x^2 - 1)^{\frac{1}{2}} + x^2(x^2 - 1)^{-\frac{1}{2}}$
f $f'(x) = (x + 1)^2 + 2x(x + 1)$

2 a $\dfrac{dy}{dx} = 2x(2x - 1) + 2x^2$
b $\dfrac{dy}{dx} = 4(2x + 1)^3 + 24x(2x + 1)^2$
c $\dfrac{dy}{dx} = 2x(3 - x)^{\frac{1}{2}} - \frac{1}{2}x^2(3 - x)^{-\frac{1}{2}}$
d $\dfrac{dy}{dx} = \frac{1}{2}x^{-\frac{1}{2}}(x - 3)^2 + 2\sqrt{x}(x - 3)$
e $\dfrac{dy}{dx} = 10x(3x^2 - 1)^2 + 60x^3(3x^2 - 1)$
f $\dfrac{dy}{dx} = \frac{1}{2}x^{-\frac{1}{2}}(x - x^2)^3 + 3\sqrt{x}(x - x^2)^2(1 - 2x)$

3 a -48 **b** $406\frac{1}{4}$ **c** $\frac{13}{3}$ **d** $\frac{11}{2}$

4 b $x = 3$ or $\frac{3}{5}$
c Domain of $\dfrac{dy}{dx}$ is $\{x \mid x > 0\}$. Domain of original function
is $\{x \mid x \geqslant 0\}$. $\dfrac{dy}{dx}$ is undefined when $x = 0$.

5 $x = -1$ and $x = -\frac{5}{3}$ **6** $x = 1$ and $x = -\frac{1}{3}$
7 a $x = \frac{2}{3}$ **b** $x = 0$ **8** $a = -\frac{7}{4}$ and $a = -\frac{20}{9}$

EXERCISE 12D

1 a $\dfrac{dy}{dx} = \dfrac{7}{(2 - x)^2}$ **b** $\dfrac{dy}{dx} = \dfrac{2x^2 + 2x}{(2x + 1)^2}$
c $\dfrac{dy}{dx} = \dfrac{-x^2 - 3}{(x^2 - 3)^2}$ **d** $\dfrac{dy}{dx} = \dfrac{2x + 1}{2\sqrt{x}(1 - 2x)^2}$
e $\dfrac{dy}{dx} = \dfrac{3x^2 - 6x + 9}{(3x - x^2)^2}$ **f** $\dfrac{dy}{dx} = \dfrac{2 - 3x}{2(1 - 3x)^{\frac{3}{2}}}$

2 a $\dfrac{4}{(3 - x)^2}$ **b** $\dfrac{-3x^2 - 3}{(x^2 - 1)^2}$
c $\dfrac{4x^3 - 3x^2}{(2x - 1)^2}$ **d** $\dfrac{2x - 20}{(x - 5)^{\frac{3}{2}}}$
e $\dfrac{3x^2 + 3}{2\sqrt{x}(3 - x^2)^2}$ **f** $\dfrac{-x^3 - 6x}{(x^2 + 3)^{\frac{3}{2}}}$

3 a 1 **b** 1 **c** $-\frac{7}{324}$ **d** $-\frac{28}{27}$

4 $f'(x) = \dfrac{x-2}{2(x-1)^{\frac{3}{2}}}$

5 a $\dfrac{dy}{dx} = -\dfrac{1}{(x+1)^2}$

b At $x = -2$, $\dfrac{dy}{dx} = -1$. At $x = 0$, $\dfrac{dy}{dx} = -1$.

So, the gradient of each tangent is -1

$\therefore$ the tangents are parallel.

6 b i never $\{\dfrac{dy}{dx}$ is undefined at $x = -1\}$

ii $x \leqslant 0$ and $x = 1$

7 b i $x = -3$ and $x = 2$ **ii** $x = -\frac{1}{2}$

8 b i $x = -2 \pm \sqrt{11}$ **ii** $x = -2$

EXERCISE 12E

1 a $f'(x) = 4e^{4x}$ **b** $f'(x) = e^x$ **c** $f'(x) = -2e^{-2x}$

d $f'(x) = \frac{1}{2}e^{\frac{x}{2}}$ **e** $f'(x) = -e^{-\frac{x}{2}}$ **f** $f'(x) = 2e^{-x}$

g $f'(x) = 2e^{\frac{x}{2}} + 3e^{-x}$ **h** $f'(x) = \dfrac{e^x - e^{-x}}{2}$

i $f'(x) = -2xe^{-x^2}$ **j** $f'(x) = -\dfrac{e^{\frac{1}{x}}}{x^2}$

k $f'(x) = 20e^{2x}$ **l** $f'(x) = 40e^{-2x}$

m $f'(x) = 2e^{2x+1}$ **n** $f'(x) = \frac{1}{4}e^{\frac{x}{4}}$

o $f'(x) = -4xe^{1-2x^2}$ **p** $f'(x) = -0.02e^{-0.02x}$

2 a $e^x + xe^x$ **b** $3x^2e^{-x} - x^3e^{-x}$ **c** $\dfrac{xe^x - e^x}{x^2}$

d $\dfrac{1-x}{e^x}$ **e** $2xe^{3x} + 3x^2e^{3x}$ **f** $\dfrac{xe^x - \frac{1}{2}e^x}{x\sqrt{x}}$

g $20e^{-0.5x} - 10xe^{-0.5x}$ **h** $\dfrac{e^x + 2 + 2e^{-x}}{(e^{-x}+1)^2}$

3 a $\dfrac{dy}{dx} = 4e^x(2+e^x)^3$ **b** $\dfrac{dy}{dx} = \dfrac{e^x}{2\sqrt{e^x - 1}}$

c $\dfrac{dy}{dx} = \frac{3}{2}(e^x + e^{-x})^{\frac{1}{2}}(e^x - e^{-x})$

d $\dfrac{dy}{dx} = -e^{2x}(e^{2x}+2)^{-\frac{3}{2}}$

4 a 108   **b** -1 **c** $\frac{9}{\sqrt{19}}$ **d** $-\dfrac{4}{e^3}$

5 a $\{x \mid x \leqslant \ln 6\}$ **b i** $P(\ln 2, 2)$ **ii** $-\frac{1}{2}$

6 $k = -9$

7 a $\dfrac{dy}{dx} = 2^x \ln 2$

c i $\dfrac{dy}{dx} = 5^x \ln 5$ **ii** $\dfrac{dy}{dx} = 8 \times 10^x \ln 10$

8 $P(0, 0)$ or $P(2, \dfrac{4}{e^2})$ **9 c** $S(x)$ **d** $\dfrac{1}{[C(x)]^2}$

EXERCISE 12F

1 a $\dfrac{dy}{dx} = \dfrac{1}{x}$ **b** $\dfrac{dy}{dx} = \dfrac{2}{2x+1}$ **c** $\dfrac{dy}{dx} = \dfrac{1-2x}{x-x^2}$

d $\dfrac{dy}{dx} = -\dfrac{2}{x}$ **e** $\dfrac{dy}{dx} = 2x \ln x + x$ **f** $\dfrac{dy}{dx} = \dfrac{1 - \ln x}{2x^2}$

g $\dfrac{dy}{dx} = e^x \ln x + \dfrac{e^x}{x}$ **h** $\dfrac{dy}{dx} = \dfrac{2 \ln x}{x}$

i $\dfrac{dy}{dx} = \dfrac{1}{2x\sqrt{\ln x}}$ **j** $\dfrac{dy}{dx} = \dfrac{e^{-x}}{x} - e^{-x} \ln x$

k $\dfrac{dy}{dx} = \dfrac{\ln(2x)}{2\sqrt{x}} + \dfrac{1}{\sqrt{x}}$ **l** $\dfrac{dy}{dx} = \dfrac{\ln x - 2}{\sqrt{x}(\ln x)^2}$

m $\dfrac{dy}{dx} = \dfrac{4}{1-x}$ **n** $\dfrac{dy}{dx} = \ln(x^2 + 1) + \dfrac{2x^2}{x^2 + 1}$

o $\dfrac{dy}{dx} = \dfrac{1 - 2\ln x}{x^3}$

2 $f'(x) = \dfrac{1}{x}$, since $\ln(kx) = \ln k + \ln x$ and $\ln k$ is a constant.

3 a $\dfrac{dy}{dx} = \ln 5$ **b** $\dfrac{dy}{dx} = \dfrac{3}{x}$ **c** $\dfrac{dy}{dx} = \dfrac{4x^3 + 1}{x^4 + x}$

d $\dfrac{dy}{dx} = \dfrac{1}{x-2}$ **e** $\dfrac{dy}{dx} = \dfrac{6}{2x+1}[\ln(2x+1)]^2$

f $\dfrac{dy}{dx} = \dfrac{1 - \ln(4x)}{x^2}$ **g** $\dfrac{dy}{dx} = -\dfrac{1}{x}$

h $\dfrac{dy}{dx} = \dfrac{1}{x \ln x}$ **i** $\dfrac{dy}{dx} = \dfrac{-1}{x(\ln x)^2}$

4 a $\dfrac{dy}{dx} = \dfrac{1}{2x-1}$ **b** $\dfrac{dy}{dx} = \dfrac{-2}{2x+3}$

c $\dfrac{dy}{dx} = 1 + \dfrac{1}{2x}$ **d** $\dfrac{dy}{dx} = \dfrac{1}{x} - \dfrac{1}{2(2-x)}$

e $\dfrac{dy}{dx} = \dfrac{1}{x+3} - \dfrac{1}{x-1}$ **f** $\dfrac{dy}{dx} = \dfrac{2}{x} + \dfrac{1}{3-x}$

5 a $f'(x) = \dfrac{9}{3x-4}$ **b** $f'(x) = \dfrac{1}{x} + \dfrac{2x}{x^2+1}$

c $f'(x) = \dfrac{2x+2}{x^2+2x} - \dfrac{1}{x-5}$

d $f'(x) = \dfrac{3}{x} - \dfrac{1}{x+4} - \dfrac{1}{x-1}$

6 2   **7** $a = 3$, $b = \dfrac{1}{e}$ **8** $a = 4$, $b = e^3$ **9** $(-3, \ln 6)$

EXERCISE 12G

1 a $\dfrac{dy}{dx} = 2 \cos 2x$ **b** $\dfrac{dy}{dx} = \cos x - \sin x$

c $\dfrac{dy}{dx} = -3 \sin 3x - \cos x$ **d** $\dfrac{dy}{dx} = \cos(x+1)$

e $\dfrac{dy}{dx} = 2 \sin(3 - 2x)$ **f** $\dfrac{dy}{dx} = 6 \sin 3x$

g $\dfrac{dy}{dx} = \frac{1}{2} \cos \frac{x}{2} + 3 \sin x$ **h** $\dfrac{dy}{dx} = 4 \cos x + 2 \sin 2x$

i $\dfrac{dy}{dx} = -3 \sin 6x - 20 \cos 4x$

2 a $2x - \sin x$ **b** $e^x \cos x - e^x \sin x$

c $-e^{-x} \sin x + e^{-x} \cos x$ **d** $\dfrac{\cos x}{\sin x}$

e $-5 \sin 5x \times e^{\cos 5x}$ **f** $-\frac{1}{2} \sin \frac{x}{2}$

g $\cos x - x \sin x$ **h** $\dfrac{x \cos x - \sin x}{x^2}$

3 a $2x \cos(x^2)$ **b** $-\dfrac{1}{2\sqrt{x}} \sin(\sqrt{x})$ **c** $-\dfrac{\sin x}{2\sqrt{\cos x}}$

d $2 \sin x \cos x$ **e** $-3 \sin x \cos^2 x$

f $-\sin x \sin 2x + 2\cos x \cos 2x$

g $-12\sin 4x \cos^2 4x$ **h** $-\dfrac{8\cos 2x}{\sin^3 2x}$

4 **a** $\dfrac{1}{\cos^2 x}$

b **i** $\dfrac{dy}{dx} = \dfrac{5}{\cos^2 5x}$ **ii** $\dfrac{dy}{dx} = \dfrac{1}{\cos^2 x} - 3\cos x$

iii $\dfrac{dy}{dx} = 2e^{2x}\tan x + \dfrac{e^{2x}}{\cos^2 x}$ **iv** $\dfrac{dy}{dx} = \tan x + \dfrac{x}{\cos^2 x}$

5 **a** $-\frac{9}{8}$ **b** 0

6 **a** $f'(x) = 0$ **b** $f(x) = 2(\cos^2 x + \sin^2 x) + 1$
$$= 2(1) + 1$$
$$= 3, \text{ a constant}$$

7 **a** tangent **B**

b $\dfrac{dy}{dx} = -\sin x + 4\cos 2x$

When $x = \frac{\pi}{6}$, $\dfrac{dy}{dx} = \frac{3}{2}$

When $x = \frac{7\pi}{6}$, $\dfrac{dy}{dx} = \frac{5}{2}$ which is $> \frac{3}{2}$ ✓

EXERCISE 12H

1 **a** $f''(x) = 6$ **b** $f''(x) = \dfrac{3}{2x^2\sqrt{x}}$

c $f''(x) = 12x - 6$ **d** $f''(x) = \dfrac{12 - 6x}{x^4}$

e $f''(x) = 8$ **f** $f''(x) = \dfrac{20}{(2x-1)^3}$

2 **a** $\dfrac{d^2y}{dx^2} = -6x$ **b** $\dfrac{d^2y}{dx^2} = 2 - \dfrac{30}{x^4}$

c $\dfrac{d^2y}{dx^2} = -\dfrac{9}{4x^2\sqrt{x}}$ **d** $\dfrac{d^2y}{dx^2} = \dfrac{8}{x^3}$

e $\dfrac{d^2y}{dx^2} = 12x^2 - 36x + 18$

f $\dfrac{d^2y}{dx^2} = 2 + \dfrac{2}{(1-x)^3}$ **g** $\dfrac{d^2y}{dx^2} = 9e^{3x}$

h $\dfrac{d^2y}{dx^2} = \dfrac{-x^2e^{-x} - 2xe^{-x} + 2 - 2e^{-x}}{x^3}$

i $\dfrac{d^2y}{dx^2} = -\dfrac{x^3 - 3x^2 - 6x - 6}{x^3 e^x}$

3 **a** $f(2) = 9$ **b** $f'(2) = 10$ **c** $f''(2) = 12$

4 **a** $x = 1$ **b** $x = 2$ or $x = 3$

5

x	-1	0	1
$f(x)$	$-$	0	$+$
$f'(x)$	$+$	$-$	$+$
$f''(x)$	$-$	0	$+$

6 **a** $f(1) = 0$ **b** $f'(1) = 3$ **c** $f''(1) = 0$

7 **a** $f(1) = 3e - 2$ **b** $f'(1) = 3e - 2$ **c** $f''(1) = 3e$

8 **a** $\dfrac{d^2y}{dx^2} = 2\cos x - x\sin x$

b $\dfrac{d^2y}{dx^2} = \dfrac{6\cos^2 x}{x^4} + \dfrac{4\sin 2x - 2}{x^3} - \dfrac{2\cos 2x}{x^2}$

c $\dfrac{d^2y}{dx^2} = -2e^{-x}\cos x$

10 **b** $f''(x) = 3\sin x \cos 2x + 6\cos x \sin 2x$ **11** $-3\sqrt{3}$

12 **a** $\dfrac{d^2y}{dx^2} = \dfrac{1}{x^2}$ **b** $\dfrac{d^2y}{dx^2} = \dfrac{1}{x}$ **c** $\dfrac{d^2y}{dx^2} = \dfrac{2}{x^2}(1 - \ln x)$

REVIEW SET 12A

1 **a** $f'(x) = 15x^2$ **b** $f'(x) = 6x^5 - 5$

c $f'(x) = 14x + \dfrac{3}{x^2}$ **d** $f'(x) = 3 + \dfrac{8}{x^3}$

e $f'(x) = 3\sqrt{x}$ **f** $f'(x) = \dfrac{2}{\sqrt{x}} + \dfrac{1}{2x\sqrt{x}}$

2 **a** $\dfrac{dy}{dx} = 6x - 4x^3$ **b** $\dfrac{dy}{dx} = 1 + \dfrac{1}{x^2}$

c $\dfrac{dy}{dx} = 2x\sqrt{x-2} + \dfrac{x^2}{2\sqrt{x-2}}$

3 **a** $f'(x) = (x^2 + 1)^{-\frac{3}{2}}$ **b** $(0, 0)$

4 **a** $\dfrac{dy}{dx} = 3x^2 e^{x^3 + 2}$ **b** $\dfrac{dy}{dx} = \dfrac{1}{x+3} - \dfrac{2}{x}$

c $\dfrac{dy}{dx} = 3x^2 e^{2x} + 2x^3 e^{2x}$

5 **a** 10 **b** -15

6 **a** $5 + 3x^{-2}$ **b** $4(3x^2 + x^{\frac{1}{2}})^3(6x + \frac{1}{2}x^{-\frac{1}{2}})$

c $2x(1 - x^2)^3 - 6x(x^2 + 1)(1 - x^2)^2$

7 $(-2, 19)$ and $(1, -2)$

8 **a** $(5\cos 5x)\ln x + \dfrac{\sin 5x}{x}$ **b** $\cos x \cos 2x - 2\sin x \sin 2x$

c $-e^{-x}\cos x - e^{-x}\sin x$

9 $\dfrac{\sqrt{3}}{2}$

11 **a** $f'(x) = \dfrac{-x^2 + 6x - 3}{e^x}$ **b** $\dfrac{2}{e}$ **c** $x = 3 \pm \sqrt{6}$

12 **a** $f'(x) = 8x(x^2 + 3)^3$

b $g'(x) = \dfrac{\frac{1}{2}x(x+5)^{-\frac{1}{2}} - 2(x+5)^{\frac{1}{2}}}{x^3}$

c $h'(x) = \dfrac{6e^{4x} - 8xe^{4x}}{(1 - 2x)^2}$

13 **a** $\dfrac{dy}{dx} = \cos^2 x - \sin^2 x$

b **Hint:** $\cos 2x = \cos^2 x - \sin^2 x$ **c** $-\frac{1}{2}$

14 **a** $f(\frac{\pi}{2}) = 1$ **b** $f'(\frac{\pi}{2}) = 0$ **c** $f''(\frac{\pi}{2}) = 2$

15 **a** $\dfrac{d^2y}{dx^2} = \frac{3}{2}x^2 + x - \frac{1}{2}$ **b** $\dfrac{d^2y}{dx^2} = -2e^{-x} + xe^{-x}$

16 **a** $f'(x) = \dfrac{1}{2\sqrt{x}}\cos 4x - 4\sqrt{x}\sin 4x$,

$f''(x) = -\dfrac{1}{4x\sqrt{x}}\cos 4x - \dfrac{4}{\sqrt{x}}\sin 4x - 16\sqrt{x}\cos 4x$

b **i** $\frac{1}{\sqrt{2}}\left(\frac{2}{\sqrt{\pi}} - \sqrt{\pi}\right)$ **ii** $-\frac{8\sqrt{2}}{\sqrt{\pi}}$

17 **a**

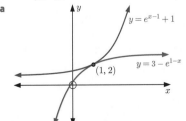

b $(1, 2)$

c The gradient is $e^0 = 1$ for both. The tangents to each of the curves at this point are the same line.

REVIEW SET 12B

1 **a** $f'(x) = 6x - 7$ **b** $f'(x) = 2x + 10$

c $f'(x) = \dfrac{1}{\sqrt{x}} + \dfrac{3}{x^2}$ **d** $f'(x) = 15x\sqrt{x}$

2 **a** $\dfrac{dy}{dx} = 6x^2 - 12x + 7$ **b** $\dfrac{dy}{dx} = -\dfrac{3}{x^2} + \dfrac{15}{x^4}$

c $\dfrac{dy}{dx} = -\dfrac{5}{x^{\frac{4}{3}}}$

3 **a** $f(3) = -17$ **b** $f'(3) = -17$ **c** $f''(3) = -6$

4 **a** $\dfrac{dy}{dx} = 3x^2(1 - x^2)^{\frac{1}{2}} - x^4(1 - x^2)^{-\frac{1}{2}}$

b $\dfrac{dy}{dx} = \dfrac{(2x - 3)(x + 1)^{\frac{1}{2}} - \frac{1}{2}(x^2 - 3x)(x + 1)^{-\frac{1}{2}}}{x + 1}$

5 **a** $\dfrac{dy}{dx} = e^x + xe^x$ **b** $(1, e)$

6 **a** $f'(x) = \dfrac{e^x}{e^x + 3}$ **b** $f'(x) = \dfrac{3}{x + 2} - \dfrac{1}{x}$

7 **a** $f'(x) = 1 - \dfrac{2}{x^2}$ **b** **i** -1 **ii** $\frac{1}{2}$

c

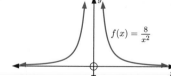

(graph showing $f(x)$, with labels: 3, gradient $= -1$, -3, 3, x, gradient $= \frac{1}{2}$, -3, $f(x) = \dfrac{x^2 + 2}{x}$)

8 when $x = 1$, $\dfrac{dy}{dx} = 0$

9 **a** $\dfrac{dy}{dx} = \dfrac{3x^2 - 3}{x^3 - 3x}$ **b** $\dfrac{dy}{dx} = \dfrac{e^x(x - 2)}{x^3}$

c $\dfrac{dy}{dx} = 2e^{2x} \sin x + e^{2x} \cos x$

10 **a** $f''(x) = 24x^2 - 24x - 18$ **b** $x = -\frac{1}{2}$ or $\frac{3}{2}$

11 **a** $10 - 10 \cos 10x$ **b** $\tan x$

c $(5 \cos 5x) \ln(2x) + \dfrac{\sin 5x}{x}$

12 $\frac{28}{9}$ **13** $a = 4$, $b = e^2$

14 **a** $-\frac{1}{4}$ **b** **Hint:** Show that $\dfrac{dy}{dx} = -\dfrac{2 \sin x + 1}{(\sin x + 2)^2}$.

15 **b** **i** $x = \frac{1}{2}$ **ii** $x \leqslant 0$

16 **a** $\dfrac{d^2y}{dx^2} = -\dfrac{10}{(1 - 2x)^3}$ **b** $\dfrac{d^2y}{dx^2} = 6x + \frac{3}{4}x^{-\frac{5}{2}}$

18 **a** $x = -6 \pm \sqrt{33}$ **b** $x = \pm\sqrt{3}$ **c** $x = -3$, 0, or 3

EXERCISE 13A

1 **a** $f'(x) = 2x - 4$ **b** $y = -2x - 1$

2 **a** $y = -7x + 11$ **b** $y = \frac{1}{4}x + 2$ **c** $y = -2x - 2$

d $y = -2x + 6$ **e** $y = -5x - 9$ **f** $y = -5x - 1$

3 **a** $y = 21$ and $y = -6$ **b** $y = 23$ and $y = -9$

c $y = 2$

4 **a** $k = -5$ **b** $y = 4x - 15$ **5** $y = -3x + 1$

6 $a = -4$, $b = 7$ **7** $a = 2$, $b = \frac{1}{2}$

9 **a** $f'(x) = 2x - \dfrac{8}{x^3}$ **b** $x = \pm\sqrt{2}$

c When $x = \sqrt{2}$, $y = 4$ and when $x = -\sqrt{2}$, $y = 4$.
$\therefore$ tangents are $y = 4$.

10 $a = 4$, $b = 3$

11 **a** $y = -e^{-2}x + 3e^{-2}$ **b** $y = -\frac{1}{3}x - \frac{1}{3} + \ln 3$

c $y = 4ex - e$ **d** $y = \dfrac{e^2}{2}x - \dfrac{3}{2}$ **e** $y = 3ex - 5e$

12 **a** Domain is $\{x \mid x < 0$ or $x > 2\}$

b $f'(x) = \dfrac{1}{x} + \dfrac{1}{x - 2}$ **c** $y = \frac{4}{3}x - 4 + \ln 3$

13 x-intercept $\frac{2}{3}$, y-intercept $-2e$ **14** $\dfrac{3}{4\sqrt{e}}$ units^2

15 **a** $y = x$ **b** $y = -\frac{1}{2}x + \frac{\pi}{12} + \frac{\sqrt{3}}{2}$ **c** $y = 1$ **d** $y = 2$

16 **Hint:** Show that there are no tangents which have gradient $= 0$.

17 $(-4, -64)$ **18** $(4, -31)$ **19** $(-1, -2)$

20 **a** $y = (2a - 1)x - a^2 + 9$

b $y = 5x$, point of contact $(3, 15)$, and
$y = -7x$, point of contact $(-3, 21)$

21 **a** $y = (2a + 4)x - a^2$

b $y = 12x - 16$, point of contact $(4, 32)$, and
$y = -4$, point of contact $(-2, -4)$

22 $y = 5x - 15$ and $y = -7x - 3$

23 **a** $y = e^a x + e^a(1 - a)$ **b** $y = ex$

24 **a** $y = -4x - 2$ and $y = 12x - 18$

b $(-1, 2)$ for $y = -4x - 2$ and
$(3, 18)$ for $y = 12x - 18$

c For a tangent to pass through $(1, 4)$, $4 = 4a - 2a^2$ must have real solutions. But $\Delta < 0$, so no real solutions.

d

(graph with labels: $y = 2x^2$, y, 24, 16, $(3, 18)$, 8, $y = 12x - 18$, $(-1, 2)$, -3, 3, 6, x, -8, $y = -4x - 2$)

25 **a**

(graph with labels: y, $f(x) = \dfrac{8}{x^2}$, x)

b $16x + a^3 y = 24a$ **c** A is $\left(\frac{3}{2}a, 0\right)$, B is $\left(0, \dfrac{24}{a^2}\right)$

d area $= \dfrac{18}{|a|}$ units^2; as $a \to \infty$, area $\to 0$

26 $\approx 63.43°$

27 **a** **Hint:** They must have the same y-coordinate at $x = b$ and the same gradient.

c $a = \frac{1}{2e}$ **d** $y = e^{-\frac{1}{2}}x - \frac{1}{2}$

28 **a** $y = 2asx - as^2$, $y = 2atx - at^2$

EXERCISE 13B

1 **a** $x + 8y = 132$ **b** $x + 7y = 26$ **c** $x - 3y = -11$
   d $x + 6y = 43$ **e** $64x + 4y = -65$ **f** $x = 2$

2 **a** $y = 4 - 2x$ **b** $y = -\frac{9}{62}x + \frac{1259}{186}$

3 **a** $y = x + 1$ **b** $ex + y = e^2 + 1$
   c $x + 2ey = 1 + 2e^2$ **d** $2x + y = \frac{2\pi}{3} + \frac{\sqrt{3}}{2}$

4 $a = 2$, $b = 4$ **5** $(-1, -2)$ and $(2, 1)$
6 $x = 0$ **7** $y = -\sqrt{14}x + 4\sqrt{14}$

EXERCISE 13C

1 **a** **i** $x \geqslant 0$ **ii** never   **b** **i** never   **ii** $-2 < x \leqslant 3$
   c **i** $x \leqslant 2$ **ii** $x \geqslant 2$ **d** **i** $x \in \mathbb{R}$ **ii** never
   e **i** $1 \leqslant x \leqslant 5$ **ii** $x \leqslant 1$, $x \geqslant 5$
   f **i** $2 \leqslant x < 4$, $x > 4$ **ii** $x < 0$, $0 < x \leqslant 2$

2 **a** **i** $x \leqslant 1$, $x \geqslant 3$ **ii** $1 \leqslant x \leqslant 3$

b $f'(x) = 3x^2 - 12x + 9$
$= 3(x - 3)(x - 1)$

3 **a** $f'(x) = 3x^2 - 12x$
$= 3x(x - 4)$

b increasing for $x \leqslant 0$ and $x \geqslant 4$
decreasing for $0 \leqslant x \leqslant 4$

4 **a** increasing for $x \geqslant 0$, decreasing for $x \leqslant 0$
   b decreasing for all $x \in \mathbb{R}$
   c increasing for $x \geqslant -\frac{3}{4}$, decreasing for $x \leqslant -\frac{3}{4}$
   d decreasing for all $x \neq 0$ **e** decreasing for all $x > 0$
   f increasing for $x \leqslant 0$ and $x \geqslant 4$,
   decreasing for $0 \leqslant x \leqslant 4$
   g increasing for $-\sqrt{\frac{2}{3}} \leqslant x \leqslant \sqrt{\frac{2}{3}}$,
   decreasing for $x \leqslant -\sqrt{\frac{2}{3}}$, $x \geqslant \sqrt{\frac{2}{3}}$
   h increasing for $-\frac{1}{2} \leqslant x \leqslant 3$,
   decreasing for $x \leqslant -\frac{1}{2}$, $x \geqslant 3$
   i increasing for $x \geqslant 0$, decreasing for $x \leqslant 0$
   j increasing for $x \leqslant 2 - \sqrt{3}$, $x \geqslant 2 + \sqrt{3}$,
   decreasing for $2 - \sqrt{3} \leqslant x \leqslant 2 + \sqrt{3}$

5 **a** $f'(x) = 3x^2 - 6x + 5$
   b $\Delta = 36 - 60 < 0$ and $a > 0$
   $\therefore$ $f'(x)$ lies entirely above x-axis.
   $\therefore$ $f'(x) > 0$ for all x.
   $\therefore$ $f(x)$ is increasing for all x.

c
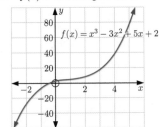

6 **a**

b increasing for $x \leqslant -3$ and $x \geqslant 3$,
decreasing for $-3 \leqslant x < 0$ and $0 < x \leqslant 3$

7 **a**

b increasing for $-1 \leqslant x \leqslant 1$,
decreasing for $x \leqslant -1$ and $x \geqslant 1$

8 **a**

b increasing for $-1 \leqslant x < 1$,
decreasing for $x \leqslant -1$ and $x > 1$

9 **a**

b increasing for $-1 \leqslant x < 1$ and $1 < x \leqslant 3$,
decreasing for $x \leqslant -1$ and $x \geqslant 3$

10 In this case, $f(x)$ is only defined when $x > 0$.
   $\therefore$ $f'(x)$ is only defined when $x > 0$.

11 **a** increasing for all $x \in \mathbb{R}$, never decreasing
   b increasing for $x > -2$, never decreasing
   c never increasing, decreasing for all $x \in \mathbb{R}$
   d increasing for $x \geqslant -1$, decreasing for $x \leqslant -1$
   e increasing for $x \geqslant 1$, decreasing for $0 < x \leqslant 1$
   f increasing for $x \geqslant e^{-\frac{1}{3}}$, decreasing for $0 < x \leqslant e^{-\frac{1}{3}}$
   g increasing for $x \leqslant -\sqrt{3}$ and $x \geqslant \sqrt{3}$,
   decreasing for $-\sqrt{3} \leqslant x < -1$ and $-1 < x < 1$ and
   $1 < x \leqslant \sqrt{3}$
   h increasing for $x \leqslant 0$, decreasing for $x \geqslant 0$
   i increasing for $x \geqslant 0$, decreasing for $x \leqslant 0$
   j increasing for $x \geqslant 2$,
   decreasing for $x < 1$ and $1 < x \leqslant 2$
   k increasing for $x \geqslant 0$, decreasing for $x \leqslant 0$
   l increasing for $x \leqslant -1$,
   decreasing for $-1 \leqslant x < 0$ and $x > 0$

EXERCISE 13D

1 **a** A - local max, O - stationary inflection, B - local min.
   b

c **i** $x \leqslant -2$ and $x \geqslant 3$ **ii** $-2 \leqslant x \leqslant 3$
   d

2 **a** P is a local maximum, Q is a local minimum.
   b $f'(x) = 3x^2 + 12x - 15 = 3(x + 5)(x - 1)$
   c P$(-5, 60)$, Q$(1, -48)$

3 **a** $f'(x) = x^2 - 9$
   $= (x + 3)(x - 3)$

b increasing for $x \leqslant -3$ and $x \geqslant 3$,
decreasing for $-3 \leqslant x \leqslant 3$
   c $(-3, 22)$ is a local maximum, $(3, -14)$ is a local minimum
   d As $x \to \infty$, $f(x) \to \infty$, as $x \to -\infty$, $f(x) \to -\infty$.

e
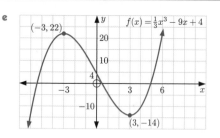

4 **a** $g'(x) = -6x^2 + 12x + 18 = -6(x - 3)(x + 1)$

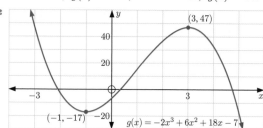

b increasing for $-1 \leqslant x \leqslant 3$,
decreasing for $x \leqslant -1$ and $x \geqslant 3$

c $(3, 47)$ is a local maximum, $(-1, -17)$ is a local minimum

d As $x \to \infty$, $g(x) \to -\infty$, as $x \to -\infty$, $g(x) \to \infty$.

e
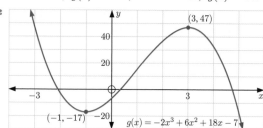

5 **a**
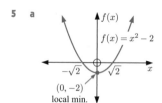

b
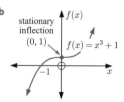

c
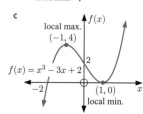

d
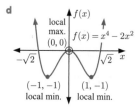

e
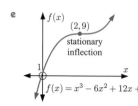

f
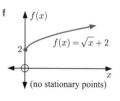

g
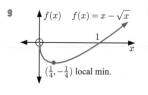

h
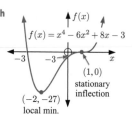

i
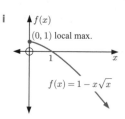

j
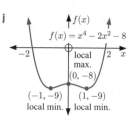

6 **a** $x = -\dfrac{b}{2a}$　**b** local min. if $a > 0$, local max. if $a < 0$

7 **a** $\left(1, \dfrac{1}{e}\right)$ is a local maximum

b $\left(-2, \dfrac{4}{e^2}\right)$ is a local maximum, $(0, 0)$ is a local minimum

c $(1, e)$ is a local minimum　**d** $(-1, e)$ is a local maximum

8 **a** $a = 9$　**b** $(-4, 113)$

9 **a** $a = -12$, $b = -13$

b $(-2, 3)$ is a local maximum, $(2, -29)$ is a local minimum

10 **a** $a = 3$, $b = 6$　**b** local minimum　**11** **a** $x > 0$

12 **a** $\left(\dfrac{\pi}{2}, 1\right)$ is a local maximum, $\left(\dfrac{3\pi}{2}, -1\right)$ is a local minimum

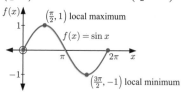

b $(0, 1)$, $(\pi, 1)$, and $(2\pi, 1)$ are local maxima,
$\left(\dfrac{\pi}{2}, -1\right)$ and $\left(\dfrac{3\pi}{2}, -1\right)$ are local minima

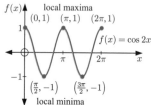

c $(0, 0)$, $(\pi, 0)$, and $(2\pi, 0)$ are local minima,
$\left(\dfrac{\pi}{2}, 1\right)$ and $\left(\dfrac{3\pi}{2}, 1\right)$ are local maxima

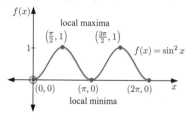

d $\left(\dfrac{\pi}{2}, e\right)$ is a local maximum, $\left(\dfrac{3\pi}{2}, \dfrac{1}{e}\right)$ is a local minimum

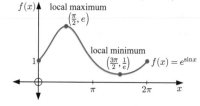

e $\left(\frac{3\pi}{4}, -\sqrt{2}\right)$ is a local minimum,

$\left(\frac{7\pi}{4}, \sqrt{2}\right)$ is a local maximum

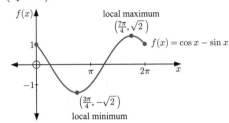

f $\left(\frac{\pi}{6}, \frac{3\sqrt{3}}{2}\right)$ is a local maximum,

$\left(\frac{5\pi}{6}, -\frac{3\sqrt{3}}{2}\right)$ is a local minimum,

$\left(\frac{3\pi}{2}, 0\right)$ is a stationary inflection

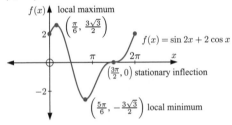

13 $P(x) = -9x^3 - 9x^2 + 9x + 2$

14 a greatest value is 63 when $x = 5$,
least value is -18 when $x = 2$

b greatest value is 4 when $x = 3$ and $x = 0$,
least value is -16 when $x = -2$

c greatest value is 20 when $x = 4$,
least value is 12 when $x = 2$

d greatest value is 0 when $x = 0$,
least value is -4 when $x = 4$

16 a $f'(x) = 6\cos^3 x - 5\cos x$

c local max. at $(0.421, 0.272)$, $(2.72, 0.272)$,
local min. at $\left(\frac{\pi}{2}, -1\right)$

d

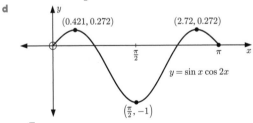

17 $a = \frac{\sqrt{e}}{2}$, $b = -\frac{1}{8}$

18 Hint: Show that $\frac{\ln x}{x}$ has only one stationary point, which is
a local maximum.

19 Hint: Show that $f(x) \geqslant 1$ for all $x > 0$.

EXERCISE 13E

1 a

Point	$f(x)$	$f'(x)$	$f''(x)$
A	+	−	+
B	−	0	+
C	+	+	0
D	+	0	−
E	0	−	−

b B is a local minimum, D is a local maximum

c C

2 a $f'(x) = 3x^2 + 6x - 5$
$f''(x) = 6x + 6$

b

c i $x \geqslant -1$ **ii** $x \leqslant -1$

3 a concave up   **b** concave down   **c** concave down

d concave up

4 a i $x \geqslant 0$ **ii** $x \leqslant 0$ **iii** $x \in \mathbb{R}$ **iv** never

b i never   **ii** $x \in \mathbb{R}$ **iii** $x \leqslant 0$ **iv** $x \geqslant 0$

c i $x \in \mathbb{R}$ **ii** never   **iii** $x \in \mathbb{R}$ **iv** never

d i $x > 0$ **ii** never   **iii** never   **iv** $x > 0$

e i $x > 0$ **ii** never   **iii** never   **iv** $x > 0$

f i $-\sqrt{6} \leqslant x \leqslant 0$ and $x \geqslant \sqrt{6}$

   ii $x \leqslant -\sqrt{6}$ and $0 \leqslant x \leqslant \sqrt{6}$

   iii $x \leqslant -\sqrt{2}$ and $x \geqslant \sqrt{2}$ **iv** $-\sqrt{2} \leqslant x \leqslant \sqrt{2}$

5 a x-intercept is $\frac{e^3 + 1}{2} \approx 10.5$

b no, $\therefore$ there is no y-intercept

c Domain is $\{x \mid x > \frac{1}{2}\}$ **d** gradient $= 2$

e $f''(x) = \frac{-4}{(2x - 1)^2} < 0$ for all $x > \frac{1}{2}$, so $f(x)$ is
concave down.

f

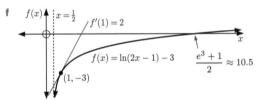

6 a $x > 0$

b $f'(x) = \frac{1}{x}$

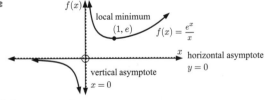

$f(x)$ is increasing for $x > 0$.

$f''(x) = -\frac{1}{x^2}$

$f(x)$ is concave down for $x > 0$.

c $ex + y = e^2 + 1$

7 a $f(x)$ does not have any x or y-intercepts.

b as $x \to \infty$, $f(x) \to \infty$, as $x \to -\infty$, $f(x) \to 0^-$

c local minimum at $(1, e)$ **d i** $x > 0$ **ii** $x < 0$

e

local minimum
$(1, e)$
$f(x) = \frac{e^x}{x}$
horizontal asymptote $y = 0$
vertical asymptote $x = 0$

f $2x + ey = -3$

EXERCISE 13F

1 a

Point	$f(x)$	$f'(x)$	$f''(x)$
A	0	−	+
B	−	0	+
C	0	+	0
D	+	0	0

b B is a local minimum.

c C is a non-stationary inflection point,
   D is a stationary inflection point.

2 a no points of inflection   **b** stationary inflection at $(0, 2)$

c non-stationary inflection at $(2, 3)$

d stationary inflection at $(0, 2)$

   non-stationary inflection at $\left(-1\frac{1}{3}, 11\frac{13}{27}\right)$

e no points of inflection

f stationary inflection at $(-2, -3)$

g non-stationary inflection at $(1, 9)$

h non-stationary inflections at $(-1, 5)$ and $(1, 5)$

3 a i local minimum at $\left(\frac{5}{2}, -\frac{9}{4}\right)$

   ii no points of inflection

   iii increasing for $x \geqslant \frac{5}{2}$, decreasing for $x \leqslant \frac{5}{2}$

   iv concave up for all $x \in \mathbb{R}$

   v

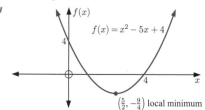

b i local maximum at $\left(-\frac{8}{3}, \frac{256}{27}\right)$,

   local minimum at $(0, 0)$

   ii non-stationary inflection at $\left(-\frac{4}{3}, \frac{128}{27}\right)$

   iii increasing for $x \leqslant -\frac{8}{3}$ and $x \geqslant 0$,

   decreasing for $-\frac{8}{3} \leqslant x \leqslant 0$

   iv concave up for $x \geqslant -\frac{4}{3}$, concave down for $x \leqslant -\frac{4}{3}$

   v

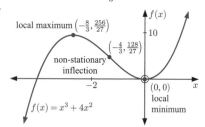

c i no turning points   **ii** no points of inflection

   iii increasing for $x > 0$, never decreasing

   iv concave down for $x > 0$, never concave up

   v

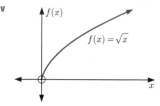

d i local maximum at $(-2, 29)$

   local minimum at $(4, -79)$

   ii non-stationary inflection at $(1, -25)$

   iii increasing for $x \leqslant -2$ and $x \geqslant 4$

   decreasing for $-2 \leqslant x \leqslant 4$

   iv concave down for $x \leqslant 1$, concave up for $x \geqslant 1$

   v

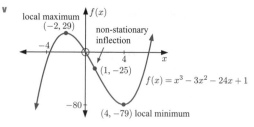

e i local minimum at $(-1, -3)$

   ii non-stationary inflection at $\left(-\frac{2}{3}, -2\frac{16}{27}\right)$

   stationary inflection at $(0, -2)$

   iii increasing for $x \geqslant -1$, decreasing for $x \leqslant -1$

   iv concave down for $-\frac{2}{3} \leqslant x \leqslant 0$

   concave up for $x \leqslant -\frac{2}{3}$ and $x \geqslant 0$

   v

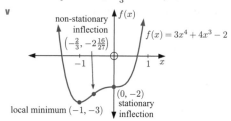

f i local minimum at $(1, 0)$

   ii no points of inflection

   iii increasing for $x \geqslant 1$, decreasing for $x \leqslant 1$

   iv concave up for all $x \in \mathbb{R}$

   v

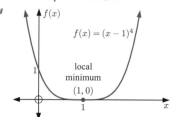

g i local minima at $(-\sqrt{2}, -1)$ and $(\sqrt{2}, -1)$,

   local maximum at $(0, 3)$

   ii non-stationary inflections at $\left(\sqrt{\frac{2}{3}}, \frac{7}{9}\right)$ and

   $\left(-\sqrt{\frac{2}{3}}, \frac{7}{9}\right)$

   iii increasing for $-\sqrt{2} \leqslant x \leqslant 0$ and $x \geqslant \sqrt{2}$

   decreasing for $x \leqslant -\sqrt{2}$ and $0 \leqslant x \leqslant \sqrt{2}$

   iv concave down for $-\sqrt{\frac{2}{3}} \leqslant x \leqslant \sqrt{\frac{2}{3}}$

   concave up for $x \leqslant -\sqrt{\frac{2}{3}}$ and $x \geqslant \sqrt{\frac{2}{3}}$

   v

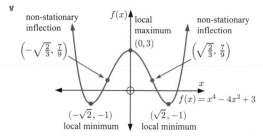

h **i** no turning points   **ii** no points of inflection
   iii increasing for $x > 0$,   never decreasing
   iv concave down for $x > 0$,   never concave up

v

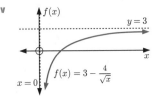

$x = 0$ $f(x) = 3 - \dfrac{4}{\sqrt{x}}$

4 **a** x-intercept $\ln \sqrt{3}$, y-intercept -2
   b $f'(x) = 2e^{2x} > 0$ for all $x \in \mathbb{R}$
   c $f''(x) = 4e^{2x} > 0$ for all $x \in \mathbb{R}$
   d as $x \to -\infty$, $e^{2x} \to 0^+$ $\therefore$ $e^{2x} - 3 \to -3^+$
   e

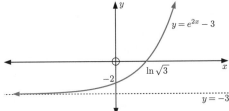

5 **a** $f(x)$: x-intercept $\ln 3$, y-intercept -2
   $g(x)$: x-intercept $\ln\left(\frac{5}{3}\right)$, y-intercept -2
   b $f(x)$: as $x \to \infty$, $f(x) \to \infty$
       as $x \to -\infty$, $f(x) \to -3^+$
     $g(x)$: as $x \to \infty$, $g(x) \to 3^-$
       as $x \to -\infty$, $g(x) \to -\infty$
   c

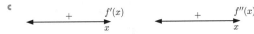

$f(x)$ is increasing and concave up for all $x \in \mathbb{R}$.

$g(x)$ is increasing and concave down for all $x \in \mathbb{R}$.

   d $(0, -2)$ and $(\ln 5, 2)$
   e

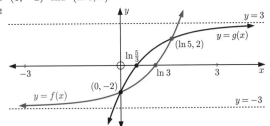

6 **a** x-intercept $\ln \sqrt{3}$, y-intercept -2
   b $f'(x) = e^x + 3e^{-x} > 0$ for all $x \in \mathbb{R}$
   c y is concave down below the x-axis and concave up above the x-axis.
   d

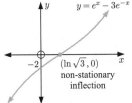

7 **a** local maximum at $\left(0, \frac{1}{\sqrt{2\pi}}\right)$,   increasing for $x \leqslant 0$,
   decreasing for $x \geqslant 0$
   b non-stationary inflections at $\left(-1, \frac{1}{\sqrt{2e\pi}}\right)$ and
   $\left(1, \frac{1}{\sqrt{2e\pi}}\right)$
   c as $x \to \infty$, $f(x) \to 0^+$,   as $x \to -\infty$, $f(x) \to 0^+$
   d

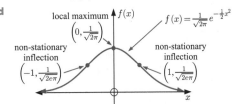

8 **a** The inflection points coincide with the x-intercepts.
   b non-stationary inflection points at $\left(\frac{\pi}{2}, 0\right)$ and $\left(\frac{3\pi}{2}, 0\right)$
   c **i** $\pi \leqslant x \leqslant 2\pi$ **ii** $0 \leqslant x \leqslant \pi$ **iii** $\frac{\pi}{2} \leqslant x \leqslant \frac{3\pi}{2}$
   iv $0 \leqslant x \leqslant \frac{\pi}{2}$ and $\frac{3\pi}{2} \leqslant x \leqslant 2\pi$
   d

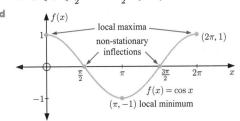

9 **a** **i** **Hint:** Show that $f'(t) = Ae^{-bt}(1 - bt)$.
   ii **Hint:** Show that $f''(t) = Abe^{-bt}(bt - 2)$.
   b

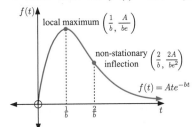

10 **a** y-intercept is $\dfrac{C}{1 + A}$ **c**

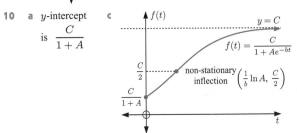

EXERCISE 13G

1 **a**

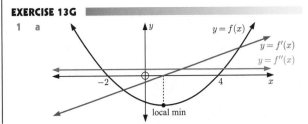

b

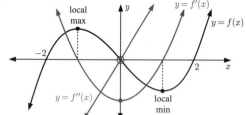

c

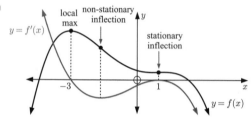

2 a

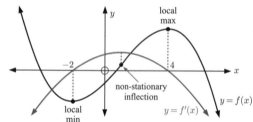

b

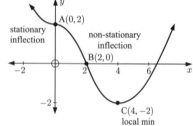

3

stationary inflection, A(0, 2), non-stationary inflection, B(2, 0), C(4, −2) local min

REVIEW SET 13A

1 a $y = 4x + 2$ **b** $y = 7x - 14$ **c** $y = -1$

   d $3x - ey = -1$ **e** $y = \dfrac{2}{e}x$

2 a $8x + 3y = 44$ **b** $y = -\dfrac{1}{6e^2}x + \dfrac{18e^4 + 1}{6e^2}$

3 $p = 1, \ q = -8$ **4** $(-2, 19)$ and $(1, -2)$

5 $a = 64$ **6** $(-2, -25)$

7 a $y = -\dfrac{1}{2e^{2a}}x + \dfrac{a}{2e^{2a}} + e^{2a}$ **b** $y \approx -1.12x$

8 $P(0, 7.5), \ Q(3, 0)$ **9** $\dfrac{3267}{152} \approx 21.5$ units^2

---

10 a $-6 \leqslant x \leqslant 2$ **b** $x \leqslant -6$ and $x \geqslant 2$

11 a local maximum at $(-2, 51)$, local minimum at $(3, -74)$

   b increasing for $x \leqslant -2, \ x \geqslant 3$
      decreasing for $-2 \leqslant x \leqslant 3$

   c as $x \to \infty$, $f(x) \to \infty$,
      as $x \to -\infty$, $f(x) \to -\infty$

   d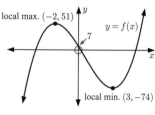

12 a $\{x \mid x \neq -3\}$ **b** x-intercept $\tfrac{2}{3}$, y-intercept $-\tfrac{2}{3}$

   c $f'(x) = \dfrac{11}{(x + 3)^2}$

   d no stationary points

13 greatest value is ≈ 10.3 when $x = 10$,
   least value is 6 when $x = 4$

14 b i $x > 0$ **ii** $x < \tfrac{1}{2}$

   c local maximum at $(\tfrac{1}{2}, \tfrac{1}{2})$

15 a increasing for $x \leqslant -\sqrt{2}$ and $x \geqslant \sqrt{2}$,
      decreasing for $-\sqrt{2} \leqslant x \leqslant \sqrt{2}$

   b increasing for $x \geqslant 1$, decreasing for $x \leqslant 1$

   c increasing for all $x \in \mathbb{R}$

16 a local maximum at $(1, 3)$, local minimum at $(\tfrac{1}{3}, \tfrac{77}{27})$

   b local maximum at $(-6, -12)$, local minimum at $(0, 0)$

17 a $(-\pi, -1)$ is a local minimum, $(\pi, 1)$ is a local maximum

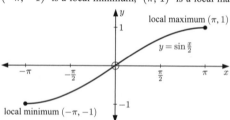

   b $(-\pi, 1), \ (0, 1),$ and $(\pi, 1)$ are local maxima,
      $(-\tfrac{\pi}{2}, 0)$ and $(\tfrac{\pi}{2}, 0)$ are local minima

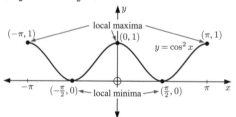

   c $(-\tfrac{5\pi}{6}, \tfrac{3}{2})$ and $(-\tfrac{\pi}{6}, \tfrac{3}{2})$ are local maxima,
      $(-\tfrac{\pi}{2}, 1)$ and $(\tfrac{\pi}{2}, -3)$ are local minima

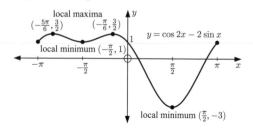

18 a $f'(x) = 6x^2 - 6x + 1$,   **b**
$f''(x) = 12x - 6$

c $x \leqslant \frac{1}{2}$ **d** $(\frac{1}{2}, -12)$

19 a concave up for $x \geqslant \frac{4}{3}$, concave down for $x \leqslant \frac{4}{3}$

b concave up for $x \leqslant -3$,
concave down for $-3 \leqslant x < 0$ and $x > 0$

c concave up for $-4 < x \leqslant 2$ and $x > 0$,
concave down for $x < -4$ and $-2 \leqslant x < 0$

20 a $x > 0$

b $f'(x) = 1 + \dfrac{1}{x}$ $f''(x) = -\dfrac{1}{x^2}$

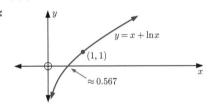

$f(x)$ is increasing and concave downwards for all $x > 0$.

c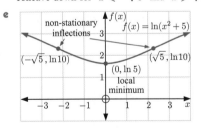

21 a $f'(x) = e^{x\sqrt{3}}(\cos x + \sqrt{3}\sin x)$ **b** $x = \frac{5\pi}{6}$ or $\frac{11\pi}{6}$

c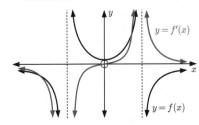

d i $0 \leqslant x \leqslant \frac{5\pi}{6}$ and $\frac{11\pi}{6} \leqslant x \leqslant 2\pi$

ii $\frac{5\pi}{6} \leqslant x \leqslant \frac{11\pi}{6}$

22 a $(0, \ln 5)$ is a local minimum

b $(-\sqrt{5}, \ln 10)$ and $(\sqrt{5}, \ln 10)$ are non-stationary inflections

c increasing for $x \geqslant 0$, decreasing for $x \leqslant 0$

d concave up for $-\sqrt{5} \leqslant x \leqslant \sqrt{5}$
concave down for $x \leqslant -\sqrt{5}$ and $x \geqslant \sqrt{5}$

e

23 a $x = \frac{\pi}{2}$

b $(0.999, 2.03)$ and $(2.14, 2.03)$ are non-stationary inflections.

24

25

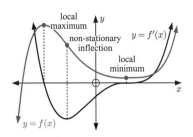

REVIEW SET 13B

1 a $y = 31x - 43$ **b** $x + 128y = 41$

c $y = 3x + \frac{3\sqrt{3}}{2} - \frac{\pi}{2}$ **d** $y = \frac{3}{4}x + \frac{1}{2}$

2 a $x = 1$ **b** $x = 0$ **3** $a = -14$, $b = 21$

5 a $f(3) = 2$, $f'(3) = -1$ **b** $f(x) = x^2 - 7x + 14$

6 a $a = 2$ **b** $y = 3x - 1$ **c** $(-4, -13)$

7 $(\frac{1}{2}, \frac{1}{4})$

8 a $2x + 3y = \frac{2\pi}{3} + 2\sqrt{3}$ **b** $x + 2\sqrt{2}y = \frac{\pi}{2} + 2$

9 $y = \frac{3}{4}x + \frac{5}{4}$ **10** $a = \frac{5}{2}$, $b = -\frac{3}{2}$

11 a $-1 \leqslant x \leqslant 0$ and $x \geqslant 4$ **b** $x \leqslant -1$ and $0 \leqslant x \leqslant 4$

12 a $a = -9$

b local maximum at $(-1, 55)$, local minimum at $(3, 23)$

13 a x-intercepts 0 and 2, y-intercept 0

b local maximum at $(\frac{2}{3}, \frac{32}{27})$, local minimum at $(2, 0)$

c increasing for $x \leqslant \frac{2}{3}$ and $x \geqslant 2$,
decreasing for $\frac{2}{3} \leqslant x \leqslant 2$

d As $x \to \infty$, $y \to \infty$, as $x \to -\infty$, $y \to -\infty$.

e

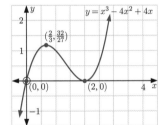

14 a local minimum at $(0, 1)$ **b** as $x \to \infty$, $f(x) \to \infty$

c $f''(x) = e^x$

$f(x)$ is concave up for all $x \in \mathbb{R}$.

d

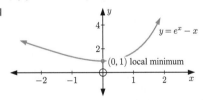

15 a

16 $(1 - a, e^{a-1})$ is a local maximum   **17** $a = 2$, $b = 3$

18 a $x \leqslant -1.96$ and $0.238 \leqslant x \leqslant 3.22$

b $-1.96 \leqslant x \leqslant 0.238$ and $x \geqslant 3.22$

c $-1 \leqslant x \leqslant 2$ **d** $x \leqslant -1$ and $x \geqslant 2$

19 **a** stationary inflection at $(0, 9)$,

   non-stationary inflection at $\left(\frac{3}{2}, \frac{63}{16}\right)$

b non-stationary inflections at $(-1, 8)$ and $\left(\frac{3}{2}, \frac{313}{16}\right)$

20 **a** $0 \leqslant x \leqslant \frac{\pi}{2}$ and $\frac{3\pi}{2} \leqslant x \leqslant 2\pi$

b $f'(x) = -\dfrac{\sin x}{2\sqrt{\cos x}}$,   increasing for $\frac{3\pi}{2} < x \leqslant 2\pi$,

   decreasing for $0 \leqslant x < \frac{\pi}{2}$

c
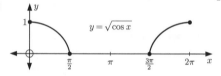

21 **a** $f'(x) = 4x^3 - 12x^2$
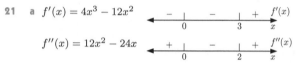

$f''(x) = 12x^2 - 24x$

b $(3, -20)$ is a local minimum

c $(0, 7)$ is a stationary inflection

   $(2, -9)$ is a non-stationary inflection

d **i** $x \geqslant 3$ **ii** $x \leqslant 3$ **iii** $x \leqslant 0$ and $x \geqslant 2$

   iv $0 \leqslant x \leqslant 2$

e
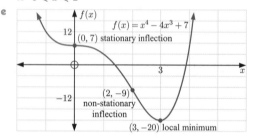

22 **a** local maxima at $(0, 1)$, $(\pi, 1)$, and $(2\pi, 1)$,

   local minima at $\left(\frac{\pi}{2}, 0\right)$ and $\left(\frac{3\pi}{2}, 0\right)$

b non-stationary inflections at $\left(\frac{\pi}{4}, \frac{1}{2}\right)$, $\left(\frac{3\pi}{4}, \frac{1}{2}\right)$,

   $\left(\frac{5\pi}{4}, \frac{1}{2}\right)$, and $\left(\frac{7\pi}{4}, \frac{1}{2}\right)$

c
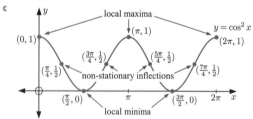

23 **a** -1 **b** $x \neq 1$

c $f'(x) \leqslant 0$ for $x < 1$ and $1 < x \leqslant 2$

   and $f'(x) \geqslant 0$ for $x \geqslant 2$

   $f''(x) > 0$ for $x > 1$, $f''(x) < 0$ for $x < 1$

   The function is decreasing for all defined values of $x \leqslant 2$,

   and increasing for all $x \geqslant 2$. The curve is concave down

   for $x < 1$ and concave up for $x > 1$.

d
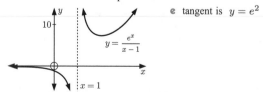

e tangent is $y = e^2$

24
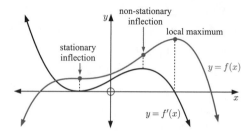

25 **a** $y = 2x - 3$ **b**
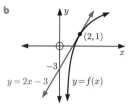

c $f'(x) > 0$ for all $x \in \mathbb{R}$

   $\therefore$ $f(x)$ is increasing

d $\frac{3}{2} < x < 2$

EXERCISE 14A

1 **a** \$118 000   **b** $\dfrac{dP}{dt} = 4t - 12$ thousand dollars per year

c 20, which means that in 8 years from now, profits will be increasing at a rate of \$20 000 per year.

2 **a** 190 m^3 per day   **b** 180 m^3 per day

3 **a** **i** $Q(0) = 100$ **ii** $Q(25) = 50$ **iii** $Q(100) = 0$

b **i** decreasing by 1 unit per year

   ii decreasing by $\frac{1}{\sqrt{2}}$ units per year

c $Q'(t) = -\dfrac{5}{\sqrt{t}} < 0$ for all $t > 0$

4 **a** 0.5 m

b **i** ≈ 15.8 m   **ii** ≈ 21.7 m   **iii** ≈ 24.9 m

c $t = 0$: 6.9 m per year, $t = 5$: 1.725 m per year,

   $t = 10$: ≈ 0.767 m per year

d $\dfrac{dH}{dt} = \dfrac{172.5}{(t + 5)^2} > 0$ for all $t \geqslant 0$

   The tree will continue to grow forever.

5 **a** $C'(x) = 6 + 8.4x^{-0.3}$ dollars per pair

b $C'(220) \approx \$7.67$,   this estimates the cost of making the 221st pair of jeans if 220 pairs are currently being made.

c $C(221) - C(220) \approx \$7.66$, this is the actual cost of making the 221st pair of jeans. The answer in **b** is a very good estimate.

6 **a** **i** 4500 euros   **ii** 4000 euros

b **i** decreasing at ≈ 210.22 euros per km h^{-1}

   ii increasing at ≈ 11.31 euros per km h^{-1}

c ≈ 79.4 km h^{-1}

7 **a** $\dfrac{dV}{dt} = -1250\left(1 - \dfrac{t}{80}\right)$ L min^{-1}

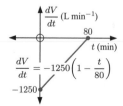

b $t = 0$ when the tap was first opened

c $\dfrac{d^2V}{dt^2} = \dfrac{125}{8} > 0$

This shows that the rate of change of V is constantly increasing, so the outflow is increasing at a constant rate.

8   a   The near part of the lake is 2 km from the sea, the furthest part is 3 km.

b $\dfrac{dy}{dx} = \dfrac{3}{10}x^2 - x + \dfrac{3}{5}$

When $x = \frac{1}{2}$, $\dfrac{dy}{dx} = 0.175$, the height of the hill is increasing as the gradient is positive.

When $x = 1\frac{1}{2}$, $\dfrac{dy}{dx} = -0.225$, the height of the hill is decreasing as the gradient is negative.

c ≈ 2.55 km from the sea, ≈ 63.1 m deep

9   a $k = \frac{1}{50}\ln 2 \approx 0.0139$

b   i   20 grams   ii ≈ 14.3 grams   iii ≈ 1.95 grams

c ≈ 216 hours or ≈ 9 days

d   i $\approx -0.0693\ \text{g h}^{-1}$ ii $\approx -2.64 \times 10^{-7}\ \text{g h}^{-1}$

e   Hint: You should find $\dfrac{dW}{dt} = -\frac{1}{50}\ln 2 \times 20e^{-\frac{t}{50}\ln 2}$

10   a $k = \frac{1}{15}\ln\left(\frac{19}{3}\right) \approx 0.123$ b $100°\text{C}$

c $c = -k \approx -0.123$

d   i   decreasing at $\approx 11.7°\text{C min}^{-1}$

ii   decreasing at $\approx 3.42°\text{C min}^{-1}$

iii   decreasing at $\approx 0.998°\text{C min}^{-1}$

11   a ≈ 43.9 cm   b ≈ 10.4 years

c   i   growing at ≈ 5.45 cm per year

ii   growing at 1.875 cm per year

12   a   When $t = 0$, $A = 0$ litres

b   i $k = \dfrac{\ln 2}{3}$ (≈ 0.231)

ii ≈ 0.728 litres of alcohol produced per hour

13   $\frac{21}{\sqrt{2}}$ cm^2 per radian

14   a $l = \sqrt{800 - 800\cos\theta}$ cm   b   10 cm per radian

15   a   i   0 volts   ii   340 volts

b   i -34000π volts per second   ii   0 volts per second

16   a   2000 bees   b $\approx 37.8\%$ c   yes, 3000 bees

d $B'(t) = \dfrac{2595}{e^{1.73t}(1 + 0.5e^{-1.73t})^2} > 0$ for all $t \geqslant 0$

$\therefore$ $B(t)$ is increasing over time.

e ≈ 0.0806 bees per month

f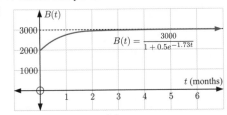

1   250 items per day   2   10 blankets per day

3   b   15 m $\times$ 30 m

4   b $L_{\min} \approx 28.3$ m, when $x \approx 7.07$

c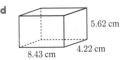

14.1 m

7.07 m

5   a   Hint: $V = 200 = 2x \times x \times h$

b   Hint: Show $h = \dfrac{100}{x^2}$ and substitute into the surface area equation.

c $A_{\min} \approx 213$ cm^2, when $x \approx 4.22$

d

5.62 cm

8.43 cm   4.22 cm

6   a   Hint: Recall that $V_{\text{cylinder}} = \pi r^2 h$ and that $1\ \text{L} = 1000$ cm^3.

b   Hint: Recall that $SA_{\text{cylinder}} = 2\pi r^2 + 2\pi rh$.

c

5.42 cm

10.8 cm

7   b   6 cm $\times$ 6 cm

8   a $0 < x < \dfrac{200}{\pi} \approx 63.7$

b $l = 100$, $x = \dfrac{100}{\pi} \approx 31.8$, $A = \dfrac{20\,000}{\pi} \approx 6370$ m^2

9   a $y = 30 - x$ b $A(x) = x(30 - x)$ cm^2

c $A'(x) = 30 - 2x$ d $x = 15$, 15 cm $\times$ 15 cm

10   a   area $= 4x\sqrt{25 - x^2}$ cm^2 b $5\sqrt{2}$ cm $\times$ $5\sqrt{2}$ cm

11   20 kettles   12 $C\left(\frac{1}{\sqrt{2}}, e^{-\frac{1}{2}}\right)$

13   b $\theta \approx 1.91$, $A \approx 237$ cm^2

14   c $\theta = \frac{\pi}{6}$,   area ≈ 130 cm^2

15   a $E'(t) = 750e^{-1.5t}(1 - 1.5t)$

b   40 minutes after the injection

16   $3\frac{1}{3}$ km   17   after ≈ 13.8 weeks

18   a   Hint: Use the cosine rule.   b ≈ 3550

c $\approx 5:36$ pm

19   c $\theta = \frac{\pi}{6}$ d

$\dfrac{dT}{d\theta}$

+   −

0        $\frac{\pi}{6}$ $\frac{\pi}{2}$ θ

e   i   Row from P to Q at an angle of $\frac{\pi}{6}$ to the diameter of the lake, then walk from Q to R.

ii   Walk from P to R.

20   a   X is between A and C.

c $x \approx 2.67$ This is the distance in km from A to X which minimises the time taken to get from B to C.

21   b ≈ 3.37 m

1   a   60 cm   b   i ≈ 4.24 years   ii ≈ 201 years

c   i   16 cm per year   ii ≈ 1.95 cm per year

2   a   £20 000   b   £146.53 per year

3   a $\$4930.25$

b   i   decreasing at $\approx \$1.39$ per km h^{-1}

ii increasing at $\approx$ \$2.83 per $km\,h^{-1}$

c ≈ 79.4 $km\,h^{-1}$

4 b $C(\sqrt{3},\,6)$

5 b $A = 200x - 2x^2 - \frac{1}{2}\pi x^2$ **c**

28.0 m

56.0 m

6 a $y = \dfrac{1}{x^2},\ x > 0$

c base is $\sqrt[3]{2} \approx 1.26$ m square, height is ≈ 0.630 m

7 a $\dfrac{dD}{dt} = -3.4476\sin(0.507t)$, this tells us the rate at which the depth of water is increasing or decreasing t hours after midnight.

b ≈ 5.15 m   **c** rising, when $t = 8$, $\dfrac{dD}{dt} \approx 2.73 > 0$

d midnight and $\approx$ 12:24 pm, maximum depth of 16.1 m

REVIEW SET 14B

1 a $C'(x) = 2.805x^{-0.15} + 1.4x^{-0.5}$ euros per item
b $C'(1000) \approx €1.04$, this estimates the cost of making the 1001st item each day.
c $C(1001) - C(1000) \approx €1.04$, this is the actual cost of making the 1001st item each day. The answer in **b** is a very good estimate.

2 a $P(0) = 20\,000$ **b** $P'(t) = \dfrac{30\,000e^{-\frac{t}{4}}}{(1 + 2e^{-\frac{t}{4}})^2}$

c Hint: Use the fact that $e^{-\frac{t}{4}}$ is never negative.
$P(t)$ is increasing for all $t \geqslant 0$.

d $P''(t) = \dfrac{7500e^{-\frac{t}{4}}(2e^{-\frac{t}{4}} - 1)}{(1 + 2e^{-\frac{t}{4}})^3}$

e 3750 per year when $t = 4\ln 2$ years
f as $t \to \infty$, $P(t) \to 60\,000^-$
g

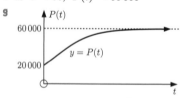

3 a $A = 242\pi(1 - \cos\theta)$ cm^2
b $121\sqrt{2}\pi \approx 538$ cm^2 per radian
4 6 cm from each end   **5** x-coordinate of P is $\ln a$.
6 $x \approx 2.11$ **7 b** $\dfrac{1}{\sqrt{2}}$ metres

EXERCISE 15A

1 a i 0.4 units^2 **ii** 0.6 units^2 **b** 0.5 units^2
2 a ≈ 0.653 units^2 **b** ≈ 0.737 units^2

3

n	A_L	A_U
10	2.1850	2.4850
25	2.2736	2.3936
50	2.3034	2.3634
100	2.3184	2.3484
500	2.3303	2.3363

A_L and A_U converge to $\frac{7}{3}$.

4 a i

n	A_L	A_U
5	0.160 00	0.360 00
10	0.202 50	0.302 50
50	0.240 10	0.260 10
100	0.245 03	0.255 03
500	0.249 00	0.251 00
1000	0.249 50	0.250 50
10 000	0.249 95	0.250 05

ii

n	A_L	A_U
5	0.400 00	0.600 00
10	0.450 00	0.550 00
50	0.490 00	0.510 00
100	0.495 00	0.505 00
500	0.499 00	0.501 00
1000	0.499 50	0.500 50
10 000	0.499 95	0.500 05

iii

n	A_L	A_U
5	0.549 74	0.749 74
10	0.610 51	0.710 51
50	0.656 10	0.676 10
100	0.661 46	0.671 46
500	0.665 65	0.667 65
1000	0.666 16	0.667 16
10 000	0.666 62	0.666 72

iv

n	A_L	A_U
5	0.618 67	0.818 67
10	0.687 40	0.787 40
50	0.738 51	0.758 51
100	0.744 41	0.754 41
500	0.748 93	0.750 93
1000	0.749 47	0.750 47
10 000	0.749 95	0.750 05

b i $\frac{1}{4}$ **ii** $\frac{1}{2}$ **iii** $\frac{2}{3}$ **iv** $\frac{3}{4}$ **c** area $= \dfrac{1}{a+1}$

5 a

n	Rational bounds for π
10	$2.9045 < \pi < 3.3045$
50	$3.0983 < \pi < 3.1783$
100	$3.1204 < \pi < 3.1604$
200	$3.1312 < \pi < 3.1512$
1000	$3.1396 < \pi < 3.1436$
10 000	$3.1414 < \pi < 3.1418$

b $n = 10\,000$

EXERCISE 15B

1 a

y
1.0
0.8 $y = \sqrt{x}$
0.6
0.4
0.2
1   x

b

n	A_L	A_U
5	0.5497	0.7497
10	0.6105	0.7105
50	0.6561	0.6761
100	0.6615	0.6715
500	0.6657	0.6677

c $\displaystyle\int_0^1 \sqrt{x}\,dx \approx 0.67$

2 **a** $A_L = \dfrac{2}{n}\displaystyle\sum_{i=0}^{n-1}\sqrt{1+x_i^3}, \quad A_U = \dfrac{2}{n}\displaystyle\sum_{i=1}^{n}\sqrt{1+x_i^3},$

where $x_i = \dfrac{2i}{n}$

b

n	A_L	A_U
50	3.2016	3.2816
100	3.2214	3.2614
500	3.2373	3.2453

c $\displaystyle\int_0^2 \sqrt{1+x^3}\, dx \approx 3.24$

3 **a**

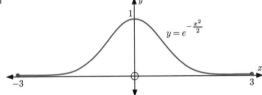

$y = e^{-\frac{x^2}{2}}$

b lower ≈ 1.2493,   upper ≈ 1.2506
c lower ≈ 1.2493,   upper ≈ 1.2506
d $\displaystyle\int_{-3}^3 e^{-\frac{x^2}{2}}\, dx \approx 2.4999, \quad \sqrt{2\pi} \approx 2.5066$

4 **a** 18   **b** 4.5   **c** 2π **5** **b** **i** 0   **ii** 22

EXERCISE 15C

1 **a** **i** $\dfrac{x^2}{2}$ **ii** $\dfrac{x^3}{3}$ **iii** $\dfrac{x^6}{6}$ **iv** $-\dfrac{1}{x}$

  v $-\dfrac{1}{3x^3}$ **vi** $\dfrac{3}{4}x^{\frac{4}{3}}$ **vii** $\dfrac{3}{2}x^{\frac{2}{3}}$ **viii** $\dfrac{3}{5}x^{\frac{5}{3}}$

  b The antiderivative of x^n is $\dfrac{x^{n+1}}{n+1}$ $(n \neq -1)$.

2 **a** **i** $\dfrac{1}{3}e^{3x}$ **ii** $\dfrac{1}{5}e^{5x}$ **iii** $2e^{\frac{1}{2}x}$ **iv** $100e^{0.01x}$

  v $\dfrac{1}{\pi}e^{\pi x}$ **vi** $3e^{\frac{x}{3}}$

  b The antiderivative of e^{kx} is $\dfrac{1}{k}e^{kx}$, where $k \neq 0$ is a constant.

3 **a** $\dfrac{d}{dx}(x^3 + x^2) = 3x^2 + 2x$

  $\therefore$ the antiderivative of $6x^2 + 4x$ is $2x^3 + 2x^2$.

  b $\dfrac{d}{dx}(x\sqrt{x}) = \dfrac{3}{2}\sqrt{x}$

  $\therefore$ the antiderivative of $\sqrt{x}$ is $\dfrac{2}{3}x\sqrt{x}$.

  c $\dfrac{d}{dx}\left(\dfrac{1}{\sqrt{x}}\right) = -\dfrac{1}{2}x^{-\frac{3}{2}} = -\dfrac{1}{2x\sqrt{x}}$

  $\therefore$ the antiderivative of $\dfrac{1}{x\sqrt{x}}$ is $-\dfrac{2}{\sqrt{x}}$.

EXERCISE 15D

1 **a** $\dfrac{d}{dx}(x^2) = 2x$

  $\therefore$ the antiderivative of $2x$ is x^2.

  b 8 units^2

2 **a** $\dfrac{2}{3}x^{\frac{3}{2}}$ **b** $\dfrac{2}{3}$ units^2

  c $\dfrac{2}{3} \approx 0.67$ $\therefore$ the answers are the same.

3 **a** **i** 4 units^2 **ii** $16\frac{1}{4}$ units^2 **iii** $20\frac{1}{4}$ units^2

  b $\displaystyle\int_0^3 x^3\, dx = \displaystyle\int_0^2 x^3\, dx + \displaystyle\int_2^3 x^3\, dx$

4 **a** $3\frac{3}{4}$ units^2 **b** $8\frac{2}{3}$ units^2 **c** $\dfrac{4\sqrt{2}-2}{3}$ units^2

  d 2 units^2

6 $\dfrac{9\pi}{4} \approx 7.07$ units^2

7 **c** **i** $\displaystyle\int_0^1 (-x^2)\, dx = -\frac{1}{3}$, the area between $y = -x^2$ and the x-axis from $x = 0$ to $x = 1$ is $\frac{1}{3}$ units^2.

  ii $\displaystyle\int_0^1 (x^2 - x)\, dx = -\frac{1}{6}$, the area between $y = x^2 - x$ and the x-axis from $x = 0$ to $x = 1$ is $\frac{1}{6}$ units^2.

  iii $\displaystyle\int_{-2}^0 3x\, dx = -6$, the area between $y = 3x$ and the x-axis from $x = -2$ to $x = 0$ is 6 units^2.

  d $-\pi$

REVIEW SET 15A

1 **a** $A = \frac{17}{4}, \ B = \frac{25}{4}$ **b** $\displaystyle\int_0^2 (4 - x^2)\, dx \approx \frac{21}{4}$

2 **a**

  $y = \sin x$

  b   lower rectangles   upper rectangles

  $y = \sin x$ $y = \sin x$

  $\dfrac{\pi(1+\sqrt{3})}{12} < \displaystyle\int_0^{\frac{\pi}{2}} \sin x\, dx < \dfrac{\pi(3+\sqrt{3})}{12}$

  or $0.715 < \displaystyle\int_0^{\frac{\pi}{2}} \sin x\, dx < 1.24$

3 **a** $\dfrac{x^5}{5}$ **b** $-\dfrac{1}{2x}$ **c** $-2e^{-\frac{1}{2}x}$ **d** $\sin x$

4 **a** 2π **b** 4

5 **a** **i** $\frac{1}{3}$ units^2 **ii** $2\frac{1}{3}$ units^2 **iii** $2\frac{2}{3}$ units^2

  b $\displaystyle\int_0^2 x^2\, dx = \displaystyle\int_0^1 x^2\, dx + \displaystyle\int_1^2 x^2\, dx$

REVIEW SET 15B

1 **a**

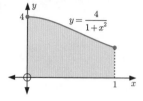

$$y = \frac{4}{1+x^2}$$

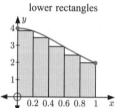

lower rectangles

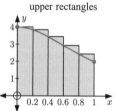

upper rectangles

b

n	A_L	A_U
5	2.9349	3.3349
50	3.1215	3.1615
100	3.1316	3.1516
500	3.1396	3.1436

c $\displaystyle\int_0^1 \frac{4}{1+x^2}\, dx$

≈ 3.1416

$\approx \pi$

2 **a** 10   **b** $\frac{\pi}{2}$

3 **a** $\dfrac{d}{dx}(x^3 - 2x) = 3x^2 - 2$

$\therefore$ the antiderivative of $3x^2 - 2$ is $x^3 - 2x$.

b $\dfrac{d}{dx}\left(x^{\frac{4}{3}}\right) = \frac{4}{3}x^{\frac{1}{3}} = \frac{4}{3}\sqrt[3]{x}$

$\therefore$ the antiderivative of $\sqrt[3]{x}$ is $\frac{3}{4}x^{\frac{4}{3}}$.

4 **a** 3   **b** $\frac{15}{2}$ **5** **a** 18 units^2 **b** 18 units^2

EXERCISE 16A

1 **a** $\dfrac{d}{dx}\left(x^7\right) = 7x^6$

$\therefore \displaystyle\int x^6\, dx = \frac{1}{7}x^7 + c$

b $\dfrac{d}{dx}\left(x^{\frac{3}{2}}\right) = \frac{3}{2}x^{\frac{1}{2}} = \frac{3}{2}\sqrt{x}$

$\therefore \displaystyle\int \sqrt{x}\, dx = \frac{2}{3}x^{\frac{3}{2}} + c$

c $\dfrac{d}{dx}\left(x^{-\frac{1}{2}}\right) = -\frac{1}{2}x^{-\frac{3}{2}}$

$\therefore \displaystyle\int x^{-\frac{3}{2}}\, dx = -2x^{-\frac{1}{2}} + c$

d $\dfrac{d}{dx}\left(x^{n+1}\right) = (n+1)x^n$

$\therefore \displaystyle\int x^n\, dx = \frac{x^{n+1}}{n+1} + c, \quad n \neq -1$

2 **a** $\dfrac{d}{dx}\left(e^{4x}\right) = 4e^{4x}$

$\therefore \displaystyle\int e^{4x}\, dx = \frac{1}{4}e^{4x} + c$

b $\dfrac{d}{dx}\left(e^{-\frac{x}{2}}\right) = -\frac{1}{2}e^{-\frac{x}{2}}$

$\therefore \displaystyle\int e^{-\frac{x}{2}}\, dx = -2e^{-\frac{x}{2}} + c$

c $\dfrac{d}{dx}\left(e^{kx}\right) = ke^{kx}$

$\therefore \displaystyle\int e^{kx}\, dx = \frac{1}{k}e^{kx} + c, \quad k \neq 0$

3 **a** $\dfrac{d}{dx}(\sin x) = \cos x$

$\therefore \displaystyle\int \cos x\, dx = \sin x + c$

b $\dfrac{d}{dx}(\cos x) = -\sin x$

$\therefore \displaystyle\int \sin x\, dx = -\cos x + c$

4 $\dfrac{d}{dx}\left(x^3 + x^2\right) = 3x^2 + 2x$

$\therefore \displaystyle\int (3x^2 + 2x)\, dx = x^3 + x^2 + c$

5 $\dfrac{d}{dx}\left(3x^4 - 2x^2\right) = 12x^3 - 4x$

$\therefore \displaystyle\int (3x^3 - x)\, dx = \frac{3}{4}x^4 - \frac{1}{2}x^2 + c$

6 **a** $f(x) + g(x)$

7 **a** $\dfrac{d}{dx}(\sin 3x) = 3\cos 3x$

$\therefore \displaystyle\int \cos 3x\, dx = \frac{1}{3}\sin 3x + c$

b $\dfrac{d}{dx}\left(\cos\left(\frac{\pi}{3} - x\right)\right) = \sin\left(\frac{\pi}{3} - x\right)$

$\therefore \displaystyle\int \sin\left(\frac{\pi}{3} - x\right) dx = \cos\left(\frac{\pi}{3} - x\right) + c$

c $\dfrac{d}{dx}\left(e^{3x+1}\right) = 3e^{3x+1}$

$\therefore \displaystyle\int e^{3x+1}\, dx = \frac{1}{3}e^{3x+1} + c$

d $\dfrac{d}{dx}\left(\sqrt{5x-1}\right) = \frac{5}{2}(5x-1)^{-\frac{1}{2}} = \dfrac{5}{2\sqrt{5x-1}}$

$\displaystyle\int \frac{1}{\sqrt{5x-1}}\, dx = \frac{2}{5}\sqrt{5x-1} + c$

e $\dfrac{d}{dx}\left((2x+1)^4\right) = 8(2x+1)^3$

$\therefore \displaystyle\int (2x+1)^3\, dx = \frac{1}{8}(2x+1)^4 + c$

8 **a** $\dfrac{1}{x}$ **b** $\dfrac{-1}{-x} = \dfrac{1}{x}$

c $\displaystyle\int \frac{1}{x}\, dx = \begin{cases} \ln x + c, & x > 0 \\ \ln(-x) + c, & x < 0 \end{cases}$

EXERCISE 16B

1 a $\frac{1}{3}x^3 + \frac{3}{2}x^2 - 2x + c$ **b** $\frac{2}{3}x^3 - \frac{3}{2}x^2 + x + c$

c $-\frac{1}{4}x^4 + \frac{4}{3}x^3 - 3x + c$ **d** $\frac{1}{4}x^2 + \frac{1}{3}x^3 + \frac{1}{4}x^4 + c$

e $\frac{1}{5}x^5 - \frac{1}{3}x^3 - \frac{1}{2}x^2 + 2x + c$ **f** $\frac{4}{3}x^3 + \ln|x| + c$

g $\frac{4}{3}x^{\frac{3}{2}} - 6x^{\frac{1}{2}} + c$ **h** $\frac{1}{3}\ln|x| + \frac{2}{x} + c$

i $\frac{2}{5}x^{\frac{5}{2}} - 9x + c$ **j** $-6x^{-\frac{1}{2}} + \frac{4}{5}x^{\frac{5}{4}} + c$

2 a $2e^x - \frac{3}{2}x^2 + c$ **b** $4\ln|x| + \frac{1}{3}x^3 - e^x + c$

c $5e^x + \frac{1}{6}x^3 + c$

3 a $-3\cos x - 2x + c$ **b** $2x^2 - 2\sin x + c$

c $-\cos x - 2\sin x + e^x + c$ **d** $\frac{2}{7}x^{\frac{7}{2}} + 10\cos x + c$

e $\frac{1}{9}x^3 - \frac{1}{6}x^2 + \sin x + c$ **f** $\cos x + \frac{4}{3}x^{\frac{3}{2}} + c$

4 a $y = 6x + c$ **b** $y = \frac{4}{3}x^3 + c$ **c** $y = -\frac{1}{x} + c$

d $y = 3x^{\frac{2}{3}} + c$ **e** $y = \frac{1}{2}x^4 - 4x + c$

f $y = x^4 + x^3 + c$ **g** $y = 2x - \ln|x| + c$

h $y = -\cos x + 2\sin x + c$ **i** $y = 2e^x - 5x + \frac{1}{2}x^2 + c$

5 a $\frac{1}{8}x^4 - \frac{1}{5}x^5 + \frac{3}{4}x^{\frac{4}{3}} + c$ **b** $-\frac{4}{x} + \frac{1}{3}x^3 - \frac{1}{16}x^4 + c$

c $x^5 + \frac{1}{12}x^4 - \frac{2}{3}x^{\frac{3}{2}} + c$

6 a $\frac{4}{3}x^3 + 2x^2 + x + c$ **b** $\frac{1}{3}x^3 + 2x - \frac{1}{x} + c$

c $-\frac{2}{\sqrt{x}} - 8\sqrt{x} + c$ **d** $\frac{4}{3}x\sqrt{x} - 2\sqrt{x} + c$

e $\frac{1}{2}x^2 - 2x + \ln|x| + c$ **f** $\ln|x| - \frac{1}{2}x^2 + c$

g $-\frac{4}{x} + 4\ln|x| + x + c$ **h** $\frac{1}{4}x^4 + x^3 + \frac{3}{2}x^2 + x + c$

i $\frac{1}{5}x^5 - x^4 + 2x^3 - 2x^2 + x + c$

j $\frac{2}{3}x\sqrt{x} + \frac{8}{\sqrt{x}} + c$ **k** $\frac{1}{2}x^2 - 4x + 10\ln|x| + c$

l $\frac{3}{2}x^2 - 2x - \frac{5}{x} + c$

7 a $f(x) = x - 2x^2 + \frac{4}{3}x^3 + c$

b $f(x) = \frac{2}{3}x\sqrt{x} - 4\sqrt{x} + c$ **c** $f(x) = x + \frac{5}{x} + c$

8 a $\frac{2}{3}x^{\frac{3}{2}} + \frac{1}{2}\sin x + c$ **b** $2e^x + 4\cos x + c$

c $3\sin x + \cos x + c$

9 a $\frac{1}{5}x^5 - x^2 - \frac{1}{x} + c$ **b** $\frac{2}{5}x^{\frac{5}{2}} - \frac{8}{3}x^{\frac{3}{2}} + 4x^{\frac{1}{2}} + c$

c $\frac{18}{7}x^{\frac{7}{2}} - \frac{12}{5}x^{\frac{5}{2}} + \frac{2}{3}x^{\frac{3}{2}} + c$

EXERCISE 16C

1 a $f(x) = x^2 - x + 3$ **b** $f(x) = x^3 + x^2 - 7$

c $f(x) = 2x + 2\sqrt{x} - 3$ **d** $f(x) = \frac{1}{2}x^2 - 4\sqrt{x} + \frac{11}{2}$

e $f(x) = \frac{2}{3}x^{\frac{3}{2}} - 2x + \frac{8}{3}$ **f** $f(x) = \ln|x| + 1$

2 $y = \frac{1}{2}x^2 - \frac{2}{3}x^3 + \frac{22}{3}$ **3** $y = x - e^x + 2e^3 - 3$

4 a $f(x) = \frac{1}{3}x^3 - 4\sin x + 3$

b $f(x) = 2\sin x + 3\cos x - 2\sqrt{2}$

c $f(x) = \frac{2}{3}x^{\frac{3}{2}} + 2\cos x - 4$

d $f(x) = e^x + 3\sin x - e^\pi$

5 $f(x) = -x^2 + x + 3$ **6** $f(x) = 3x^3 + 1$

7 a $f(x) = \frac{1}{3}x^3 + \frac{1}{2}x^2 + x + \frac{1}{3}$

b $f(x) = 4x^{\frac{5}{2}} + 4x^{\frac{3}{2}} - 4x + 5$

c $f(x) = -\cos x - x + 4$ **d** $f(x) = \frac{1}{3}x^3 - \frac{16}{3}x + 5$

8 $f(x) = 3e^{-x} - x + 1$

EXERCISE 16D

1 a $\frac{1}{8}(2x+5)^4 + c$ **b** $\frac{1}{2(3-2x)} + c$

c $\frac{-2}{3(2x-1)^3} + c$ **d** $\frac{1}{32}(4x-3)^8 + c$

e $\frac{2}{9}(3x-4)^{\frac{3}{2}} + c$ **f** $-4\sqrt{1-5x} + c$

g $-\frac{3}{5}(1-x)^5 + c$ **h** $-2\sqrt{3-4x} + c$

i $-\frac{5}{6(3x-2)^2} + c$

2 $y = \frac{1}{3}(2x-7)^{\frac{3}{2}} + 2$ **3** $(-8, -19)$

4 a $\frac{1}{2}(2x-1)^3 + c$ **b** $\frac{1}{12}(4x-5)^3 + c$

c $-\frac{1}{12}(1-3x)^4 + c$ **d** $-\frac{1}{15}(2-5x)^3 + c$

e $-\frac{8}{3}(5-x)^{\frac{3}{2}} + c$ **f** $\frac{1}{35}(7x+1)^5 + c$

5 $y = \frac{1}{2}x^2 - \frac{5}{1-x} - 7$

6 a $-\frac{1}{3}\cos 3x + c$ **b** $-\frac{1}{2}\sin(-4x) + x + c$ **c** $6\sin\frac{x}{2} + c$

d $-\frac{3}{2}\cos 2x + e^{-x} + c$ **e** $-\cos\left(2x + \frac{\pi}{6}\right) + c$

f $3\sin\left(\frac{\pi}{4} - x\right) + c$ **g** $\frac{1}{2}\sin 2x - \frac{1}{2}\cos 2x + c$

h $-\frac{2}{3}\cos 3x + \frac{5}{4}\sin 4x + c$ **i** $\frac{1}{16}\sin 8x + 3\cos x + c$

7 a $2e^x + \frac{5}{2}e^{2x} + c$ **b** $\frac{3}{5}e^{5x-2} + c$

c $-\frac{1}{3}e^{7-3x} + c$ **d** $\frac{1}{2}e^{2x} + 2x - \frac{1}{2}e^{-2x} + c$

e $-\frac{1}{2}e^{-2x} - 4e^{-x} + 4x + c$

f $\frac{1}{3}e^{3x} - 10e^x - 25e^{-x} + c$

8 $y = x - 2e^x + \frac{1}{2}e^{2x} + \frac{11}{2}$

9 $p = -\frac{1}{4}$, $f(x) = \frac{1}{2}\cos\frac{x}{2} + \frac{1}{2}$ **11** $f(x) = -e^{-2x} + 4$

12 $y = \frac{2}{3}x^{\frac{3}{2}} - \frac{1}{8}e^{-4x} + \frac{1}{8}e^{-4} - \frac{2}{3}$

13 $\int (\sin x + \cos x)^2\, dx = x - \frac{1}{2}\cos 2x + c$

14 a $\sin^2 x = \frac{1}{2} - \frac{1}{2}\cos 2x$, $\cos^2 x = \frac{1}{2} + \frac{1}{2}\cos 2x$

b **i** $\frac{1}{2}x - \frac{1}{4}\sin 2x + c$ **ii** $\frac{1}{2}x + \frac{1}{4}\sin 2x + c$

15 a $\frac{5}{2}x + \frac{1}{4}\sin 2x + c$ **b** $\frac{1}{2}x - \frac{1}{4}\sin 2x + 2x^2 + c$

c $\frac{3}{2}x + \frac{1}{8}\sin 4x + c$ **d** $\frac{5}{2}x + \frac{1}{12}\sin 6x + c$

e $\frac{1}{4}x + \frac{1}{32}\sin 8x + c$ **f** $\frac{3}{2}x + 2\sin x + \frac{1}{4}\sin 2x + c$

g $x - \frac{1}{2}\sin 2x + \cos x + c$

h $\frac{11}{2}x + 6\cos x - \frac{9}{4}\sin 2x + c$

16 a $6\ln|x+4| + c$ **b** $\frac{1}{2}\ln|2x-1| + c$

c $-3\ln|1-x| + c$ **d** $-\frac{5}{3}\ln|1-3x| + c$

e $x - x^2 + 4\ln|x-3| + c$ **f** $4x + \frac{1}{5}\ln|5x-2| + c$

g $-e^{-x} - 2\ln|2x+1| + c$

h $\ln|x+2| + 2\ln|x-3| + c$

i $5\ln|x-6| - \frac{2}{3}\ln|3x-1| + c$

17 Both are correct. Recall that:

$$\frac{d}{dx}\left(\ln(Ax)\right) = \frac{d}{dx}\left(\ln A + \ln x\right) = \frac{1}{x}, \quad A, \, x > 0$$

18 $\displaystyle\int \frac{3x-1}{x+2}\, dx = 3x - 7\ln|x+2| + c$

19 $f(x) = x^2 + 2\ln|1-x| + 2 - 2\ln 2$

EXERCISE 16E

1 $\qquad \dfrac{d}{dx}\left((x^2 - x)^3\right) = 3(x^2-x)^2(2x-1)$

$\therefore \displaystyle\int (2x-1)(x^2-x)^2 \, dx = \frac{1}{3}(x^2-x)^3 + c$

2 $\qquad \dfrac{d}{dx}\left(\sin(x^2)\right) = 2x\cos(x^2)$

$\therefore \displaystyle\int x\cos(x^2)\, dx = \frac{1}{2}\sin(x^2) + c$

3 $\dfrac{d}{dx}\left(\ln(5 - 3x + x^2)\right) = \dfrac{2x-3}{5-3x+x^2}$

$\therefore \displaystyle\int \frac{4x-6}{5-3x+x^2}\, dx = 2\ln\left|5 - 3x + x^2\right| + c$

4 **a** $\frac{1}{5}(x^3+1)^5 + c$ **b** $\frac{1}{3}e^{x^3+1} + c$ **c** $\frac{1}{5}\sin^5 x + c$
   d $\sin(x^2 - 3) + c$

5 **a** $\frac{1}{4}(2+x^4)^4 + c$ **b** $2\sqrt{x^2+3} + c$

   c $-\dfrac{1}{3(2x^3-1)^3} + c$ **d** $\frac{1}{5}(x^3 + 2x + 1)^5 + c$

   e $\dfrac{1}{8(1-x^2)^4} + c$ **f** $-\dfrac{1}{2(x^2+4x-3)} + c$

6 **a** $e^{1-2x} + c$ **b** $e^{x^2} + c$ **c** $2e^{\sqrt{x}} + c$

7 **a** $\ln\left|x^2+1\right| + c$ **b** $-\frac{1}{2}\ln\left|2-x^2\right| + c$
   c $\ln\left|x^2 - 3x\right| + c$

8 **a** $-\frac{1}{9}(3-x^3)^3 + c$ **b** $-\frac{1}{3}(1-x^2)^{\frac{3}{2}} + c$
   c $-\frac{1}{2}e^{1-x^2} + c$ **d** $\frac{1}{4}(\ln x)^4 + c$
   e $-e^{x-x^2} + c$ **f** $-\frac{1}{3}\ln\left|x^3 - 3x\right| + c$

9 **a** $\frac{1}{8}\sin^8 x + c$ **b** $-\frac{1}{6}\cos^6 x + c$
   c $-2\sqrt{\cos x} + c$ **d** $-\ln|\cos x| + c$
   e $\frac{2}{3}(\sin x)^{\frac{3}{2}} + c$ **f** $-(2 + \sin x)^{-1} + c$
   g $\ln|1 - \cos x| + c$ **h** $\frac{1}{2}\ln|\sin 2x - 3| + c$
   i $-\frac{1}{2}\cos(x^2) + c$

10 **a** $-\frac{1}{3}\sin^3 x + \sin x + c$ **b** $\frac{1}{8}\sin^4 2x + c$

REVIEW SET 16A

1 $\qquad \dfrac{d}{dx}\left(x^4 - x^2\right) = 4x^3 - 2x$

$\therefore \displaystyle\int (2x^3 - x)\, dx = \frac{1}{2}x^4 - \frac{1}{2}x^2 + c$

2 $\qquad \dfrac{d}{dx}\left(\sin(\frac{\pi}{3} - 2x)\right) = -2\cos(\frac{\pi}{3} - 2x)$

$\therefore \displaystyle\int \cos(\frac{\pi}{3} - 2x)\, dx = -\frac{1}{2}\sin(\frac{\pi}{3} - 2x) + c$

3 **a** $\frac{2}{3}x\sqrt{x} + \frac{2}{x} + c$ **b** $x^2 - \frac{9}{2}x^{\frac{2}{3}} + c$
   c $4x\sqrt{x} + 10\sqrt{x} + c$

4 **a** $8\sqrt{x} + c$ **b** $\frac{1}{12}x^4 + x^2 + c$ **c** $-\dfrac{1}{2x^2} + \dfrac{2}{x} + c$

5 **a** $-\frac{3}{5}x^5 + 2x^3 + c$ **b** $\frac{3}{2}x^2 - x + \frac{1}{x} + c$
   c $\frac{4}{3}x^3 - \frac{8}{5}x^{\frac{5}{2}} + \frac{1}{2}x^2 + c$ **d** $4e^x - 3\ln|x| + c$
   e $-\frac{1}{4}\cos(4x - 5) + c$ **f** $-\frac{1}{3}e^{4-3x} + c$

6 **a** $y = -3e^{-x} - 2\cos(\frac{\pi}{2} - x) + c$
   b $y = \frac{1}{4}\sin 4x - \frac{1}{6}x^3 + c$

7 $f(x) = x^3 - 2x^2 + x + 2$ **8** $y = -2x^2 + 3x + 2$

9 $f(x) = \frac{3}{2}e^{2x} + \frac{1}{2}$

10 **a** $\frac{1}{2}x^2 - 7\ln|x| + c$ **b** $\frac{1}{2}e^{2x-3} - \frac{2}{3}\ln|3x - 1| + c$
   c $-\frac{1}{12}(4 - 3x)^4 + \frac{1}{2}\cos(-2x) + c$

11 $a = 6\sqrt{2}, \quad f(x) = 2\sqrt{2}\sin 3x - 1$

12 $\frac{3}{2}x + 2\cos x - \frac{1}{4}\sin 2x + c$

13 $\qquad \dfrac{d}{dx}\left(\sqrt{x^2 - 4}\right) = \dfrac{x}{\sqrt{x^2-4}}$

$\therefore \displaystyle\int \frac{x}{\sqrt{x^2-4}}\, dx = \sqrt{x^2 - 4} + c$

14 $-\frac{1}{2}\cos(x^2 + \frac{\pi}{3}) + c$

15 **a** $\frac{1}{2}\ln\left|x^2 + 4x\right| + c$ **b** $e^{x^2-1} + c$
   c $\frac{1}{10}\sin^{10} x + c$ **d** $-\frac{1}{2}\ln|\cos 2x| + c$

REVIEW SET 16B

1 $\qquad \dfrac{d}{dx}\left(6e^{-2x}\right) = -12e^{-2x}$

$\therefore \displaystyle\int e^{-2x}\, dx = -\frac{1}{2}e^{-2x} + c$

2 $\qquad \dfrac{d}{dx}\left(\ln(2x+1)\right) = \dfrac{2}{2x+1}$

$\therefore \displaystyle\int \frac{1}{2x+1}\, dx = \frac{1}{2}\ln|2x+1| + c$

3 **a** $x + \dfrac{2}{x} + c$ **b** $3x^3 - 12x^2 + 16x + c$ **c** $4x - \frac{2}{3}x^3 + c$

4 **a** $\frac{3}{4}x^{\frac{4}{3}} + 3x + c$ **b** $x^3 - 2x + c$ **c** $9x + 6x^2 + \frac{4}{3}x^3 + c$

5 $f(x) = \frac{1}{3}x^3 - \frac{3}{2}x^2 + 2x + 2\frac{1}{6}$

6 **a** $y = \frac{1}{5}x^5 - \frac{2}{3}x^3 + x + c$ **b** $y = 400x - 40x^{\frac{1}{2}} + c$

7 **a** $\frac{1}{2}x^4 - \frac{5}{2}x^2 + 7x + c$ **b** $\frac{3}{2}x^2 - \ln|x| + c$
   c $x - x^3 + \frac{3}{5}x^5 - \frac{1}{7}x^7 + c$ **d** $-2e^{-x} + 3x + c$
   e $2\sin 2x + c$ **f** $9x + 3e^{2x-1} + \frac{1}{4}e^{4x-2} + c$

8 $f(x) = 2\ln|x| - x + e + 2 - 2\ln 2$

9 $y = -\frac{3}{68}x^3 + \frac{21}{68}(x-1)^{\frac{3}{2}} + \frac{275}{68}$

10 $f(x) = -2\sqrt{4-3x} + 8$

11 $\displaystyle\int (\sin x - \cos x)^2\, dx = x + \frac{1}{2}\cos 2x + c$

12 **a** $-\frac{1}{2}\ln|3 - 2x| + c$ **b** $\frac{4}{5}\ln|5x + 1| + c$

13

$$\frac{d}{dx}\left((3x^2+x)^3\right)=3(3x^2+x)^2(6x+1)$$

$$\therefore \int (3x^2+x)^2(6x+1)\,dx=\tfrac{1}{3}(3x^2+x)^3+c$$

14 a $2\sqrt{x^2-5}+c$ **b** $\dfrac{1}{3\cos^3 x}+c$ **c** $-2e^{-x^2}+c$

  d $-\cos x+\tfrac{1}{3}\cos^3 x+c$

15 a $\tfrac{1}{2}\ln\left|x^2-9\right|+c$ **b** $\ln\left|\cos\left(\sin^{-1}\left(\tfrac{x}{3}\right)\right)\right|+c$

EXERCISE 17A

1 a $\displaystyle\int_1^4 \sqrt{x}\,dx=\tfrac{14}{3},\quad \int_1^4 (-\sqrt{x})\,dx=-\tfrac{14}{3}$

  b $\displaystyle\int_0^1 x^7\,dx=\tfrac{1}{8},\quad \int_0^1 (-x^7)\,dx=-\tfrac{1}{8}$

2 a $\tfrac{1}{3}$ **b** $\tfrac{7}{3}$ **c** $\tfrac{8}{3}$ **d** 1

3 a -4 **b** $6\tfrac{1}{4}$ **c** $2\tfrac{1}{4}$ **4 a** $\tfrac{1}{3}$ **b** $\tfrac{2}{3}$ **c** 1

5 a $\tfrac{1}{4}$ **b** $\tfrac{2}{3}$ **c** 18 **d** $1\tfrac{1}{2}$ **e** $16\tfrac{5}{6}$ **f** $6\tfrac{2}{3}$

  g $\tfrac{2}{3}$ **h** $20\tfrac{1}{3}$ **i** $21+\ln 4$

6 $m=-1$ or $\tfrac{4}{3}$ **7 a** $68\tfrac{1}{5}$ **b** 2 **c** $4\tfrac{2}{3}$

8 a $e-1$ **b** $2e^3-11$ **c** $\tfrac{1}{3}(e^6-1)$

  d $e-1$ **e** $\tfrac{3}{2}$ **f** $-\dfrac{1}{2e^4}-\dfrac{3}{2e^2}+\dfrac{2}{e}+1$

9 a 2 **b** $\tfrac{1}{2}$ **c** $\tfrac{1}{2}$ **d** $\tfrac{1}{3}$ **e** 1 **f** $\tfrac{1}{\sqrt{2}}$

10 $\tfrac{\pi}{8}+\tfrac{1}{4}$ **11** $\tfrac{\pi}{4}$ **12** $-\tfrac{1}{6}$ **13** $\ln 4$

14 a $-\ln 3$ **b** $\ln 3$ **c** $\tfrac{4}{3}\ln 2$ **d** $2\ln\left(\tfrac{13}{5}\right)$

15 $m=-5$ **17 a** ≈ 1.30 **b** ≈ 1.49 **c** ≈ -0.189

19 a $\displaystyle\int_2^7 f(x)\,dx$ **b** $\displaystyle\int_4^6 f(x)\,dx$ **c** $\displaystyle\int_1^9 g(x)\,dx$

20 a -5 **b** 4

21 a 4 **b** 0 **c** -8 **d** $k=-\tfrac{7}{4}$ **22** 0

23 a $\tfrac{1}{4}(x^2-1)^4+c$ **b** $\tfrac{81}{4}$

24 a $-\tfrac{1}{4}e^{-2x^2}+c$ **b** $\dfrac{e^6-1}{4e^8}$

25 a $-\tfrac{1}{2}\ln\left|2-x^2\right|+c$ **b** $\tfrac{1}{2}\ln\left(\tfrac{2}{7}\right)$

26 a $-\dfrac{1}{2(x^2+2)}+c$ **b** $\tfrac{1}{12}$

27 a $\tfrac{1}{3}\sin^3 x+c$ **b** $\tfrac{1}{24}$

EXERCISE 17B

1 a 6 units^2 **b** 6 units^2

2 a 30 units^2 **b** $4\tfrac{1}{2}$ units^2 **c** $13\tfrac{1}{2}$ units^2

3 a $5\tfrac{1}{3}$ units^2 **b** $12\tfrac{2}{3}$ units^2

4 a $\tfrac{1}{3}$ units^2 **b** $63\tfrac{3}{4}$ units^2 **c** $2\tfrac{1}{6}$ units^2

5 a $A(-2,0)$, $B(3,0)$ **b** $20\tfrac{5}{6}$ units^2

6 a $4\tfrac{1}{2}$ units^2 **b** 9 units^2 **c** $4\sqrt{3}$ units^2

8 1 unit^2 **9** $\tfrac{2}{3}$ units^2

10 a region A

  b A: $\tfrac{1}{2}$ units^2, B: $1-\tfrac{1}{\sqrt{2}}\approx 0.293$ units^2

  $\therefore$ region A is larger.

11 a $\tfrac{\pi}{4}$ **b** $-\ln|\cos x|+c$ **c** $\ln\sqrt{2}$ units^2

12 a $\tfrac{1}{2}$ units^2 **b** $(e-1)$ units^2 **c** $4\tfrac{1}{2}$ units^2

  d 18 units^2 **e** $\left(2e-\dfrac{2}{e}\right)$ units^2

13 b $\left(\dfrac{\sin 2}{1+\cos 2}\right)$ units^2 (≈ 1.56 units^2)

14 a $b=\left(\tfrac{3}{2}\right)^{\frac{2}{3}}\approx 1.3104$ **b** $a=\sqrt{3}$

  c $k=\dfrac{3e^{0.4}-1}{2}\approx 1.7377$ **d** $k=2\sqrt{5}$

EXERCISE 17C

1 a $4\tfrac{1}{2}$ units^2 **b** $(1+e^{-2})$ units^2

  c 2 units^2 **d** $2\tfrac{1}{4}$ units^2

2 a $40\tfrac{1}{2}$ units^2 **b** 8 units^2 **c** 8 units^2

3 a $\displaystyle\int_3^5 f(x)\,dx=-$ (area between $x=3$ and $x=5$)

  b $\displaystyle\int_1^3 f(x)\,dx-\int_3^5 f(x)\,dx+\int_5^7 f(x)\,dx$

4 Region B is larger.

  $\displaystyle\int_{-2}^4 f(x)\,dx=$ area of region $A+(-$ area of region $B)$

  $\{$region B is below the x-axis$\}$

  $=$ area of region $A-$ area of region B

  $=-6$

  $\therefore$ area of region $B>$ area of region A

5 $k=\tfrac{3}{2}$ or 6

6 a

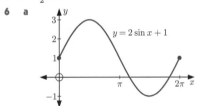

  b $\left(2\sqrt{3}-\dfrac{2\pi}{3}\right)$ units^2 (≈ 1.37 units^2)

7 a $33\tfrac{1}{3}$ cm^2 **b** ≈ 66.7 L **8 a** $\tfrac{1}{3}\sin(x^3)+c$

EXERCISE 17D

1 a

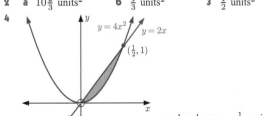

  b $(1,-2)$ and $(3,0)$

  c $1\tfrac{1}{3}$ units^2

2 a $10\tfrac{2}{3}$ units^2 **b** $\tfrac{1}{3}$ units^2 **3** $\tfrac{1}{2}$ units^2

4

enclosed area $=\tfrac{1}{12}$ units^2

5 **a** $A(\frac{1}{2}, \frac{5}{2})$, $B(2, 1)$ **b** $\left(\frac{21}{8} - \frac{5}{2}\ln\left(\frac{5}{2}\right)\right)$ units^2

6 $k \approx 2.3489$

7

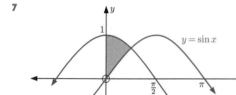

enclosed area $= (\sqrt{2} - 1)$ units^2

8 **a** C_1 is $y = 4\sin x$, C_2 is $y = \sin x$ **b** 6 units^2

9 **a** C_1 is $y = \cos^2 x$, C_2 is $y = \cos 2x$

  b $A(0, 1)$, $B(\frac{\pi}{4}, 0)$, $C(\frac{\pi}{2}, 0)$, $D(\frac{3\pi}{4}, 0)$, $E(\pi, 1)$

10 **a**

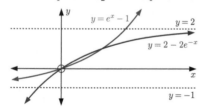

  b $(0, 0)$ and $(\ln 2, 1)$ **c** $(3\ln 2 - 2)$ units^2

11 **a** $A = \displaystyle\int_{-2}^{-1} (x^3 - 7x - 6)\, dx + \int_{-1}^{3} (-x^3 + 7x + 6)\, dx$

  b $32\frac{3}{4}$ units^2

12 **a**

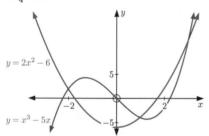

  b $x = -2$, 1, and 3 **c** $21\frac{1}{12}$ units^2

13 **a** 8 units^2 **b** $101\frac{3}{4}$ units^2

14 **a** C_1 is $y = \sin 2x$, C_2 is $y = \sin x$

  b $A(\frac{\pi}{3}, \frac{\sqrt{3}}{2})$ **c** $2\frac{1}{2}$ units^2

EXERCISE 17E

1 **a** 20 cars per minute   **b** $\approx$ 8:05 am

  c

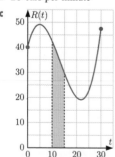

$\displaystyle\int_{10}^{15} R(t)\, dt$ represents the total number of cars going past the pedestrian crossing from 8:10 am to 8:15 am.

d 1031 cars

2 **a** **i** $\approx$ 1.65 L per minute   **ii** $\approx$ 1.09 L per minute

  b The rate of water leaking into the kayak is greater than the rate of water being bailed from the kayak after 2 minutes. So, the amount of water in the kayak is increasing after 2 minutes.

  c **i** $\displaystyle\int_0^3 R_1(t)\, dt \approx 3.72$

   About 3.72 litres of water have leaked into the kayak in the first 3 minutes.

  ii $\displaystyle\int_2^5 R_2(t)\, dt \approx 5.27$

   About 5.27 litres of water have been bailed out of the kayak from $t = 2$ minutes to $t = 5$ minutes.

  iii $\displaystyle\int_0^8 [R_1(t) - R_2(t)]\, dt \approx 5.09$

   There are about 5.09 litres of water in the kayak 8 minutes after striking the rock.

  d $\approx$ 6.31 litres

3 **a** C_1 is $y = 3\sin\frac{\pi t}{10}$, C_2 is $y = \sin\frac{\pi t}{10}$ **b** $\frac{40}{\pi}$ units

  c The area in **b** represents the total amount of energy that enters the greenhouse in the first 10 hours.

4 **a**

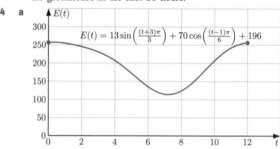

$E(t) = 13\sin\left(\frac{(t+3)\pi}{3}\right) + 70\cos\left(\frac{(t-1)\pi}{6}\right) + 196$

  b **i** $\displaystyle\int_3^4 E(t)\, dt \approx 220.12$

   The power consumption of the United Kingdom in April is about 220.12 TWh.

  ii $\displaystyle\int_5^8 E(t)\, dt \approx 392.96$

   The power consumption of the United Kingdom from June 1st to September 1st is about 392.96 TWh.

  iii $\displaystyle\int_0^{12} E(t)\, dt = 2352$

   The yearly power consumption of the United Kingdom is 2352 TWh.

REVIEW SET 17A

1 **a** 8   **b** $\frac{1}{8} - \frac{1}{3\sqrt{2}}$ **c** $11\frac{13}{15}$

2 **a** $b = 3$ **b** $b \approx 1.86$

3 **a** $12\frac{4}{9}$ **b** $\sqrt{2}$ **c** $2\ln 3$

4 $a = \frac{1}{2}\ln 2$ **5** $\frac{\pi}{12} - \frac{1}{4}$

6 $\dfrac{d}{dx}\left(e^{-2x}\sin x\right) = e^{-2x}(\cos x - 2\sin x)$

  $\therefore \displaystyle\int_0^{\frac{\pi}{2}} \left[e^{-2x}(\cos x - 2\sin x)\right]\, dx = e^{-\pi}$

7 **a** $\approx 1.236\,17$ **b** $\approx 1.952\,49$

8 **a** $\frac{1}{4}(x^2+1)^4 + c$ **b** **i** $\frac{15}{4}$ **ii** $-\frac{609}{8}$

9 **a** $-\frac{1}{3}e^{1-x^3} + c$

10 **a** 9 units^2 **b** $(3\pi + 1)$ units^2 **c** 36 units^2
   d $(3\ln 3 - 2)$ units^2

11 **a** 39 units^2 **b** $\left(\frac{16}{3} - 2\sqrt{3}\right)$ units^2 **c** 3 units^2

12 **a**
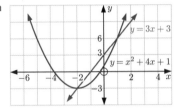
   b $(-2, -3)$ and $(1, 6)$
   c $4\frac{1}{2}$ units^2

13 No, total area shaded $= \int_{-1}^{1} f(x)\,dx - \int_{1}^{3} f(x)\,dx$.

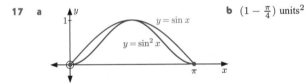

14 $k = \sqrt[3]{16}$ **15** **a** $a = \ln 3$ **b** $b = \ln 5$ **16** $40\frac{1}{2}$ units^2

17 **a**
   b $\left(1 - \frac{\pi}{4}\right)$ units^2

18 **a** **i** $\int_{0}^{\frac{1}{2}} R_2(t)\,dt \approx 0.655$

   About 655 millilitres of water leak from the watering can in the first 30 seconds.

   ii $\int_{0}^{1} [R_1(t) - R_2(t)]\,dt \approx 5.03$

   There are about 5.03 litres of water in the watering can after 1 minute.

   b ≈ 199 seconds

19 **a** $-\frac{1}{2}\cos(x^2) + c$

REVIEW SET 17B

1 **a** $2 - \frac{2\sqrt{2}}{\sqrt{3}}$ **b** -3 **c** $\frac{8}{15}$ **2** $a = \frac{3}{2}$

3 **a** $\frac{2}{3}(\sqrt{5} - \sqrt{2})$ **b** $4\ln\left(\frac{4}{3}\right)$ **c** $\frac{\pi}{4} + \sqrt{2}$

4 $b = \frac{\pi}{4}$ or $\frac{3\pi}{4}$ **5** $\frac{\pi}{6} + \frac{\sqrt{3}}{4}$

6 **a** ≈ 3.528 **b** ≈ 2.963

7 **a** 6   **b** 3   **c** $k = -\frac{5}{3}$

8 **b** $\frac{\pi}{4} - \frac{1}{2}$

9 **a** $e^{3x} + 6e^{2x} + 12e^x + 8$ **b** $\frac{1}{3}e^3 + 3e^2 + 12e - 7\frac{1}{3}$

10 **a** $-\dfrac{1}{2(1+\sin x)^2} + c$ **b** $\frac{5}{18}$

11 **a** 22 units^2 **b** $\ln 3$ units^2 **c** $\dfrac{e^4 - 1}{2}$ units^2
   d $\frac{4\pi}{3}$ units^2

12 $4\frac{1}{2}$ units^2 **13** $(3 - \ln 4)$ units^2

14 **a**
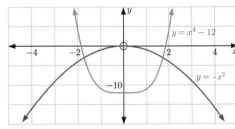
   b $(-\sqrt{3}, -3)$ and $(\sqrt{3}, -3)$ **c** $\frac{92\sqrt{3}}{5}$ units^2

15 $k = \frac{4}{3}$ **16** $m = \frac{\pi}{3}$ **17** $21\frac{1}{12}$ units^2

18 **a** $a = -3$ **b** A has x-coordinate $\sqrt[3]{4}$.

19 **a** $\int_{5}^{12} E(t)\,dt \approx 10.7$

   The solar energy transferred into Callum's solar panels from 5 am to 12 pm is about 10.7 kWh.

   b $\int_{12}^{20} E(t)\,dt \approx 12.9$

   The solar energy transferred into Callum's solar panels from 12 pm to 8 pm is about 12.9 kWh.

   c $\int_{5}^{20} E(t)\,dt \approx 23.5$

   The solar energy transferred into Callum's solar panels from 5 am to 8 pm is about 23.5 kWh.

EXERCISE 18A

1 **a** 5 cm to the right of the origin
   b **i** 2 cm to the right of the origin
      ii 5 cm to the left of the origin
   c at $t = 5$ s
   d No, the displacement function $s(t)$ is linear, so it has no turning points.
   e

2 **a** 1 m to the right of the origin   **b**
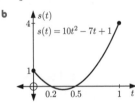
   c $t = 0.35$ s, 0.225 m to the left of the origin
   d at $0 \leqslant t < 0.2$ s and $0.5 < t \leqslant 1$ s
   e

3 **a** at $t = 0$ s, $t = 0.125$ s, and $t = 0.25$ s
   b
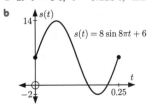

c 14 cm to the right of the origin, at $t = 0.0625$ s, and 2 cm to the left of the origin, at $t = 0.1875$ s

d

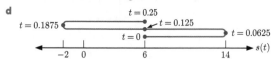

EXERCISE 18B.1

1 a i 3 m   **ii** -3 m   **b** -2 m s^{-1} **c** $-\frac{2}{3}$ m s^{-1}

2 a -2 m s^{-1} **b** $v(t) = 2t - 6$ m s^{-1}

c i -4 m s^{-1} **ii** 4 m s^{-1}

3 a 2 cm to the left of the origin   **b** $t = 6$ s
c to the right   **d** $t = 3$ s and $t = 9$ s
e i

f 1 cm s^{-1}

4 a $\frac{2}{3}$ cm s^{-1} **b** 3 cm to the right of the origin

c $v(t) = \dfrac{1}{\sqrt{t}}$ cm s^{-1} **d i** $\frac{1}{2}$ cm s^{-1} **ii** $\frac{1}{4}$ cm s^{-1}

5 a $v(t) = 3t^2 - 22t + 24$ m s^{-1}
b The object is initially at the origin, moving to the right at 24 m s^{-1}.
c

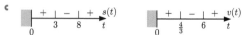

d at 0 s, 3 s, and 8 s
e at $\frac{4}{3}$ s and 6 s; $s(\frac{4}{3}) \approx 14.8$ m, $s(6) = -36$ m
f The object starts at O, and moves towards the right at 24 m s^{-1}. Its velocity is decreasing. After $\frac{4}{3}$ seconds, when it is 14.8 m to the right of O, it changes direction and moves to the left, passing O after 3 seconds. After 6 seconds, when it is 36 m to the left of O, it changes direction again and moves towards the right, passing O once more after 8 seconds.
g

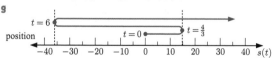

6 b i 69.58 m s^{-1} **ii** ≈ 247 m

EXERCISE 18B.2

1 110 m

2 a i travelling forwards
  ii travelling backwards (opposite direction)
b 16 km   **c** 8 km from starting point (on positive side)
3 a

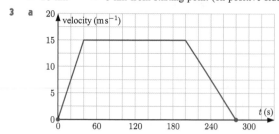

b 3.3 km

4 a

velocity (km h^{-1}) graph — trapezoidal shape with axes marked 10, 20, 30, 40, 50 on velocity and 0, 2, 4, 6, 8, 10, 12, 14, 16, 18 on t (mins)

b $6\frac{1}{6}$ km

5 a at $t = \frac{1}{2}$ second   **b** $\frac{1}{2}$ cm   **c** 0 cm

6 a $s(t) = \frac{1}{3}t^3 - \frac{1}{2}t^2 - 2t$ cm   **b** $5\frac{1}{6}$ cm
c $1\frac{1}{2}$ cm left of its starting point

7 a $s(t) = 29.4t - 4.9t^2 + 1$ m   **b** 45.1 m

8 a $s(t) = 32t + 2t^2 + 16$ m
b There is no change in direction,
  so displacement $= s(\tau) - s(0) = \displaystyle\int_0^\tau (32 + 4t)\, dt$
c 160 m

9 a 1 m   **b** $s(\frac{\pi}{3}) = \dfrac{\sqrt{3}+2}{4}$ m

10 a

$v(t)$ (cm per second) graph — sinusoidal curve with axes marked 5, 10, 15, 20, 25 and t (seconds) 0 to 6; labelled $v(t) = 20 + 5\sin 4t$

b ≈ 16.2 cm s^{-1} **c** ≈ 41.4 cm

11 a $s(t) = -4t + \frac{2}{3}t^{\frac{3}{2}}$ m   **b** $t = 16$ s
c ≈ 10.5 m left of the origin   **d** ≈ 32.2 m

12 a i 10 m s^{-1} **ii** $10\sqrt{2}$ m s^{-1} **b** $s(t) = \frac{20}{3}t^{\frac{3}{2}}$ m
c $\displaystyle\int_0^2 v(t)\, dt \approx 18.9$ The motorcyclist travels about 18.9 m in the first 2 seconds.
d i 4 seconds
  ii Yes, he only needs $53\frac{1}{3}$ m to reach the required speed.

13 a ≈ 513 m   **b** ≈ 0.637 cm

EXERCISE 18C

1 a 16 cm s^{-1} **b** 6 cm s^{-2}
c $a(t) = 10 - 2t$ cm s^{-2} **d** 4 cm s^{-2}

2 a $s(2) = -1$ m, $v(2) = 8$ m s^{-1}, $a(2) = 10$ m s^{-2}
b $t = \frac{1}{3}$ s

3 a $v(t) = 98 - 9.8t$ m s^{-1} $a(t) = -9.8$ m s^{-2}

$v(t)$ number line diagram (+ from 0 to 10, − from 10 to 20) and $a(t)$ number line diagram (− from 0 to 20)

b $s(0) = 0$ m above the ground, $v(0) = 98$ m s^{-1} upward
c At $t = 5$ s, the stone is 367.5 m above the ground and moving upward at 49 m s^{-1}. It has acceleration -9.8 m s^{-2}. At $t = 12$ s, the stone is 470.4 m above the ground and moving downward at 19.6 m s^{-1}. It has acceleration -9.8 m s^{-2}.
d 490 m   **e** 20 seconds

4 a $v(t) = 100 - 40e^{-\frac{t}{5}}$ cm s^{-1}, $a(t) = 8e^{-\frac{t}{5}}$ cm s^{-2}
  b $s(0) = 200$ cm to the right of the origin
  $v(0) = 60$ cm s^{-1}, $a(0) = 8$ cm s^{-2}
  c as $t \to \infty$, $v(t) \to 100$ cm s^{-1} (below)
  d as $t \to \infty$, $a(t) \to 0$ cm s^{-2}

5 b $v(t) = 1 - \dfrac{2}{2t+1}$ cm s^{-1}
  c **i** $t > \frac{1}{2}$ **ii** $0 \leqslant t < \frac{1}{2}$ **e** $\frac{4}{25}$ cm s^{-2}
  f $1 + \ln\left(\frac{4}{5}\right) \approx 0.777$ cm

6 a 40 m s^{-1} **b** ≈ 47.8 m s^{-1} **c** $2\ln 2 \approx 1.39$ seconds
  d as $t \to \infty$, $v(t) \to 50$ from below
  e $a(t) = 5e^{-0.5t}$ and as $e^x > 0$ for all x, then $a(t) > 0$ for all t.
  f $t = 2\ln\left(\frac{5}{2}\right)$ seconds
  g   **h** ≈ 134 m

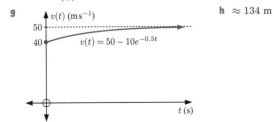

7 a $v(t) = \dfrac{t^2}{20} - 3t + 45$ m s^{-1}
  b $\displaystyle\int_0^{60} v(t)\,dt = 900$ The train travels a total of 900 m in the first 60 seconds.

8 a **Hint:** Show that $v(t) = 100 - 80e^{-\frac{1}{20}t}$ m s^{-1} and as $t \to \infty$, $v(t) \to 100$ m s^{-1}.
  b ≈ 370 m

9 a $v(t) = -\dfrac{1}{(t+1)^2} + 1$ m s^{-1}
  b $s(t) = \dfrac{1}{t+1} + t - 1$ m
  c The particle is $\frac{4}{3}$ m to the right of the origin, moving to the right at $\frac{8}{9}$ m s^{-1}, and accelerating at $\frac{2}{27}$ m s^{-2}.

EXERCISE 18D

1 a $v(t) = 2t - 6$ m s^{-1} $a(t) = 2$ m s^{-2}

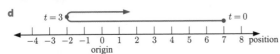

  b $s(0) = 7$ m, $v(0) = -6$ m s^{-1}, $a(0) = 2$ m s^{-2}
  Initially, the object is 7 m to the right of O, moving to the left at 6 m s^{-1}, with acceleration 2 m s^{-2}.
  c 2 m to the left of O
  d

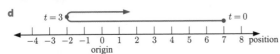

  e $0 \leqslant t \leqslant 3$

2 a 1.2 m
  b $s'(t) = 28.1 - 9.8t$ represents the instantaneous velocity of the ball.
  c ≈ 41.5 m
  d **i** 28.1 m s^{-1} **ii** 8.5 m s^{-1} **iii** 20.9 m s^{-1}

3 a $v(t) = 12 - 6t^2$ cm s^{-1}, $a(t) = -12t$ cm s^{-2}
  b $s(0) = -1$ cm, $v(0) = 12$ cm s^{-1}, $a(0) = 0$ cm s^{-2}
  The particle started 1 cm to the left of the origin and was travelling to the right at a constant speed of 12 cm s^{-1}.
  c $t = \sqrt{2}$ s, $s(\sqrt{2}) = 8\sqrt{2} - 1$ cm
  d **i** $t \geqslant \sqrt{2}$ s   **ii** never
  e

4 a $v(t) = -\dfrac{1}{2\sqrt{t+1}}$ m s^{-1} $a(t) = \dfrac{1}{4(t+1)^{\frac{3}{2}}}$ m s^{-2}

  b $s(0) = 3$ m, $v(0) = -\frac{1}{2}$ m s^{-1}, $a(0) = \frac{1}{4}$ m s^{-2}
  Initially, the particle is 3 m to the right of O, moving to the left at $\frac{1}{2}$ m s^{-1} with acceleration $\frac{1}{4}$ m s^{-2}.
  c After 3 seconds, the particle is 2 m to the right of O, moving to the left at $\frac{1}{4}$ m s^{-1}, with acceleration $\frac{1}{32}$ m s^{-2}.
  d The particle's speed is continuously decreasing.

5 a $k \approx 1.87$
  b $v(t) = -9.8t + 4.9$ m s^{-1} $a(t) = -9.8$ m s^{-2}

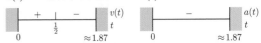

  c **i** decreasing   **ii** increasing

6 a $x(0) = -1$ cm, $v(0) = 0$ cm s^{-1}, $a(0) = 2$ cm s^{-2}
  b At $t = \frac{\pi}{4}$ seconds, the particle is $(\sqrt{2} - 1)$ cm to the left of O, moving to the right at $\sqrt{2}$ cm s^{-1}, with acceleration $\sqrt{2}$ cm s^{-2}.
  c changes direction when $t = \pi$ s, $x(\pi) = 3$ cm
  d increasing for $0 \leqslant t \leqslant \frac{\pi}{2}$ and $\pi \leqslant t \leqslant \frac{3\pi}{2}$

7 a **i** right   **ii** left   **b** $v(t) = 4\cos\frac{t}{2}$ m s^{-1}
  c **i** left   **ii** right   **d** $a(t) = -2\sin\frac{t}{2}$ m s^{-2}
  e decreasing

8 a

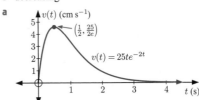

  c $0 \leqslant t \leqslant \frac{1}{2}$ **d** $t \geqslant \frac{1}{2}$

9 a lion: ≈ 13.6 m s^{-1},   zebra: ≈ 1.90 m s^{-1}
  b

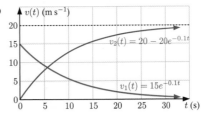

  The lion's speed $v_1(t)$ decreases over time whereas the zebra's speed $v_2(t)$ increases over time.

c $\displaystyle\int_0^3 v_1(t)\,dt = 150 - 150e^{-0.3} \approx 38.9$

The lion has travelled about 38.9 m in the first 3 seconds.

d $\displaystyle\int_0^3 [v_1(t) - v_2(t)]\,dt = 290 - 350e^{-0.3}$
≈ 30.7

In the first 3 seconds, the lion has gained about 30.7 m on the zebra.

e At the time when $v_1(t) = v_2(t)$, the lion and the zebra will be moving at the same speed. Since the lion's speed decreases over time and the zebra's speed increases over time, the zebra will be faster than the lion after that time. So, they will be closest at the point when their speeds are equal.

f $-10\ln\left(\frac{4}{7}\right) \approx 5.60$ s

g No, the lion was about 1.92 m from the zebra at their closest point.

REVIEW SET 18A

1 a 12 m to the right of the origin
   b i 10 m to the right of the origin   c $t = 6$ s
      ii 6 m to the right of the origin
   d No, the displacement function is linear, so it has no turning points.
   e

2 a 13 cm s^{-1} b i 9 cm s^{-1} ii 17 cm s^{-1}
   c $a(t) = 4$ cm s^{-2}
3 a $v(t) = 6t^2 - 18t + 12$ cm s^{-1}, $a(t) = 12t - 18$ cm s^{-2}

   b $s(0) = 5$ cm to left of origin
      $v(0) = 12$ cm s^{-1} towards origin
      $a(0) = -18$ cm s^{-2} (decreasing speed)
   c At $t = 2$, the particle is 1 cm to the left of the origin, is instantaneously stationary, and is beginning to accelerate.
   d at $t = 1$ s, $s = 0$ cm, and at $t = 2$ s, $s = -1$ cm
   e
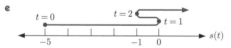
   f Speed is increasing for $1 \leqslant t \leqslant 1\frac{1}{2}$ and $t \geqslant 2$.
4 a
   b The particle moves in the positive direction initially, then at $t = 2$, $6\frac{2}{3}$ m from its starting point, it changes direction. It changes direction again at $t = 4$, $5\frac{1}{3}$ m from its starting point, and at $t = 5$, it is $6\frac{2}{3}$ m from its starting point again.
   c $6\frac{2}{3}$ m   d $9\frac{1}{3}$ m
5 a i 2.75 m s^{-1} ii ≈ 1.62 m s^{-1}
   b Hint: Show that $a(t)$ and $v(t)$ are opposite in sign for all $0 \leqslant t \leqslant 6$.
   c $\displaystyle\int_0^2 v(t)\,dt \approx 4.54$ The kayak travels approximately 4.54 m in the first 2 seconds after the kayaker stops paddling.

6 a $v(t) = 15 + \dfrac{120}{(t+1)^3}$ cm s^{-1}, $a(t) = -\dfrac{360}{(t+1)^4}$ cm s^{-2}
   b At $t = 3$, the particle is 41.25 cm to the right of O, moving to the right at ≈ 16.9 cm s^{-1}, with decreasing speed $(a(3) \approx -1.41$ cm s$^{-2})$.
   c The particle's speed is never increasing.
7 a $x(0) = 3$ m, $x'(0) = 2\pi$ m s^{-1}, $x''(0) = 0$ m s^{-2}
   b $t = \frac{1}{2}, 1\frac{1}{2}, 2\frac{1}{2}, 3\frac{1}{2}, 4\frac{1}{2}$ s   c 20 m
8 a 1 m   b 6 m   c 4 m
9 a $v(t) = -2t + 65$ m s^{-1} b $s(t) = -t^2 + 65t$ m
   c i 31 s   ii 1054 m
10 a $v(0) = 25$ m s^{-1}, $v(3) = 4$ m s^{-1}
    b as $t \to \infty$, $v(t) \to 0$ from above
    c
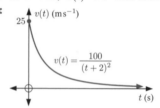
    d $\displaystyle\int_0^2 v(t)\,dt = 25$ The boat travels a total distance of 25 m in the first 2 seconds after its engine is turned off.
    e 3 seconds

REVIEW SET 18B

1 a 1 m to the right of the origin   b 8 m s^{-1}
   c $v(t) = 2t + 4$ m s^{-1} d 6 m s^{-1}
2 200 m
3 a $v(t) = 3t^2 - 30t + 27$ cm s^{-1}
   b -162 cm (162 cm to the left of the origin)
4 a $v(t) = 3 - \frac{3}{2}\sqrt{t}$ cm s^{-1} $a(t) = -\dfrac{3}{4\sqrt{t}}$ cm s^{-2}

   b $x(0) = 0$, $v(0) = 3$
      The particle is initially at the origin, moving to the right at 3 cm s^{-1}.
   c The particle is ≈ 3.17 cm to the right of the origin, travelling to the right at ≈ 0.879 cm s^{-1}, with decreasing speed $(a(2) \approx -0.530$ cm s$^{-2})$.
   d at $t = 4$ s, 4 cm to the right of O   e $0 \leqslant t \leqslant 4$
   f

   g ≈ 4.70 cm
5 a i 7.2 m s^{-2} ii 9.6 m s^{-2} iii 0 m s^{-2}
      iv -12 m s^{-2}
   b $\displaystyle\int_0^3 v(t)\,dt = 27$ The human cannonball travels 27 m in the first 3 seconds.
   c ≈ 3.14 s
6 a $v(t) = -8e^{-\frac{t}{10}} - 40$ m s^{-1}
      $a(t) = \frac{4}{5}e^{-\frac{t}{10}}$ m s^{-2} $\{t \geqslant 0\}$
   b $s(0) = 80$ m, $v(0) = -48$ m s^{-1}, $a(0) = 0.8$ m s^{-2}

c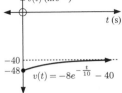

d $t = 10 \ln 2$ seconds

7 a $v(0) = 0$ cm s^{-1}, $v(\frac{1}{2}) = -\pi$ cm s^{-1}, $v(1) = 0$ cm s^{-1},
$v(1\frac{1}{2}) = \pi$ cm s^{-1}, $v(2) = 0$ cm s^{-1}

b $0 \leqslant t \leqslant 1$, $2 \leqslant t \leqslant 3$, $4 \leqslant t \leqslant 5$, and so on
So, for $2n \leqslant t \leqslant 2n+1$, $n \in \{0, 1, 2, 3, ...\}$

8 a ≈ 6.76 m s^{-1}
b $a(t) = 0.15(t^{1.1} + 3t)^{0.5}(1.1t^{0.1} + 3)$ m s^{-2}
c ≈ 1.79 m s^{-2} **d** ≈ 109 m

9 a $s(t) = -\frac{1}{96}t^4 - \frac{1}{24}t^2 + 2$ m   **b** ≈ 3.46 s

10 a Tyson

b $\int_0^5 v_1(t)\, dt \approx 42.0$ Tyson has travelled about 42.0 m in the first 5 seconds of the race.

c $s_1(t) = 10t + 8e^{-1.25t} - 8$ m   **d** Tyson
$s_2(t) = 10.5t + 10.5e^{-t} - 10.5$ m

e Hint: Find t such that $s_1(t) = 100$.   **f** Maurice

EXERCISE 19A

1 a weak, positive, linear correlation, with no outliers
b strong, negative, linear correlation, with one outlier
c no correlation
d strong, negative, non-linear correlation, with one outlier
e moderate, positive, linear correlation, with no outliers
f weak, positive, non-linear correlation, with no outliers

2 a *Hours worked* is the explanatory variable.
Number of customers is the response variable.

b

c i Monday and Friday   **ii** Wednesday and Sunday
d The more hours that Tiffany works, the more customers she is likely to have.

3 a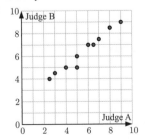

b There appears to be **strong**, **positive**, **linear** correlation between Judge A's scores and Judge B's scores. This means that as Judge A's scores increase, Judge B's scores **increase**.

c No, the scores are related to the quality of the ice skaters' performances.

4 a i job G   **ii** job C

b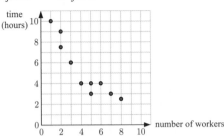

c There is a strong, negative, non-linear correlation between *number of workers* and *time*.

5 a D   **b** A   **c** B   **d** C

6 a There is a moderate, positive, linear correlation between *hours of study* and *marks obtained*.
b The test is out of 50 marks, so the outlier (> 50) appears to be an error. It should be discarded.
c Yes, this is a causal relationship as spending more time studying for the test is likely to cause a higher mark.

7 a Not causal, dependent on genetics and/or age.
b Not causal, dependent on the size of the fire.
c Causal, an increase in advertising is likely to cause an increase in sales.
d Causal, the childrens' adult height is determined by the genetics they receive from their parents to a great extent.
e Not causal, dependent on population of town.

EXERCISE 19B

1 weak, positive correlation

2 a B   **b** A   **c** D   **d** C   **e** E

3 a i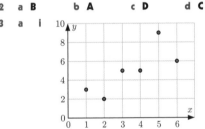
ii $r \approx 0.786$
iii moderate, positive correlation

b i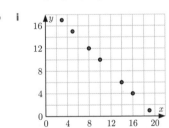
ii $r = -1$
iii perfect, negative correlation

c i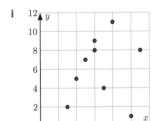
ii $r \approx 0.146$
iii very weak, positive correlation

4 a

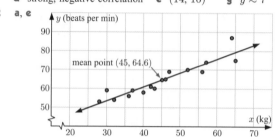

(scatter plot: text messages received vs phone calls received)

b $r \approx 0.816$
c moderate, positive correlation
d Those students who receive several phone calls are also likely to receive several text messages and vice versa.

5 a $r \approx 0.917$
b strong, positive correlation
In general, the higher the young athlete's age, the further they can throw a discus.

6 a

(scatter plot: drying time (y minutes) vs temperature (x °C))

b $r \approx -0.987$ **c** very strong, negative correlation

7 a

(scatter plot: number of car accidents vs number of supermarkets)

b $r \approx 0.572$
c The point $(3, 37)$, which represents 37 car accidents in a town with 3 supermarkets, is an outlier.
d   **i** $r \approx 0.928$
   ii strong, positive correlation
   iii Removing the outlier had a very significant effect on the value of r.
e No, it is not a causal relationship. Both variables depend on the number of people in each town, not on each other.

8 a

(scatter plot: MS incidence per 100 000 vs latitude (degrees))

b $r \approx 0.849$ **c** moderate, positive correlation
d The incidence of MS is higher near the poles.

EXERCISE 19C

1 a, f

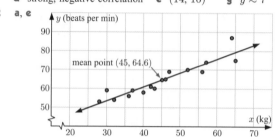

(scatter plot with mean point (14, 16))

b negatively correlated   **c** $r \approx -0.881$
d strong, negative correlation   **e** (14, 16)   **g** $y \approx 7$

2 a, e

(scatter plot: y (beats per min) vs x (kg), mean point (45, 64.6))

b $r \approx 0.929$
c There is a strong, positive correlation between *weight* and *pulse rate*.
d (45, 64.6)
f ≈ 68 beats per minute. This is an interpolation, so the estimate is reliable.

3 a, e

(scatter plot: y (m) vs x (cm), mean point (45, 15.7))

b (20, 22)   **c** very tall and thin   **d** (45, 15.7)
f ≈ 37 m. This is an extrapolation, so the prediction may not be reliable.
g ≈ 25 cm. This is an interpolation, so the estimate is reliable.

EXERCISE 19D

1 a, c

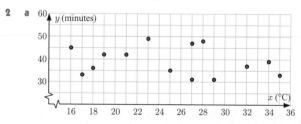

(scatter plot)

b $y \approx 1.92x - 0.0667$

2 a

(scatter plot: y (minutes) vs x (°C))

b $r \approx -0.219$

c There is a very weak, negative correlation between *temperature* and *time*.

d No, as there is almost no correlation.

3 a $r \approx -0.924$

b There is a strong, negative, linear correlation between the *petrol price* and the *number of customers*.

c $y \approx -4.27x + 489$

d ≈ -4.27; this indicates that for every cent per litre the petrol price increases by, the number of customers will decrease by approximately 4.27.

e ≈ -5.10 customers   **f** ≈ 105.3 cents per litre

g In **e**, it is impossible to have a negative number of customers. This extrapolation is not valid.
In **f**, this is an interpolation, so this estimate is likely to be reliable.

4 a

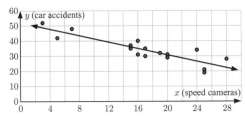

b $r \approx -0.878$

c There is a strong, negative correlation between *number of speed cameras* and *number of car accidents*.

d $y \approx -1.06x + 52.0$

e gradient: ≈ -1.06; this indicates that for every additional speed camera, the number of car accidents per week decreases by an average of 1.06.
y-intercept: ≈ 52.0; this indicates that if there were no speed cameras in a city, an average of 52.0 car accidents would occur each week.

f ≈ 41.4 car accidents

5 a, d

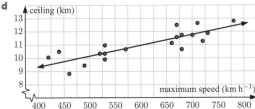

b $r \approx 0.840$

c moderate, positive, linear correlation

d $y \approx 0.008\,12x + 6.09$

e $\approx 0.008\,12$; this indicates that for each additional $km\,h^{-1}$, the ceiling increases by an average of 0.008 12 km or 8.12 m.

f ≈ 11.0 km   **g** ≈ 605 $km\,h^{-1}$

6 a, d

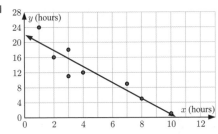

b $r \approx -0.927$

c There is a strong, negative, linear correlation between *time exercising* and *time watching television*.

d $y \approx -2.13x + 22.1$

e gradient: ≈ -2.13; this indicates that for each additional hour a child exercises each week, the number of hours they spend watching television each week decreases by 2.13.
y-intercept: ≈ 22.1; this indicates that for children who do not spend time exercising, they would watch television for an average of 22.1 hours per week.

f **i** 9 hours per week   **ii** ≈ 7.22 hours per week
   iii This particular child spent more time watching television than predicted.

7 a

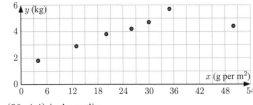

(50, 4.4) is the outlier.

b **i** reduces the strength of the correlation
   ii decreases the gradient of the regression line

c **i** $r \approx 0.798$ **ii** $r \approx 0.993$

d **i** $y \approx 0.0672x + 2.22$ **ii** $y \approx 0.119x + 1.32$

e The one which excludes the outlier, as this will be more accurate for an interpolation.

f Too much fertiliser often kills the plants. In this case, the outlier should be kept when analysing the data as it is a valid data value. If the outlier is a recording error caused by bad measurement or recording skills, it should be removed before analysing data.

EXERCISE 19E

1 a The y variable, money spent on fast food, can be measured exactly. The x variable, time spent on homemade meals, will not be measured exactly.

b $x \approx -0.0576y + 8.29$

c **i** ≈ 5.70 hours   **ii** $\approx \$57.13$

2 a

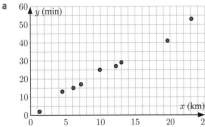

b x against y, since a student's time taken to travel to school can be more precisely measured than their distance from school.

c ≈ 33.9 min

d This is an interpolation, so this estimate is likely to be reliable.

3 a, c

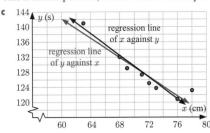

b i $y \approx -1.28x + 219$ **ii** $x \approx -0.693y + 160$
c The two regression lines are very similar. The regression line of x against y is slightly steeper.

4 b The regression lines are the same if $r^2 = 1$.

REVIEW SET 19A

1 a strong, positive, linear correlation, with no outliers
  b weak, negative, linear correlation, with one outlier
  c strong, negative, non-linear correlation, with no outliers

2 a The correlation between water bills and electricity bills is likely to be positive, as a household with a high water bill is also likely to have a high electricity bill, and vice versa.
  b No, there is not a causal relationship. Both variables mainly depend on the number of occupants in each house.

3 a

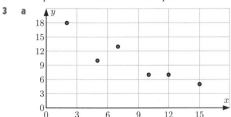

  b negative   **c** $r \approx -0.906$

4 a

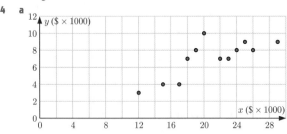

  b $r \approx 0.776$ **c** moderate, positive correlation

5 a mean time ≈ 13.3 min, mean spending $\approx €57.07$
  b

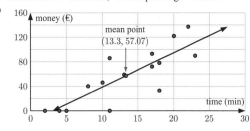

  c There is a moderate positive linear correlation between *time in the store* and *money spent*.

6 a

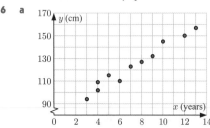

  b $y \approx 5.98x + 80.0$
  c ≈ 5.98; this indicates that each year, a child grows taller by an average of 5.98 cm.
  d ≈ 110 cm   **e** ≈ 10 years old

7 a

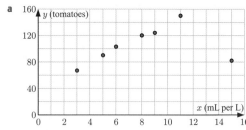

  b $r \approx 0.340$. There is a very weak, positive, linear correlation between spray concentrations and yield.
  c Yes, $(15, 82)$ is an outlier.
  d $r \approx 0.994$. Yes it is now reasonable to draw a regression line.
  e $y \approx 9.93x + 39.5$
  f gradient: ≈ 9.93; this indicates that for every additional mL per L the spray concentration increases, the yield of tomatoes per bush increases on average by 9.93.
    y-intercept: ≈ 39.5; this indicates that if the tomato bushes are not sprayed, the average yield per bush is approximately 39.5 tomatoes.
  g i ≈ 109 tomatoes per bush   **ii** ≈ 16.2 mL per L
  h In **g i**, this is an interpolation, so this estimate is likely to be reliable.
    In **g ii**, this is an extrapolation, so this estimate may not be reliable.

8 a

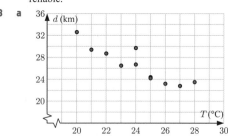

  b The values for the distance travelled d are more precisely measured than the daily temperature which Thomas is just estimating.
  c $T \approx -0.689d + 42.3$ **d** ≈ 17.9 km

REVIEW SET 19B

1 a Negative correlation. As prices increase, the number of tickets sold is likely to decrease.
    Causal. Less people will be able to afford tickets as the prices increase.
  b Positive correlation. As ice cream sales increase, the number of shark attacks is likely to increase.
    Not causal. Both of these variables are dependent on the number of people at the beach.

2 a

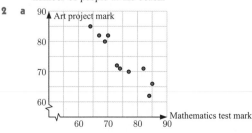

  b There is a strong, negative, linear correlation between Mathematics and Art marks.
  c $r \approx -0.930$

3 a (50, 2.51)

b

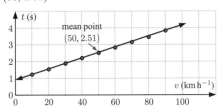

c i ≈ 2.7 seconds   **ii** ≈ 4.4 seconds

d The estimate in **c i**, since it is an interpolation.

4 a $r \approx 0.983$ **b** $y \approx 3.36x + 8.64$ **c** ≈ 42.2

5 a, d

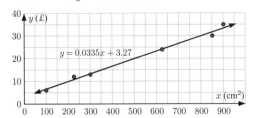

b $r \approx 0.994$

c There is a very strong, positive correlation between *area* and *price*.

e ≈ £43.42, this is an extrapolation, so it may be unreliable.

6 a

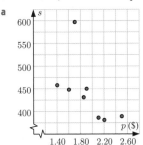

b Yes, the point $(1.7, 597)$ is an outlier. It should not be deleted as there is no evidence that it is a mistake.

c $s \approx -116p + 665$

d ≈ −116; this indicates that with every additional dollar the price increases by, the number of sales decreases by 116.

e No, the prediction would not be accurate, as it is an extrapolation.

7 a, d

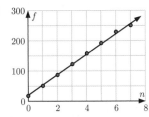

There is a very strong, positive correlation between number of waterings and flowers produced.

b $f \approx 34.0n + 19.3$

c Yes, plants need water to grow, so it is expected that an increase in watering will result in an increase in flowers.

e i 104 flowers $(n = 2.5)$, 359 flowers $(n = 10)$

ii $n = 2.5$ is reliable, as it is an interpolation.
$n = 10$ is unreliable as it is an extrapolation and over-watering could be a problem.

8 a

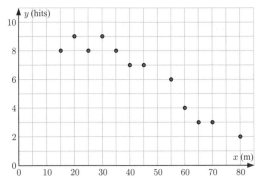

b The number of hits can be counted exactly, while the distance from the target will not be exact.

c $x \approx -7.89y + 93.7$

d ≈ −0.8 hits, but it is impossible to make a negative number of shots. This extrapolation is not valid.

EXERCISE 20A

1 a continuous   **b** discrete   **c** continuous
   d continuous   **e** discrete   **f** discrete
   g continuous   **h** continuous

2 a i $X =$ the height of water in the rain gauge
   ii continuous   **iii** $0 \leqslant X \leqslant 400$ mm

   b i $X =$ stopping distance   **ii** continuous
   iii $0 \leqslant X \leqslant 50$ m

   c i number of switches until failure
   ii discrete   **iii** any integer $\geqslant 1$

3 a X has a set of distinct possible values.
   b $X = 2, 3, 4, 5, 6, 7, 8, 9,$ or 10

4 a $X = 4, 5, 6,$ or 7   **b i** $X = 5$ **ii** $X = 6$ or 7

5 a $X = 0, 1, 2, 3,$ or 4

b ✓✓✓✓ ✓✓✓✗ ✓✓✗✗ ✗✗✗✓ ✗✗✗✗
         ✓✓✗✓ ✓✗✓✗ ✗✗✓✗
         ✓✗✓✓ ✓✗✗✓ ✗✓✗✗
         ✗✓✓✓ ✗✗✓✓ ✓✗✗✗
                  ✗✓✗✓
                  ✗✓✓✗

   $(X = 4)$ $(X = 3)$ $(X = 2)$ $(X = 1)$ $(X = 0)$

c i $X = 2$ **ii** $X = 2, 3,$ or 4

6 a $X = 0, 1, 2,$ or 3

b HHH   HHT   TTH   TTT
           HTH   THT
           THH   HTT
   $(X = 3)$ $(X = 2)$ $(X = 1)$ $(X = 0)$

c No, for example there is probability $\frac{1}{8}$ that $X = 3$, and probability $\frac{3}{8}$ that $X = 2$.

EXERCISE 20B

1 a i yes   **ii** no   **iii** yes   **iv** no
   b For **a iii**, X is a uniform random variable.

2 a $k = 0.2$ **b** $k = \frac{1}{7}$

3 a $a = 0.2$
   b No, as the probabilities of each outcome are not all equal.
   c 2   **d** $P(X \geqslant 2) = 0.65$

4 a $P(2) = 0.1088$
   b $a = 0.5488$ is the probability that Jason does not hit a home run in a game.

c $P(1) + P(2) + P(3) + P(4) + P(5) = 0.4512$ and is the probability that Jason will hit one or more home runs in a game.

d
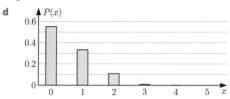

e mode $= 0$ home runs,   median $= 0$ home runs

5 a $k = 0.04$ **b** 0 tyres

c $P(X > 1) = 0.12$ which is the probability that more than 1 tyre will need replacing on a car being inspected.

6 a

x	1	2	3	4
$P(X = x)$	$\frac{3}{8}$	$\frac{2}{8}$	$\frac{1}{8}$	$\frac{2}{8}$

b
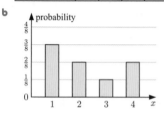

c mode $= 1$, median $= 2$ **d** $P(X \leqslant 3) = \frac{3}{4}$

7 a $X = 1, 2, 3,$ or 4

b

x	1	2	3	4
$P(X = x)$	0.24	0.35	0.27	0.14

c mode $= 2$ bedrooms, median $= 2$ bedrooms

8 a $X = 1, 2, 3,$ or 4

b

x	1	2	3	4
$P(X = x)$	0.48	0.28	0.08	0.16

c mode $= 1$ shot, median $= 2$ shots

9 a $P(0) = \frac{1}{10}$, $P(1) = \frac{2}{10}$, $P(2) = \frac{3}{10}$, $P(3) = \frac{4}{10}$

$0 \leqslant P(x_i) \leqslant 1$ in each case, and

$\sum_{i=1}^{n} P(x_i) = \frac{1}{10} + \frac{2}{10} + \frac{3}{10} + \frac{4}{10} = 1$

$\therefore$ $P(x)$ is a valid probability function.

b $P(1) = \frac{6}{11}$, $P(2) = \frac{3}{11}$, $P(3) = \frac{2}{11}$

$0 \leqslant P(x_i) \leqslant 1$ in each case, and

$\sum_{i=1}^{n} P(x_i) = \frac{6}{11} + \frac{3}{11} + \frac{2}{11} = 1$

$\therefore$ $P(x)$ is a valid probability function.

10 a $k = \frac{1}{12}$ **b** $k = \frac{12}{25}$

11 a $a = 10$ **b** $P(X = 1) = \frac{3}{10}$ **c** 2

12 a $\frac{3}{2}$ **b** $a = \frac{2}{3}$ **13** $a = \frac{3}{5}$

EXERCISE 20C.1

1 a $E(X) = 1.7$ **b** $E(X) = 2.5$ **c** $E(X) = 3.85$

d $E(X) = 30$

2 a $a = \frac{1}{2}$ **b** 3   **c** $\mu = 2\frac{2}{5}$

3 ≈ 11.7 points   **4** 1.57 fish

5 a $a = 0.25$ **b** 4 books   **c** 3.13 books

6 5.25 lollies   **7 a** $\frac{4}{15}$ **b** ≈ 8.93 pins

8 $a = 0.1$, $b = 0.4$

9 a offensive strategy: $P(\text{draw}) = 0.15$
defensive strategy: $P(\text{draw}) = 0.5$

b offensive strategy: 1.05 points per game
defensive strategy: 1.1 points per game

c defensive strategy

d Yes, an offensive strategy would then be better.

10 a   **i** car park B   **ii** car park A   **iii** car park B

b Zoe should choose car park A as the expected cost for car park A is $14.80 whereas the expected cost for car park B is $15.25 .

11 $390

EXERCISE 20C.2

1 fair   **2 a** $3.50   **b** $-$0.50   **c** no

3 a $\approx -$0.05   **b** lose $\approx $5.41   **4** $-$0.75

5 a   **i** 0.3   **ii** 0.1   **b** $E(X) = 2.5$ tokens

c No, as the player can expect to lose half a token on average per game.

6 a Expected gain $\approx -$0.67 $\neq$ $0   **b** $30

7 a $P(X \leqslant 3) = \frac{1}{12}$, $P(4 \leqslant X \leqslant 6) = \frac{1}{3}$,   **c** $a = 7$

$P(7 \leqslant X \leqslant 9) = \frac{5}{12}$, $P(X \geqslant 10) = \frac{1}{6}$

d The organisers would lose $2.50 per game.   **e** $4010

8 $4.75

EXERCISE 20D

1 a The binomial distribution applies, as tossing a coin has two possible outcomes (H or T) and each toss is independent of every other toss.

b The binomial distribution applies, as this is equivalent to tossing one coin 100 times.

c The binomial distribution applies as we can draw out a red or a blue marble with the same chances each time.

d The binomial distribution does not apply as the result of each draw is dependent upon the results of previous draws.

e The binomial distribution does not apply, assuming that ten bolts are drawn without replacement. We do not have a repetition of independent trials. However, since there is such a large number of bolts in the bin, the trials are approximately independent, so the distribution is approximately binomial.

2 a $(p + q)^4 = p^4 + 4p^3q + 6p^2q^2 + 4pq^3 + q^4$

b **i** $\left(\frac{1}{2}\right)^4 = \frac{1}{16}$ **ii** $4\left(\frac{1}{2}\right)^3\left(\frac{1}{2}\right) = \frac{1}{4}$

iii $6\left(\frac{1}{2}\right)^2\left(\frac{1}{2}\right)^2 = \frac{3}{8}$

3 a $(p + q)^5 = p^5 + 5p^4q + 10p^3q^2 + 10p^2q^3 + 5pq^4 + q^5$

b **i** $5\left(\frac{1}{2}\right)^4\left(\frac{1}{2}\right) = \frac{5}{32}$ **ii** $10\left(\frac{1}{2}\right)^2\left(\frac{1}{2}\right)^3 = \frac{5}{16}$

iii $\left(\frac{1}{2}\right)^4\left(\frac{1}{2}\right) = \frac{1}{32}$

4 a $\left(\frac{2}{3} + \frac{1}{3}\right)^4 = \left(\frac{2}{3}\right)^4 + 4\left(\frac{2}{3}\right)^3\left(\frac{1}{3}\right) + 6\left(\frac{2}{3}\right)^2\left(\frac{1}{3}\right)^2$

$+ 4\left(\frac{2}{3}\right)\left(\frac{1}{3}\right)^3 + \left(\frac{1}{3}\right)^4$

b **i** $\left(\frac{2}{3}\right)^4 = \frac{16}{81}$ **ii** $6\left(\frac{2}{3}\right)^2\left(\frac{1}{3}\right)^2 = \frac{8}{27}$ **iii** $\frac{8}{9}$

5 a $\left(\frac{3}{4} + \frac{1}{4}\right)^5 = \left(\frac{3}{4}\right)^5 + 5\left(\frac{3}{4}\right)^4\left(\frac{1}{4}\right) + 10\left(\frac{3}{4}\right)^3\left(\frac{1}{4}\right)^2$

$+ 10\left(\frac{3}{4}\right)^2\left(\frac{1}{4}\right)^3 + 5\left(\frac{3}{4}\right)\left(\frac{1}{4}\right)^4 + \left(\frac{1}{4}\right)^5$

b **i** $10\left(\frac{3}{4}\right)^3\left(\frac{1}{4}\right)^2 = \frac{135}{512}$ **ii** $\frac{53}{512}$ **iii** $\frac{47}{128}$

6 b $\binom{n}{x}$, p^x, $(1-p)^{n-x} \geqslant 0$ $\therefore$ $P(x) \geqslant 0$

Now $\displaystyle\sum_{x=0}^{n} P(x) = 1$ $\therefore$ $P(x) \leqslant 1$

$\therefore$ $0 \leqslant P(x) \leqslant 1$ for all $x = 0, 1, ..., n$.

c $P(x)$ is a valid probability distribution.

EXERCISE 20E

1 a ≈ 0.0305 **b** ≈ 0.265

2 a ≈ 0.476 **b** ≈ 0.840 **c** ≈ 0.160 **d** ≈ 0.996

3 a ≈ 0.0280 **b** $\approx 0.002\,46$ **c** ≈ 0.131 **d** ≈ 0.710

4 $\approx 0.000\,864$ **5 a** ≈ 0.998 **b** ≈ 0.807

6 a ≈ 0.0388 **b** ≈ 0.405 **c** ≈ 0.573 **7** ≈ 0.0341

8 a ≈ 0.863 **b** ≈ 0.475 **9 a** $\frac{1}{36}$ **b** ≈ 0.846

10 a ≈ 0.0905 **b** ≈ 0.622

c Yes, the probability that Shelley is on time for work each day of a 5 day week is now $\approx 87.2\%$.

11 a ≈ 0.0388 **b** 25 solar components

EXERCISE 20F

1 a i $\mu = 3$, $\sigma \approx 1.22$

ii

x_i	0	1	2	3
$P(x_i)$	0.0156	0.0938	0.2344	0.3125

x_i	4	5	6
$P(x_i)$	0.2344	0.0938	0.0156

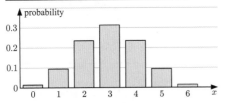

iii The distribution is symmetric.

b i $\mu = 1.2$, $\sigma \approx 0.980$

ii

x_i	0	1	2	3
$P(x_i)$	0.2621	0.3932	0.2458	0.0819

x_i	4	5	6
$P(x_i)$	0.0154	0.0015	0.0001

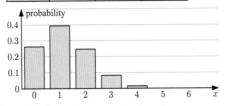

iii The distribution is positively skewed.

c i $\mu = 4.8$, $\sigma \approx 0.980$

ii

x_i	0	1	2	3
$P(x_i)$	0.0001	0.0015	0.0154	0.0819

x_i	4	5	6
$P(x_i)$	0.2458	0.3932	0.2621

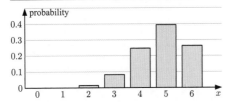

iii The distribution is negatively skewed and is the exact reflection of **b**.

2 $\mu = 5$, $\sigma^2 = 2.5$

3 a $\mu = 1.2$, $\sigma \approx 1.07$ **b** $\mu = 28.8$, $\sigma \approx 1.07$

4 $\mu = 3.9$, $\sigma \approx 1.84$

5 a $\mu = 28.5$, $\sigma \approx 2.67$ **b** ≈ 0.740

6 a $\mu_X = np$ $\quad\quad$ $\mu_Y = np$

$= 100 \times \frac{1}{2}$ $\quad\quad$ $= 300 \times \frac{1}{6}$

$= 50$ $\quad\quad\quad$ $= 50$

b $\sigma_X = 5$, $\sigma_Y \approx 6.45$

c X is more likely to lie between 45 and 55 inclusive because the standard deviation of X is lower than that of Y, which means there are more values of X which lie close to the mean.

d i ≈ 0.729 **ii** ≈ 0.606

REVIEW SET 20A

1 a discrete **b** continuous **c** discrete

2 a i yes **ii** no **iii** no **iv** yes **v** yes **vi** yes

b the distribution in **a iv**

3 a $a = \frac{5}{9}$ **b** $\frac{4}{9}$

4 a $k = 0.05$ **b** 0.15 **c** 2 **d** $E(X) = 1.7$

5 a X has a set of distinct possible values.

b $X = 0$, 1, or 2

c

x	0	1	2
$P(X = x)$	$\frac{1}{10}$	$\frac{3}{5}$	$\frac{3}{10}$

d 1.2 green balls

6 ≈ 3.83

7 a \$7 **b** No, she would lose \$1 per game in the long run.

8 a $a = -\frac{1}{84}$ **b** 4 marsupials

9 a $\left(\frac{4}{5} + \frac{1}{5}\right)^5 = \left(\frac{4}{5}\right)^5 + 5\left(\frac{4}{5}\right)^4\left(\frac{1}{5}\right) + 10\left(\frac{4}{5}\right)^3\left(\frac{1}{5}\right)^2$

$+ 10\left(\frac{4}{5}\right)^2\left(\frac{1}{5}\right)^3 + 5\left(\frac{4}{5}\right)\left(\frac{1}{5}\right)^4 + \left(\frac{1}{5}\right)^5$

b i $\frac{64}{3125} = 0.020\,48$ **ii** $\frac{128}{625} = 0.2048$

10 a

pentagonal spinner $\quad$ square spinner $\quad$ **b** $\frac{11}{20}$

c i $X \sim B(10, \frac{11}{20})$

ii $P(X = 1) = \binom{10}{1}\left(\frac{11}{20}\right)\left(\frac{9}{20}\right)^9 \approx 0.004\,16$

$P(X = 9) = \binom{10}{9}\left(\frac{11}{20}\right)^9\left(\frac{9}{20}\right) \approx 0.0207$

It is more likely that exactly one red will occur 9 times.

11 a 40 days **b** ≈ 2.83 days

12 a i ≈ 0.0751 **ii** ≈ 0.166 **b** ≈ 4.97 games

13 a i ≈ 0.544 **ii** ≈ 0.456

b i $P(X = 0) = \binom{n}{0}\left(\frac{3}{100}\right)^0\left(\frac{97}{100}\right)^n$ **ii** $n = 12$

$= (0.97)^n$

REVIEW SET 20B

1 **a** X is the number of hits that Sally has in a match.
$X = 0, 1, 2, 3, 4,$ or 5
   b **i** $k = 0.23$ **ii** $P(X \geqslant 2) = 0.79$
      iii $P(1 \leqslant X \leqslant 3) = 0.83$
   c mode $= 3$ hits,   median $= 3$ hits

3 **a** 2   **b** 3   **c** 2.7

4 **b** $p_1 = \frac{1}{3}$ is the highest probability in the probability mass function.
$\therefore$ the mode is 1.

5 **a** **i** Naomi   **ii** Rosslyn   **b** Rosslyn

6 **a** **i** $\frac{2}{5}$ **ii** $\frac{1}{10}$ **iii** $\frac{1}{10}$ **b** $2.70 per game

7 $a = 0.15$, $b = 0.35$

8 **a** $\frac{4}{5}$ **b** **i** ≈ 0.0881 **ii** ≈ 0.967

9 **a** The probability of rolling a two is not the same for each die. So X is not a binomial random variable.
   b

x	0	1	2
$P(X=x)$	$\frac{15}{24}$	$\frac{1}{3}$	$\frac{1}{24}$

   c $\frac{5}{12}$

10 **a** $E(X) = 2.1$ **b** $E(Y) = 1.9$

11 **a** The probability of spinning a 3 is the same for each spin.
   b $\mu = 4$, $\sigma \approx 1.79$

12 **a** 42 donations   **b** **i** ≈ 0.334 **ii** ≈ 0.0931

13 **a**

coin toss	bowling	probability
	$\frac{1}{9}$ ↗ 2 strikes	$\frac{1}{4} \times \frac{1}{9} = \frac{1}{36}$
$\frac{1}{4}$ ↗ 2 heads $\frac{4}{9}$ → 1 strike		$\frac{1}{4} \times \frac{4}{9} = \frac{1}{9}$
$\frac{4}{9}$ ↘ 0 strikes		$\frac{1}{4} \times \frac{4}{9} = \frac{1}{9}$
$\frac{1}{2}$ → 1 head $\frac{1}{3}$ → 1 strike		$\frac{1}{2} \times \frac{1}{3} = \frac{1}{6}$
$\frac{1}{4}$ $\frac{2}{3}$ ↘ 0 strikes		$\frac{1}{2} \times \frac{2}{3} = \frac{1}{3}$
↘ 0 heads 1 → 0 strikes		$\frac{1}{4} \times 1 = \frac{1}{4}$

   b

x	0	1	2
$P(X=x)$	$\frac{25}{36}$	$\frac{5}{18}$	$\frac{1}{36}$

   c $\approx \$3.33$
   d $\approx -\$1.67$, Suvi should not play the game many times.

EXERCISE 21A.1

1 **B**, **D**, and **F**

2 **a** The diameters may be affected by:
   - the type of lathe used
   - the steadiness of the woodworker's hand
   - the operating speed of the lathe.

   b The scores may be affected by:
   - the time spent studying
   - natural ability (for example, memory, learning ability)
   - general knowledge.

   c The times may be affected by:
   - the distance that the students live from their school
   - walking speed
   - physical fitness
   - the terrain.

3 **a** The variable is not likely to be normally distributed as it is more likely that there would be more people younger than the mean age than there are older. The distribution may be positively skewed.

   b The variable is likely to be normally distributed as the long jumper is likely to jump the same distance consistently, but it will vary due to factors such as the speed at which the long jumper runs before the jump, and the positioning of their body before hitting the sand.

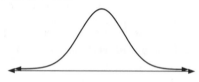

   c The variable is not likely to be normally distributed as each number has the same chance of being drawn. The distribution should be uniform.

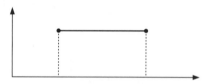

   d The variable is likely to be normally distributed as the lengths of the carrots will be generally centred around the mean, but will vary due to factors such as soil quality, different weather conditions, harvest times, and so on.

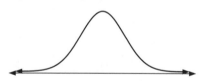

   e The variable is not likely to be normally distributed. People are most likely to be served quite quickly. The distribution is likely to be negatively skewed.

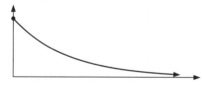

   f The variable is not likely to be normal as it is a discrete variable. Each egg has the same probability of being brown, so the distribution is binomial.

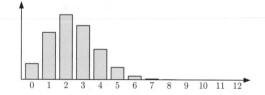

g The variable is not likely to be normally distributed as it is a discrete variable. Most families will have 0 - 2 children, and there will be much fewer families with more than 2 children. The distribution will be positively skewed.

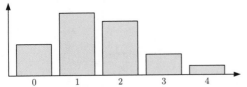

h The variable is not likely to be normally distributed as there will tend to be many more shorter buildings than tall buildings in a city. The distribution will be positively skewed.

EXERCISE 21A.2

1 **a** B   **b** D   **c** A   **d** C

2

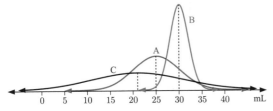

3 **a**

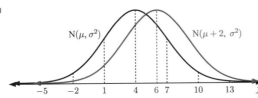

b

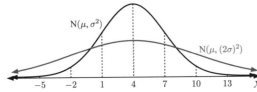

c

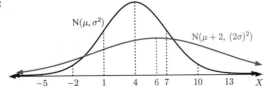

d

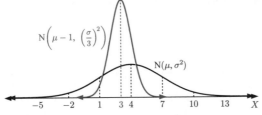

e

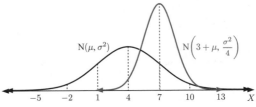

EXERCISE 21B.1

1 **a** **i** 40   **ii** 25
   b **i** 1 standard deviation above the mean
      ii 2 standard deviations below the mean
      iii 3 standard deviations above the mean
   c

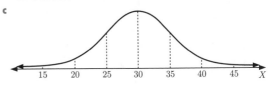

   d $\approx 34.13\%$ **e** ≈ 0.1359

2 **a** $\mu = 20$, $\sigma = 4$
   b **i** $\approx 34.13\%$ **ii** $\approx 13.59\%$ **iii** $\approx 2.28\%$

3 **a**

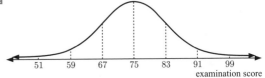

examination score

   b **i** $\approx 15.87\%$ **ii** $\approx 2.28\%$ **iii** $\approx 81.85\%$

4 **a** ≈ 0.6826 **b** ≈ 0.0228

5 **a** **i** $\approx 34.13\%$ **ii** $\approx 47.72\%$
   b **i** ≈ 0.0228 **ii** ≈ 0.8413
   c ≈ 68 students   **d** $k \approx 178$

6 **a** ≈ 459 babies   **b** ≈ 446 babies

7 **a** ≈ 41 days   **b** ≈ 254 days   **c** ≈ 213 days

8 **a** ≈ 5 competitors   **b** ≈ 32 competitors
   c ≈ 137 competitors

9 **a** $\mu \approx 176$ g, $\sigma \approx 24$ g   **b** $\approx 81.85\%$

10 **a** **i** $\approx 84.13\%$ **ii** $\approx 2.28\%$
   b **i** ≈ 0.0215 **ii** ≈ 0.9544 **c** ≈ 0.0223

EXERCISE 21B.2

1 **a**

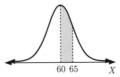

P$(60 \leqslant X \leqslant 65) \approx 0.341$

b

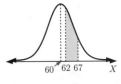

P$(62 \leqslant X \leqslant 67) \approx 0.264$

c

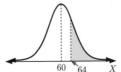

P$(X \geqslant 64) \approx 0.212$

d

P$(X \leqslant 68) \approx 0.945$

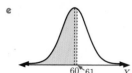

$P(X \leqslant 61) \approx 0.579$

$P(57.5 \leqslant X \leqslant 62.5)$
≈ 0.383

2 **a** ≈ 0.334 **b** ≈ 0.166 **3** ≈ 0.378

4 **a** ≈ 0.303 **b** ≈ 0.968 **c** ≈ 0.309

5 **a** ≈ 0.0509 **b** $\approx 52.1\%$ **c** ≈ 47 eels

6 **a** **i** $\approx 90.4\%$ **ii** $\approx 4.78\%$ **b** $\$4160$

7 **a** **i** $\approx 12.7\%$ **ii** $\approx 52.0\%$

   b **i** 21.6 kL   **ii** ≈ 76 customers

8 **a** **i** $\approx 21.5\%$ **ii** $\approx 95.2\%$

   b **i** Enrique   **ii** Damien

9 **a** $\approx 10.3\%$ **b** ≈ 0.456

10 **a** $\approx 84.1\%$ **b** ≈ 0.879

EXERCISE 21C.1

1 **a** Emma's z-scores:
English ≈ 1.82, Mandarin ≈ 2.33, Geography ≈ 1.61,
Biology $= 0.9$, Mathematics ≈ 2.27

   b Mandarin, Mathematics, English, Geography, Biology

   c The scores in each of Emma's classes are normally distributed.

2 **a** Sergio's z-scores:
Physics ≈ -0.463, Chemistry ≈ 0.431,
Mathematics ≈ 0.198, German ≈ 0.521,
Biology ≈ -0.769

   b German, Chemistry, Mathematics, Physics, Biology

3 **a** Frederick's z-scores:
50 m freestyle ≈ 1.95, 100 m backstroke ≈ -1.07,
200 m breaststroke ≈ -0.578, 100 m butterfly ≈ 0.345

   b Lower times are better as they indicate that the person swims faster.

   c 100 m backstroke, 200 m breaststroke, 100 m butterfly, 50 m freestyle

EXERCISE 21C.2

1 **a**
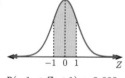

$P(-1 < Z < 1) \approx 0.683$

   b
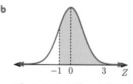

$P(-1 \leqslant Z \leqslant 3) \approx 0.840$

   c
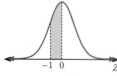

$P(-1 < Z < 0) \approx 0.341$

   d
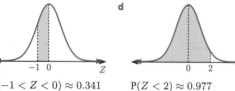

$P(Z < 2) \approx 0.977$

   e
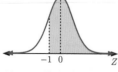

$P(-1 < Z) \approx 0.841$

   f
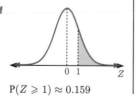

$P(Z \geqslant 1) \approx 0.159$

2 **a** $a = -1$, $b = 2$ **b** $a = -0.5$, $b = 0$

   c $a = 0$, $b = 3$

3 **a**
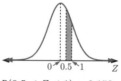

$P(0.5 \leqslant Z \leqslant 1) \approx 0.150$

   b
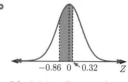

$P(-0.86 \leqslant Z \leqslant 0.32)$
≈ 0.431

   c
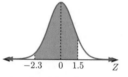

$P(-2.3 \leqslant Z \leqslant 1.5)$
≈ 0.922

   d
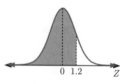

$P(Z \leqslant 1.2) \approx 0.885$

   e
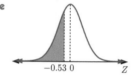

$P(Z \leqslant -0.53) \approx 0.298$

   f
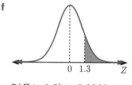

$P(Z \geqslant 1.3) \approx 0.0968$

   g

$P(Z \geqslant -1.4) \approx 0.919$

   h
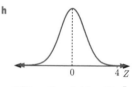

$P(Z > 4) \approx 3.17 \times 10^{-5}$

   i
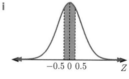

$P(-0.5 < Z < 0.5)$
≈ 0.383

   j
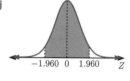

$P(-1.960 \leqslant Z \leqslant 1.960)$
≈ 0.950

   k
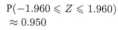
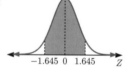

$P(-1.645 \leqslant Z \leqslant 1.645)$
≈ 0.900

   l
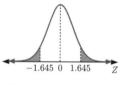

$P(|Z| > 1.645)$
≈ 0.100

4 **a** **ii** ≈ 0.976 **b** **i** ≈ 0.910 **ii** ≈ 0.302

5 **a** **i** $z_1 \approx -0.859$, $z_2 \approx 1.18$ **ii** ≈ 0.687

EXERCISE 21D.1

1 **a**
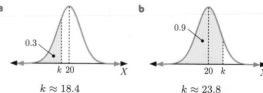

     $k \approx 18.4$ $k \approx 23.8$

c

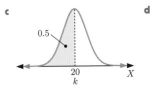

$k = 20$

d

$k \approx 22.5$

e

$k \approx 20.9$

f

$k \approx 23.4$

2 a

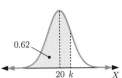

$k \approx 0.878$

b

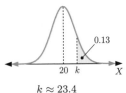

$k \approx 0.202$

c

$k \approx -0.954$

d

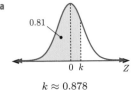

$k \approx -1.64$

e

$k \approx -1.28$

f

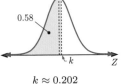

$k \approx 0.228$

3 a

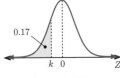

$\therefore \quad a > 30$

b $a \approx 30.9$

c **i** 0.43
  ii 0.07

4 a $k \approx 12.5$ **b** $k \approx 18.8$ **c** $k \approx 4.93$
5 a ≈ 0.212 **b** $k \approx 75.1$
6 a $a \approx 42.0$ **b** $a \approx 46.7$ **c** $a \approx 40.1$
7 ≈ 24.7 cm   **8** ≈ 75.2 mm
9 ≈ 501.8 mL to 504.0 mL   **10** $\approx 31.0°$C

EXERCISE 21D.2

1 a Greater. Data values less than 40 make up only 20% of all values.
  b $\mu \approx 45.0$
2 $\sigma \approx 3.90$ **3** ≈ 112 **4** ≈ 0.193 m
5 $\approx €96.48$ **6** $\approx 4{:}01{:}24$ pm
7 $\mu \approx 23.6, \quad \sigma \approx 24.3$
8 a $\mu \approx 52.4, \quad \sigma \approx 21.6$ **b** $\approx 54.3\%$

9 a $\mu \approx 4.00$ cm, $\sigma \approx 0.003\,53$ cm   **b** ≈ 0.603
10 a $\mu \approx 2.00$ cm, $\sigma \approx 0.0305$ cm   **b** ≈ 0.736
  c ≈ 0.153

REVIEW SET 21A

1 a The distribution of times taken for students to read a novel is likely to be positively skewed, and hence not normal.
  b The mean amount spent on groceries at a supermarket is likely to occur most often, with variations around the mean occurring symmetrically as a result of random variation in the prices of items bought and/or the quantities of items bought (for example weights of fruits and vegetables). So the distribution is likely to be normal.

2 a

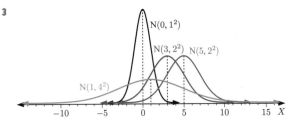

  b **i** $\approx 47.72\%$ **ii** $\approx 2.28\%$

3

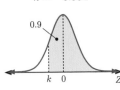

4 a $\approx 2.28\%$ **b** $\approx 68.26\%$ **c** $\approx 95.44\%$
5 a $\approx 50.2\%$ **b** ≈ 7 oysters
6 a Harri's test score is 2 standard deviations below the mean.
  b $\approx 97.72\%$ **c** 7
7 a ≈ 0.364 **b** ≈ 0.356 **c** $k \approx 18.2$
8 a $\approx 6.68\%$ **b** ≈ 0.854
9 a ≈ 0.260 **b** ≈ 29.3 weeks
10 a $k \approx 28.1$ **b** $k \approx 26.5$ **c** $k \approx 25.0$
11 ≈ 0.842
12 a $\mu = 29, \quad \sigma \approx 10.7$ **b** **i** ≈ 0.713 **ii** ≈ 0.250
13 a **i** ≈ 0.0736 **ii** ≈ 0.0406 **b** ≈ 0.644

REVIEW SET 21B

1

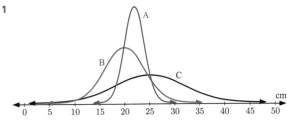

2 a $\mu = 32, \quad \sigma = 5$
  b **i** $\approx 34.13\%$ **ii** $\approx 84.13\%$ **iii** $\approx 2.28\%$
3 a **i** $\approx 2.28\%$ **ii** $\approx 84.0\%$ **b** ≈ 0.3413
4 a **i** $\approx 76.1\%$ **ii** $\approx 96.0\%$ **b** ≈ 0.598
  c $x \approx 61.9$
5 $k \approx 1.96$
6 a ≈ 0.479 **b** ≈ 0.0766 **c** $k \approx 55.2$

7 ≈ 162 seconds

8 a $a \approx 9.05$ **b** $a \approx 13.7$ **c** $a \approx 10.4$ **9** 8.97

10 ≈ 0.0708 units^2

11 a   i ≈ 0.0362   **ii** ≈ 0.610   **iii** ≈ 0.566
   b $k \approx 74.4$ **c** $a \approx 81.0$, $b \approx 102$ **d** ≈ 0.506

12 a ≈ 68.3%   **b** ≈ 0.0884

13 a   i ≈ 0.722   **ii** ≈ 0.798   **b** ≈ 0.0563

INDEX